Power Plant Performance

Dedicated To My Wife
and
Keir, Ian and Quintin

Page	Line	
283	9	$\ldots = \left(\frac{0.5}{1.0}\right)^2 h$
290	2	$\ldots = 1.7223 + 2.48.$
290	14	To read, So $P + \frac{\rho v^2}{2} + g\rho H = K.$
290	23	To read, So $P_1 + \frac{\rho^2 v_1^2}{2} + \rho g H_1 = P_2 + \frac{\rho v_2^2}{2} + \rho g H_2.$
292	3	To read, $V_2 = \frac{1}{\sqrt{(1-m^2)}} \sqrt{\frac{2(P_1 - P_2)}{\rho}}$
292	11	To read, and ρ_w is the density.
293	4	$A_2 = \quad \ldots \frac{\pi d^2}{4 \times 10^6}$
293		Appendix 2 should start $P_1 + H_1\rho_1 g = P_2 + H_2\rho_1 g + hm\rho_2 g.$
293		Appendix 2, lines 5, 6 and 7. All should be $\ldots + h_m\rho_2.$
294	3	So $h_m = \frac{h\rho g}{(\rho_2 - \rho_1)g}$
296	23	$E = \frac{1}{\sqrt{(1-m^2)}}$
306	9, 12	$(H - 0/8)$
307	4	Should be $\ldots \left[\frac{8}{3}C + 8\left(H - \frac{0}{8}\right) + S\right]$
318		Last line, Loss $= \left[\frac{100}{12(CO_2 + CO)} \times \ldots\right]$
319		3rd line from bottom $\ldots \times 1.88\ (149 - 20.6) = \ldots$
320	16	Loss $= \frac{0.02}{13.73 + 0.02} \ldots$
346		Item 6 $\ldots = 121.7$ grams
347		Last line should be $\ldots \times 10^{-4}.$
350	26	Should be $W_f = \ldots \times 10^{-4}.$
362		Next to last line should be: $\left[\frac{14.0 + (9 \times 3.6)}{22\,725} - \frac{17.7 + (9 \times 3.66)}{22\,080}\right]$
372	4	Should be, $\ldots y = 100(1 - e^{-k})$
412	18	Should be $4\left[\frac{uVi}{V_i^2} - \frac{u^2}{V_i^2}\right]$
423		Table 10.4, item 3. $= \frac{(2)^2}{44.72^2}$
478	19	To read 'Then $Q_B \alpha Q_f$' ...
564		Figure 12.24(a) Bled steam to 6 heater should be 22.46
566	1	To read $\ldots = \frac{300(991.1 - 854.6)}{(3071.2 - 1008.4)} = \ldots$
572		Figure 12.27. Turbine gland L/O. should be 0.33 kg/s.
573		3rd line from bottom. Flash steam = 0.19 kg/s
582	17	Flash steam to No. 4 heater $= \frac{(6.33 + 7.98)(822.5 - 709.3)}{2064.9}$
586		Last line, add 'satisfactory'.
611	2	Should be, So $mV = (m.mb) + Z$
630		Figure 14.6. Caption should read 'Effect of loading on turbine condition line (nozzle control)'
634		Last line should read $F_a = F_0 \sqrt{\frac{(P_a v_0}{(P_a v_a)}}$
656	7	Should read ... = Fixed heat + (incremental heat × load)

Gill: Power Plant Performance — Errata

Page	*Line*	
vi	8	Mr C. Clay *not* Mr C. Clag
21	Fig. 1.16	Caption to read — General arrangement of supercritical pressure boiler (CEGB)
78	10	$\frac{\pm 8 \text{ cm}}{\sqrt{(1000)}}$ and $\frac{\pm 8 \text{ cm}}{\sqrt{(4000)}}$
101	24	Formula should be $\frac{4fv^2L}{2gD}$
117	20	Suction pipe 7.0 m
117	21	1 medium radius bend $= 25 \times 0.35$ 8.8 m
119	24	To read, Q is in m^3/s
146	3	To read, $N_s = \frac{3.6 \text{ rev/min} \times \sqrt{m^3/h}}{H^{0.75}}$
151	11	$\left(\frac{1}{\text{Efficiency}} - 1\right)$
158		Item 4. 1st line should be $n^{-1}\, d^{\alpha}\, \rho^{\beta}\, u^{\gamma} = 0$ Item 5. First line should be $n^{-1} \ldots = 0$
159	3	Should be L $\alpha = -1$
160	5	Delete title "Enthalpy of compressed water in kJ/kg"
166		3rd line from bottom. Should be, 1 bar static head + 1 bar friction loss
176	9	$\ldots V_1 = Va + Vb$
176	12	...keeping T_2 at 0°C
213	5	The line of best fit will pass through $\bar{X}$ and $\bar{Y}$
213	6	where $\bar{X} = \frac{\Sigma X}{N}$ and $x = X - \bar{X}$
214	3	Delete, So $\bar{X} = 67.47$ and $\bar{Y} = 20.93$
214		Insert above line 5. $Z = \bar{Y} - m\bar{X} = 0.972$.
218	14	Should be $\frac{3000}{0.6}$
221	4	Delete Law of transducer $X = s(mV - 0.609)$ bar (g).
222		Bottom of column xy delete $\eta\Sigma y$; insert Σxy.
231	2	Should read $\left[1 + \left(\frac{6}{150}\right)^2\right]$
236	2	Should read $\therefore V = \sqrt{\frac{(2\rho w Hg)}{\rho}} = \ldots$
254	17	$\therefore \rho = 0.8696 \text{ kg/m}^3 \sqrt{\rho} = 0.9327$
256	18	So $h_1\rho_1 = h_2\rho_2$
263	14	m.m.w.g. to less than 370 times the upstream...
265		R.H.S. column heading should be $R_{ed}^{-0.5}$ $(\times 10^3)$
278	10	So $dw = 0.432 \times 76.299 = \ldots$
280		Last line ... say, h to 2200.

(continued overleaf)

Power Plant Performance

A B Gill C ENG, MIEE, MI Mech. E
Site Efficiency Engineer
Drakelow Power Stations

Butterworths
London Boston Durban Singapore
Sydney Toronto Wellington

First published 1984

British Library Cataloguing in Publication Data

Gill, A.B.
Power plant performance,
1. Electric generators
I. Title
621.31'3 TK2661
ISBN 0-408-01427-X

Library of Congress Cataloging in Publication Data

Gill, A.B. (Allan Bennett)
Power plant performance.

Bibliography: p.
Include index.
1. Electric power-plants—Efficiency. 2. Heat engineering. I. Title.
TK1005. G5 1984 621.31'2132 84-5881
ISBN 0-408-01427-X

Typeset by PRG Graphics Ltd. Redhill, Surrey
Printed in England by Robert Hartnoll Ltd., Bodmin, Cornwall

Preface

The considerable rise in electricity demand throughout the world has resulted in an enormous increase in the size of power plant installations. The capacity of a typical turbo-alternator thirty-five years ago was about 30 MW. Today, machines rated at 1300 MW are in service and the capacity of boiler and ancillary plant has kept pace with this rapid growth.

This expansion, coupled with the escalating cost of fuel, has imposed an increasingly urgent need to ensure that the plant is operated and maintained as near to optimum conditions as possible. At current UK fuel prices, if a large unit is operated at an efficiency one percentage point lower than design it will incur an additional fuel cost of over two million pounds per year. It is clear that it is of great importance that all power engineers should be aware of the causes of poor efficiency and the means to rectify such trends. That is the purpose of the book. Although written primarily for power engineers, others, such as marine engineers and engineering students, will find the material of interest.

As far as possible mathematics and thermodynamic theory have been kept to a minimum, the aim being to stress the practical application of the subject matter. Each chapter contains self-test questions, exercises and projects. The exercises are quite straightforward and should present little difficulty, whereas the projects are more demanding.

SI units have been standard within the CEGB for several years now so it is appropriate that they are used throughout the book. Also, the CEGB publications *Steam Tables in SI Units* and *Abridged Steam Tables in SI Units* have been used.

The basic model used is a British coal-fired station but, of course, much of the material is also applicable to other stations, whether nuclear or fired by oil or gas and no matter what the country. British practice may differ from that in other countries somewhat in particular aspects of design and, where this is so, reference is made to it.

The 'Performance' referred to in the title is thermal, as opposed to mechanical, performance. Thus, purely mechanical subjects such as vibration, turbine line-out and so on are not covered. However, pumps are so important in power station work that a chapter has been devoted to the subject.

The views expressed are those of the author and he is solely responsible for any errors or omissions.

Sincere thanks are due to the many people who have helped in the preparation of the work. They are too numerous to mention individually, but a special word of thanks is due to the following:

Mr J. Porteous, Director-General, Midlands Region, CEGB, for his kind permission to publish the book, to use illustrations from CEGB sources and for other facilities; Mr R. Mason and Mr T. Westcombe of the Efficiency Department at Drakelow Power Station for their help in reading the text and the preparation of many of the illustrations; Mr J.R. Jackson of the CEGB National Training Resources Unit for his valuable advice and encouragement; the Management and various staff at Drakelow Power Station for their help and co-operation; Mr F. Carlin, Midlands Region Scientific Services Department, Mr C. Clag and Mr P. Adams of the Hydraulic and Temperature Calibration Centre at Hams Hall for checking the material in Part 2, and last, but by no means least, the various organizations who have given permission to publish illustrations and other material.

Allan B. Gill

Acknowledgements

The author and publishers would like to thank Mr J. Porteous, Director-General, Midlands Region, Central Electricity Generating Board, for permission to reproduce many of the illustrations in this book. Thanks are due also to the following companies who supplied illustrations:

General Descaling Co. Ltd.
Budenberg Gauge Co. Ltd.
Airflow Developments. Ltd.
Furmanite International Ltd.
Negretti and Zambra Ltd.
Davidson and Co. Ltd.
Land Combustion Ltd.

Figures 7.1, 7.5 and 7.14 are from BS 1042, Part 1, 1964, and are reproduced by kind permission of the British Standards Institution, 2 Park Steet, London W1A 2BS, from whom complete copies of the Standard can be obtained.

Contents

Part I

General Plant Considerations

1 Ideal steam cycles

The temperature–entropy (T–S) diagram

The basic diagram is shown in *Figure 1.1.* Note that the boiling water line

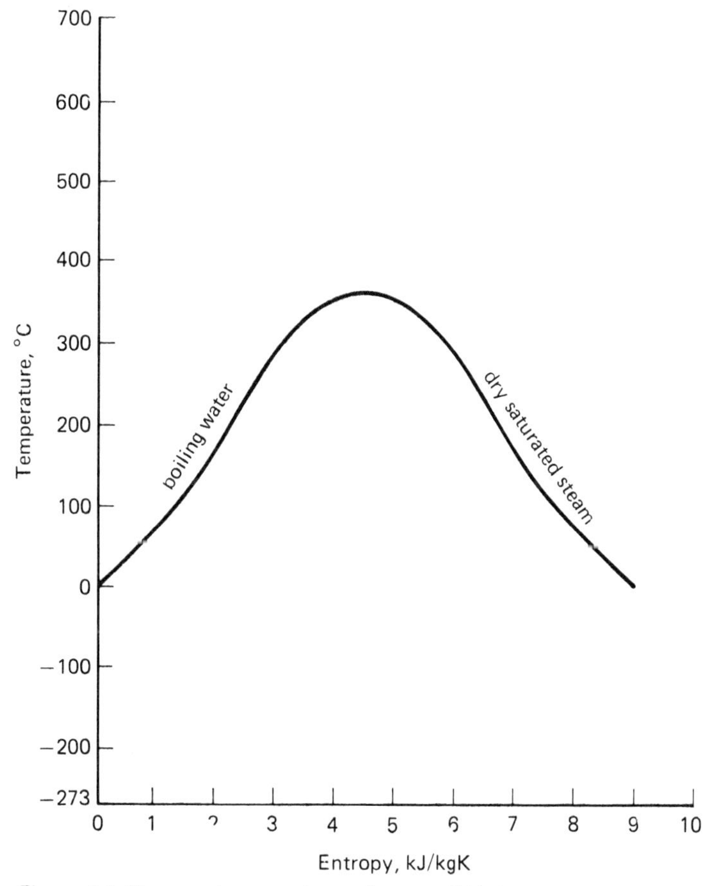

Figure 1.1. Temperature – entropy diagram SI Units

starts at 0°C and the temperature scale at absolute zero, i.e. (−)273.15°C. Also note that the entropy scale starts from zero.

Heat is the product of absolute temperature and change of entropy, and so on a T–S diagram it is represented by an area.

For example, consider the latent heat required to convert 1 kg of boiling water at 100 bar abs. into dry saturated steam.

The boiling temperature is 311.0°C = 584.111 K. The entropy of the boiling water is 3.3605 kJ/kgK and of the dry saturated steam 5.6198 kJ/kgK.

$$\begin{aligned} \text{So latent heat required} &= T\,(S_2 - S_1) \\ &= 583.111\,(5.6198\text{-}3.3605) \\ &= 583.111 \times 2.2593 \\ &= 1319.7\ \text{kJ/kg} \end{aligned}$$

This is illustrated in *Figure 1.2.*

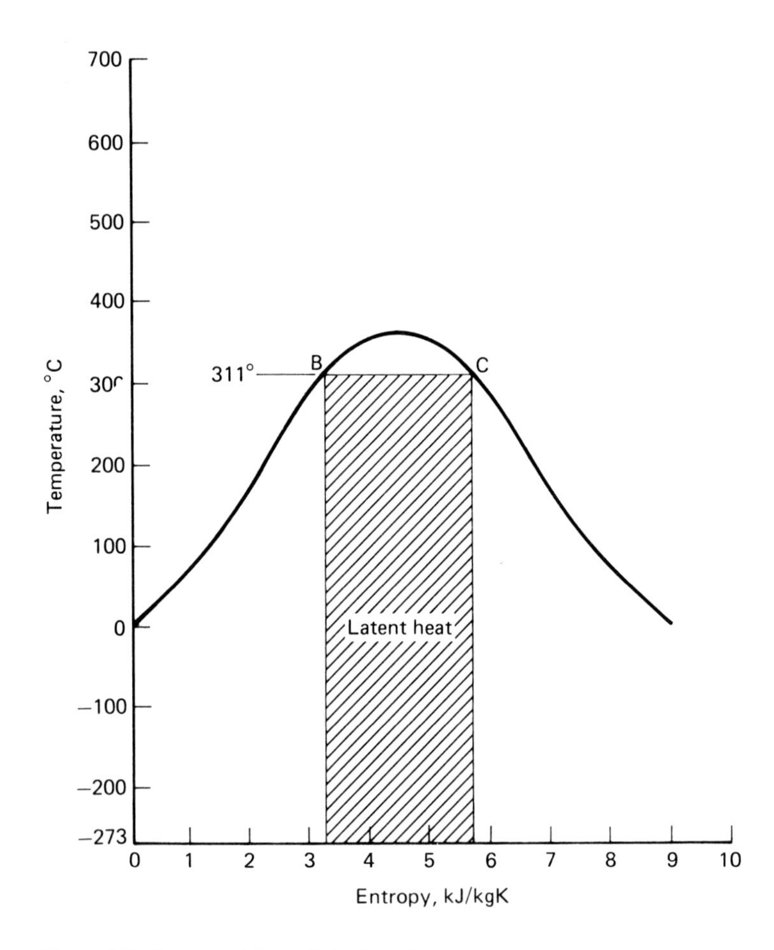

Figure 1.2. Representation of latent heat

Lines of constant pressure are horizontal in the water/steam zone and rise rapidly in the superheat region as shown in *Figure 1.3(a)*, while lines of

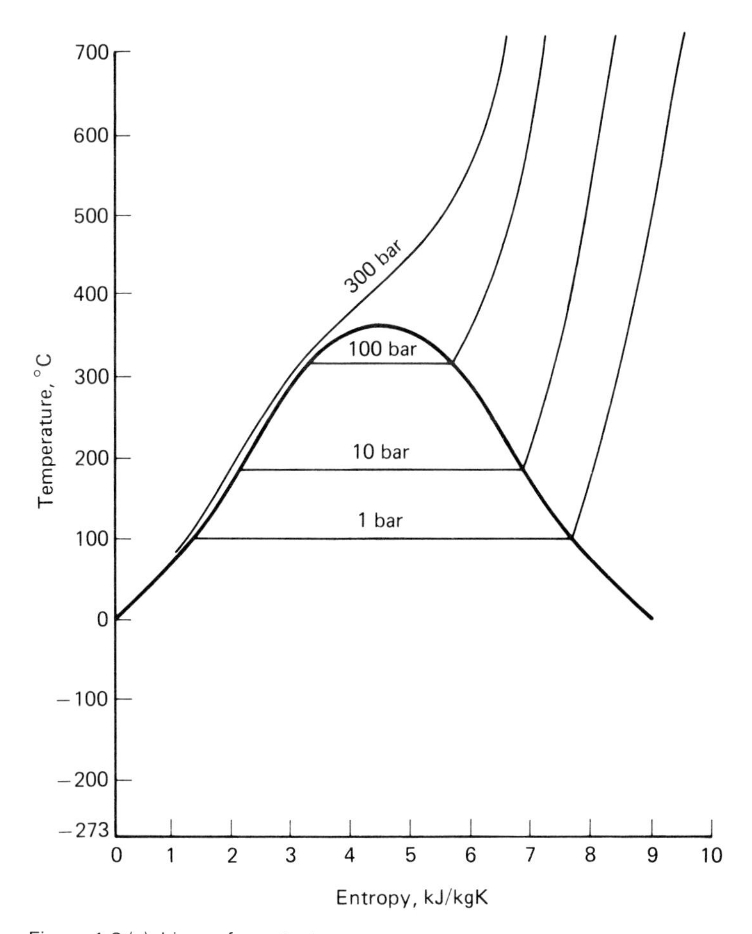

Figure 1.3 (a). Lines of constant pressure

constant wetness are shown in *Figure 1.3(b)*. Of course a line of constant dryness of, say, 90% is the same as a line of constant wetness of 10%.

Supercritical conditions

Reference to the temperature–entropy diagram shows that the 'boiling water line' and the 'dry saturated steam lines' come closer together, the higher the temperature. In other words, the quantity of latent heat required to convert the boiling water to steam becomes less.

A point is reached where the boiling water and dry saturated steam lines meet and so the associated latent heat is zero. This is known as the 'Critical

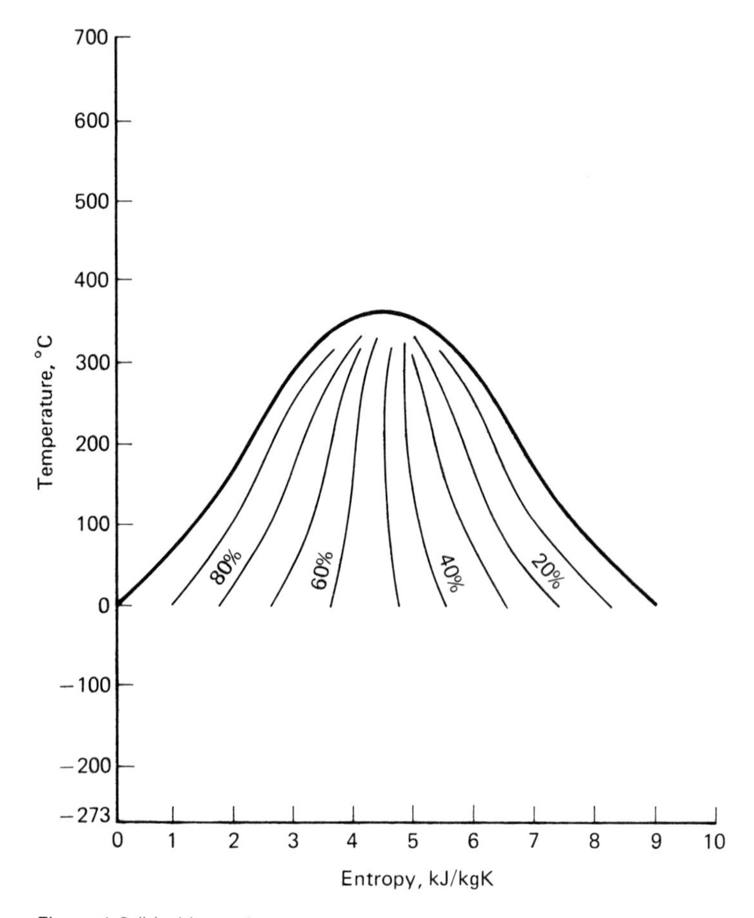

Figure 1.3 (b). Lines of constant wetness

Point' and occurs at the following conditions:

Critical pressure	221.2 bar absolute
Critical temperature	374.15°C
Critical volume	3.17 dm^3/kg

At more elevated conditions the steam is 'supercritical'. Thus, if water is at a supercritical pressure and is heated the temperature will increase until, at a particular value, the water will flash instantaneously into steam and superheating will commence. There is no change of specific volume from the liquid to the dry steam state.

The temperature at which water at a given supercritical pressure will flash to steam is not precisely known, but the pseudo transition locus shown in *Figure 1.4* gives an indication. The supercritical boilers at Drakelow operate at about 250 bar and so the transition from water to steam takes place at about 385°C.

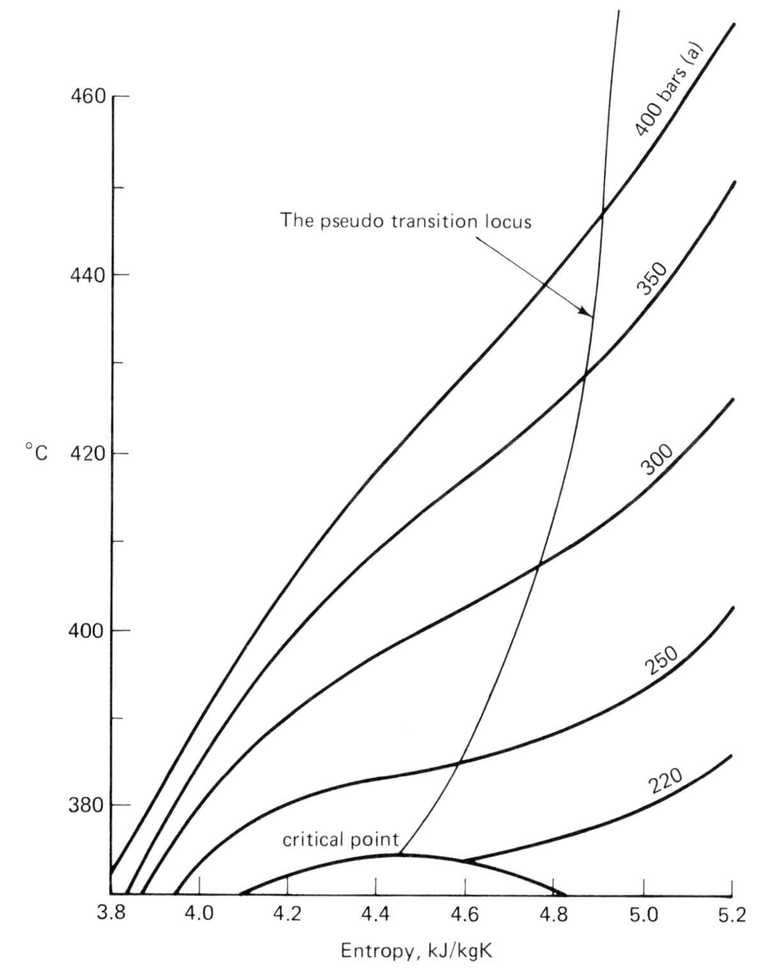

Figure 1.4. The pseudo transition locus

The Ideal (or Rankine) cycle

It is axiomatic that every component in an ideal cycle works perfectly. Thus, the condensate is heated such that it is continuously at saturation temperature from the time it leaves the condenser until it is at boiler pressure; work is done in the turbine by isentropic expansion of the steam; in the condenser only the latent heat of the steam is removed, and so the condensate is at the boiling temperature corresponding to the back pressure, and so on.

The basic cycle is shown in *Figure 1.5*, which shows the conditions for:

Steam pressure	100 bar absolute
Steam temperature	566°C (839K)
Back pressure	30 mbar (saturation temp. 24.1°C)

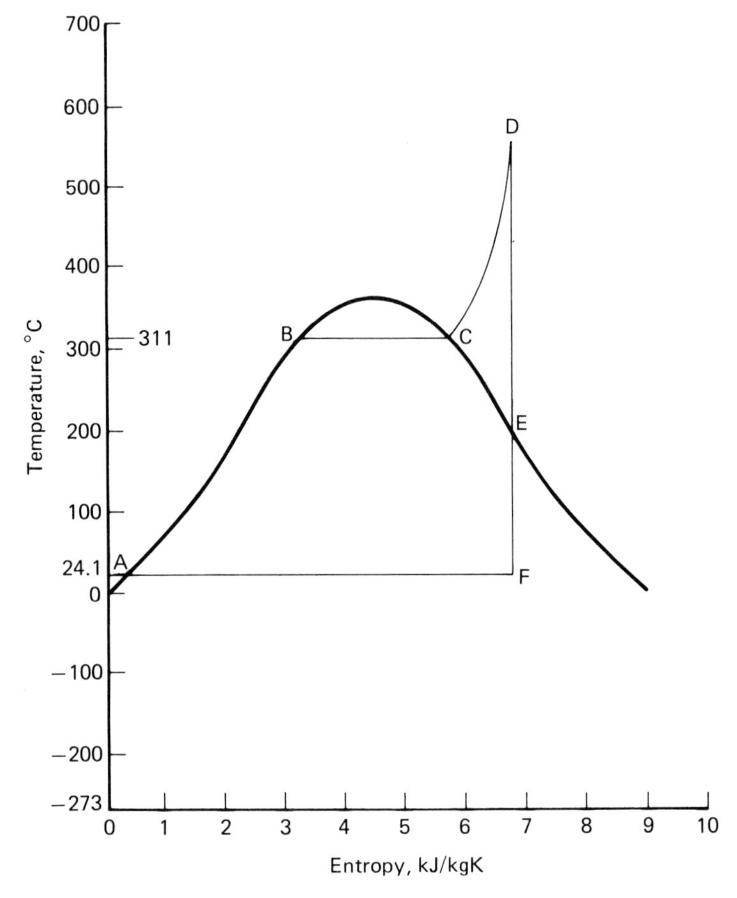

Figure 1.5. Basic Rankine cycle

At point A the condensate is at the boiling temperature corresponding to the back pressure. It is then returned to the boiler via a heating system such that as the temperature increases so does the pressure, and so the feed is continuously at the boiling temperature corresponding to the pressure. At B the boiling water is at a pressure of 100 bar where it is evaporated in the boiler. The latent heat addition is represented by the line BC and at C all the water has been evaporated and superheating commences. This is shown by CD and at point D the superheated steam temperature is 566°C.

The steam then expands isentropically inside the turbine as shown by the line DEF. At point E there is no superheat left in the steam and so from E to F there is increasing wetness. At F the steam is at a pressure of 30 mbar and is passed out of the turbine to the condenser and condensation of the steam takes place as represented by the line FA. At point A the steam has all been condensed and the condensate is at boiling temperature ready to begin another cycle.

To summarize the above:

AB – heating of feed water (i.e. sensible heat addition)
BC – evaporation of water in boiler (i.e. latent heat addition)
CD – superheating of steam (i.e. superheat addition)
DF – expansion of steam in turbine. Point E is the demarcation between superheated and wet steam
FA – condensation of the steam in the condenser

More detailed study of the ideal cycle

(a) *Sensible heat addition*

In *Figure 1.6* the sensible heat is represented by the area under the line AB. At point A the temperature is 24.1°C and at B it is 310.961°C, the values being obtained from steam tables. Also from the tables the sensible heat from A to B is 1408 − 101 = 1307 kJ/kg.

If, however, the heat represented by the area 0°C YB in *Figure 1.6* were known, the heat at B could have been calculated from:

Heat at B = area under YB − area 0°C YB
= (absolute temperature at B × entropy change from 0 to B) − area 0°C YB

Willard Gibbs determined values for the areas such as 0°C YB and he called them the 'Negative Thermodynamic Potential', but the common name is 'Gibbs Function'. In the 1939 Callender's steam tables it is denoted by G; in the 1972 *C.E.G.B. Abridged Steam Tables* it is denoted by g and called 'specific free enthalpy'.

To find the sensible heat using Gibbs' function in the above case first calculate the heat at point B, i.e. 310.961°C and 3.3605 entropy:

∴ Sensible heat at B = $[(310.961 + 273.15) \times 3.3605] - g$

From steam tables the value of g = 554.9 kJ/kg.
So heat at B = 1962.90 − 554.9
= 1408.00 kJ/kg

But the water was already at 24.1°C before heating took place, so it already contained the equivalent heat of water at 297.25 K, 0.3544 entropy.

So initial heat = $(297.25 \times 0.3544) - g$
From steam tables $g = 4.4$ kJ/kg
∴ initial heat = $105.4 - 4.4$
= 101.0 kJ/kg
Therefore the added heat to raise the water from 24.1°C to 310.961°C
= 1408.00 − 101.0
= 1307 kJ/kg as before

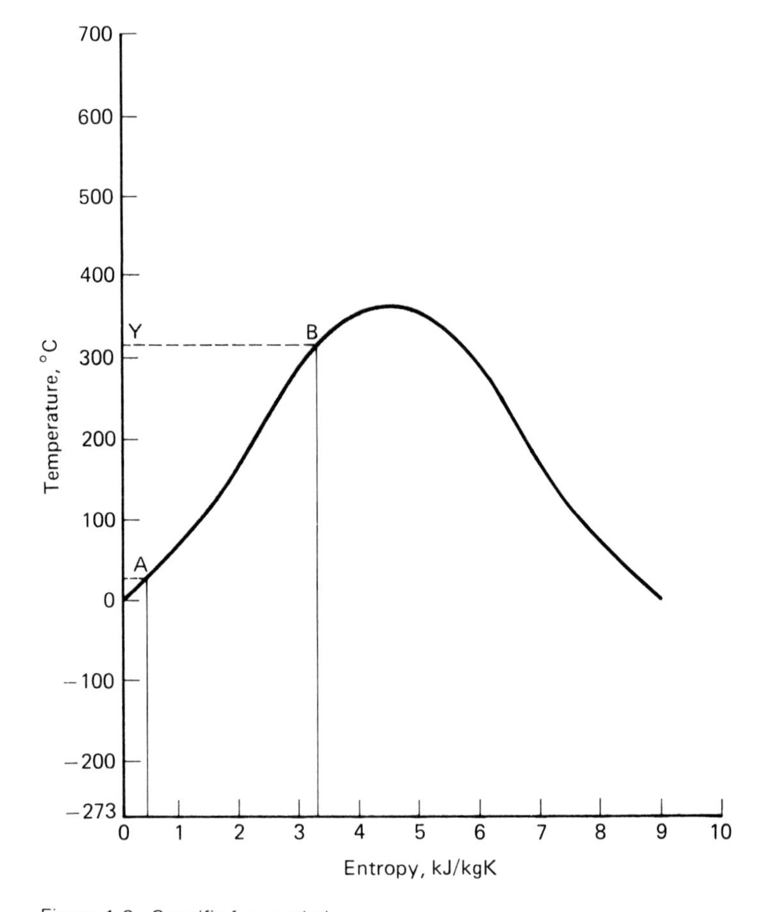

Figure 1.6. Specific free enthalpy

Increasing the pressure increases the quantity of sensible heat per kilogram of water as shown in the random examples shown in *Table 1.1* and in *Figure 1.7*.

Usually, increased pressure is associated with increased output of the turbo-alternator, so not only does increasing the pressure mean more sensible heat

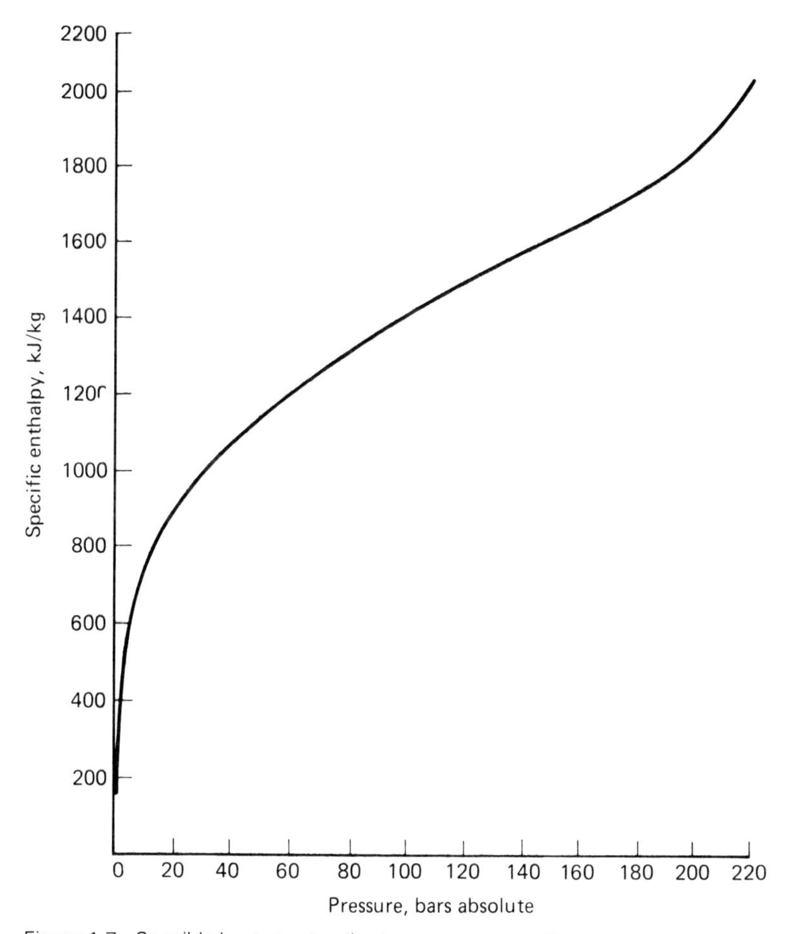

Figure 1.7. Sensible heat at saturation temperature at various pressures

Table 1.1 Sensible heat of water at saturation temperature

Absolute pressure (bar)	*Saturation temperature (°C)*	*Sensible heat (kJ/kg)*
50	263.9	1154.5
100	311.0	1408.0
150	342.1	1611.0
200	365.7	1826.5
221.2	374.15	2107.4

per kilogram, but also that there will usually be more kilograms to heat per second. Therefore the physical heat exchange surface must also increase.

The usual consequence of this is that the number of feed heaters increases, the more elevated the steam conditions. Typical examples are given in *Table 1.2.*

Table 1.2. Number of feed heaters for typical UK and USA installations

Output (MW)	*Final feed Water temp. (°C)*	*Number of heaters*	*Country*
120	224	6	UK
125	241	5	USA
275	252	7	UK
350	238	6	USA
350	252	7	UK
500	252	7	UK
510	256	7	USA
600	252	8	UK
660	244	7	USA
800	254	8	USA
860	254	7	USA

Some idea of the size of a feed heater can be gained from *Figure 1.8*. Note the size of the man compared to the heater nest from a moderate-sized unit.

Latent heat addition

The sensible heat is almost all supplied in the feed heaters and economizer. When the water is supplied to the boiler walls it is almost at boiling temperature. The last bit of sensible heat is added to the water at the lower part of the water wall tubes and then latent heat addition takes place. As there is no temperature change associated with latent heat absorption it follows that the water/steam mixture is at about constant temperature from the bottom to the top of the tubes.

Consider the latent heat addition required for the 100 bar cycle already considered in *Figure 1.5*. The latent heat addition is represented in *Figure 1.2*, where B marks the beginning and C the end. Thus, the heat added is represented by the shaded area below BC and amounts to 1319.7 kJ/kg.

The amount of latent heat required to convert boiling water entirely to dry saturated steam varies with pressure as shown by the examples in *Figure 1.9* and *Table 1.3*.

So the proportion of latent heat absorbing surface required for each kilogram of water/steam becomes progressively less as the pressure rises until, at the critical pressure of 221.2 bar absolute, it is zero, and remains zero for higher pressures. The effect is to physically alter the proportions of the boiler surface required for this function.

For example, low output boilers (say up to 100 MW) are associated

Figure 1.8. High pressure heater for 350 MW. unit – during construction (CEGB)

Table 1.3 Variation of latent heat with pressure

Absolute pressure (bar)	*Saturation temp. (°C)*	*Latent heat (kJ/kg)*
50	263.9	1639.7
100	311.0	1319.7
150	342.1	1004.0
200	365.7	591.9
212.2	374.15	0

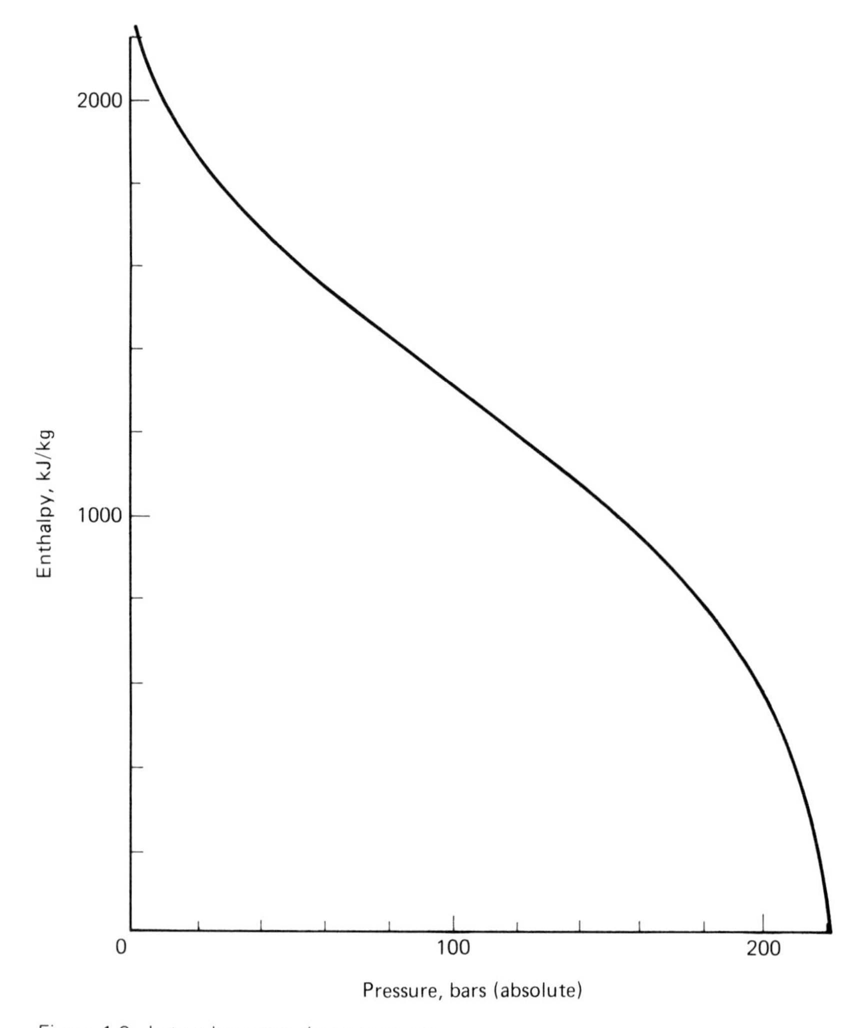

Figure 1.9. Latent heat at various pressures

usually with moderate steam conditions, and so the whole of the furnace walls are devoted to latent heat absorption plus a small amount of sensible heat absorption. As the boiler pressures become higher the proprtion of furnace wall for latent heat absorption becomes less until, on the supercritical pressure units, it is zero. It may be of interest to note that on supercritical plant it is common to arrange the furnace tubes horizontally as shown in *Figures 1.10* and *1.11*. With this type of boiler there is no drum, the heat absorbing surface being, in effect, one continuous tube. Therefore, they are known as 'once-through, supercritical pressure' boilers.

The water in the boiler is pressurized by the boiler feed pump. Sensible heat is added in the feed heaters, economizer and furnace tubes until the

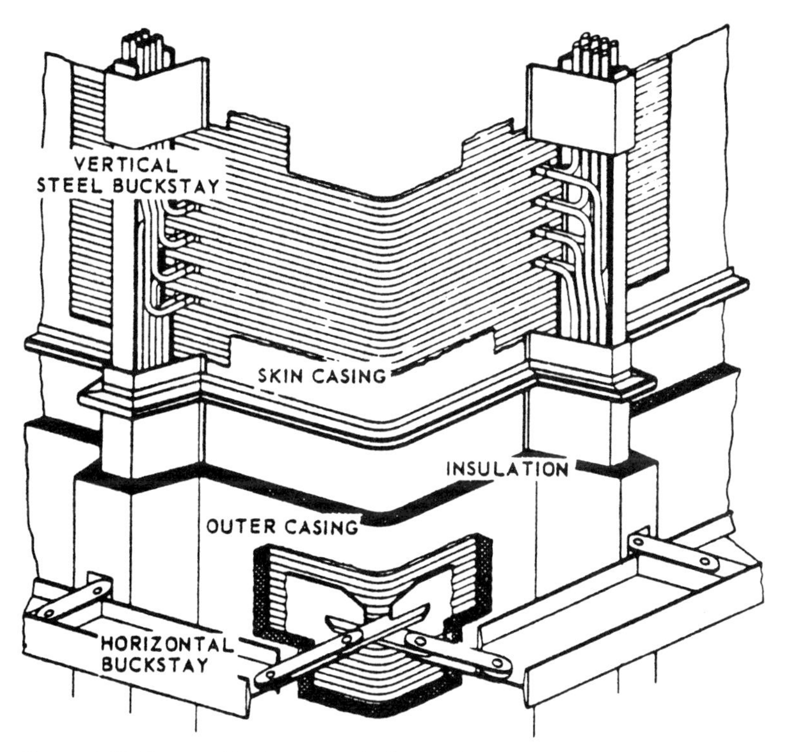

Figure 1.10. Supercritical pressure boiler, wall construction (CEGB)

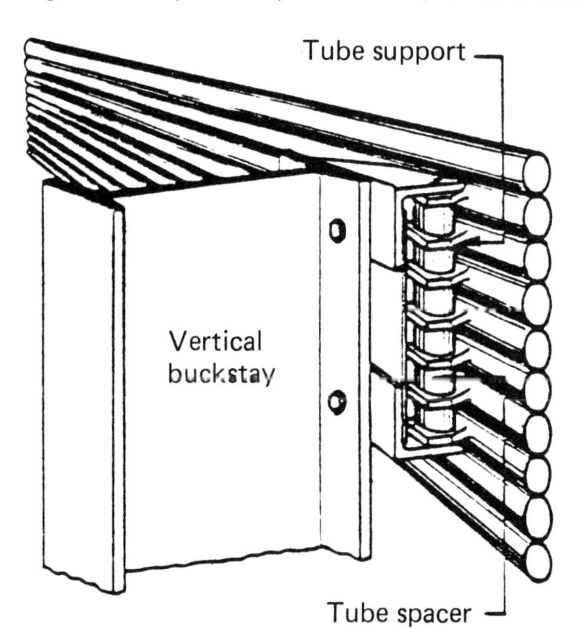

Figure 1.11. Supercritical pressure boiler tube wall support (CEGB)

water attains saturation temperature and flashes *instantaneously* to dry saturated steam and superheating commences. The location in the boiler where the change from water to steam takes place is known as the *transition zone*. Of course, there is no necessity for water level gauge glasses on a supercritical pressure boiler.

Returning to general boiler considerations it is interesting to compare the relationship between the volume of a furnace and the heat absorping surface area surrounding the furnace. Consider the cube-shaped furnace shown in *Figure 1.12(a)* with no top and no bottom. The volume has to be such that

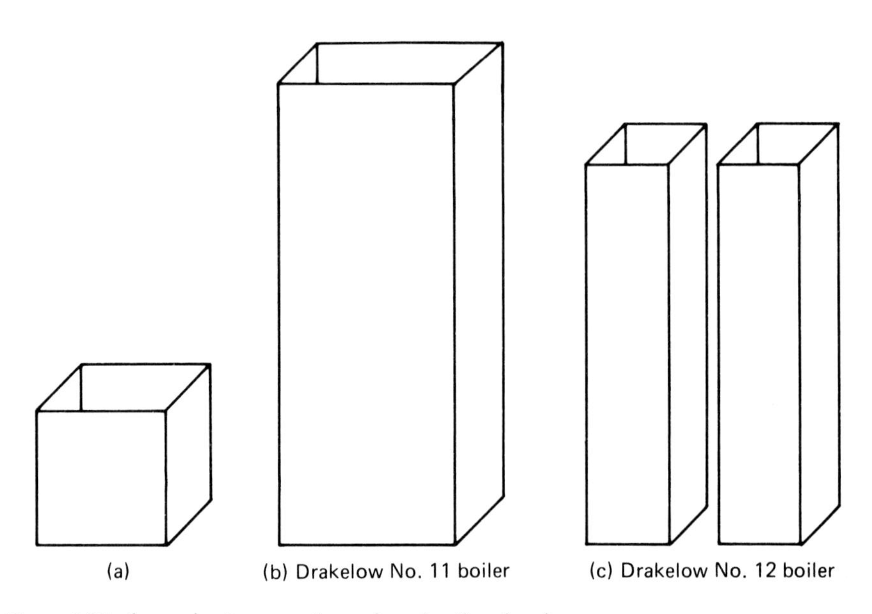

Figure 1.12. Approximate proportions of combustion chambers

combustion of the fuel is complete and the gas temperature reduced to an acceptable level before leaving the combustion chamber. Meanwhile, the surrounding wall tubes must be capable of absorbing the correct quantity of heat to achieve the required gas temperature reduction.

Suppose each side of the furnace is 2 units long, then:

Volume $= 2 \times 2 \times 2 = 8$ cubic units

Surface area = 4 walls, each of $2 \times 2 = 4$ square units, a total of 16 square units.

Hence, the surface area to volume ratio = 2 : 1

If, now, the length of each side is doubled, then:

Volume $= 4 \times 4 \times 4 = 64$ cubic units

Surface area $= 4 \times (4 \times 4) = 64$ square units

So, surface area to volume ratio = 1 : 1

It is apparent that as the volume increases the proportion of surface area decreases. The balance can be restored by the following:

(a) Increase the height of the chamber.
(b) Insert a division wall.
(c) Use twin furnaces.

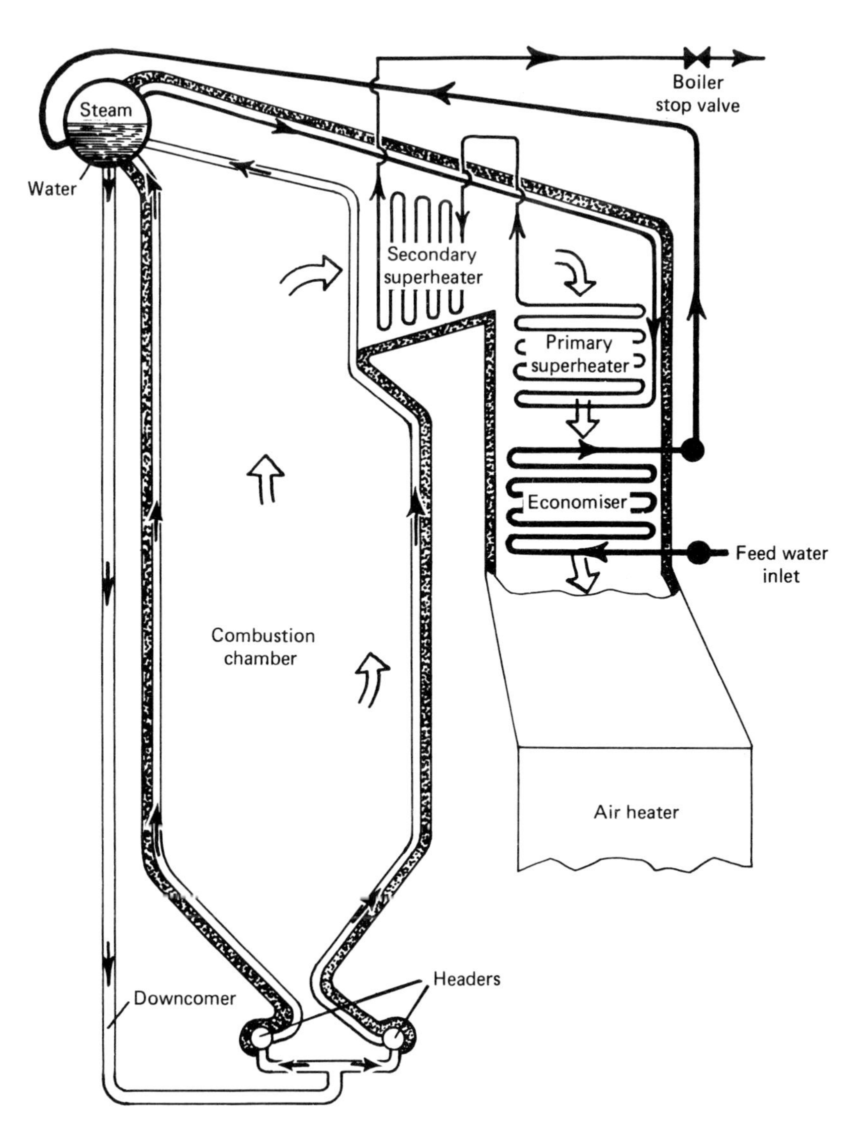

Figure 1.13. Natural circulation boiler (C.E.G.B)

For example, *Figures 1.12(b)* and *(c)* represent to scale the combustion chambers of two 375 MW boilers with identical steam conditions of flow, temperature and pressure, but made by different manufacturers. The No. 11 boiler has no division wall, but is about 7 metres higher than No. 12.

Natural and assisted circulation

Boilers operating at less than 160 bar are usually of the natural circulation type as shown in *Figure 1.13.* With this arrangement water is fed to the drum at lower than boiling temperature, and then fed via external downcomers to the bottom water wall headers. These supply the water wall tubes where some of the water is converted to steam. The downcomers and water walls form U-tubes in which the density of water in the downcomers exceeds that of the steam/water mixture in the wall tubes. Consequently the circulation is down the downcomers and up the wall tubes at such a rate that frictional resistance balances the driving force. Natural circulation is simple, efficient and reliable.

However, the density of boiling water becomes progressively lower as the pressure increases, while that of saturated steam increases, as shown in *Figure 1.14.* At about 160 bar the density differential is getting rather low for

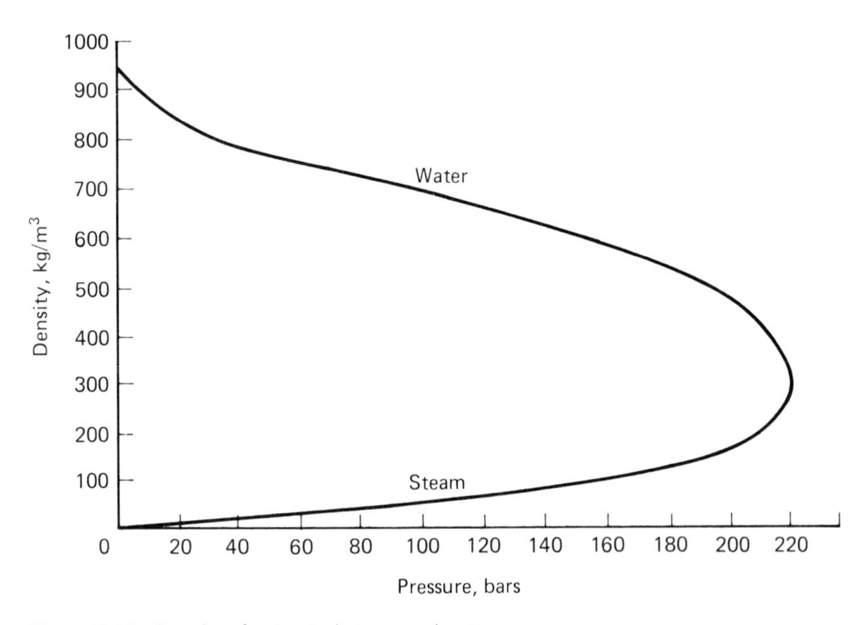

Figure 1.14. Density of saturated steam and water

natural circulation to be maintained easily in a boiler, and so most manufacturers make the change to assisted circulation at about this pressure. This is achieved by fitting boiler circulating pumps at the bottom of the down-comers. On one sub-critical pressure boiler the pumps have the following duty:

No. off	4	
Suction pressure	192.8 bar	
Discharge pressure	194.8 bar	
Differential pressure	2.0 bar	
Pumped quantity	0.979 m^3/s	
Net positive suction head above vapour pressure	15 m	
Water temperature	363°C	
Specific gravity	0.518	
	Hot	*Cold*
Power absorbed	242 kW	466 kW
Current at 415 V	454 A	887 A

Two boiler circulating pumps are required in service at all times when the unit is on load so the combined pumped quantity will be of the order of 1.6 m^3/s. This seems a very high figure as the 100% boiler feed pump discharge is only 0.4 m^3/s. However, the reason is that all boilers have a circulation factor which is the ratio of the water circulating in the boiler compared to the amount of water supplied. Commonly for each kilogram of water supplied the quantity circulating is between 3 and 4 kg. Hence, for the boilers being considered above, each of the two circulation pumps handle about twice the output of the 100% boiler feed pump.

Figure 1.15 shows a boiler circulating pump and motor. Once the change to assisted circulation is made the boiler designer has much more flexibility of layout and tube sizing at his disposal. For example, the circuit resistance is no longer a critical factor and so the water wall tubes can be of smaller bore.

At supercritical pressures the density difference between steam and water is zero. Consequently, there is no need for steam/water separation and so the boilers do not require a drum. This means that they can be of the 'once-through' type where the principle is that water is pumped in at one end of a tube and comes out at the other end as steam at boiler stop valve conditions. Actually there would be several tubes in parallel and, as mentioned earlier, they can be horizontal in the combustion chamber. This offers various advantages, one being that boiler deposits will affect the heat transfer in each circuit by about the same amount. *Figure 1.16* shows the general arrangement of a 'once-through supercritical pressure boiler'.

Superheat addition

Returning to the 100 bar cycle shown in *Figure 1.5* it is already established

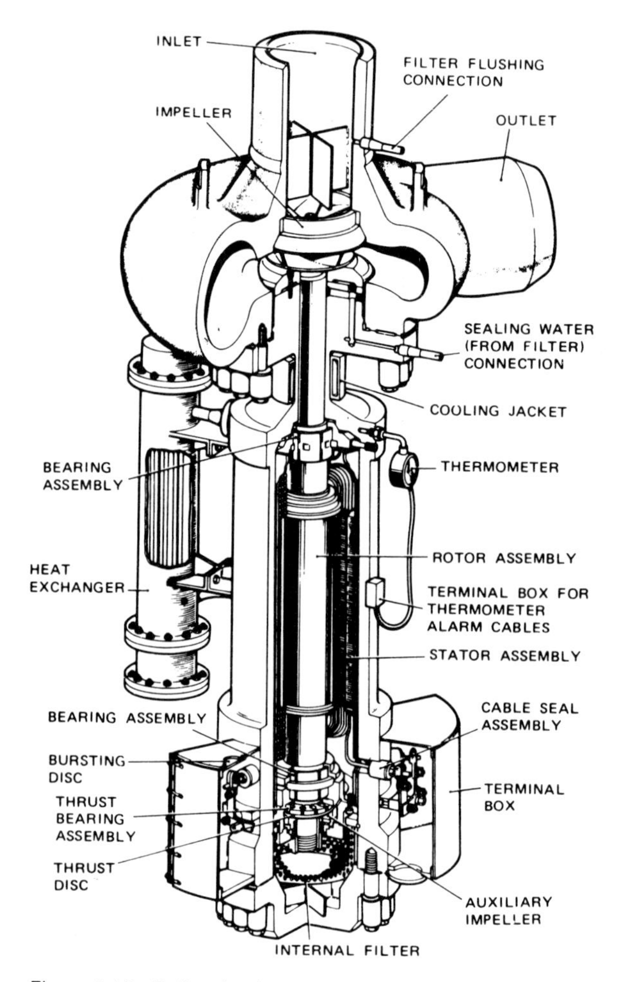

Figure 1.15. Boiler circulation pump (CEGB)

that the sensible heat and latent heat components are 1307.0 and 1319.7 kJ/kg respectively as shown in *Figure 1.17*.

It is now necessary to consider the addition of superheat. The line CD represents the steam state while being superheated at a constant pressure of 100 bar absolute to the required stop valve temperature of 566°C. The heat required for this is obtained by deducting the total heat at C from the total heat at D (*Figure 1.17*) and is equal to 811.6 kJ/kg.

The quantity of heat required to superheat steam to a given temperature varies with pressure as shown in *Table 1.4* and also in *Figure 1.18*. For convenience the final superheated steam temperature is 570°C.

Figure 1.19 illustrates the highest and lowest cases listed in *Table 1.4*, i.e. 10 and 200 bar. The entropy change at 10 bar is 1.3690 kJ/kg K, whereas for 200 bar it is 1.4653. The slope of the superheat line reduces the area under

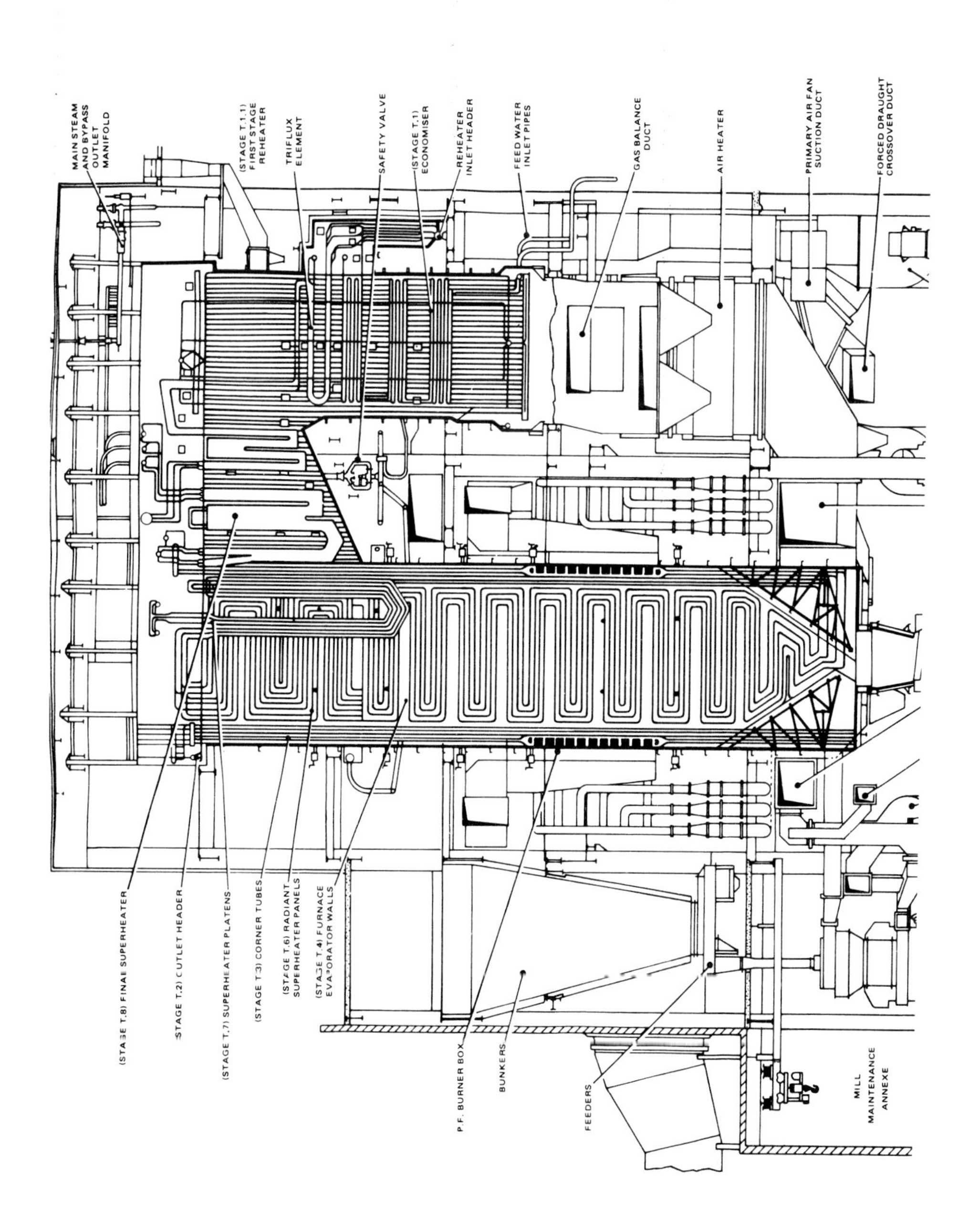
MAIN STEAM AND BYPASS OUTLET MANIFOLD
(STAGE T.1.1) FIRST STAGE REHEATER
TRIFLUX ELEMENT
SAFETY VALVE
(STAGE T.1) ECONOMISER
REHEATER INLET HEADER
FEED WATER INLET PIPES
GAS BALANCE DUCT
AIR HEATER
PRIMARY AIR FAN SUCTION DUCT
FORCED DRAUGHT CROSSOVER DUCT
(STAGE T.8) FINAL SUPERHEATER
(STAGE T.2) OUTLET HEADER
(STAGE T.7) SUPERHEATER PLATENS
(STAGE T.3) CORNER TUBES
(STAGE T.6) RADIANT SUPERHEATER PANELS
(STAGE T.4) FURNACE EVAPORATOR WALLS
P.F. BURNER BOX
BUNKERS
FEEDERS
MILL MAINTENANCE ANNEXE

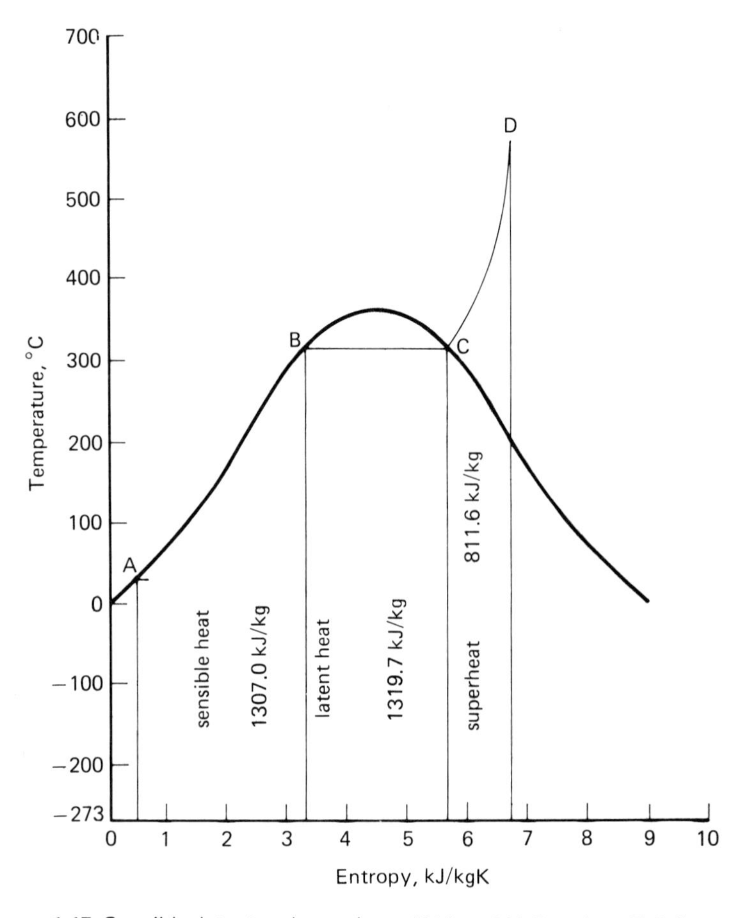

Figure 1.17. Sensible, latent and superheat, 100 bar, 566°C cycle on T-S diagram

Table 1.4 Variation of superheat for various pressures (final temperature 570°)

Abs pressure (bars)	Superheat required (kJ/*kg*)
10	854.8
50	800.9
100	821.5
150	885.4
200	1033.2

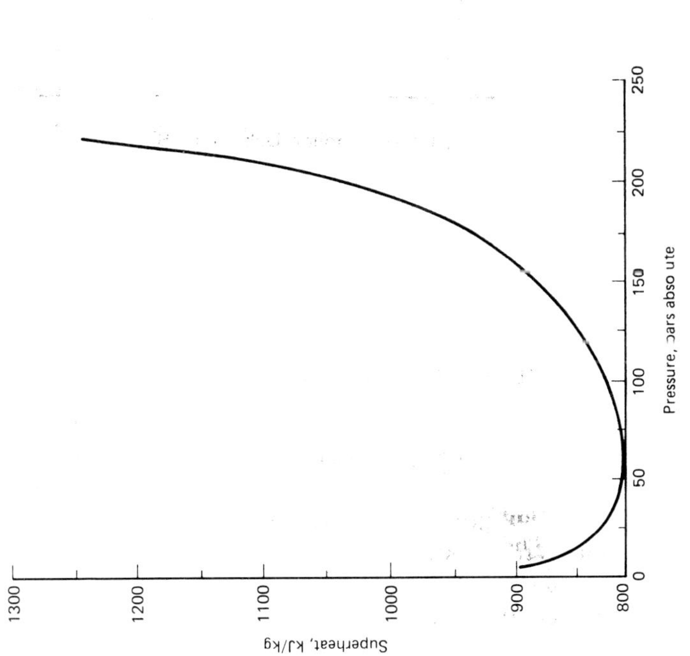

Figure 1.18. Variation of superheat with pressure for steam at 570°C

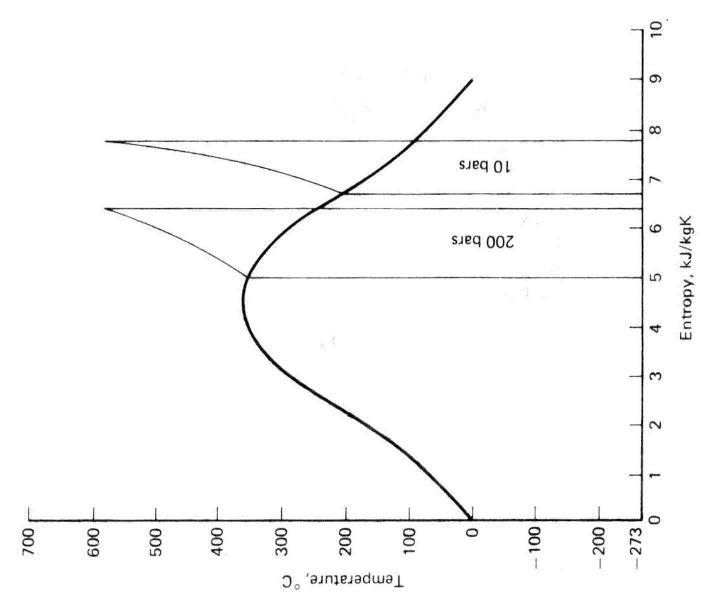

Figure 1.19. Comparison of superheat addition at low and high pressure

the curve by a proportionately greater extent at lower pressures.

Above about 60 bar the superheat requirement increases, so it is necessary to provide more heat exchange surface for this purpose the more advanced the steam conditions. The trend towards increased superheat surface is shown clearly in *Figures 1.20(a), (b), (c)* and *(d)*.

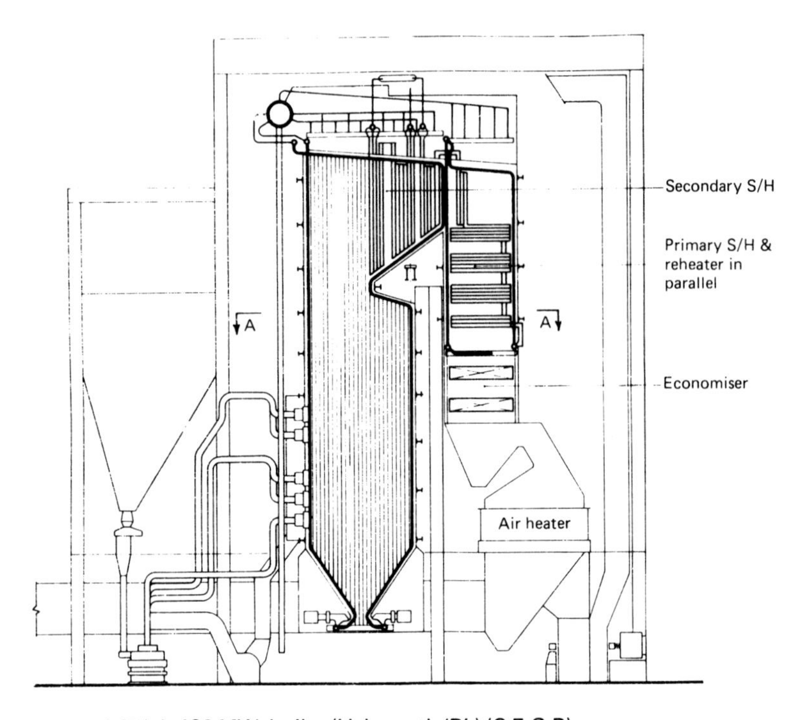

Figure 1.20(a). 120 MW. boiler (Uskmouth 'B'.) (C.E.G.B)

Superheat temperature control

The normal way to control the temperature is by means of water sprays. Direct spray injection has become possible only with the production of very high quality water. A case in point is silica contamination. If silica compounds are carried over to the turbine with the steam they may condense on to the blading. Although some of these compounds are water soluble others are not and some are extremely difficult to remove. So it is most important that strict control is kept over this item, the more so at increased pressures.

Front wall radiant s/h
Secondary s/h
Reheater
Primary s/h
Reheater

Figure 1.20 (b). 200 MW. boi er (West Thurrock) (C.E.G.B)

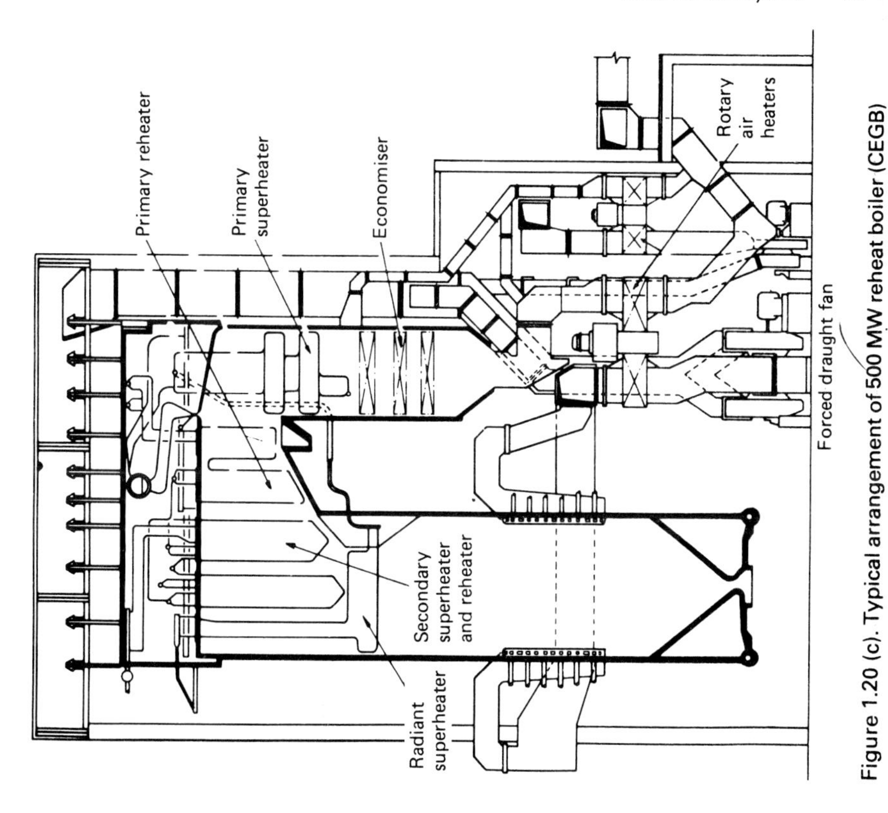

Figure 1.20 (c). Typical arrangement of 500 MW reheat boiler (CEGB)

	Cycle								(projected)
Superheater outlet pressure (bar)	43	65.5	110	110	110	170	165	252	252
Superheater outlet temperature (°C)	463	496	571	529	543	568	568	599	543
Feedwater temperature (°C)	174	196	204	232	230	246	254	273	292
First reheater outlet pressure (bar)	–	–	–	28.3	27.6	31.5	40.8	49.2	67.4
First reheater outlet temperature (°C)	–	–	–	513	541	541	568	568	541
Second reheater outlet pressure (bar)	–	–	–	–	–	–	–	–	17
Second reheater outlet temperature (°C)	–	–	–	–	–	–	–	–	541
	1125	1104	1144	1182	1218	1203	1178	1180	1133
Second reheat									10.8%
First reheat				11.4%	12.5%	14.1%	13.6%	16.6%	12.4%
Super heat	21.3%	24.6%	31.8%	27.1%	27.5%	34.3%	35.2%	44.8%	40.2%
Latent heat	63.7%	58.6%	45.5%	44%	42.7%	27.8%	28.6%		
Sensible heat	15%	16.8%	22.7%	17.5%	17.3%	23.8%	22.6%	38.6%	36.6%

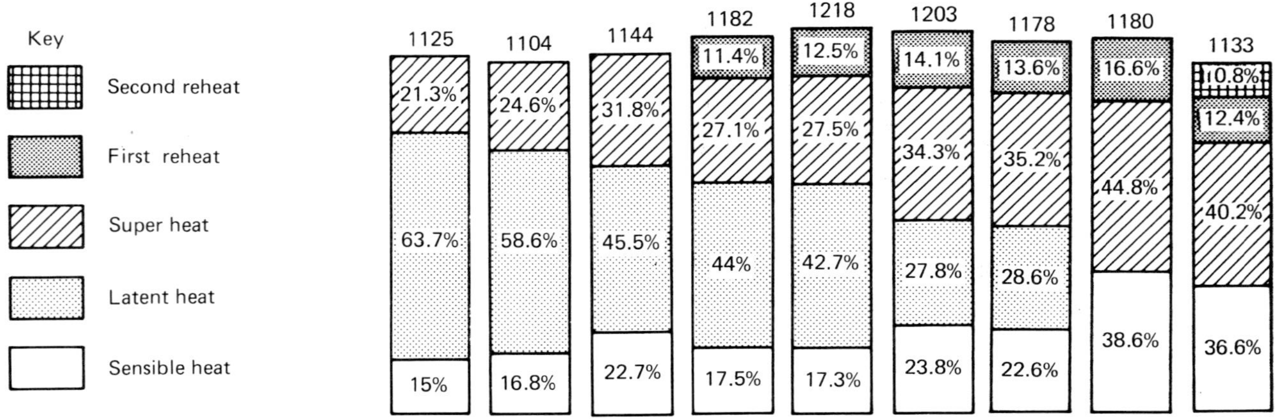

Key: Second reheat; First reheat; Super heat; Latent heat; Sensible heat

Division of total heat absorbtion (CEGB)

Figure 1.21 shows how, for a given quantity in the feed water, the quantity of silica in steam at low pressures is very low but increases rapidly above about 120 bar until, at the critical pressure, for every kilogram of silica in the water there will be a kilogram in the steam.

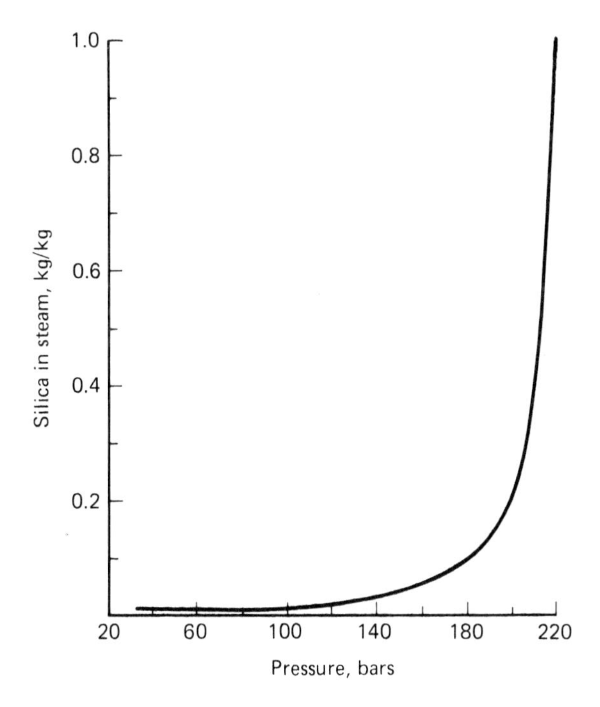

Figure 1.21. Silica in steam at various pressures

It follows that silica control becomes more important the higher the pressure. This, then, is the kind of consideration that led to the development of extremely efficient water treatment plants whose output water contains practically zero undesirable contaminants. Having achieved such a quality it was a logical step to use it for direct spray injection for superheater and, if required, reheater temperature control.

Summary of heat addition

From the previous sections it has been established that for the 100 bar/566°C case considered, the addition of sensible, latent and superheat resulted in a total heat addition of:

Sensible heat	1307.0 kJ/kg
Latent heat	1319.7 kJ/kg
Superheat	811.6 kJ/kg
	3438.3 kJ/kg at 100 bar 566° C

Remember, this is the heat contained in the steam above *absolute zero* temperature as shown in *Figure 1.17*.

Work done in the turbine and thermal efficiency

In the Ideal Cycle the steam expands in the turbine and the expansion is assumed to be frictionless and adiabatic. (An adiabatic expansion is one in which all the work done by the steam is at the expense of its internal energy, no heat being accepted or rejected during the expansion.) Hence, the expansion takes place at constant entropy. So in the case being considered the steam would enter the turbine at 100 bar abs. 566°C and entropy 6.8043 kJ/kg K. The expansion of the steam would continue at this entropy until its pressure was reduced to 30 mbar, (24.1°C). Condensation at a constant temperature of 24.1°C would then take place until all the latent heat had been removed. So the heat to be removed from the steam in the condenser is represented by the rectangle under FA in *Figure 1.22*.

$$\begin{aligned}\text{So heat rejected} &= (\text{absolute temperature of FA}) \times (6.8043 - 0.3544)\\ &= (24.1 + 273.15) \times (6.8043 - 0.3544)\\ &= 297.25 \times 6.4499\\ &= 1917.2\ \text{kJ/kg}\end{aligned}$$

It is clear from the diagram that the rejected heat represents a considerable proportion of the total.

The efficiency of the cycle is determined as follows:

$$\text{Thermal efficiency} = \frac{\text{useful heat}}{\text{total heat}}$$

$$\text{But useful heat} = \text{Total heat} - \text{rejected heat}$$

$$\text{So thermal efficiency} = \frac{\text{Total heat} - \text{rejected heat}}{\text{total heat}}$$

$$= 1 - \frac{\text{rejected heat}}{\text{total heat}}$$

In the case being considered the total heat is 3438.2 kJ/kg and the heat rejected is 1917.2 kJ/kg.

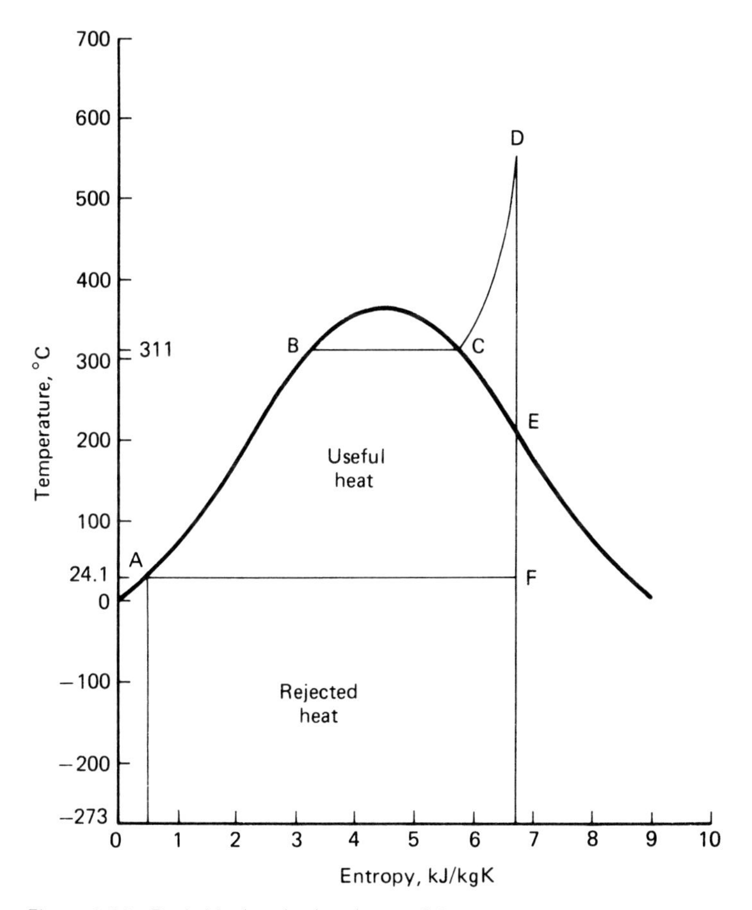

Figure 1.22. Basic ideal cycle showing useful and rejected heat components

$$\text{So the thermal efficiency} = 1 - \frac{1917.2}{3438.2}$$

$$= \mathbf{0.4423 \text{ or } 44.23\%}$$

This is the highest efficiency possible for a basic Rankine cycle with steam at 100 bar absolute, 566°C and condensing at 30 mbar. It assumes that every component is perfect, so in practice the efficiency achieved would be considerably less.

There are two ways to improve the basic Rankine efficiency:

1. Reduce the rejected heat component.
2. Increase the useful heat component.

The rejected heat component is dependent primarily upon the condensation temperature and this, in its turn, is determined by the cooling water temperature. Usually there is little control over this.

The useful heat component is determind largely by the steam temperature and this is limited by the temperature of the superheater metal. As better materials have been developed so the possible steam temperatures have increased. Thus there is only limited scope for increasing the steam temperature until the metallurgists can provide suitable materials for even more elevated conditions.

Reheating

One available way to improve the efficiency while still operating within the restricting limits of upper and lower temperature is to resort to reheating. The first reheat boiler was installed at North Tees Power Station in England in 1921. The turbine stop valve conditions were 31 bar, 343°C. As higher superheat temperatures were achieved reheating became unnecessary until after World War II.

Consider the previous 100 bar cycle, but this time with reheat. Suppose the reheating takes place when the steam pressure is 20 bar absolute. The cycle is shown in *Figure 1.23*. Reheating takes place to 566°C. The total heat is now the same as for the non-reheat cycle considered earlier PLUS the area under the curve GH.

So total heat = 3438.2 + (heat at H − heat at G)
= 3438.2 + (3613.0 − 3048.2)
= 3438.2 + 564.8
= **4003.0 kJ/kg**

Heat rejected = Area under line JA
= abs. temp. at J × Entropy change from J to A
= 297.25 (7.6134 − 0.3544)
= **2157.7 kJ/kg**

$$\text{Thermal efficiency} = 1 - \frac{\text{rejected heat}}{\text{total heat}}$$

$$= 1 - \frac{2157.7}{4003.0}$$

= 0.4609 = **46.09%**

So reheating has improved the Ideal Cycle efficiency from 44.23% to 46.09%. A further advantage of reheating is that the wetness of the exhaust steam is reduced considerably.

The Ideal Cycle efficiency for turbine conditions of 158.6 bar/566°C/566°C (the standard conditions for modern UK plant) is about 47.20%. The only difference between these conditions and the 100 bar case considered above is the steam pressure, i.e. 158.6 bar compared to 100 bar. This indicates that it is advantageous to use not only the highest economical temperature, but also the highest economical pressure.

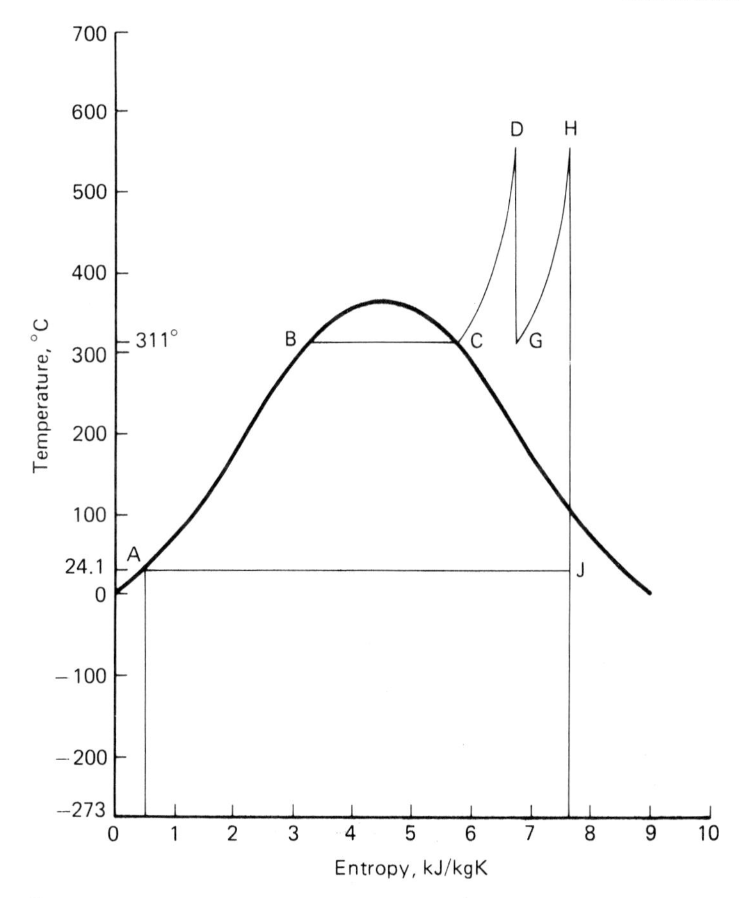

Figure 1.23 Modified basic cycle to incorporate reheat

Feed heating

One other very important way to improve the cycle efficiency has not yet been discussed and that is by feed heating. Steam bled from a turbine for feed heating will surrender its superheat, latent heat and, possibly, some sensible heat to the feed water thus relieving the boiler of a comparable amount of work. If there had been no feed heating the steam would have surrendered a large quantity of heat to the C.W. system where it is a waste, whereas with feed heating it is employed usefully.

Consider the cycle shown in *Figure 1.24*. The steam expands isentropically in the turbine until the temperature is 250°C after which some steam is bled to an infinite number of feed heaters. The result is that the quantity of heat represented by the area under the curve KL is transferred to the water side shown by the area under the curve AM. Note that M and K are both at 250°C

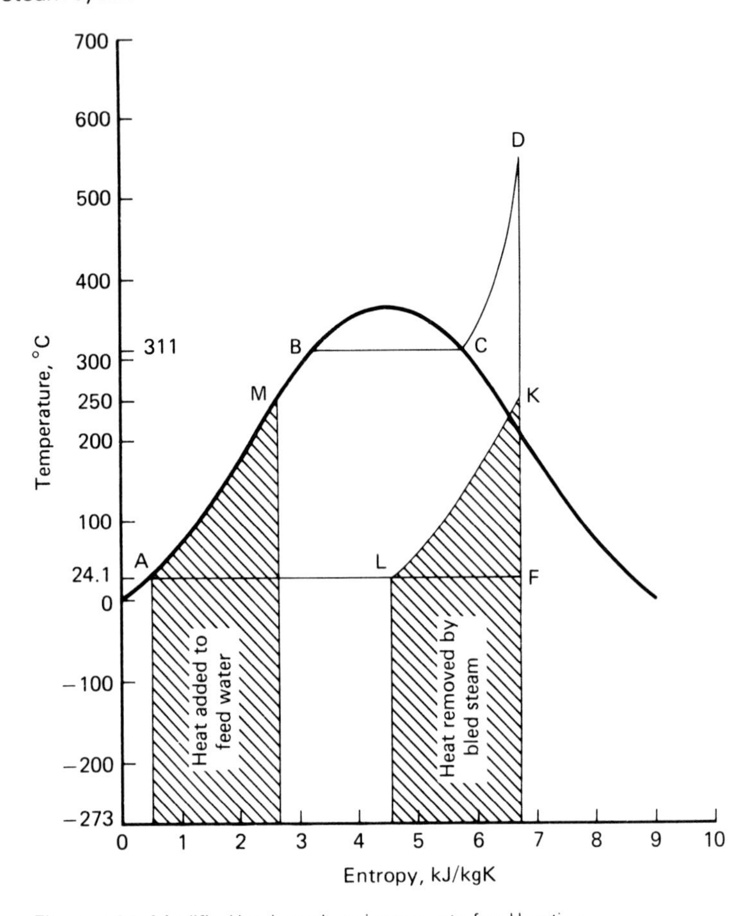

Figure 1.24 Modified basic cycle to incorporate feed heating

and the curve KL is identical to the curve MA. So the result is that the water now has a final feed temperature of 250°C. The heat represented by the area under LF has been given to the feed whereas before it would have been rejected in the condenser. The heat represented by the area LKF has also been transferred to the feed water, whereas formerly it would have done useful work in the turbine so this represents a loss of work, but on balance it is better to lose the power from the triangle LKF to save the heat represented by the large rectangle that would have been wasted.

The cycle with feed heating can be represented in two ways as shown in *Figures 1.25* and *1.26*. The magnitude of the Useful Heat and Rejected Heat areas are the same in each case. *Figure 1.26* is convenient for many calculations. In *Figure 1.25* point K indicates the point at which bleeding commences. The quantity of bled steam increases from K to L and the amount of

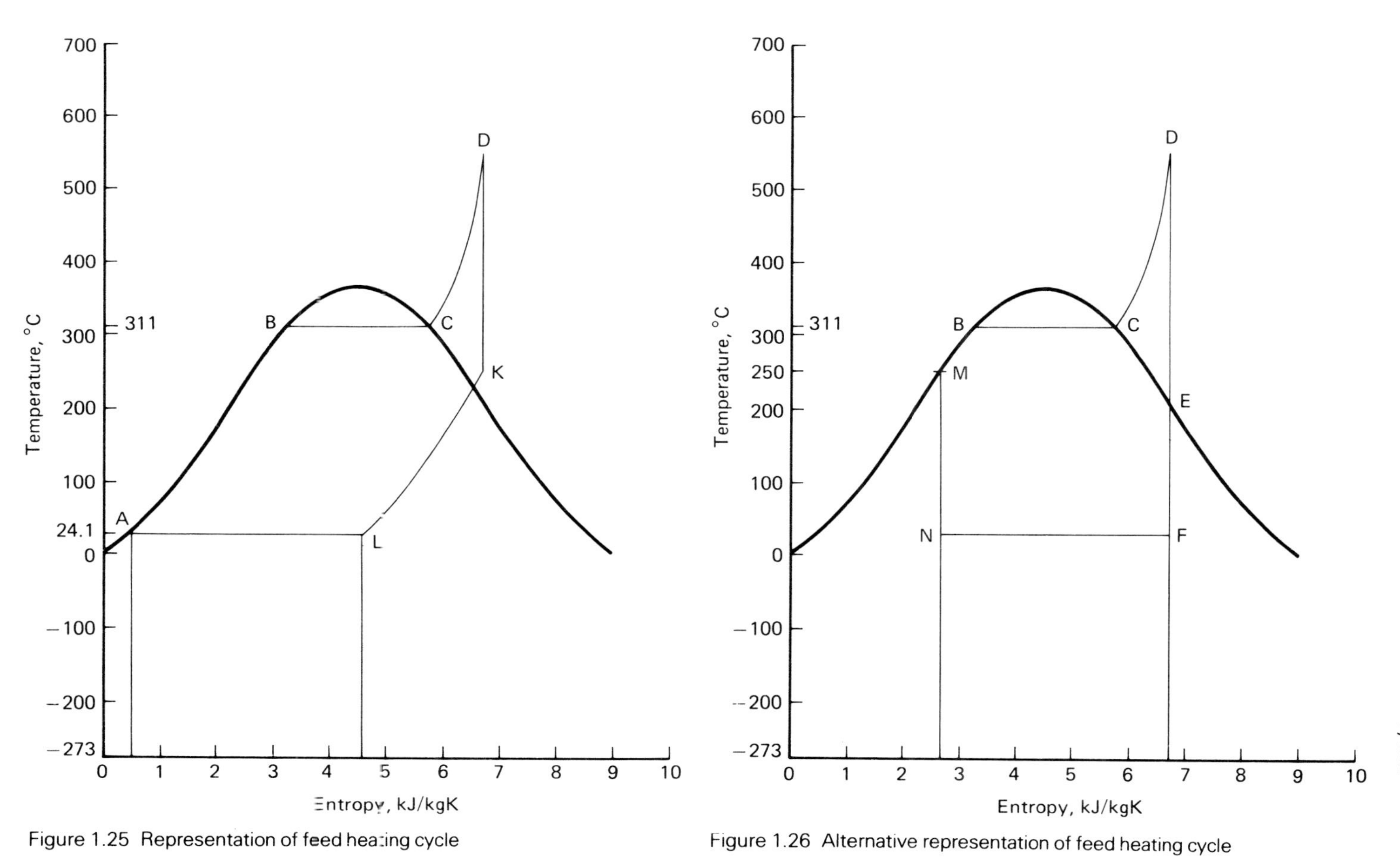

Figure 1.25 Representation of feed heating cycle

Figure 1.26 Alternative representation of feed heating cycle

bled steam is calculated as shown in *Figure 1.27*, i.e. the length of the line Y represents one kilogram of steam entering the condenser when there is no feed heating. The length of the line is proportional to the entropy change.

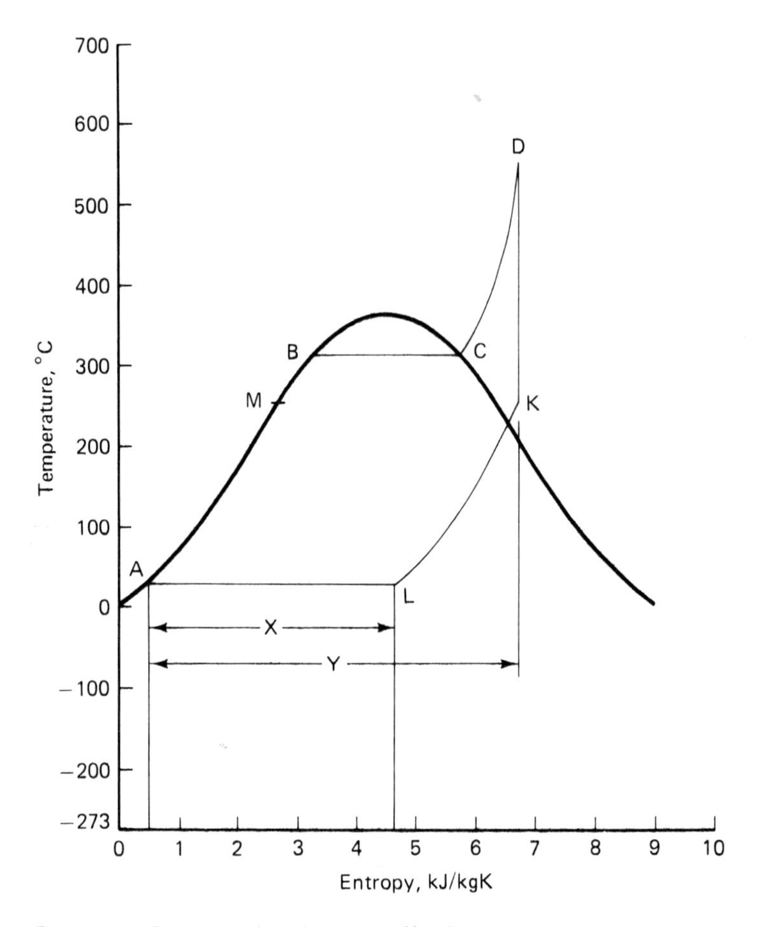

Figure 1.27 Determination of quantity of bled steam

The length of the line X represents the quantity of steam entering the condenser when there is feed heating.

The entropy change of $Y = 6.4495$ and of $X = 4.0104$.

So the steam to condenser with feed heating $= \frac{4.01}{6.45} = 0.62$ kg/kg of steam at the turbine stop valve. Thus the bled steam quantity $=$ 0.38 kg/kg steam.

Feed heating elevates the condensate temperature represented at A along the boiling water line to M and the remaining sensible heat is supplied in the economizer and boiler to point B.

The efficiency of the cycle is calculated as follows – refer to *Figure 1.26*.

Total heat supplied = sensible heat from M to B + latent heat + superheat.

The latent and superheats have already been calculated and amount to 1319.7 and 811.6 kJ/kg respectively.

Sensible heat = total heat at B − total heat at M
= 1408.0 − 1085.8 (from steam tables)
= **322.2 kJ/kg**

So total heat supplied = 322.2 + 1319.7 + 811.6
= **2453.5 kJ/kg**

Heat rejected = area under NF
= absolute temperature at F × entropy change from F to N
= 297.25 (6.8043 − 2.7935)
= **1192.2 kJ/kg**

$$\text{So efficiency} = 1 - \frac{\text{rejected heat}}{\text{total heat}}$$

$$= 1 - \frac{1192.2}{2453.5} = 1 - 0.4860$$

= **0.5140** or **51.4%**

Notice how the efficiency has changed by introducing reheating and feed heating:

Basic cycle efficiency (*Figure 1.22*) = 44.23%
Reheat cycle efficiency (*Figure 1.23*) = 46.09%
Feed heating cycle efficiency (*Figure 1.25*) = 51.40%

A combination of reheating and feed heating will give an even higher ideal cycle efficiency.

The Carnot Cycle

From the foregoing it is pertinent to consider what is the ultimate efficiency possible. *Figure 1.28* is a reproduction of *Figure 1.22*. Within the limits of the stipulated upper and lower temperatures, it is clear that to obtain the *maximum* useful heat for the given quantity of rejected heat the area ABCDF should be as large as possible, i.e. ideally it should be a rectangle as shown by AWDF.

$$\text{Thermal efficiency} = \frac{\text{added heat} - \text{rejected heat}}{\text{added heat}}$$

Added heat = abs. temp. at W × (entropy change from W to D)
Rejected heat = abs. temp. at A × (entropy change from A to F)

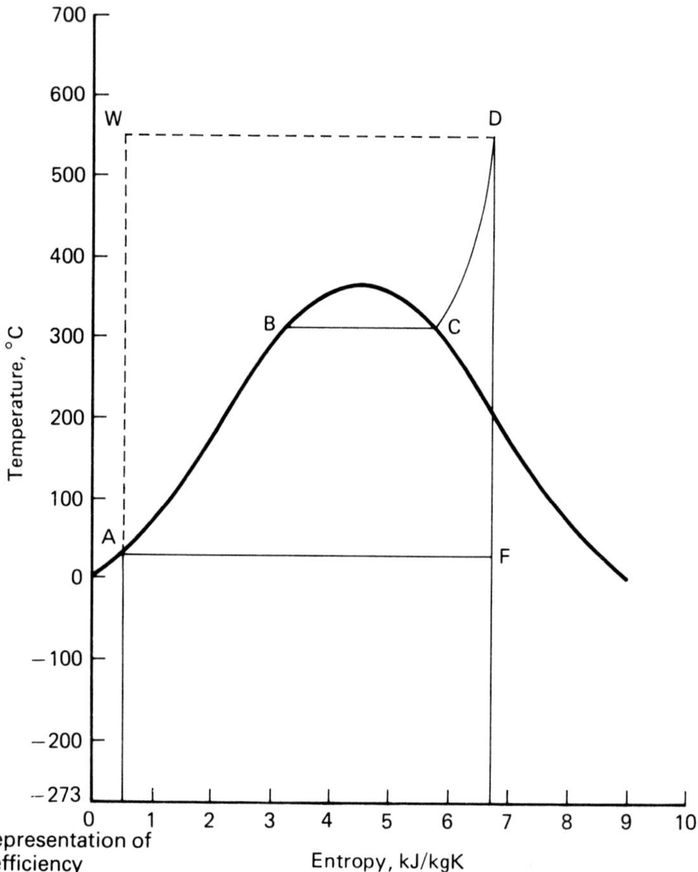

Figure 1.28 Representation of Carnot cycle efficiency

but the entropy change WD is identical to AF, and let it be denoted by $S_2 - S_1$.

Then thermal efficiency =

$$\frac{(566 + 273.15)(S_2 - S_1) - (24.1 + 273.15)(S_2 - S_1)}{(566 + 273.15)(S_2 - S_1)}$$

$$= \frac{(566 + 273.15) - (24.1 + 273.15)}{(566 + 273.15)}$$

$$= \frac{839.15 - 297.25}{839.15}$$

$= \mathbf{0.6458}$ **or 64.58%**

This is the Carnot efficiency and is the *maximum possible for any substance working between those limits of temperature.*

In general terms the Carnot efficiency $= \dfrac{T_1 - T_2}{T_1}$

where T_1 = the upper absolute temperature
T_2 = the lower absolute temperature

Notice that the heat addition and heat rejection are isothermal processes (i.e. are carried out at constant temperature), and that the expansion and compression of the working substance is isentropic. Of course no such substance as portrayed in the Carnot cycle exists, but the Carnot efficiency is important as it enables the maximum possible thermal efficiency to be determined for any given upper and lower temperature limits irrespective of the working substance used. The name 'Carnot' is used because the originator of the concept was the French thermodynamicist Sadi Carnot (1796–1832)

Modified Rankine Cycle to allow for pumping

In all the Rankine cycles that have been considered so far the effects of pumping have been ignored. However, if these effects are to be considered the cycle will be as in *Figure 1.29.*

At point A the water is pressurized to the pressure corresponding to the saturation temperature at B, in this case 100 bar abs. As the water has had work done on it its temperature will rise isentropically as shown from A to P. Subsequent feed heating is represented by the constant pressure line PB. It is clear that there has now been a slight change of heat to the cycle as represented by the area APB. *Figure 1.30* shows the approximate temperature rise that will result from isentropic compression of water. In the case being considered it will only be about 0.4°C. The quantity of heat represented by the area APB is small and may normally be ignored – see *Figure 1.31.*

The equivalent Carnot Cycle

The Equivalent Carnot Cycle is one which is the equivalent of a given Rankine Cycle. The temperature is assumed to be constant at the average temperature at which heat is received in the Rankine Cycle. The temperature at which heat is rejected is the same for both cycles – see *Figure 1.32.*

Consider the basic 100 bar/566°C cycle considered earlier. The total heat supplied amounted to 3438.2 kJ/kg and the entropy change was from 6.8039 to 0.3544 kJ/kgK, i.e. 6.4495 kJ/kgK. Therefore, the average temperature is

$$\frac{3438.2}{6.4495} = 533.1 \text{ K}$$

The temperature at which the heat is rejected is 297.25 K. The equivalent Carnot Cycle is shown dotted in *Figure 1.32.*

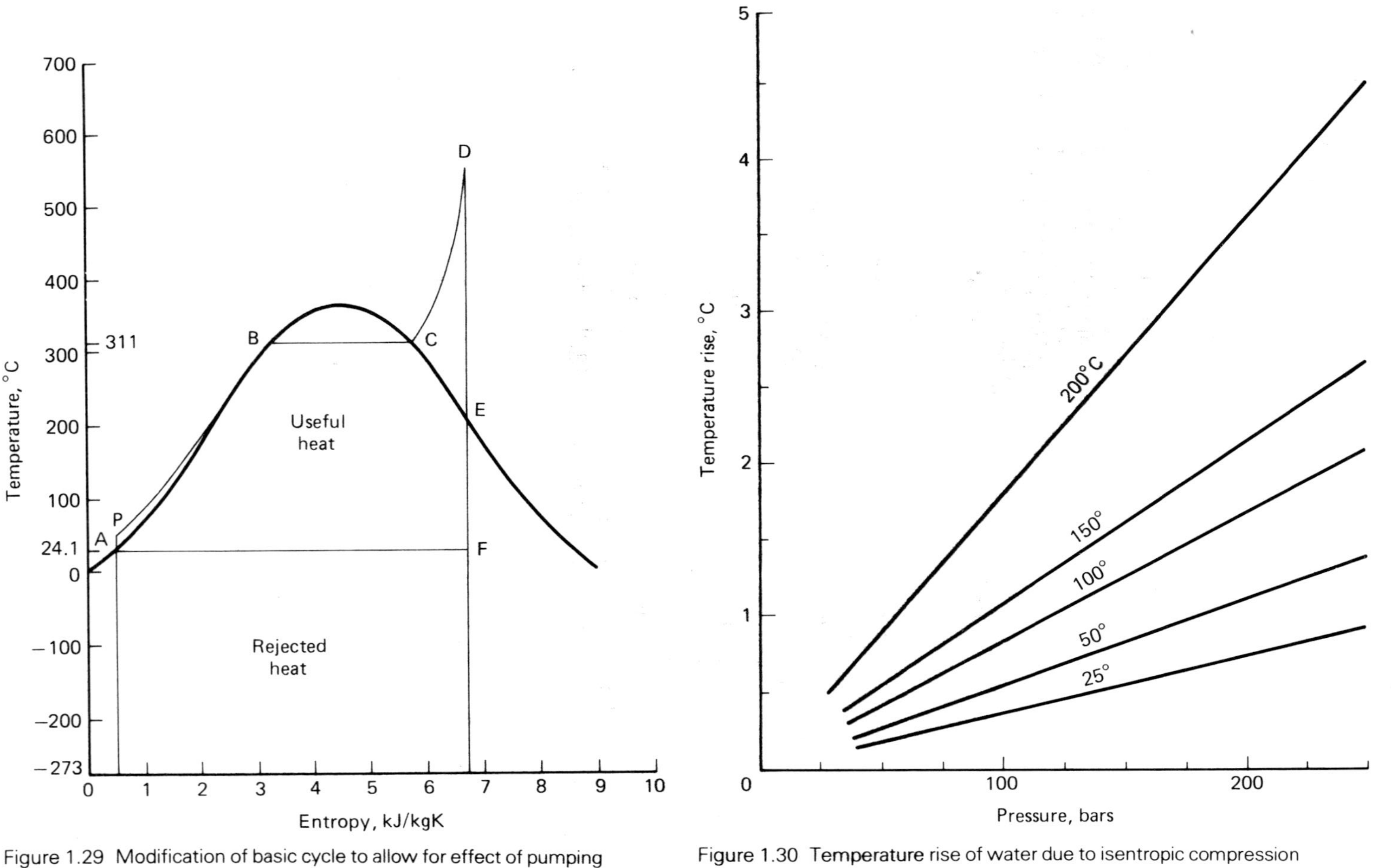

Figure 1.29 Modification of basic cycle to allow for effect of pumping

Figure 1.30 Temperature rise of water due to isentropic compression

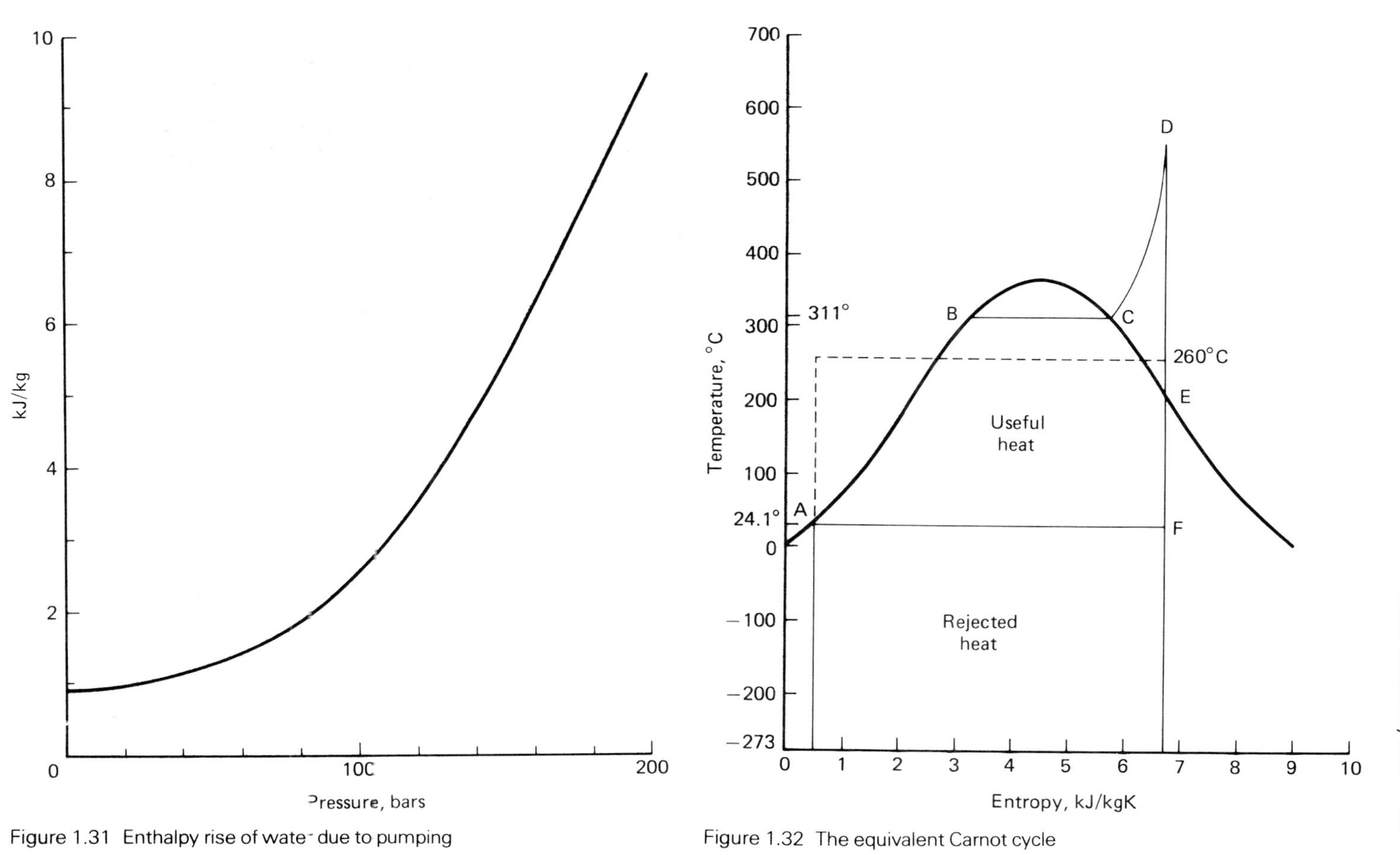

Figure 1.31 Enthalpy rise of wate- due to pumping

Figure 1.32 The equivalent Carnot cycle

$$\text{So the equivalent Carnot Cycle efficiency} = \frac{533.1 - 297.25}{\mathbf{533.1}} = \mathbf{44.24\%}$$

Thus the Rankine cycle efficiency and the equivalent Carnot cycle efficiency give the same result (see *Figures 1.22* and *1.32*). This makes the Equivalent Carnot Cycle very useful for comparing the merits of, say, using different pressures for cycles with a given rejection temperature. For example, consider a simple cycle wherein the steam temperature is 560°C and the condensation temperature is 25°C. Compare the efficiencies if the pressure of the steam is 50, 150 and 300 bar absolute respectively. The three cycles are drawn in *Figure 1.33*.

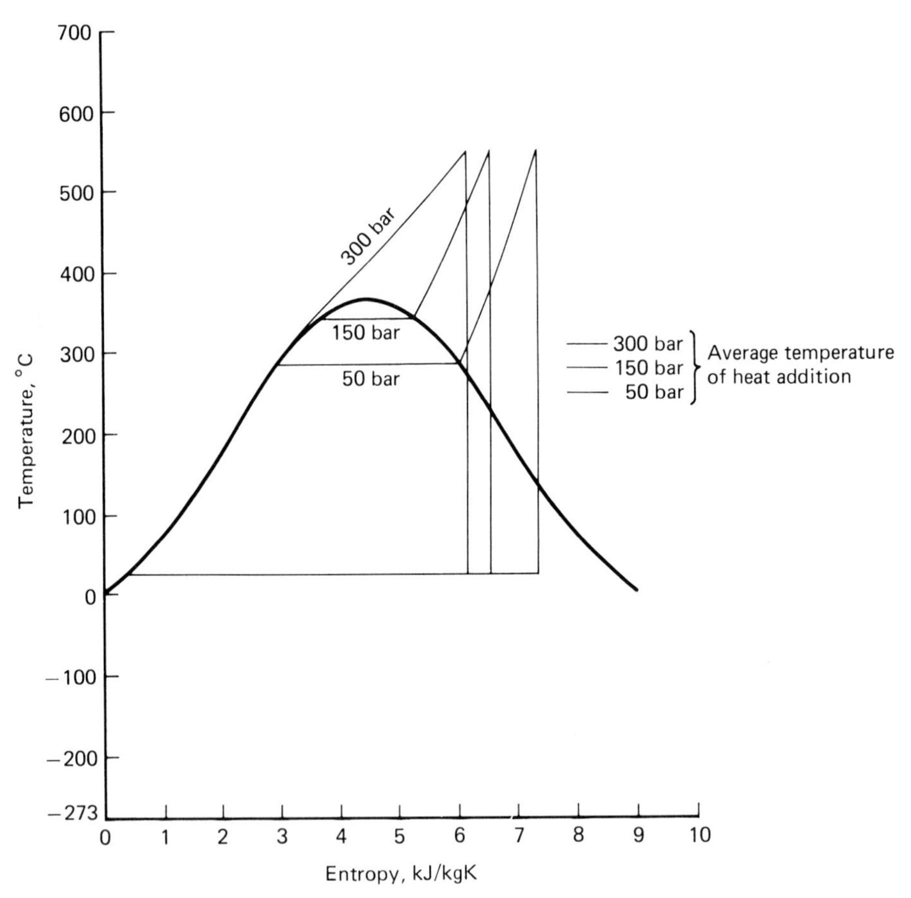

Figure 1.33 Rankine cycle and equivalent Carnot cycle temperatures for different pressures

Reference to *Figure 1.33* shows that the 300 bar cycle efficiency is highest because the heat addition line is continually rising, whereas in the 150 bar

Table 1.5 Equivalent Carnot efficiency

1	Abs. pressure at TSV	bar	50	150	300
2	Temperature at TSV	°C	560	560	560
3	Total heat at TSV	kJ/kg	3572.0	3475.0	3312.1
4	Entropy at TSV	kJ/kg K	7.1494	6.5535	6.0805
5	Entropy of condensate	kJ/kg K	0.3670	0.3670	0.3670
6	Entropy change	kJ/kg K	6.7824	6.1865	5.7135
7	Average temp. of heating $= \frac{(3)}{(6)}$	K	526.7	561.7	579.7
8	Average temp. of heat rejection	K	298.15	298.15	298.15
9	Equivalent Carnot efficiency $= \frac{(7)-(8)}{(7)} \times 100$	%	43.4	46.9	48.6

case there is a plateau of latent heat addition which does not increase the temperature and in the 50 bar cycle the plateau is even more pronounced.

On the other hand the exhaust wetness increases with pressure, and for a practical cycle the maximum wetness is 12%. Thus there is a limiting value of pressure for a given wetness.

The total heat–entropy (H–S) diagram

The temperature–entropy diagram is very useful for certain purposes. However, a more often used diagram for practical work was devised by Richard Mollier (1863–1935) and so is often called a Mollier Chart, although the correct name is the Total Heat Entropy Diagram. The larger the diagram, of course, the more accurately it can be read. A coloured chart measuring 106 cm × 80 cm is available from Edward Arnold Ltd.

Vertical distances on these charts represent heat (enthalpy) change. *Figure 1.34* shows the skeleton of a total heat–entropy diagram. On it the line 'bc' represents a throttling expansion, 'cd' isentropic expansion and 'ce' a practical expansion. Notice that the heat drop is greater for 'cd' than for 'ce'. This is because, in a practical turbine, the steam is subjected to the effects of friction, eddies and other forms of inefficiency. The effect of them is to cause some reheating of the steam and so, of the isentropic heat drop theoretically available, only about 85% of it is realized in practice.

The turbine conditions line 'ce' is shown in *Figure 1.34* as a straight line, but a more accurate representation is shown in *Figure 1.35*. The steam is throttled from turbine stop valve to after throttle valve conditions represented by the horizontal line. It then does work in the turbine. Because of the relatively inefficient first stage in many turbines the first part of the expansion line slopes from left to right more than the subsequent portion. Towards the bottom of the condition line it curves more and more to the right because the steam is in the wet region and so the expansion is becoming less and less efficient. Finally the steam leaves the last row of moving blades at exhaust pressure with considerable kinetic energy. If the steam could be

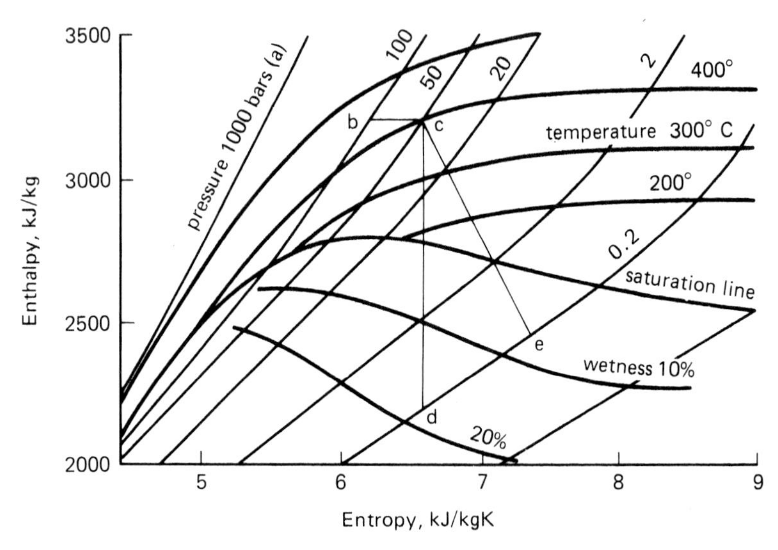

Figure 1.34 Skeleton of an enthalpy-entropy diagram

brought to rest the final state point would be as shown.

The maximum tolerable wetness of the steam is normally regarded as 12% at the last stage. With an isentropic expansion the maximum pressure for a non-reheat machine is about 28 bar. In fact, though, in a real turbine there are inefficiencies which cause the expansion line to slope from left to right. Hence, in a real cycle it is possible to operate at a pressure of 103 bar and still not have excessive wetness at the exhaust.

For example there are 100 MW non-reheat machines in the UK which operate at 103 bar, 566°C inlet steam, 30 mbar back-pressure conditions, so the wetness at the exhaust is close to the limit (*Figure 1.36*). In hot countries the attainable back pressure may only be of the order of 80 mbar or higher. In such cases, of course, it is possible to have more elevated inlet steam conditions without excessive wetness at the exhaust, although a compromise will usually be reached between them. For example, some turbines in New Delhi, India, operate at 87.2 bar, 510°C inlet steam, 85 mbar back pressure. The exhaust wetness is about 9%.

Referring again to *Figure 1.36* it is seen that with the stated back pressure even using the highest steam temperature the wetness would be intolerable at pressures higher than 140 bar. If higher pressures are used it follows that it will be necessary to resort to reheating. *Figure 1.37* shows the condition lines for the expansion of the steam in a reheat turbine with a bled steam boiler feed pump turbine whose steam is supplied from the HP cylinder exhaust.

Until it is possible to operate with higher steam temperatures, reheating will remain necessary. *Figure 1.38* shows a Rankine cycle with reheat, operating at 160 bar, 570°C. If the steam temperature could be raised to 760°C the reheating would be unnecessary.

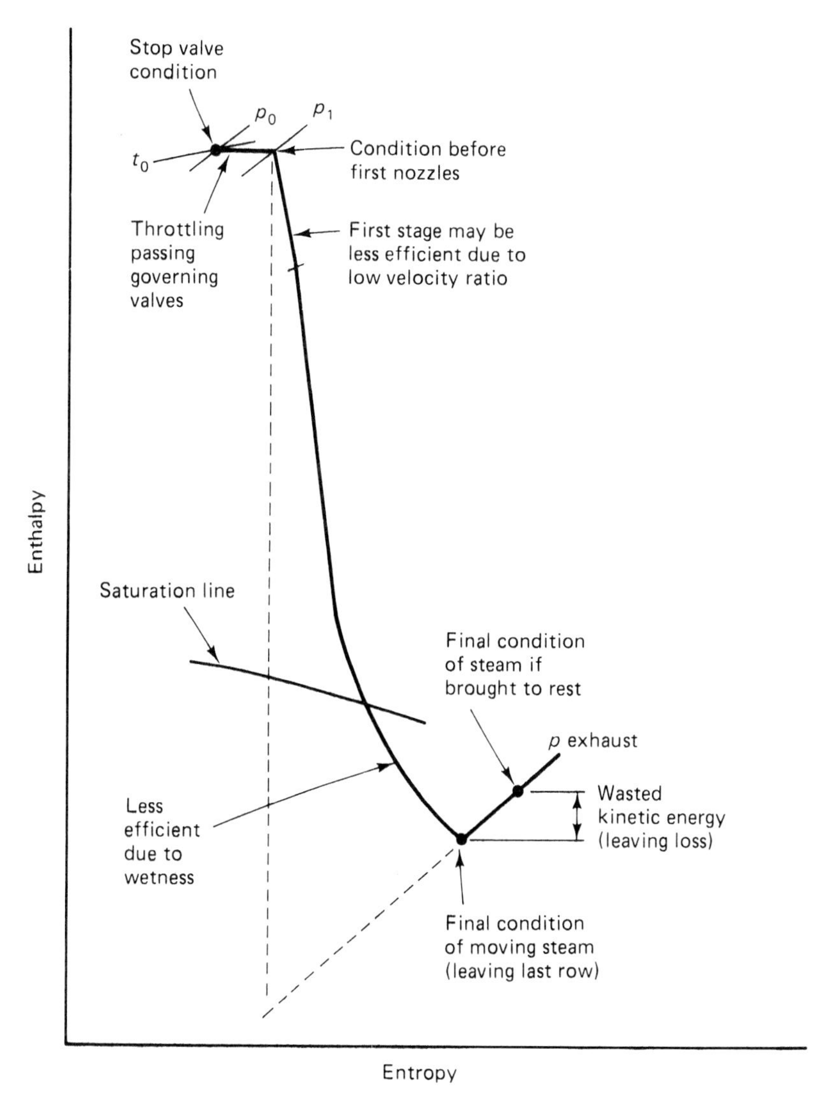

Figure 1.35. Typical turbine condition line on an enthalpy-entropy diagram (CEGB)

Questions on steam cycles

1. What is Gibbs Function?
2. What is the latent heat required to evaporate boiling water whose temperature is 205°C and the entropy change required is 4.0 kJ/kgK?
3. What is 'circulation factor'?
4 Why are boiler circulation pumps required?
5 Is the proportion of superheat surface greater or less in a large modern boiler than a small one? Why?

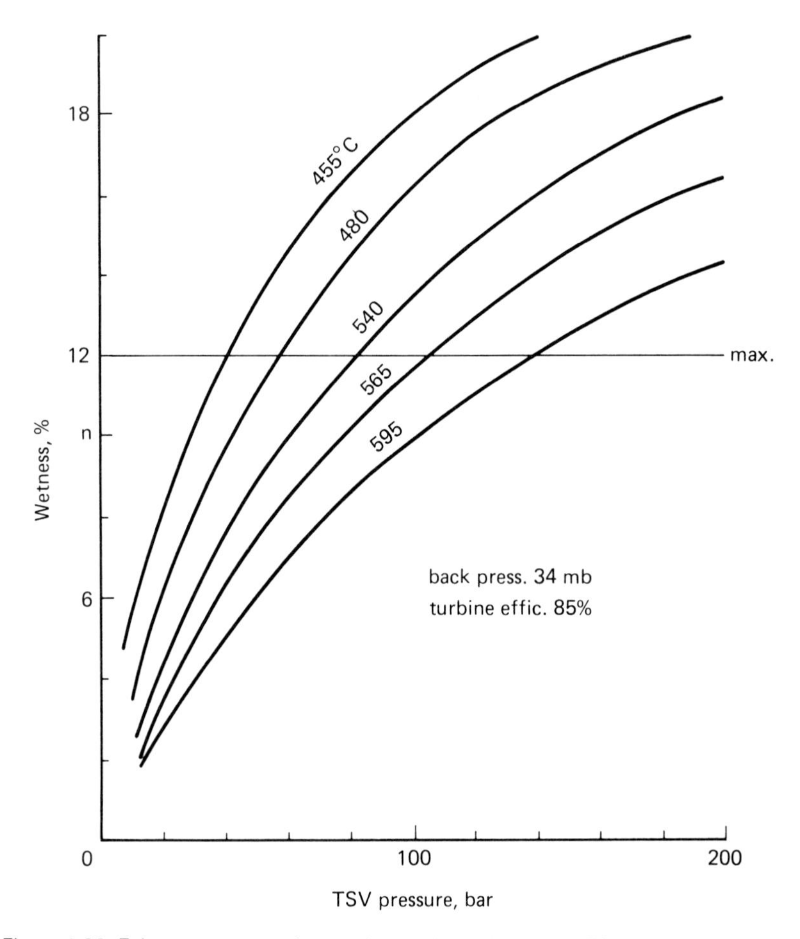

Figure 1.36 Exhaust wetness of non-reheat turbines for various TSV steam temperatures and pressures

6 What factors led to the introduction of spray desuperheaters?
7 What is the heat and entropy of water at 0°C?
8 What methods are used to increase the efficiency of a basic Rankine cycle?
9 What is the maximum possible efficiency of a cycle working between temperature limits of 500°C and 50°C?
10 What is the 'transition' zone?
11 As pressure increases with a basic Rankine cycle what happens to the:

(a) sensible heat; (b) latent heat; (c) superheat; (d) Rankine efficiency; (e) wetness at exhaust; (f) entropy change? Assume the TSV and condensation temperatures remain constant.

12 Why is reheating necessary?
13 What is one use of the Equivalent Carnot Cycle?
14 Why are boiler circulation pumps of such large capacity?

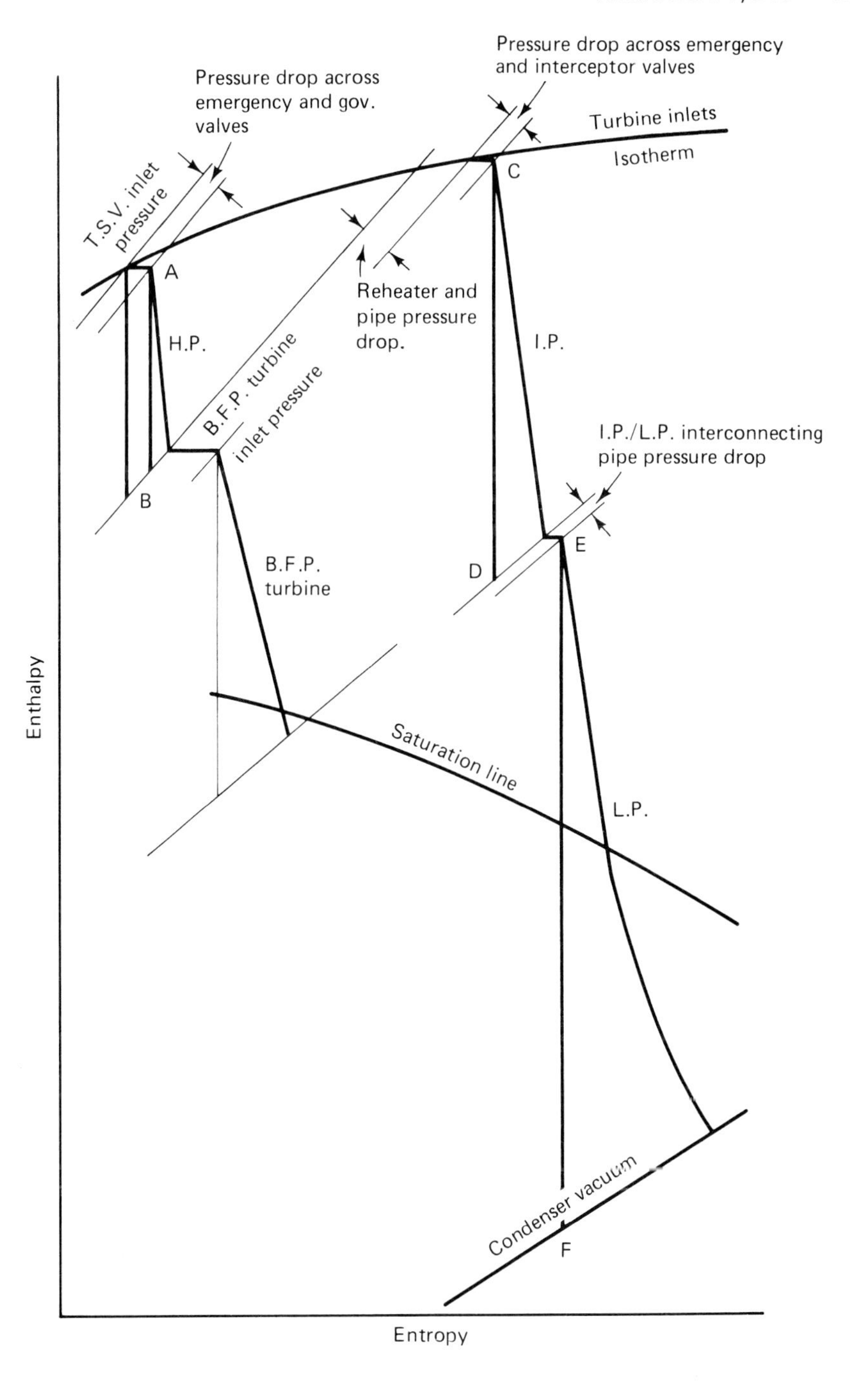

Figure 1.37 Condition lines for a practical reheat turbine incorporating a boiler feed pump turbine supplied from the H.P. cylinder exhaust (CEGB)

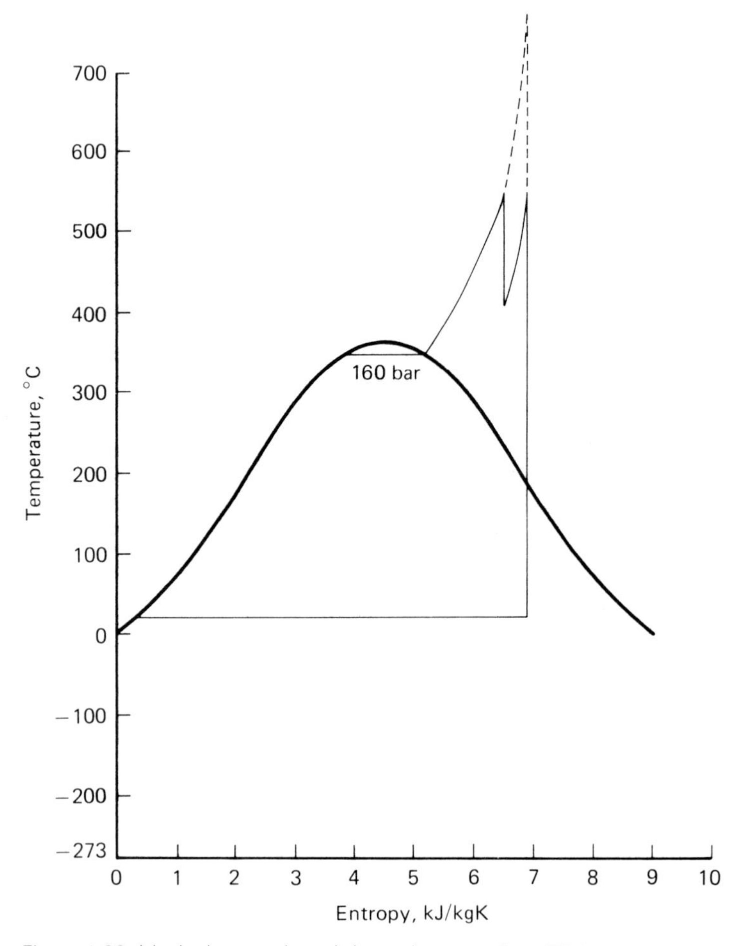

Figure 1.38 Ideal reheat cycle and alternative non-reheat TSV temperature

15 Why do some supercritical boiler furnace wall tubes run horizontally?
16 What causes natural circulation in a boiler?
17 In a T–S diagram showing a feed heating cycle, what is the wetness of the steam at the exhaust?
18 Why does feed heating improve the cycle efficiency?
19 What are the causes of inefficiency in a practical turbine?
20 Would operating a turbine with a lower TSV temperature than design, increase or decrease the wetness at the exhaust on a reheat turbine?

Exercise 1

The terminal conditions of the 62.5 MW non-reheat turbines at Indraprastha Power Station in New Delhi are:

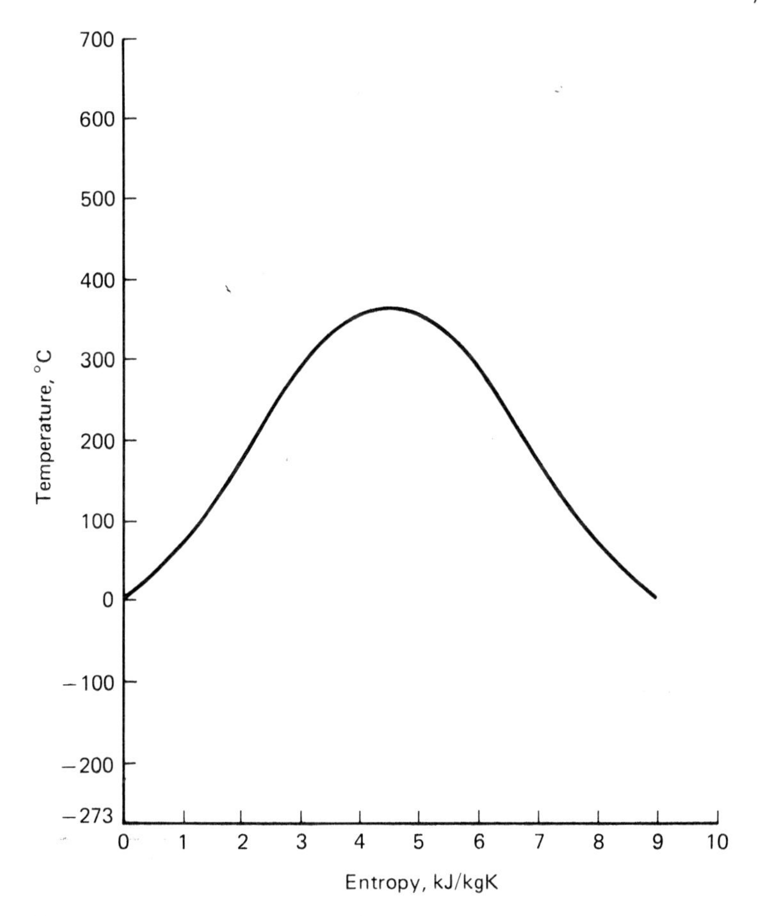

Figure 1.39 T-S diagram for use with Exercise 1

TSV absolute temperature and pressure	= 87.2 bar/510°C
Final feed temperature	= 217°C
Back pressure	= 84.66 mbar
Saturation temperature at back pressure	= 42.5°C
Saturation temperature at 87.2 bar abs.	= 301°C

(a) Draw the ideal cycle on a T–S diagram.
(b) Calculate the ideal cycle efficiency.
(c) Calculate the equivalent Carnot cycle efficiency.
(d) If the alternator output is 80% of the available heat what is the overall turbo-alternator efficiency?
(e) Calculate the Carnot cycle efficiency.

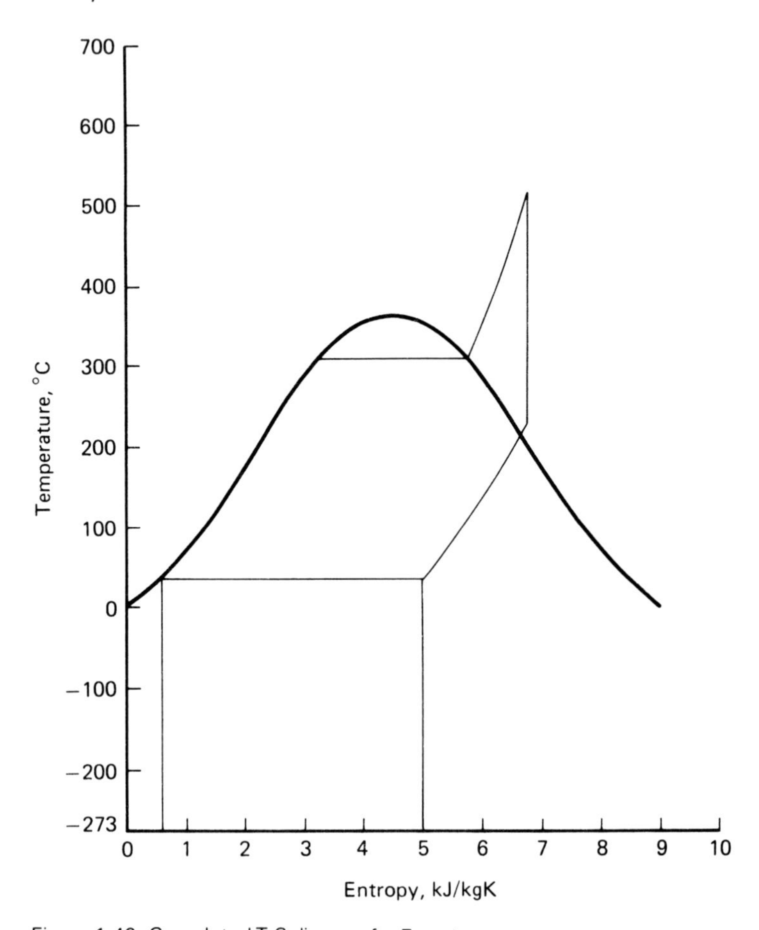

Figure 1.40 Completed T-S diagram for Exercise 1

Exercise 1 (Answer)

Indraprastha Power Station

1	Rating	MW	62.5
2	TSV pressure	bar abs.	87.2
3 T_1	TSV temperature	°C/K	510/783.15
4	Back pressure	mbar	84.66
5	Final feed temperature	°C	217.0
6 H_1	Total heat at TSV	kJ/kg	3415
7 Lf	Sensible heat in final feed	kJ/kg	929.8
8 T_2	Condensate temperature	°C/K	42.5/315.65
9 S_2	Entropy at TSV	kJ/kg K	6.7097
10 S_1	Entropy of final feed	kJ/kg K	2.4899
11 $H_1 - Lf$	Heat supplied	kJ/kg K	2485.2

12 S_2-S_1	Entropy change during heat rejection	kJ/kg K	4.2198
13 $T_2(S_2-S_1)$	Heat rejected	kJ/kg	1332.0
14 (11)−(13)	Work done	kJ/kg	1153.2
15	Rankine Cycle efficiency $= \frac{(14) \times 100}{(11)}$	%	46.4
16 T_3	Average temperature of heat supplied $= \frac{(11)}{(12)}$	K	588.9
17 T_4	Condensate temperature	K	315.65
18	Equivalent Carnot Cycle efficiency $= \frac{(16)-(17)}{(16)} \times 100$	%	46.4
19	T/A efficiency	%	80.0
20	Overall efficiency $= \frac{(18) \times (19)}{100}$	%	37.1
21	Carnot efficiency $\frac{T_1 - T_2}{T_1} \times 100$	%	59.7

Project No. 1 – Ideal Steam Cycles

Calculate:

(a) The ideal cycle efficiency of the two units whose conditions are listed. Use a different method for each.

	Unit 1	*Unit 2*
TSV pressure (absolute) (bars)	105	240
TSV temperature (°C)	540	590
Final feed temperature (°C)	224	270
Back pressure (mb)	35	30
Reheat temperature (°C)	540	570
Reheat pressure (absolute) (bars)	26	50

(b) The efficiency, if Unit 1 converts 81% and Unit 2 converts 83% of the available heat into electrical output.

(c) Draw the ideal cycle diagrams.

Project No. 1 Answer

			Unit 1	Unit 2
(a) Condensate temperature	T	°C/K	26.7/299.7	24.1/297.1
Entropy of final feed	S_1	kJ/kgK	2.5548	2.9763
Total heat at TSV	H_1	kJ/kg	3469.8	3469.9
Entropy at TSV	S	kJ/kgK	6.6987	6.3539
Total heat at R/H inlet	H_2	kJ/kg	3050.0	3013.0
Total heat at IP inlet	H_3	kJ/kg	3549.6	3595.1
Entropy at IP inlet	S_2	kJ/kgK	7.4170	7.1769
Heat in final feed water	h_f	kJ/kg	962.2	1185.2
Heat added in boiler = $H_1 - h_f$		kJ/kg	2507.6	2284.7
Heat added in R/H. = $H_3 - H_2$		kJ/kg	499.6	582.1
Total heat added	(1)	kJ/kg	3007.2	2866.8
Entropy change = $(S_2 - S_1)$	(2)	kJ/kgK	4.8622	4.2006
Heat rejected = $T(S_2 - S_1)$	(3)	kJ/kg	1457.2	1248.0
Work done = (1) − (3)	(4)	kJ/kg	1550.0	1618.8
Ideal cycle efficiency = $\frac{(4)100}{(1)}$	(5)	%	*51.5*	*56.5*
Alternatively				
Average temp. = (1) ÷ (2)	(6)	K	618.5	682.5
Equivalent Carnot efficiency = $\frac{(6)-T}{(6)} \times 100$	(7)	%	*51.5*	*56.5*
(b) Overal efficiency		%	41.7	46.9

Project 2

(a) What is the efficiency of the 100 bar reheat cycle shown in *Figure 1.23* if there is also feed heating to a final feed temperature of 250°C?
(b) Draw the cycle on the T–S diagram.
(c) What proportion of the steam is bled to the heaters?

Project 2 (Answer)

(a) Heat at M = 1085.8 kJ/kg (i.e. enthalpy of final feed)
Heat at B = 1408.0 kJ/kg
Latent heat addition = 1319.7 kJ/kg (*Figure 1.17*)
Superheat addition = 811.6 kJ/kg (*Figure 1.17*)
Reheat addition = 564.8 kJ/kg (*Figure 1.23*)
So total heat = (1408.0 − 1085.8) + 1319.7 + 811.6 + 564.8
= 3018.3 kJ/kg
Heat rejected = 297.25 × [entropy of J (*Figure 1.23*) − entropy of N (*Figure 1.26*)]

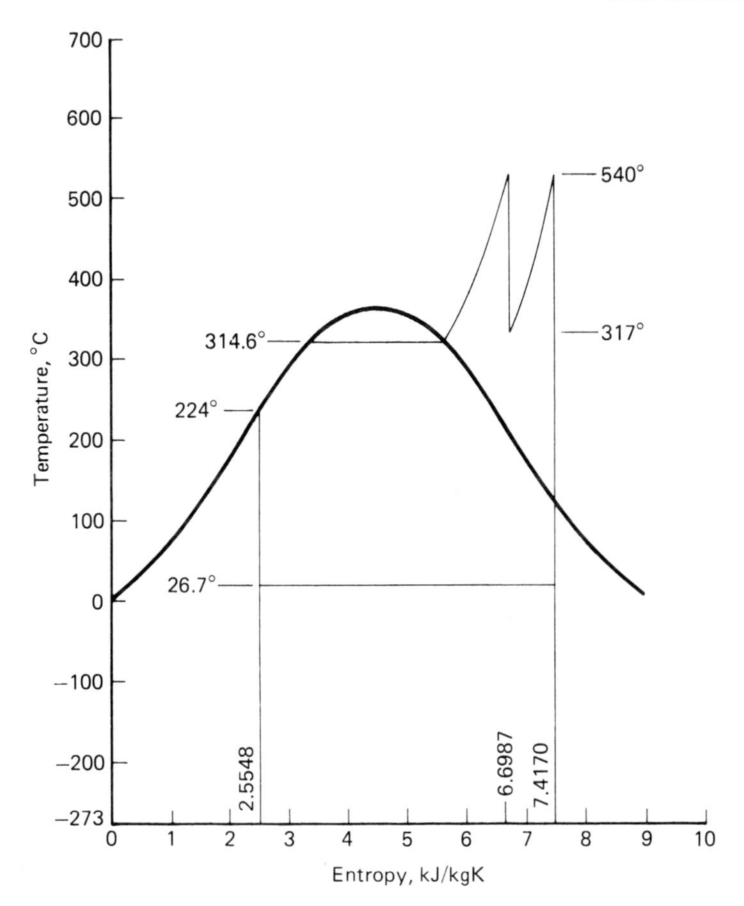

Figure 1.41 Completed T-S diagram for Project No. 1 (Unit No. 1.)

$$= 297.25 \times (7.6134 - 2.7935) = 1432.7 \text{ kJ/kg.}$$

$$\text{So efficiency} = 1 - \frac{1432.7}{3018.3} = 1 - 0.4747$$

$$= 0.5253 \text{ or } 52.53\%$$

(b) See *Figure 1.44*

(c) Proportion of steam to condenser is given by $\frac{X}{Y}$ in the figure.

$X = 7.6134 - 2.7935 = 4.8199$
$Y = 7.6134 - 0.3544 = 7.2590$
$\frac{X}{Y} = 0.664$, so 33.61% of the steam is bled.

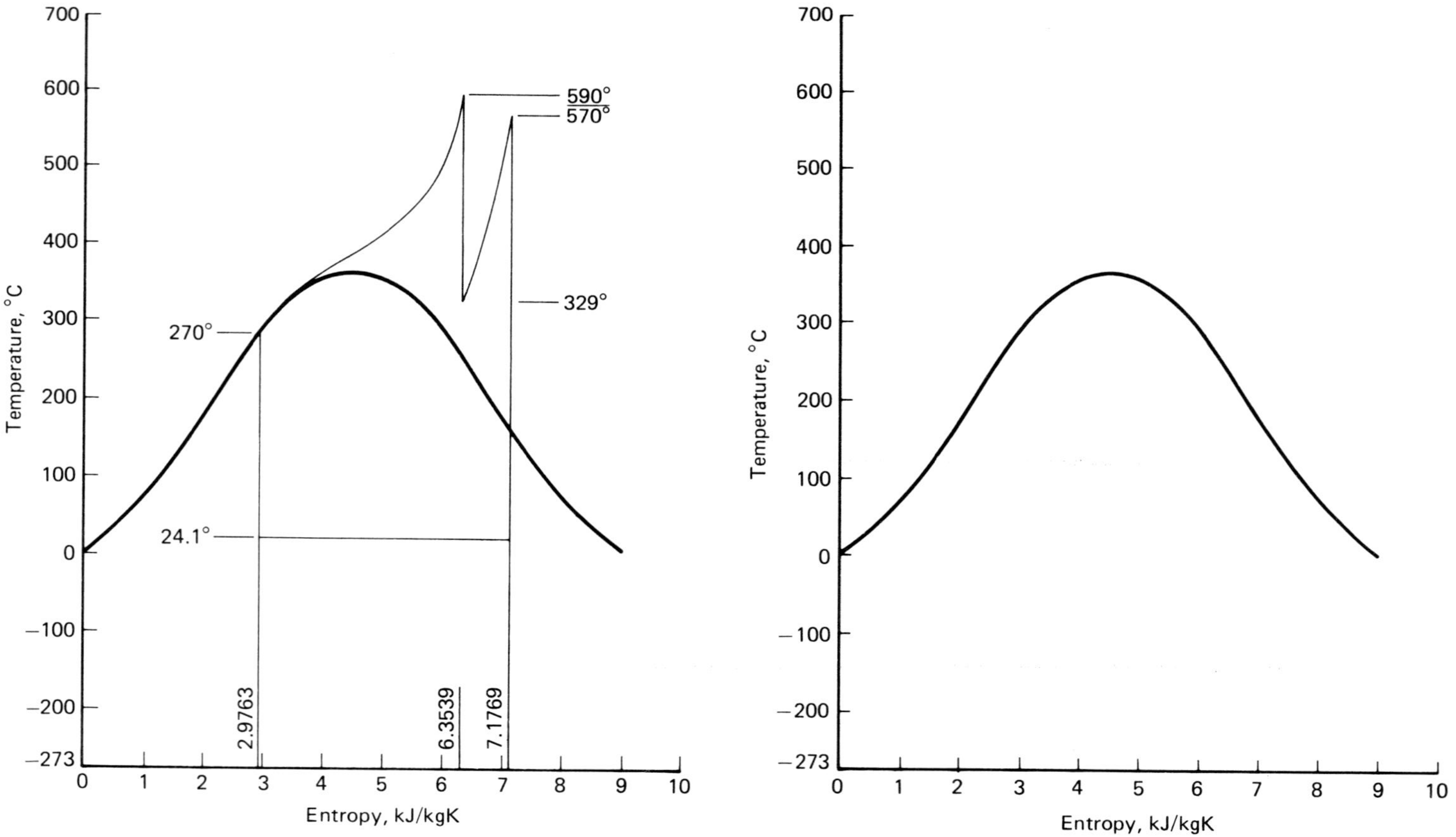

Figure 1.42 Complete T-S diagram for Project No. 1 (Unit No. 2)

Figure 1.43 T-S diagram for use with Project No. 2

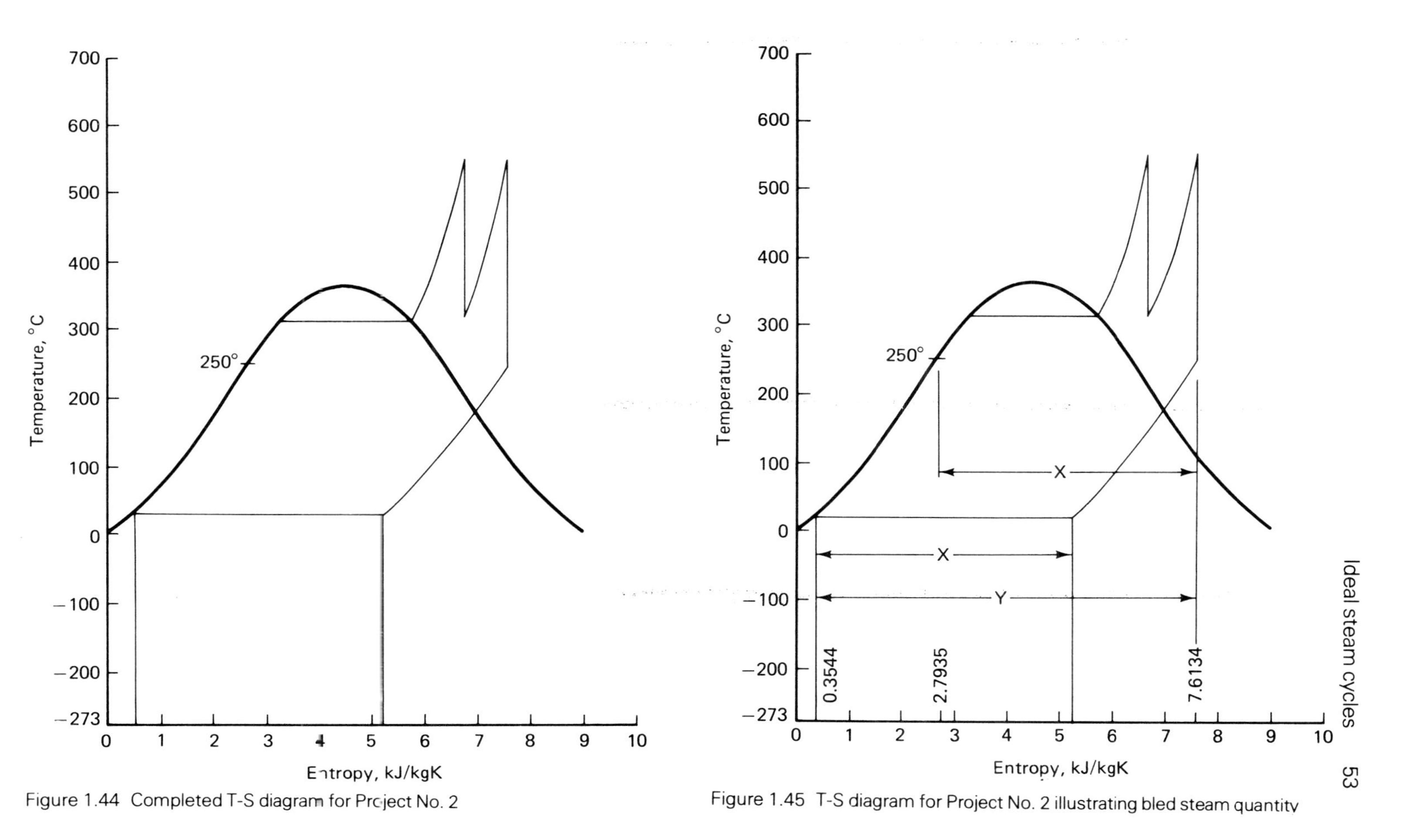

Figure 1.44 Completed T-S diagram for Project No. 2

Figure 1.45 T-S diagram for Project No. 2 illustrating bled steam quantity

Additional Reading

1 LEWITT, E.H., *Thermodynamics Applied to Heat Engines*, Pitman.
2 FENTON, K., *Thermal Efficiency and Power Production*, Pitman
3 KEARTON, W.J., *Steam Turbine Theory and Practice*, Pitman
4 SORENSON, H.A., *Principles of Thermodynamics*, Holt, Rinehart and Winston

2 Coal

General

The basic requirement for effective coal sampling is to produce a small quantity of coal for preparation and analysis by the Chemist which is in almost every way (e.g. large and small pieces, moisture content, ash, chemical analysis, etc.) representative of the consignment in bulk. This is easy to say, but very difficult to achieve in practice because coal is such an intractable material to deal with. If it is dry it is usually dusty and some of the dust is liable to blow away; if it is wet it is sticky or, if very wet, a thick paste; if it is frozen pieces bind together to form lumps.

So the very nature of the material presents the first problem.

Manual sampling from conveyors

The next problem is how to obtain an unbiased sample. Ideally a conveyor carrying the coal should be stopped and a sample frame used to segregate an increment of coal from the remainder. The frame must 'bottom' on the conveyor and must span the entire width. If the sides are obstructed by lumps of coal all the lumps on one side of the frame should be pushed into, and all those on the other side pushed away from, the sample. The coal thus collected will be removed from the sampler and placed in a container to form an increment. The required number of such increments should be taken (see *Table 2.1*)

If a sample frame is not available a similar result can be achieved by scooping a path of constant width across the coal, *all* the coal within the path being removed to form an increment. The belt must have the normal coal flow on it, i.e. it must not be deloaded for convenience while obtaining a sample, but if necessary, the loading on the belt can be kept at a reduced flow rate for the whole sampling period.

However, it is normally impractical to obtain samples as described above, and so the coal must be sampled while in motion.

Hand sampling should not be attempted if the speed of the belt exceeds

1.5 m/s or 200 tonne/h. Also it is essential that the operator can work in safety and have easy access to all the sampling positions he will require. He may obtain samples using a scoop or by manually operating a device such as a Pollock sampler. If using a scoop it should move with the flow and should scrape the bottom of the coal across the whole width of the belt. If this is not possible the alternate increments should be obtained from opposite sides of the belt.

Manual sampling from a falling stream

A ladle is used for this purpose. The method should not be used if the coal has an upper size greater than 25 mm. The ladle is traversed through the stream from one side to the other at a constant speed in one direction, the next traverse being in the opposite direction. If the ladle will be filled before a traverse is complete it is necessary to take increments from specified parts of the stream, e.g. the left-hand half of the stream followed by the right-hand half. The ladle should be moved such that the increment is collected in one direction, e.g. from the front to the back of the stream.

If the coal is being sampled from a bucket conveyor the entire content of a bucket should be regarded as an increment. However, if such a method results in too large a gross sample it is in order to reject a part of the increment in a rotary sample divider or riffle.

Manual sampling from stationary vehicles

Sampling from, say, rail wagons is done by means of an auger or by digging holes at selected locations at least 0.3 metre deep and then taking a sample from the bottom of the hole. It is important that every part of the volume of coal in the wagon is statistically included, i.e. the sides are accounted for as much as the middle, and so on. Thus, if a wagon has three increments taken from it in a diagonal across the wagon the next one should have its increments taken along an opposite diagonal. If a wagon is to have, say, nine increments removed from it they should be taken as shown in *Figure 2.1.*

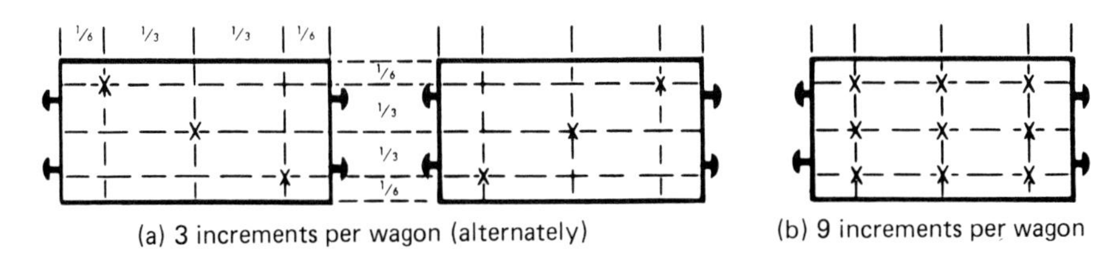

Figure 2.1 Hand sampling from wagons (CEGB)

Manual sampling of coal stocks

This is the most difficult situation of all, and consequently the results obtained should be regarded with care. An auger should be used and a large number of increments obtained to make the best of a fundamentally unsatisfactory situation.

Summary

Hand sampling should preferably be carried out where the coal stream is in motion, either on a conveyor or where the conveyor discharges. The aim should be to eliminate bias as completely as possible, and this is done by having a suitable number of pre-determined locations from which the samples will be obtained in a systematic and regular manner. In other words the aim should be to copy an automatic sampler. All instructions to the sampler should be clear and precise as to how to obtain the increments to eliminate human bias as much as possible. Implements used for manual sampling are shown in *Figure 2.2.*

Figure 2.2 British Standard hand scoops (CEGB)

Automatic sampling

Most power stations are fitted with automatic samplers. This is the only satisfactory way of sampling the very large amounts of coal being handled in modern plants with large units (see *Figure 2.3(f)*).

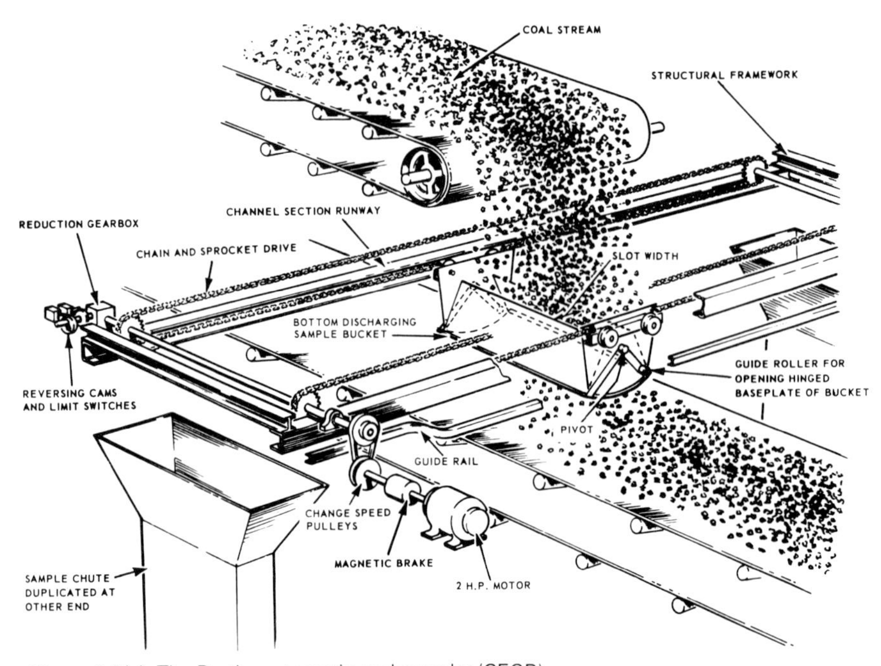

Figure 2.3(a) The Bretby automatic coal sampler (CEGB)

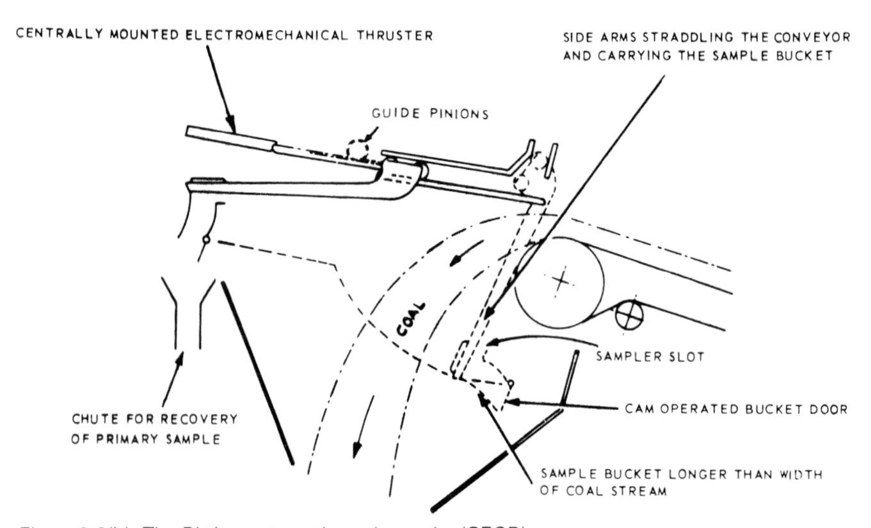

Figure2.3(b) The Birtley automatic coal sampler (CEGB)

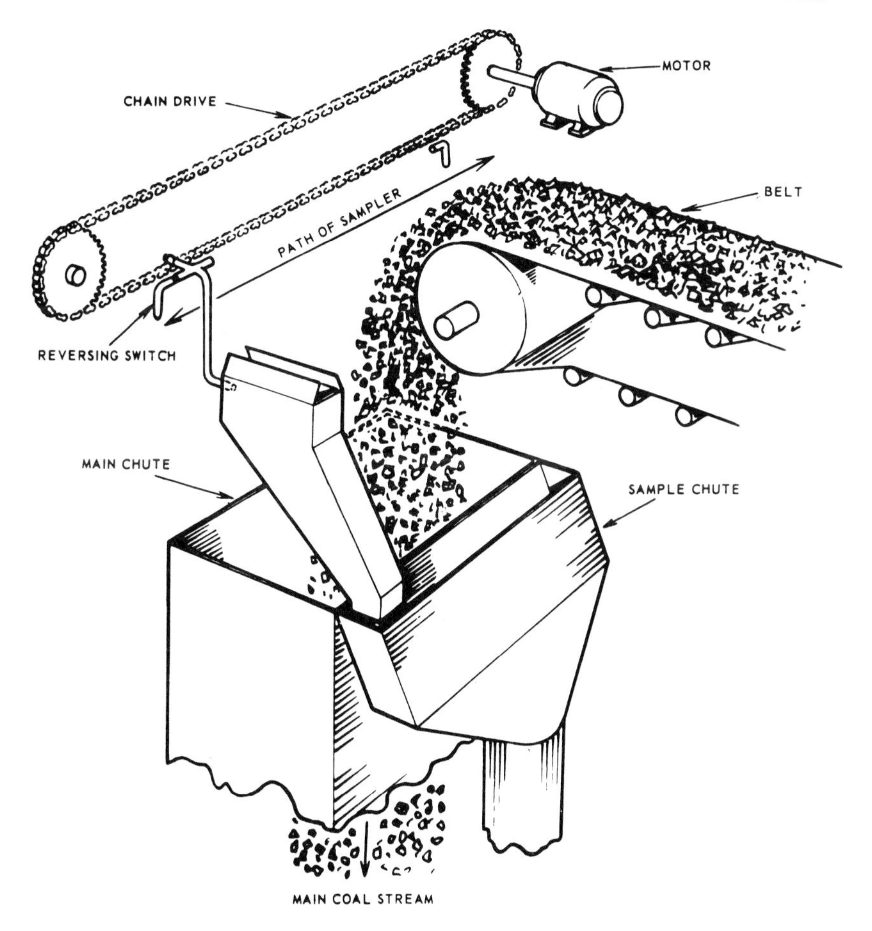

Figure 2.3(c) The GECO automatic coal sampler (CEGB)

The automatic sampler incorporates a primary grinding and sample reduction stage as the increments are large and the sample may weigh over a tonne. Five types of automatic sampler are shown in *Figure 2.3*, they are:

1. Bretby (*a*)
2. Birtley (*b*)
3. Geco (*c*)
4. Seaborne (*d*)
5. Pollock (*e*)

It is essential that, whatever type of sampler is used, adequate maintenance is provided if consistently acceptable results are to be achieved.

Number of increments required to form a gross sample

The minimum number of increments to be collected per 1000 tonnes is given in *Table 2.1.*

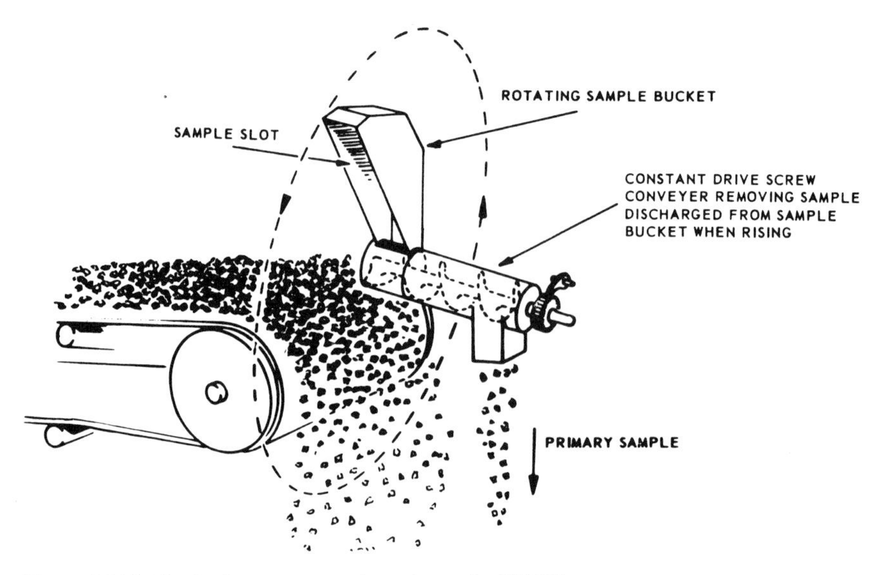

Figure 2.3(d) The Seaborne automatic coal sampler (CEGB)

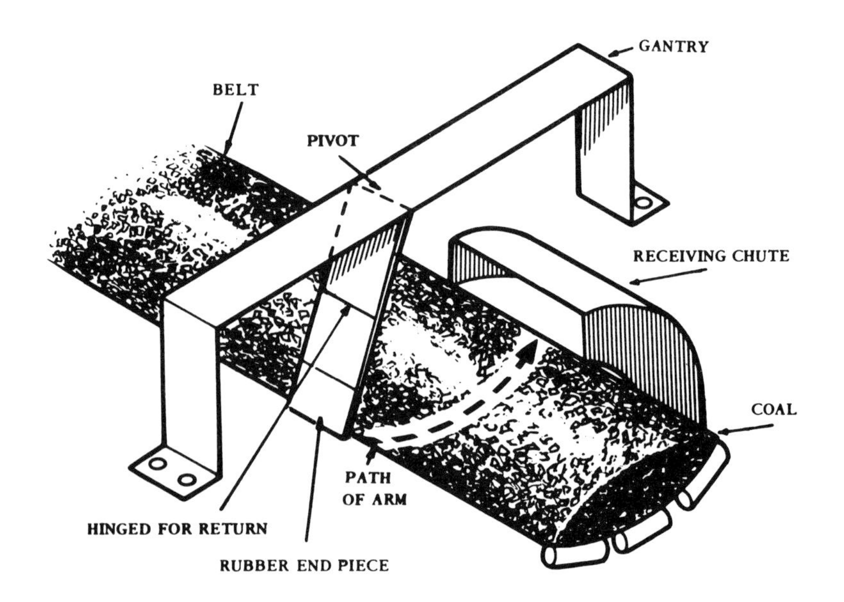

Figure 2.3(e) The Pollock automatic coal sampler (CEGB)

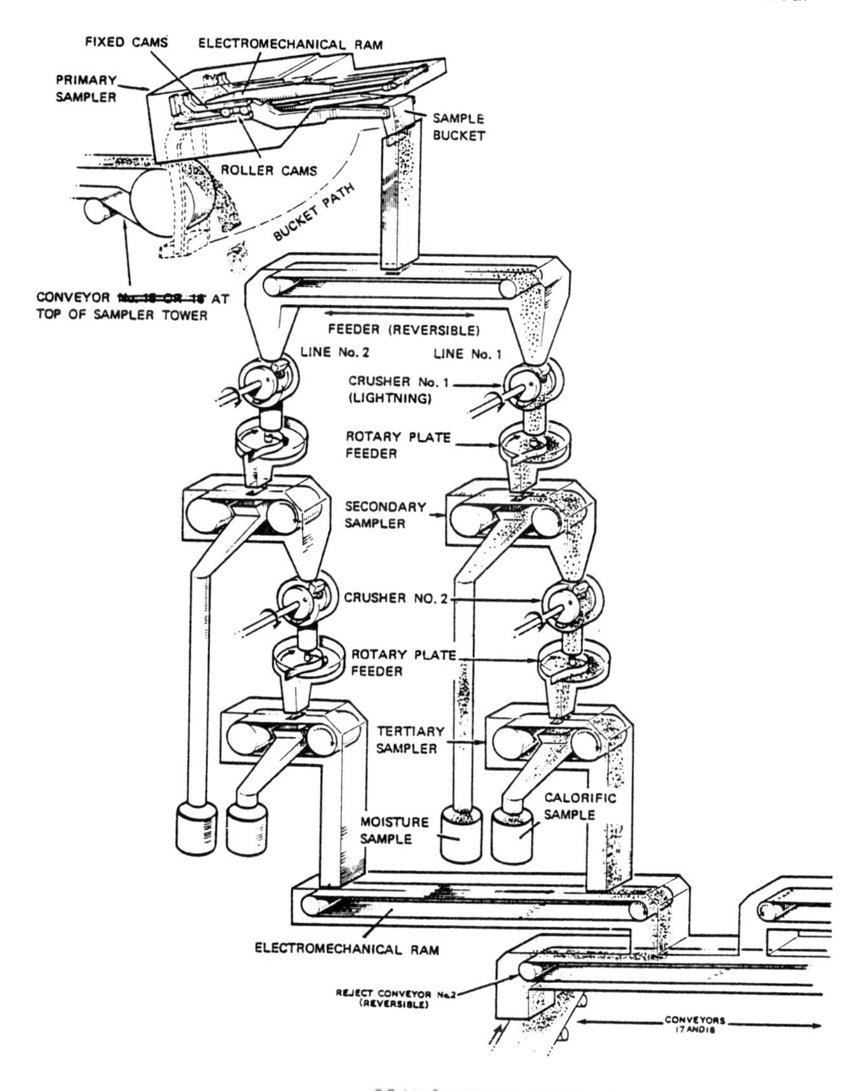

Figure 2.3(f) General arrangement of coal sampling equipment (CEGB)

For consignments greater than 1000 tonnes the number of increments required is either:

(i) the number in the table multiplied by the number of 1000-tonne units there are in the consignment.
(ii) the number $\times \sqrt{}$ (number of 1000-tonne units)

The minimum mass of each increment is given in *Figure 2.4*.

Table 2.1 Number of increments required per 1000 tonnes to form a gross sample

	Streams	*Wagons & Lorries*	*Stockpiles*
General analysis sample			
'Sized' coals	20	25	35
Blended and 'unknown' coals	35	50	65
Total moisture sample			
'Sized' coals	20	20	20
Blended and 'unknown' coals	35	35	35

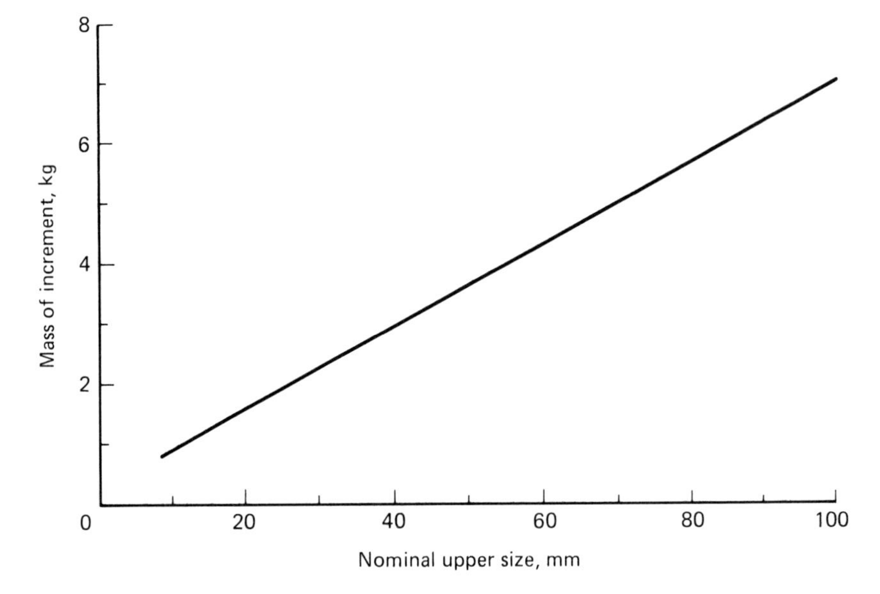

Figure 2.4 Minimum mass of increments

Moisture determination

If a sample is collected for moisture determination care must be taken to prevent any change in the moisture content of the sample. Each increment must be put into a suitable container such as a clean dustbin which is covered with wet sacking. Alternatively, a polythene bag can be put in the bin and the sample kept in the bag which must be kept sealed, except when increments are put in.

Preparation of the laboratory sample

If the sampling method is beyond reproach the gross sample will be representative of the consignment in bulk. It will have the same proportions of large and small lumps, dust, ash and so on, as are in the consignment within very small tolerances. However, the sample will still be too large for use by the Chemist as he only requires between 1 kg and 50 grams for the analysis. But, of course, these few grams must still remain a faithful representation of the original quantity. Normally the sample is required for:

(a) total moisture determination; (b) general analysis, and the stages for each are shown in the following chart:

Notice that air drying of the sample is carried out as an early step in each case.

The purpose of the initial measured air drying of the moisture sample is to ensure that it will pass through the subsequent sample reduction and grinding equipment without loss or gain of moisture to the atmosphere in the coal preparation room. The general analysis sample is dried to assist milling and to prevent blockage of the fine mill outlet screens.

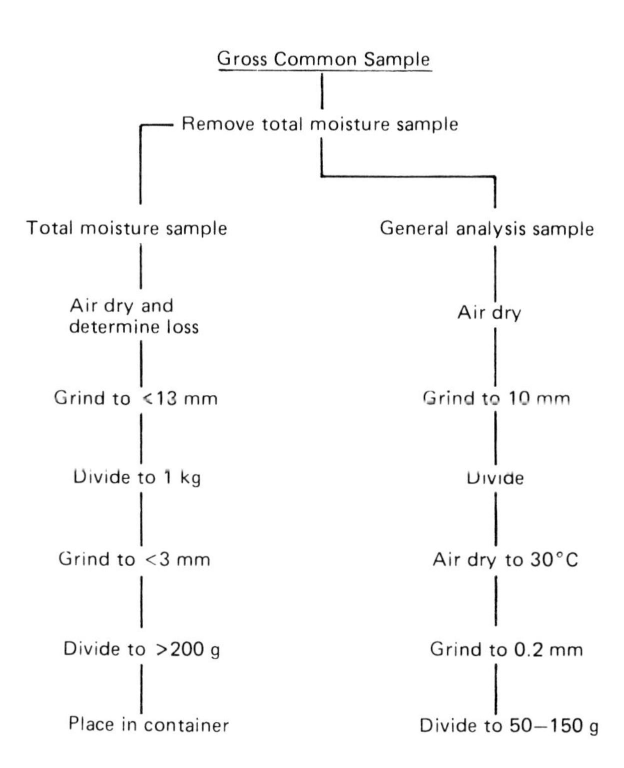

Particle size reduction

Having air dried the coal it is next crushed in a *mechanical* mill – hand crushing is not acceptable as it will lead to biased results. Various mill types are available. A particularly good one is a totally enclosed, slow speed conical mill which crushes the sample between a tungsten carbide rotating cone and a fixed jacket. Swing hammer mills are also widely used as they grind a lot of sample quickly, but the very fine particles can be lost unless air filters are fitted (*Figure 2.5*).

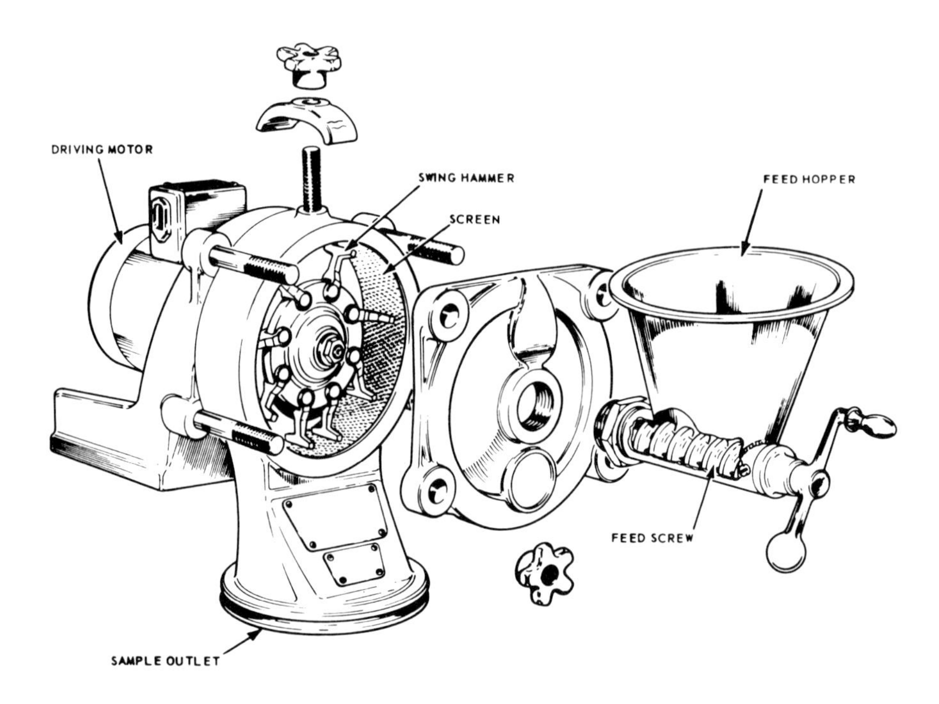

Figure 2.5(a) Exploded view of laboratory Raymond mill (CEGB)

Sample division

This can be done manually, using a riffle or, preferably, mechanically using a rotary divider. Division by coning and quartering gives biased results and so should not be used. Care is required whatever equipment is used and it may be that several passes are required to end up with an acceptably small sample. For example, the coal passed through a riffle is divided into two piles. So, to obtain a one-sixteenth sample will require four passes.

Figures 2.5(a), *(b)*, *(c)* and *(d)*, show a suitable mechanical divider and reducers.

Figure 2.5(b) Baby Hammac mill (CEGB)

Laboratory analysis

If the sampling and preparation have been carried out carefully and in accordance with BS 1017 the Chemist will now have two samples of about 200 grams of coal, one crushed to pass 0.2 mm mesh and the other crushed to pass 3 mm mesh ready for analysis.

A *proximate analysis* is carried out on the first sample (0.2 mm mesh), usually called the 'analysis' sample. This gives:

'As-tested' moisture;
Ash;
Volatile matter;
Gross calorific value;

from which the 'Dry' basis analysis can be calculated.

Figure 2.5(c) (right) Pascalt rotary divider (left) Glenn Creston Mill

Figure 2.5(d) BS sieves and Raymond mill for size reduction (CEGB)

The second sample will be derived from the bulk moisture sample or a 10–20 kg portion abstracted from the main sample. The moisture sample must be placed in a sealed container immediately to prevent loss of moisture to the atmosphere. This container is then weighed with and without its contents. The contents are allowed to air-dry at ambient temperature in the sample preparation room, and then re-weighed. The loss of weight (which is often referred to as the 'free' moisture) is recorded.

The air-dry coal is then further ground to pass a 3 mm mesh and the bulk is reduced to about 200 grams. The remainder of the moisture can then be determined and the 'total' moisture calculated. This is usually called the 'Moisture' sample. From the 'dry' basis analysis and the total moisture the Proximate analysis of the original sample can be calculated.

If a full *'Ultimate' analysis* is required, a difficult and protracted series of laboratory analyses is necessary using the 'Analysis' sample as a starting point. The ultimate analysis requires the separate determination of:

Carbon, hydrogen, nitrogen, oxygen, sulphur, and chlorine,

in addition to the total moisture and ash already determined in the proximate analysis.

If only hydrogen and carbon are required they can be calculated from various formulae (the most commonly used being Parr's formula, which will be discussed later), provided the proximate analysis and CV are known. The sulphur and chlorine contents are sometimes required if slagging or superheater fouling problems are encountered, electro-static precipitator performance is being investigated, or if fireside corrosion is evident. In addition it is sometimes desirable to determine the softening and fusion temperatures of the ash.

Reporting of results

Suppose the Chemist determines the following analysis for the 'As-tested' (i.e. air-dried) sample:

	'As-tested' basis	%
Fixed Carbon	*FC*	47.8
Volatile matter	*VM*	30.5
Ash	*A*	12.1
Moisture	M_a	9.5
Gross CV	kJ/kg	26 660

'As-received' basis

The above result is derived from the analysis sample and so it is obtained on an 'air-dried' basis. To convert it to the original 'as-received' basis it is necessary to multiply each constituent (except the moisture) by:

$$\frac{100 - M_t}{100 - M_a} = \frac{100 - 14.0}{100 - 9.5} = \mathbf{0.951}$$

where M_t = total moisture (%) in the 'as-received' sample, in this case, say, 14.0%

M_a = moisture (%) in the 'analysis' sample.

This gives the following results:

	As received	*As tested*
FC	45.5	47.8
VM	29.0	30.5
A	11.5	12.1
M	14.0	9.5
GCV	25 353	26 660

When a chemist issues the result of an analysis it is normally on an 'As-received' basis. However, it may be that any one of several other possible bases is required, as given below.

'Dry' basis

As the name implies, this is the analysis that would be obtained if the coal contained no moisture at all.

The multiplier to apply to the 'As-tested' analysis is $\frac{100}{100 - M_a}$

In this case it is $\frac{100}{100 - 9.5} = 1.105$ and so the results are:

	'As-tested' basis	*'Dry'*
FC	47.8	52.8
VM	30.5	33.7
A	12.1	13.4
M_a	9.5	—
GCV	26 660	29 459

'Dry ash-free' basis (DAF)

In this case the constituents in the 'as-tested' sample (excluding moisture and ash) are multiplied by

$\frac{100}{100 - (M_a + A_a)}$ where 'A_a' is the ash content of the 'as-tested' sample (%)

So the multiplier is $\frac{100}{100 - (9.5 + 12.1)} = 1.276$, which gives:

	'As tested'	*'Dry ash free'*
FC	47.8	61.0
VM	30.5	38.9
A	12.1	—
M_a	9.5	—
GCV	26 660	34 018

'Dry mineral–matter–free' basis

The mineral matter (MM) is calculated by one of the following methods:

(a) $MM = 1.13\,A_a + 0.5\,S_p + 0.8\,CO_2 - 2.8\,S_a + 2.8\,S_s + 0.5\,Cl$
(b) $MM = 1.10\,A_a + 0.53\,S_t + 0.74\,CO_2 - 0.32$
(c) $MM = 1.1\,A_a + K$

Where S_p = % pyritic sulphur in the air-dried sample
S_a = % ash sulphur in the air-dried sample
S_t = % total sulphur in the air-dried sample
CO_2 = % carbon dioxide (from carbonate) in the air-dried sample
Cl = % chlorine in the air-dried sample
K = a constant, e.g. for S. Wales coals K = 0.2 > 0.4

Of the three methods, (a) is the best and (c) the least desirable, although if the coal is low in CO_2, Cl and S, it may be satisfactory.

The 'as-tested' constituents (VM, FC and GCV) are multiplied by:

$$\frac{100}{100 - (M_a + MM)}$$

In this case assume that $MM = 12.68$

Then the multiplier $= \frac{100}{100 - (9.5 + 12.68)} = \mathbf{1.285}$

(Note that the volatile constituents of the mineral matter must be deducted from the air-dried volatile matter, in this case say 1.7%)

	'As tested'	*'Dry mineral-matter-free'*
FC	47.8	61.4
VM	30.5–1.7	37.0
A	12.1	—
M_a	9.5	—
GCV	26 660	34 258

The dry mineral-matter free analysis is probably more of academic interest than practical use, and consequently it is not normally calculated.

To summarize the various results for the different bases we have:

	As received	*As tested*	*Dry*	*DAF*	*Dry mineral-matter free*
FC (%)	45.5	47.8	52.8	61.0	61.4
VM (%)	29.0	30.5	33.7	38.9	37.0
A (%)	11.5	12.1	13.4	—	—
M (%)	14.0	9.5	—	—	—
GCV (kJ/kg)	25353	26660	29459	34018	34258

Of course, instead of the Proximate analysis the Ultimate analysis could have been used.

The variations from one basis to another are considerable and so it is essential that there is no ambiguity regarding which is being reported. Normally it will be the 'As-received' basis, although the 'Dry' and 'DAF' are also quite common. DAF analyses are of interest because coal from one source usually has a fairly constant dry ash-free CV and volatile matter, even though the ash and moisture vary from day to day.

An expression which has come into common use recently is 'Total Inerts'. The inert substances in a coal are the moisture and ash. As coal is bought by weight the purchaser is buying moisture and ash that are of no use to him at all – in fact he must use works power to grind the ash in the coal mills, and is involved in considerable expense to collect and dispose of the ash. Similarly the moisture has to be evaporated and disposed of up the chimney. So the 'useful' part of the coal is what is left after the 'total inerts' have been removed, i.e. the 'dry ash-free' coal.

Determination of ultimate from Proximate coal analysis

Frequently in the absence of a complete analysis of a coal, the Proximate analysis may be available. In such cases an approximation of the complete analysis may be determined by the use of one of the following methods:

1. 'Gebhardt' Formula

Given the Proximate analysis:

	%
Fixed carbon	FC
Volatile matter	V
Ash	A
Moisture	M

Then,

$$\textit{Hydrogen}\ \mathrm{H} = \mathrm{V}\left(\frac{7.35}{\mathrm{V}+10} - 0.013\right)$$

Where H = Hydrogen in combustible
V = volatile in combustible

Nitrogen N = 0.07V for anthracite and semi-anthracite
N = 2.10–0.012V for bituminous coal and lignite

Total Carbon C = Fixed carbon + volatile carbon
= FC + $0.02V^2$ for anthracite
= FC + 0.9(V − 10) for semi-anthracite
= FC + 0.9(V − 14) for bituminous coal
= FC + 0.9(V − 18) for lignites

where C = % of total carbon in combustible
FC = % of fixed carbon from Proximate analysis

Sulphur increases the value of V; hence the calculated value of 'C' is too high by practically the sulphur content of the combustible.

Oxygen is determined by difference after obtaining the values of H, C, ash, moisture and nitrogen.

Example (using Gebhardt formula)

Laboratory determinations					
Proximate analysis			Ultimate analysis		
		%			%
Fixed carbon	FC	45.5	Carbon	C	61.0
Volatile matter	V	29.0	Hydrogen	H	4.0
Ash	A	11.5	Nitrogen	N	1.4
Moisture	M	14.0	Sulphur	S	1.6
			Oxygen	O	6.5
			Ash	A	11.5
Gross CV	25353 kJ/kg		Moisture	M	14.0

Ultimate analysis by calculation

Hydrogen $H = V\left(\dfrac{7.35}{V + 10} - 0.013\right)$

$= 29\left(\dfrac{7.35}{39} - 0.013\right) = \mathbf{5.1\%}$

Total carbon C = FC + 0.9 (V − 14)
= 45.5 + 0.9 (29 − 14) = **59.0%**

Nitrogen N = 2.1 − 0.012V
= 2.1 − (0.012 × 29) = **1.7%**

Sulphur S not known

Oxygen O = 100 − (H + C + N + S + A + M)
= 100 − (5.1 + 59.0 + 1.7 − 11.5 + 14.0) = **8.7%**

2. 'Parr's' Formula

Sulphur 'S' is taken as the typical percentage sulphur content of coals normally burned at the Station.

Carbon C is calculated from the formula:

$C = (1 - 0.01Z)(Cp) + 0.05A - 0.5S$

where Z = mineral matter content of the fuel burnt, %
$= M + 1.1A + 0.1S$
M = Moisture content of fuel %
A = Ash content of fuel %
S = Typical sulphur content %
Cp = Carbon content (mineral matter free, Parr basis), %
$= 1.5782 \times 10^{-3}Qp - 0.2226Vp + 37.69$
Qp = Calorific value (Parr basis), kJ/kg
$= \dfrac{100 \times Q}{100 - Z}$
Q = CV of fuel burnt, kJ/kg
Vp = Volatile matter content (Parr basis), %
$= \dfrac{100(V - 0.1A - 0.1S)}{100 - Z}$
V = Volatile matter content of the fuel burnt, %

When the value of hydrogen H is not known it should be calculated from the Parr formula as follows:

$H = (1 - 0.01Z)Hp + 0.01A - 0.015S$

where Hp = hydrogen content (mineral matter free, Parr basis), %
$= (0.1707Qp \times 10^{-3}) + 0.0653Vp - 2.92$

Example (using Parr's formula)

Laboratory determinations

Proximate analysis		%	*Ultimate analysis*		%
Fixed carbon	FC	45.5	Carbon	C	61.0
Volatile matter	V	29.0	Hydrogen	H	4.0
Ash	A	11.5	Nitrogen	N	1.4
Moistue	M	14.0	Sulphur	S	1.6
			Oxygen	O	6.5
			Ash	A	11.5
Gross CV = 25353 kJ/kg			Moisture	M	14.0

Ultimate Analysis by Calculation

$Z = M + 1.1A + 0.1S$
$= 14.0 + (1.1 \times 11.5) + (0.1 \times 1.6)$
$= \mathbf{26.8\%}$

$$QP = \frac{100 \times Q}{100 - Z} = \frac{100 \times 25\,353}{100 - 26.8} = \mathbf{34\,635\ kJ/kg}$$

$$\mathrm{Vp} = \frac{100(\mathrm{V} - 0.1\mathrm{A} - 0.1\mathrm{S})}{100 - \mathrm{Z}}$$

$$= \frac{100\,[29 - (0.1 \times 11.5) - (0.1 \times 1.6)]}{100 - 26.8}$$

$$= \frac{100\,(29 - 1.15 - 0.16)}{73.2}$$

$$= \mathbf{37.8}$$

$$\mathrm{Cp} = 1.5782 \times 10^{-3}\,\mathrm{Qp} - (0.2226\mathrm{Vp} + 37.69$$

$$= 1.5782 \times 10^{-3} \times 34\,635 - (0.2226 \times 37.8) + 37.69$$

$$= 54.66 + 29.3 = \mathbf{83.9}$$

$$\mathrm{C} = (1 - 0.01\mathrm{Z})\,(\mathrm{Cp}) + 0.05\mathrm{A} - 0.5\mathrm{S}$$

$$= 1 - (0.01 \times 26.8) \times 83.9 + (0.05 \times 11.5) - (0.5 \times 1.6)$$

$$= (1 - 0.268)\,83.9 + 0.57 - 0.8$$

$$= 61.4 + 0.57 - 0.8$$

$$= \mathbf{61.2\%}$$

$$\mathrm{Hp} = 0.1707\mathrm{Qp} \times 10^{-3} + 0.0653\mathrm{Vp} - 2.92$$

$$= (0.1707 \times 34635) + (0.0653 \times 37.8) - 2.92$$

$$= 5.9 + 2.5 - 2.92$$

$$= \mathbf{5.5}$$

$$\mathrm{H} = (1 - 0.01\mathrm{Z})\mathrm{Hp} + 0.01\mathrm{A} - 0.015\mathrm{S}$$

$$= [1 - (0.01 \times 26.8)] \times 5.5 + (0.01 \times 11.5) - (0.01 \times 1.6)$$

$$= 4.03 + 0.115 - 0.016$$

$$= \mathbf{4.1\%}$$

So calculated ultimate analysis:

Carbon	C	61.2%
Hydrogen	H	4.1%
Nitrogen	N	not determined
Sulphur	S	1.6% assumed
Oxygen	O	not determined
Ash	A	11.5%
Moisture	M	14.0%
	Total	**92.4%**

Note that the nitrogen and oxygen are not determined in the Parr formula, but are in the Gebhardt formula. The Proximate analyses considered in the example for the use of each formula were the same. The nitrogen value determined using the Gebhardt formula was 1.7%

Substituting this into the Parr formula results gives a final analysis of:

	Calculated (%)	*Laboratory (%)*
Carbon	61.2	61.0
Hydrogen	4.1	4.0
Nitrogen	1.7	1.4
Sulphur	1.6	1.6
Oxygen	5.9	6.5
Ash	11.5	11.5
Moisture	14.0	14.0
	100.0	100.0

The oxygen is determined by subtracting the sum of all the other constituents from 100.0%.

3. The modified Seyler chart

If the volatile matter and the calorific value of a coal are known, the hydrogen and carbon can be deduced from the modified Seyler Chart (see *Figure 2.6*). The results are claimed to be accurate to ±0.25% for carbon and

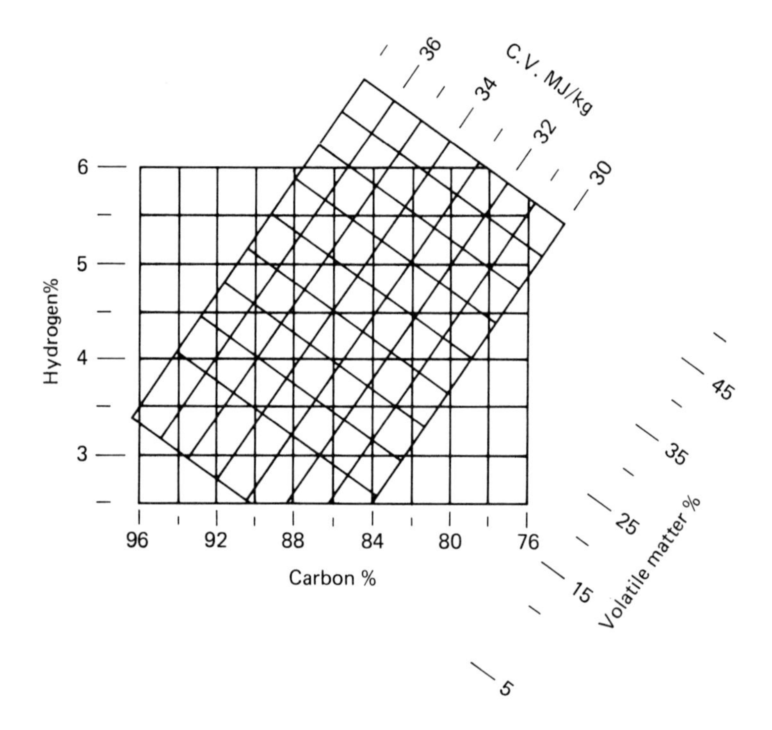

Figure 2.6 Modified Sayler chart

0.005% for hydrogen for normal coals. The values on the chart are on a 'Dry ash-free' basis.

The method of use is best shown by an example.

Example
A coal has the following Proximate analysis:

Fixed Carbon	FC	45.5%
Volatile matter	V	29.0%
Ash	A	11.5%
Moisture	M	14.0%
Gross calorific value	GCV	25 400 kJ/kg

Step 1
Find the volatile matter and gross calorific value on a 'dry ash-free' basis as follows:

Multiply each item by $\dfrac{100}{100 - (A + M)}$

$$\frac{100}{100 - (11.5 + 14)} = 1.34$$

So dry ash-free analysis is:

Volatile matter $= 29.0 \times 1.34$
$= 38.9\%$

Gross Calorific Value $= 25400 \times 1.34$
$= \mathbf{34036\ kJ/kg}$

Step 2
From the figure at the intersection of 38.9% volatile matter and 34 036 kJ/kg calorific value, read off:

Hydrogen = 5.5%; carbon = 83.0%

Step 3
Convert the hydrogen and carbon values to the original 'as-received' basis by multiplying each by $\dfrac{100 - (A + M)}{100}$

$$\frac{100 - (A + M)}{100} = \frac{100 - (11.5 + 14)}{100} = 0.745$$

So 'as-received' hydrogen = 5.5 × 0.745 = 4.1%
'As-received' total carbon = 83.0 × 0.745 = **61.8%**

A comparison of the 'derived' values and the laboratory determinations gave:

	Derived %	*Laboratory %*
Total carbon	61.8	61.0
Hydrogen	4.1	4.0
Moisture	14.0	14.0
Ash	11.5	11.5

4. Simplified Seyler–Dulong formula

An alternative to using the previous method is to use the following formulae:

$$\% \text{ Hydrogen (dry ash-free)} = 0.069\left(\frac{Qd}{419} + V\right) - 2.86$$

$$\% \text{ Total carbon (dry ash-free)} = 0.59\left(\frac{Qd}{419} - \frac{1.1V}{3}\right) + 43.4$$

where Qd = dry ash-free gross calorific value (kJ/kg)
V = dry ash-free volatile matter (%)

Example
A coal has the following Proximate analysis:

Fixed carbon	FC	= 45.5%
Volatile matter	V	= 29.0%
Ash	A	= 11.5%
Moisture	M	= 14.0%
Gross calorific value	GCV	= **25 400 kJ/kg**

Step 1
Obtain 'dry ash-free' values of V and GCV.

$$\text{Factor} = \frac{100}{100 - (A + M)} = \frac{100}{100 - (11.5 + 15)} = 1.34$$

V = dry ash-free volatile matter = 29.0 × 1.34
= **38.9%**

Qd = Calorific value of dry ash-free coal = 25400 × 1.34
= 34036 kJ/kg

$$\text{So dry ash-free hydrogen} = 0.069\left(\frac{34{,}036}{419} + 38.9\right) - 2.86$$

$$= 0.069\,(81.23 + 38.9) - 2.86$$

= **5.43%**

$$\text{Dry ash-free total carbon} = 0.59\left[\frac{34{,}036}{419} - \frac{(1.1 \times 38.9)}{3}\right] + 43.4$$

= **82.9%**

So 'as-fired' values are: H = 5.43/1.34 = 4.05%
C = 82.9/1.34
= **61.9%**

Assessment of coal stocks

General

The value of the coal on stock at a power station is considerable. Of course the actual quantity at any station at any time varies throughout the year and so the assessment is normally done when stocking out and reclaiming coal is at a minimum. Every effort should be made to assess accurately the quantity of coal as it is so valuable. Equally important is the necessity to ensure that the 'book' stock agrees quite well with the actual stock, as this provides a valuable indication of the accuracy of the station efficiency determinations.

One method of assessing the quantity of coal on stock is to have a 'fly-over' and a density check of the coal piles. The fly-over consists of taking overlapping aerial photographs of the stock from which a stereoscopic picture of the piles of coal can be constructed and the volume determined. The density is calculated by lowering a gamma-ray source into holes in the coal pile. The 'count' of the gamma-rays at a Geiger counter depends upon the density of the material between the detector and the source so the density can be determined if the equipment is calibrated. Once the volume and average density have been determined the weight of coal is easily determined.

One advantage of carrying out the assessment of the stock when the change is low is that if there is a time difference between the fly-over and the density determination the stock change will be minimal.

Volume determination

Two items of information are required before the fly-over:

1. A ground plan of the coal stock area detailing variations of the ground level.
2. The location of fixed 'control points' (e.g. pylon bases, railway sleepers, lamp-post bases or any other permanent features). The height of each control point is accurately determined with reference to ordnance survey data.

The 'fly-over' photographs are taken from a height of 400 to 450 metres, and they have a 60% overlap. Contours of the coal piles are drawn from the stereoscopic pictures and from these the volume is determined. The photographs are printed on glass so that distortion effects are minimal. When the plates are inserted in the plotting machine heights can be measured to less than 30 μm (i.e. 0.00003 m).

The camera focal length is 15.0 cm and so the scale of the photographs (assuming they are taken from 400 metres) is given by:

$$\text{Scale} = 1 \text{ in } \frac{40\ 000}{15.0} = 1 \text{ in } 2666$$

The plotting error will be within $\pm$ 30μ m and so the full-scale error will be within $\pm$ 30 μm × 2666, i.e. $\pm$ 8 cm.

Now, the contours are actually determined from a large number of spot heights, and each spot height (as we have shown) could be 8 cms in error. Generally the number of spot heights per stock is between 1000 and 4000. The resulting error will thus be between:

$$\sqrt{\frac{\pm 8 \text{ cm}}{(1000)}} \text{ and } \sqrt{\frac{\pm 8 \text{ cm}}{(4000)}}$$

and these are equal to $\pm$ 0.25 cm to $\pm$ 0.13 cm.

It follows that very little accuracy is lost from this cause.

Of far greater importance is the setting-up of the photographs in the first place. This requires the control points (i.e. the permanent features whose height is accurately known) on the base plan to be aligned with those on the photographs. Once again the possible error is $\pm$ 8 cm for each point and so the resultant error could be significant, particularly for stocks of low vertical height. The order of possible error from this cause is shown in *Figure 2.7*. Normally stocks are higher than 4 m and so the percentage error would be less than $\pm$ 2%.

Density determination

Generally an accuracy of $\pm$ 4% (with 95% confidence) is aimed for, although better accuracies can be obtained if required. The method of obtaining the density is described in some detail. The station staff must supply a sketch of the coal piles with a note of the height of the coal and the number of holes to be drilled. The required number of readings is at least 24. A reading is obtained at every metre depth of the holes, each hole being drilled to the bottom of the coal pile. Four holes should be drilled in each pile, each hole being situated randomly in a level part of a different segment of the pile, the segments each being roughly the same area.

So in the case of the typical station submission illustrated in *Figure 2.8*, the number of readings will be:

'A' stock 4 holes each with 11 readings (i.e. one reading per metre of depth).

'B' stock 4 holes each with 10 readings.

It is next necessary for the density team to determine the Gieger counter

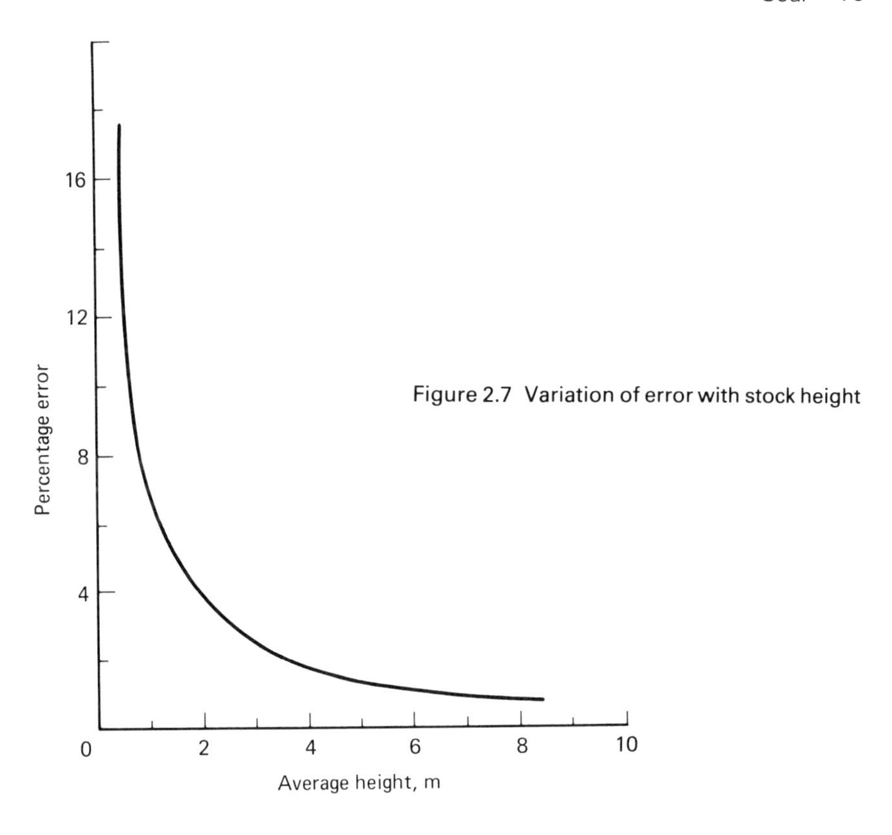

Figure 2.7 Variation of error with stock height

reading at each location, from which the density is calculated. In the case mentioned above the densities were, say:

Depth	*Stock 'A' (kg/m³)*				*Stock 'B' (kg/m³)*			
m	*1*	*2*	*3*	*4*	*1*	*2*	*3*	*4*
1	1153	1139	1216	1170	1128	1100	1079	1056
2	1141	1135	1102	1033	1042	1065	1016	1127
3	1176	1099	989	987	1055	1027	1097	1144
4	1101	1128	1007	980	990	980	1107	1171
5	1142	1121	950	946	1027	988	1164	1158
6	1136	1064	1050	1020	860	973	1196	1169
7	1042	1050	1013	1007	1037	996	1158	1148
8	1046	1043	962	1057	1010	1016	1214	1204
9	1032	984	978	981	1004	998	1189	1173
10	978	912	971	–	1022	1035	1155	1138
11	988	1037	–	–	–	–	–	–

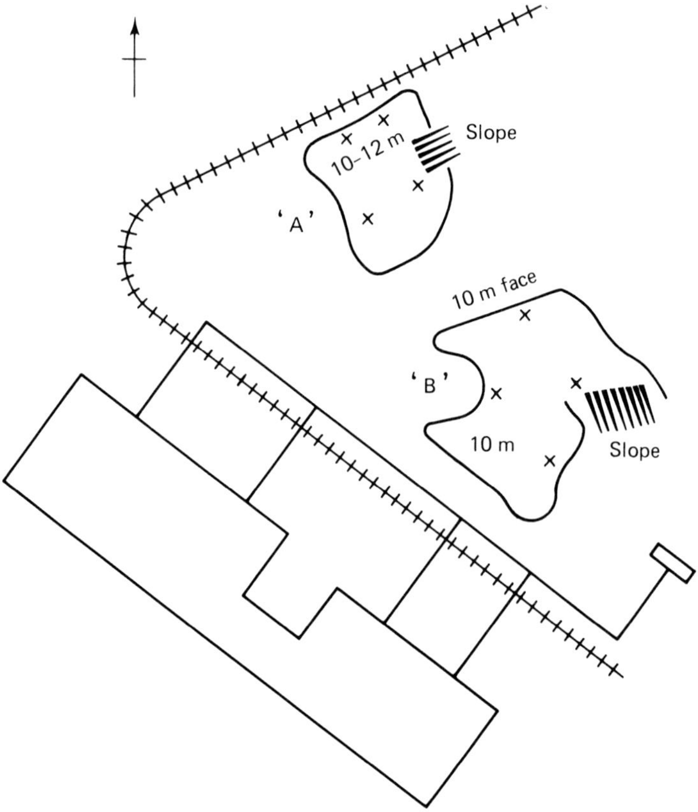

Figure 2.8 Sketch of 'A' and 'B' coal stocks

The following information is obtained from the table:

1. Number of readings (N) = 41 for 'A' stock and 40 for 'B'.
2. Average density (D) = 1050 kg/m^3 for 'A' and 1080 kg/m^3 for 'B'.
3. Highest density = 1216 kg/m^3 for 'A' and 1214 kg/m^3 for 'B'.
4. Lowest density = 912 kg/m^3 for 'A' and 973 kg/m^3 for 'B'.
5. The Density range (R) = 304 kg/m^3 for 'A' and 241 kg/m^3 for 'B'.

Reference to the nomogram (*Figure 2.9*) enables the accuracy achieved to be determined.

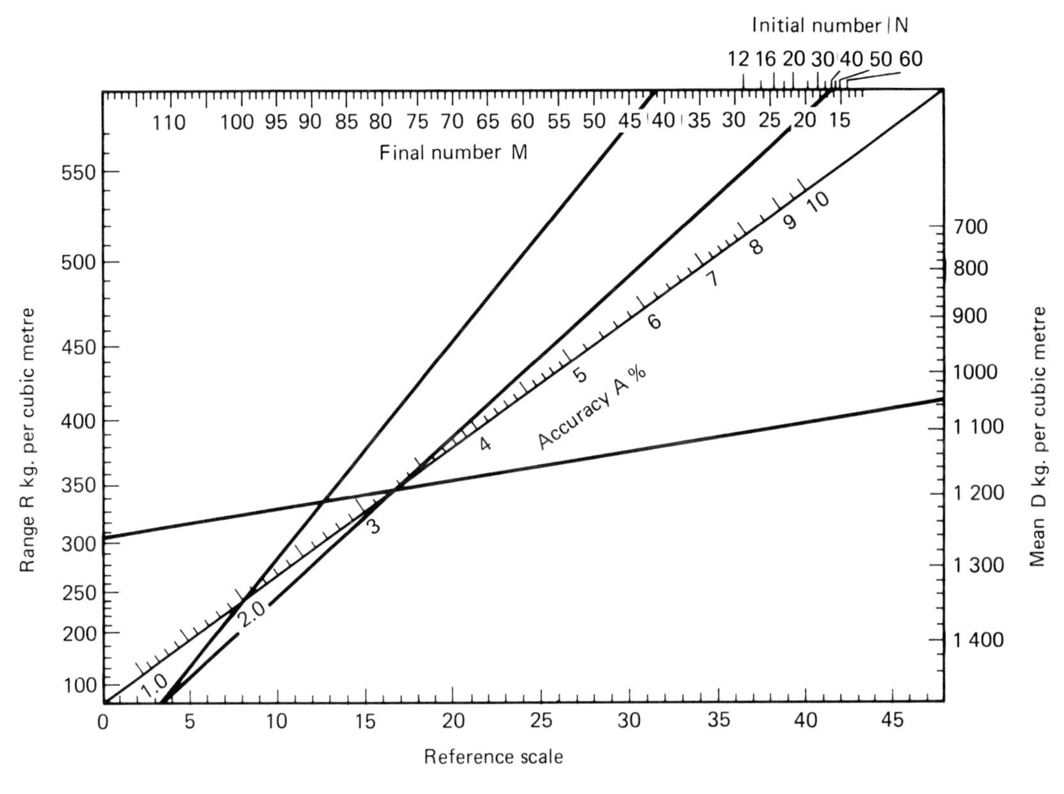

Figure 2.9 Nomogram of accuracy of coal density determination (CEGB)

The method is as follows – using the 'A' stock results:

1. Draw a line from R = 304 to D = 1050.
2. Draw a line from the intersection of line RD with line 'A' to N = 41, and extend the line to the bottom reference scale, which it cuts at 3.4.
3. From 3.4 on the reference scale draw a line to M, the final number of readings taken, which in this case is the same as N, i.e. 41.
4. Where the line intersects line 'A' read off the accuracy as 2.1%

This is well within the desired tolerance of 4.0%. However, suppose it is required to achieve an accuracy better than 2.1% – say 1.5%. Then the number of readings required is determined by plotting a line from 3.4 on the reference scale through 1.5% on scale 'A' and noting where it cuts line M – in this case M = 77. 41 readings have already been taken and 77 are required so a further 36 are needed to give an accuracy of 1.5% with 95% confidence.

Coal stock assessment

Thus, in the example being considered, the volumetric assessment for 'A' stock pile was 46 341 cubic metres and that for 'B' 184 055 cubic metres (see *Figure 2.10*).

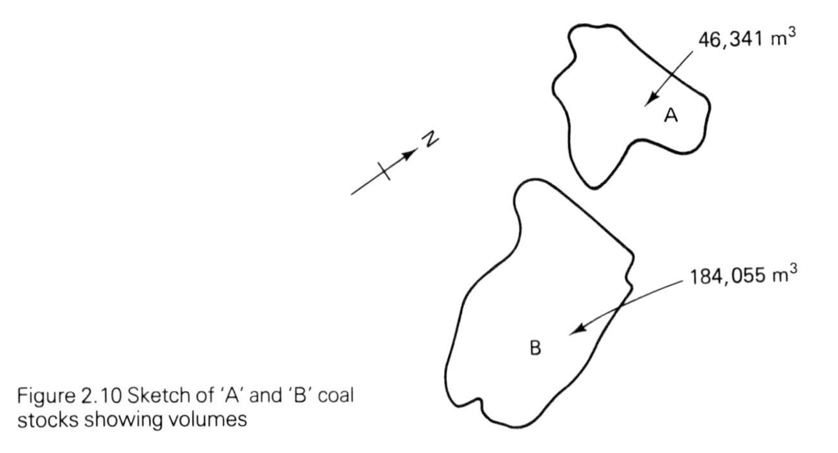

Figure 2.10 Sketch of 'A' and 'B' coal stocks showing volumes

So the 'A' stock = 46 341 × 1050 = 48 658 050 kg
= 48 658.1 tonnes

Suppose at that time the 'A' 'book' stock = 50 348.6 tonnes.

The result would be submitted as follows:

			'A' Stock
1	Aerial survey		48 658.1 tonnes
2	Book stock		50 348.6 tonnes
3	Difference	(1) − (2)	(−) 1690.5 tonnes
4	Difference	$\frac{(3) \times 100}{(2)}$	(−) 3.36%

Overall accuracy

Investigations at a number of power stations show that the total error of the assessment of stocks varies between about ± 2.0% to ± 7.5%. As one would expect, the largest errors are normally associated with stations with many small stocks.

Exercise 1 – Stock assessment

(a) What is the difference between the stock and survey figure for 'B' if the book stock is 203 420.5 tonnes?
(b) What is the accuracy of the density determination?

Exercise 1 (Answer)

(a) 'B' stock = 1080 kg/m^3 × 184 055 m^3
= 198 779 400 kg
198 779.4 tonnes

		'B' Stock
1	Aerial survey	198 799.4 tonnes
2	Book stock	203 420.5 tonnes
3	Difference (1) − (2)	(−) 4641.1 tonnes
4	Difference $\frac{(3) \times 100}{(2)}$	(−) 2.28%

(b) N = 40
D = 1080 kg/m^3
Highest density = 1214 kg/m^3
Lowest density = 973 kg/m^3
R = 241 kg/m^3
From nomogram, accuracy = 1.6% with 95% confidence.

Coal allocation

A common problem is to determine the best allocation of coal to a number of power stations from a number of pits, and the solution is found by a technique known as *linear programming*.

The total cost of fuel used at a station is determined by:

(a) The pit head price;
(b) The cost of transportation;
(c) The efficiency with which it is burned.

The coal costs to each station are reduced to a common basis, say the heat-tonne. Of course, any convenient units can be used.

Example of method
Three pits X, Y, and Z supply coal to three power stations A, B and C as shown in (1).

(1)

Pit output (heat-tonne/week)		*Station consumption (heat-tonne/week)*	
X	30000	A	40000
Y	60000	B	80000
Z	80000	C	50000
	170000		170000

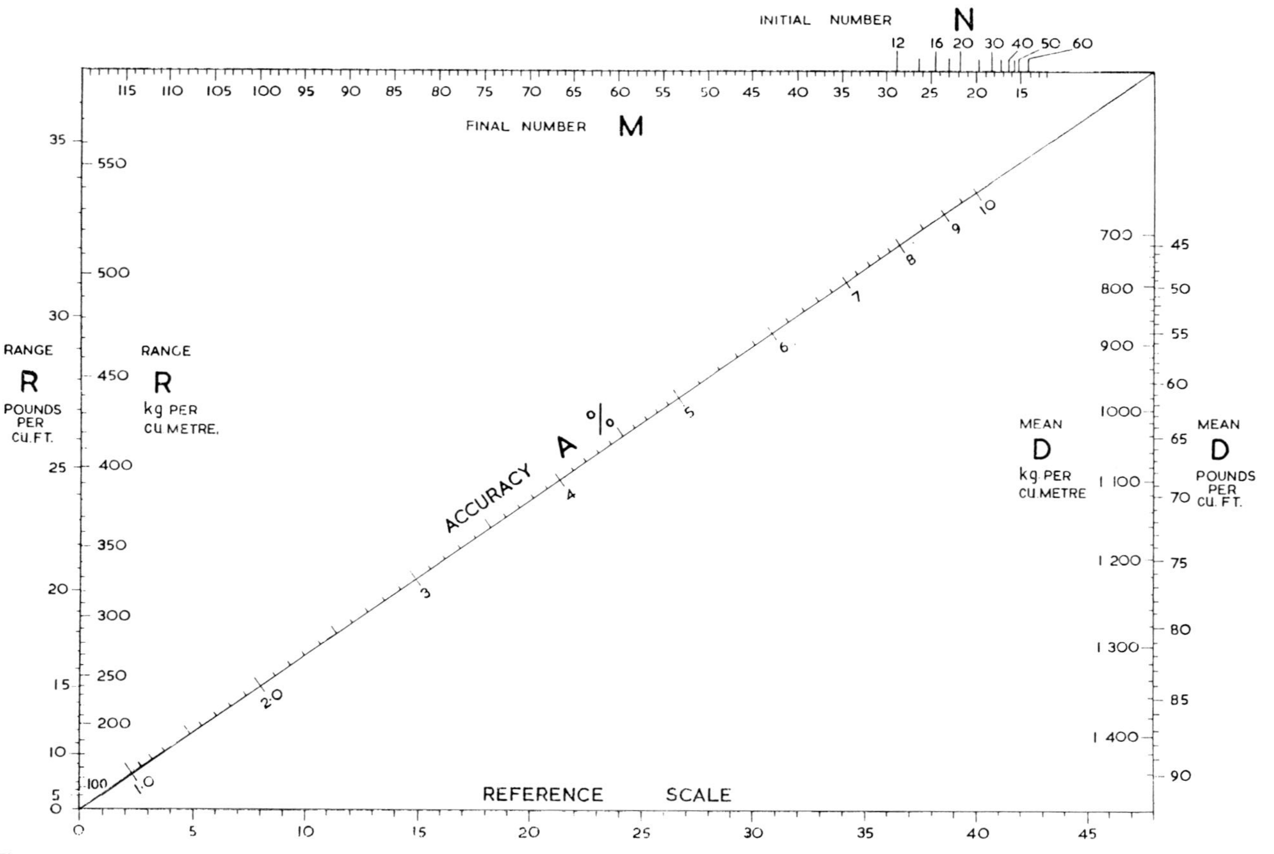

Figure 2.11 Nomogram for determination of density (CEGB)

The delivered cost in pence per heat-tonne is given in (2) along with the outputs and consumption in 1000s of tonnes.

(2)

	A40	B80	C50
X 30	1780p	1810p	1800p
Y 60	1800p	1790p	1820p
Z 80	1770p	1790p	1800p

The commonsense allocation is to supply as much coal as possible to the station with the cheapest cost, i.e. send 40 000 t to A from Z at 1770p– see (2).

The next cheapest is Z to B and Y to B each at 1790p, so send the remaining 40 000 t from Z to B plus another 40 000 t from Y to B, and so on as shown in (3).

(3)

	A 40	B 80	C 50	Totals
X 30			30	30
Y 60		40	20	60
Z 80	40	40		80
Totals	40	80	50	

The total cost of this solution is:

X to C, 30 000 t at 1800p = £540 000
Y to B, 40 000 t at 1790p = £716 000
Y to C, 20 000 t at 1820p = £364 000
Z to A, 40 000 t at 1770p = £708 000
Z to B, 40 000 t at 1790p = £716 000
Total £3 044 000

From (2) it is clear that the minimum possible cost of coal:

From X is to A, i.e. 30 000 t at 1780p = £534 000;
From Y is to B, i.e. 60 000 t at 1790p = £1074 000;
From Z is to A, i.e. 40 000 t at 1770p = £708 000.

So in (2), reduce each item in row:
X by 1780p and add £534 000 to adjust fuel cost;

Thus (2) becomes changed to (4):
(4)

	A	B	C	Fuel cost adj. (£k)
X	0	30	20	534
Y	10	0	30	1074
Z	0	20	30	708

Next determine which *columns* in (4) do not contain a zero. In this case it is only column C. The lowest figure is at XC, i.e. 20. So reduce all items in column C by 20 and adjust cost by 20 × 1800p = £360, as shown in (5).

(5)

	A	B	C	Cost. adj. (£k)
X	0	30	0	534
Y	10	0	10	1074
Z	0	20	10	708
Cost adj. (£k)			0.36	

So total cost adjustment = £k2616 + £k0.36 = £k2 616.36

Note: Irrespective of whatever final allocation is made it cannot possibly be less than £2 616 360.

(3) and (5) are now combined to give (6). 'Fictitious cost elements' (FCEs) are allocated to each row and column such that their sum equals the tonnage from (3) in the appropriate boxes. Start with column A FCE as zero.

(6)

	A	B	C	FCEs
X	[0]	[30]	[0] 30	−30
Y	[10]	[0] 40	[10] 20	−20
Z	[0] 40	[20] 40	[10]	0
FCEs	0	20	+30	

The only 'occupied' box in column A is ZA (i.e. the only one with a tonnage inserted from (3)). The zero in the small rectangle in the box must equal the sum of row Z and column A FCEs. As A is zero then Z must also be zero. In column B the small rectangle in BZ shows that the B column FCE must be 20. Continue until all the FCEs are established from consideration of the occupied boxes as shown in (6).

Next proceed to fill in the *unoccupied* boxes by entering the sum of the appropriate row and column FCEs, e.g. the figure for box XA is −30 + 0 = −30 as shown in (7) and shown encircled. Proceed in the same way for each unoccupied box.

(7)

	A	B	C	FCEs
X	[0] (−30)	[30] (−10)	[0] 30	−30
Y	[10] (−20)	[0] 40	[10] 20	−20
Z	[0] 40	[20] 40	[10] (+30)	0
FCEs	0	20	30	

If any encircled figure is greater than the corresponding figure in the small rectangle in the same box, the overall allocation is *not* a minimum. This applies in (7) to only one box, ZC.

Mark the box ZC with a (+). Look along the same row for an 'occupied' box and mark it (−). Look in that column for an occupied box and mark it (+), and so on until you arrive back at the starting point as shown in (8).

(8)

	A	D	C
X			
Y		+40	−20
Z		−40	+

Having determined the route move as large a number as possible into ZC, adding and subtracting to preserve the pit and station totals. In this case add 20 to each to give (9).

Note: Negative values are meaningless and so, for example, ZB is entered as 20 and *not* −20.

Box YC will have zero in it. Therefore the appropriate row and column fictitious cost elements add together to give +10 and this is shown in YC encircled.

(9)

	A	B	C	FCE
X	(−30) [0]	(−10) [30]	30 [0]	−30
Y	(−20) [10]	60 [0]	(+10) [10]	−20
Z	40 [0]	20 [20]	20 [10]	0
FCE	0	20	30	

In (9) there is no encircled figure larger than the corresponding figure in the rectangle in the same box. Hence the allocation is a minimum.

The reduction in cost from (3) is given by 20p × 20 k tonne (from ZC in (7) and ZC in (9)). In other words the saving is 20 000 t × 20p = £4000.

This is also obtained by totalizing the cost of the optimum allocation in (9) as follows:

X to C	30 000 t at 1800p	= £540 000
Y to B	60 000 t at 1790p	= £1 074 000
Z to A	40 000 t at 1770p	= £708 000
Z to B	20 000 t at 1790p	= £358 000
Z to C	20 000 t at 1800p	= £360 000
		£3 040 000

This total is £4000 less than that of £3 044 000 derived from (3).

It is evident that, even with this simple case, linear programming is a long and tedious task. In a real situation where a large number of pits supply many power stations the calculation can take several days. Thus, this type of problem is ideal for solution by computer, which is now normally done.

It is also clear, though, from the calculations that substantial savings are often possible by merely re-allocating supplies.

Questions

1 What is the aim of coal sampling?
2 What is the ideal method of obtaining a sample?

3 How would you manually sample from a moving conveyor belt?
4 What precautions must be observed?
5 How would you manually sample from a rail wagon?
6 How would you manually sample from a coal stock?
7 Name three types of automatic sampler.
8 What is one use of the modified Seyler chart?
9 How many increments would you obtain from a 4000-tonne consignment?
10 Why is air-drying of the sample an early step in the coal preparation process?
11 What is a Proximate analysis? An ultimate analysis?
12 State the precautions to be observed when collecting a sample for moisture determination?
13 How is the 'free' moisture determined?
14 The chemist analyses the coal samples on one basis and reports them on another. Why? What are they?
15 How would you determine the ultimate analysis of a coal?
16 What is the purpose of 'linear programming'?
17 There is an unexpectedly large discrepancy between the aerial survey and book stock. What are possible causes of this?

Project 1

It is desired to determine the efficiency of a power station which burns between 5000 and 6000 tonnes of coal per day. The ash content is about 20% and the coal is 'unknown'. A 'common' sample is required from which the total moisture, proximate analysis and gross calorific value will be determined. Sampling is from a falling stream of coal passing over the end of a conveyor belt and is carried out manually. The maximum size of the coal is 40 mm.

(a) (i) How many increments are required per 10-hour working day?
  (ii) What is the mass of each increment?
  (iii) What precautions should be taken with the samples?
(b) The volatile matter is 30.25% and the gross calorific value is 22 000 kJ/kg.
  The ash is 18.73%, moisture 11.96%
  Assume the sulphur is 1.0%
  Calculate the ultimate analysis.
(c) What is the average 'sent-out' thermal efficiency of the station over a 30-day period if the total 'sent-out' units were 300×10^6, and 156 000 tonnes of coal plus 100 tonnes of oil were burned. The gross calorific value of the oil is 40 000 kJ/kg.

Project 1(Answer)

(a) (i) Refer to *Table 2.1* (Page 62). For 6000 tonnes the number of increments is either:

$\sqrt{6} \times 35 = 86$ per day
or $6 \times 35 = 210$ per day

Until confidence has been established in the sampling, the latter is preferred, but the former is probably adequate for the purpose specified. So samples should be taken at intervals of:

$$\frac{600}{86} = 7 \text{ minutes per increment}$$

(ii) The mass of each increment is given in *Figure 2.4* as 3.0 kg.

(iii) The increments must be placed immediately in a suitable container (say a clean dustbin) with a wet sack over the top of the bin. Alternatively the sample may be placed in a polythene bag inside a bin and the bag kept closed; or an airtight container can be used. The sample should be kept cool.

(b) Refer to *Figure 2.6*

$$\frac{100}{100 - 30.69} = 1.44$$

∴ On a DAF basis GCV $= 22\,000 \times 1.44 = 31\,680$ kJ/kg
and VM $= 30.25\% \times 1.44 = 43.56\%$
Hence, from chart, C = 78% (*Figure 2.6*)
and H = 5.3%
So 'as fired', C $= 78\% \div 1.44 = 54.17\%$
and H $= 5.3\% \div 1.44 = 3.7\%$

From the Gebhardt formula:

$$N = 2.10 - (0.012 \times 30.25) = 1.74\%$$

Thus, the ultimate analysis as calculated is as follows. Also given, for comparison, is the laboratory analysis:

	Calculated %	*Laboratory* %
Moisture	11.96	11.96
Ash	18.73	18.73
Carbon	54.17	54.22
Hydrogen	3.70	3.70
Nitrogen	1.74	1.11
Sulphur	1.00	1.43
Oxygen (by difference)	8.70	8.85
	100.00	100.00

(c) Total heat supplied from coal = 156 000 × 22 000 × 1000
= 3 432 000 GJ
Total heat supplied from oil = 100 × 40 000 × 1000
= 4000 GJ
So total heat = 3 436 000 GJ

$$\therefore \text{Sent-out thermal efficiency} = \frac{300 \times 3600 \times 100}{3436000}$$

$$= \mathbf{31.43\%}$$

Additional Reading

1 BS 410 *Test sieves*
2 BS 1016, *Methods for the analysis and testing of coal and coke* (17 parts).
3 BS 1017, *Methods for sampling coal and coke* (2 parts).
4 BS 1796, *Methods for test sieving.*
5 BRAME, J.S.S., and KING, J.G. *Fuel – Solid, Liquid and Gaseous*, Edward Arnold.
6 FRANCIS, W., *Coal – Its Formation and Composition*, Edward Arnold.
7 FRANCIS, W., *Boiler House and Power Station Chemistry*, Edward Arnold.

3 Pumps and pumping

Many types and sizes of pump are used in power stations, ranging from large outputs (e.g. cooling water and boiler feed) to very small ones. The types represented may include mixed-flow C.W., screw or gear oil; reciprocating jacking oil; water-operated portable and various others. However, by far the most common type is the centrifugal pump. Also the most common fluid handled is water and so the bulk of this section will be devoted to aspects of pumping water using centrifugal pumps.

Papin first described a centrifugal pump in the 17th century, but it was not until the 19th century that manufacturing skills enabled the first practical models to be built. *Figure 3.1* illustrates a typical pump.

Pump types

There are three broad catagories of pump:

1. Positive displacement
2. Rotodynamic
3. Miscellaneous

The main sub-divisions of these are shown in *Figure 3.2*.

Positive-displacement pumps

These embrace many different types and a few will be described shortly. However, probably the best known are the various reciprocating pumps. These deliver a definite quantity of fluid every stroke, the actual value being dependent upon the swept volume and the speed. Thus, the only ways to vary the output of a reciprocating pump are to:

(a) Vary the stroke; (b) Vary the speed.

Table 3.1 shows the general classification of reciprocating pumps.

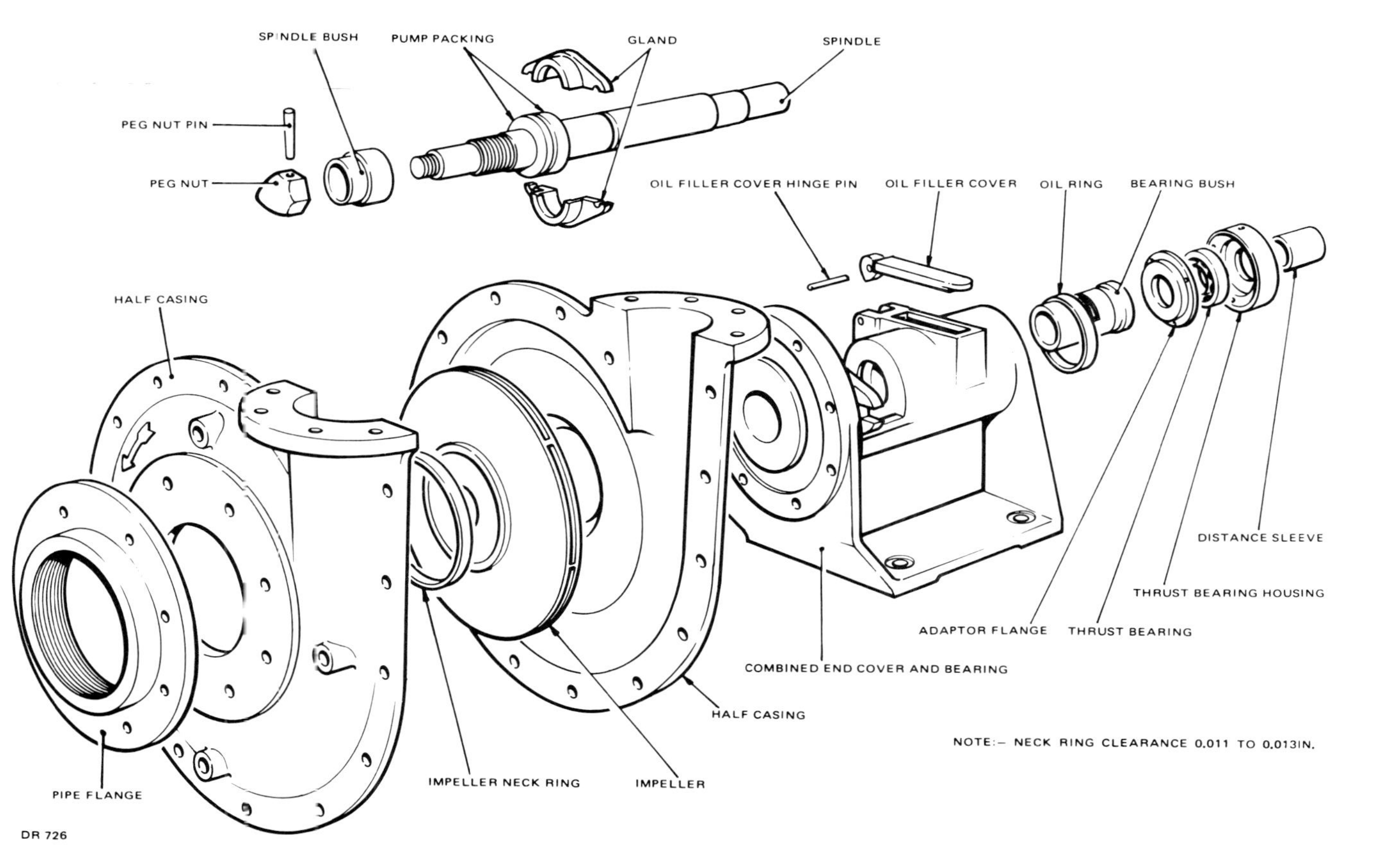

Figure 3.1 Condenser extraction pump (CEGB)

Classification	*Type*	*Method*
Positive displacement	Rotary	Gear, cam Helical screw Vane, lobe
	Reciprocating	Bucket, force. Diaphragm Ram, piston
	Peristaltic	Roller
Rotodynamic	Axial flow	Propeller
	Mixed flow	
	Centrifugal	Volute Guide vane
Miscellaneous	Jet Injector Air lift	

Figure 3.2 Main sub-divisions of pumps

Table 3.1 Reciprocating pump classification

Stroke	*Average speed (strokes/min)*	*Class*	*Ratio of bore to stroke*
Very short	150–300	Express	1 : 0.25
Short	100	Quick	1 : 1
Average	80	Normal	1 : 1.25
Long	50	Slow	1 : 2.25

The reciprocating components are stationary at the end of each stroke and then must be accelerated in the reverse direction. In addition, the delivery of water is stopped and started as the valves are operated each stroke. It follows that, where possible, long-stroke pumps are preferred because fewer reversals are required in a given time.

A few positive-displacement pumps are described in the next few pages.

Lift pumps

Most people are familiar with this type (see *Figure 3.3*). The piston (which is often referred to as the 'bucket') contains a valve which permits water to pass from the underside only. A second valve is situated at the bottom of the barrel and it is known as a suction valve. In operation, the action of the pump is as follows, starting with the barrel full of water and the piston at the top of

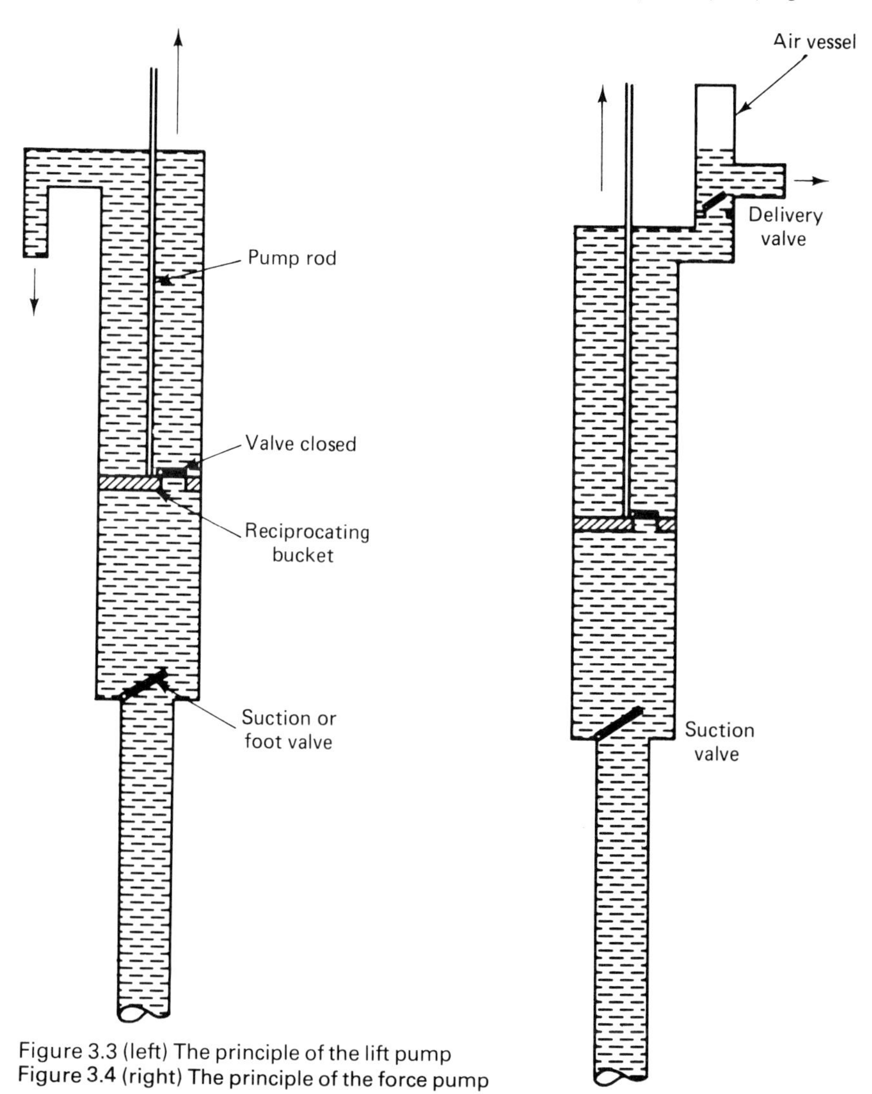

Figure 3.3 (left) The principle of the lift pump
Figure 3.4 (right) The principle of the force pump

its stroke. As the piston descends the suction valve is kept closed by the force of the water above it. However, the waterway in the piston is open and so the piston can descend easily. No work is done on the downstroke. When the piston completes the descent and starts to rise the whole column of water above the piston is *lifted*. Meanwhile the suction valve opens because of the reduced pressure above it due to the piston being raised. This allows water to enter the barrel. When the piston reaches the top of its stroke the cycle of events repeats.

Notice that a lift pump only has 'single-acting' properties, i.e. work is done on only one stroke per cycle, all during the upward stroke. Also note that there is no need for a valve in the discharge pipe.

Force pumps

The top of the working barrel is fitted with a cover and a stuffing box, and the delivery pipe is led away at any desired angle. The delivery pipe is usually of smaller bore than the barrel and often an air vessel is fitted such as illustrated in *Figure 3.4.* The vessel contains very little water, the rest being filled with air. When the delivery water is pressurized the air in the vessel is compressed. When the water pressure is reduced the air expands and sustains some of the pressure on the water. Thus, the pressure fluctuations are smoothed. The delivery valve is necessary to enable the air vessel to function properly. Also it reduces the loadings imposed on the suction valve.

The water in the discharge is pressurized so the water can be routed to any location as required, and therefore this pump is much more useful than the lift pump described earlier.

Ram or piston pumps

The trouble with the force pump just described is that the delivery pressure cannot be very high. If higher pressures are required a 'ram' or 'piston' type can be used. The one illustrated in *Figure 3.5* is double acting because each

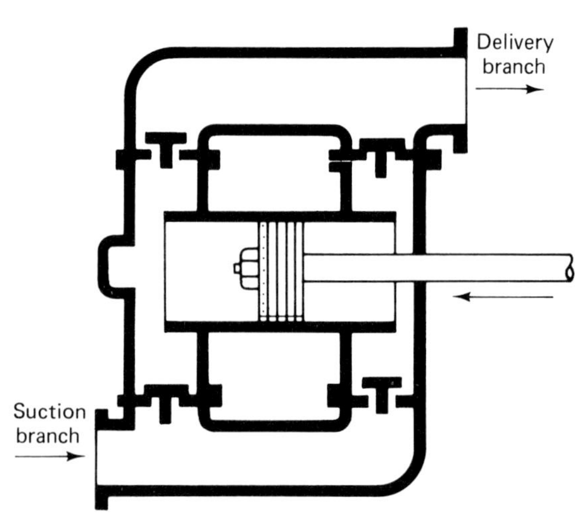

Figure 3.5 The principle of the double-acting piston pump

side of the piston does the pumping. Notice that four valves are required, whereas three were needed for the force pump. Consequently they each have different working cycles. When the piston moves to the left, water enters the pump body by way of the right-hand suction valve, and is discharged from the left-hand delivery valve. When it moves to the right the other two valves operate.

Gear pumps

These are positive-displacement devices. *Figure 3.6* shows the principle of

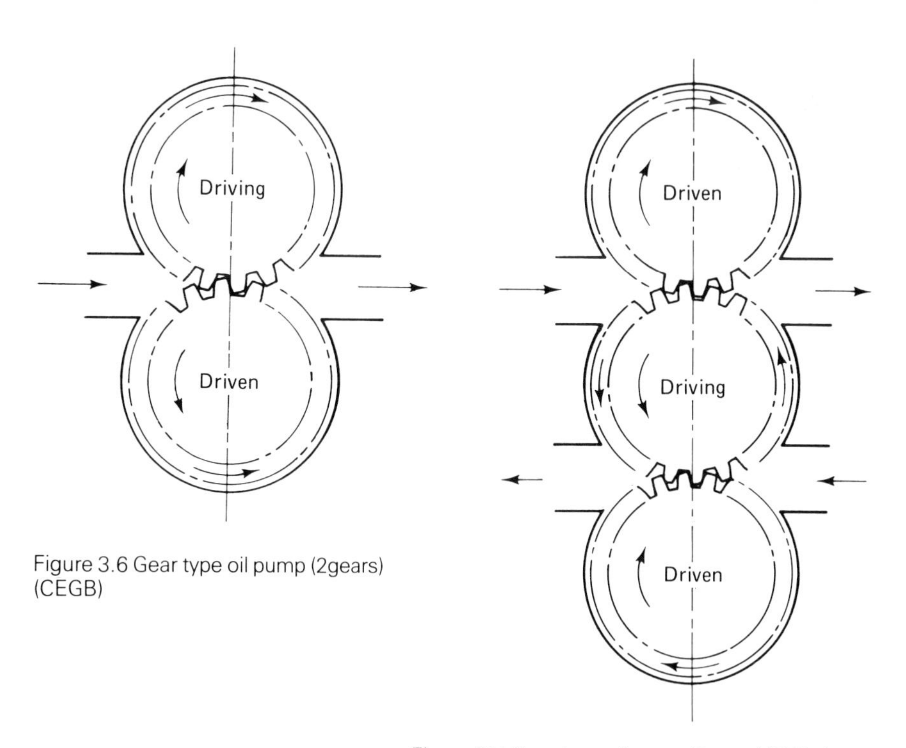

Figure 3.6 Gear type oil pump (2gears) (CEGB)

Figure 3.7 Gear type oil pump (3gears)(CEGB)

operation. Oil is admitted to the pump and is carried by the two gears in the direction of rotation and then discharged. On smaller turbines they were often used as the main oil pump, operating at about 100 rev/min, and did not require priming. By adding a third gear wheel the output is doubled as can be seen in *Figure 3.7*.

Peristaltic pumps

These are usually of small capacity. The fluid to be pumped is passed through a flexible tube. The tube is compressed by a series of rollers and as each roller moves along the tube the fluid contained between it and the roller in front is moved forward (see *Figure 3.8*).

Figure 3.8 A laboratory peristaltic pump (CEGB)

Centrifugal pumps

This type depends upon the rotation of the impeller for its action. There are two broad divisions:

(a) Volute; (b) Guide-vane.

Volute type

The pump casing forms a volute that surrounds the impeller and forms the collecting chamber. It has an increasing area in the direction of rotation which becomes a maximum at the point of discharge as shown in *Figure 3.9.*

Guide-vane type

Guide-vane pumps have diffuser vanes around the impeller and discharge to the next impeller as shown in *Figure 3.10.* Their function is to convert as much velocity energy as practicable to pressure energy. Generally, volute pumps are used if low discharge heads (e.g. extraction pumps) or large flows

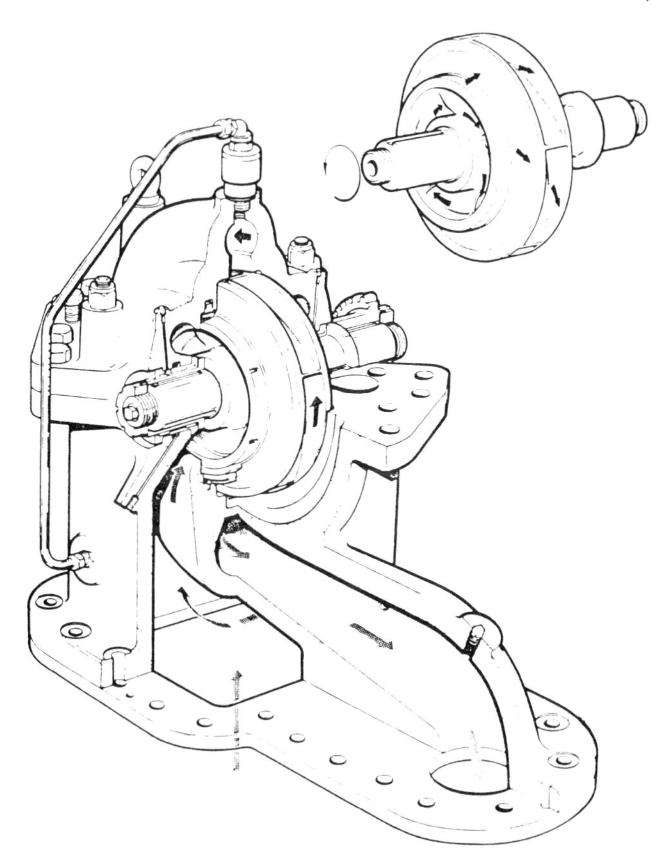

Figure 3.9 A volute oil pump (CEGB)

(e.g. C.W. pumps) are involved. For high-head work, such as boiler feed, multi-stage guide-vane pumps are used. It is apparent that guide vanes add complications to a pump and so increase the cost.

Some terms used in pump studies

Before proceeding with more detailed study it is necessary to be familiar with a few terms.

Head

If a mass of water is raised to a vertical height h then it will have been given energy by virtue of its elevation. The unit of energy is the joule (1J = 1 Nm), but in pump work it is common to say merely that the water has 'h metres head'.

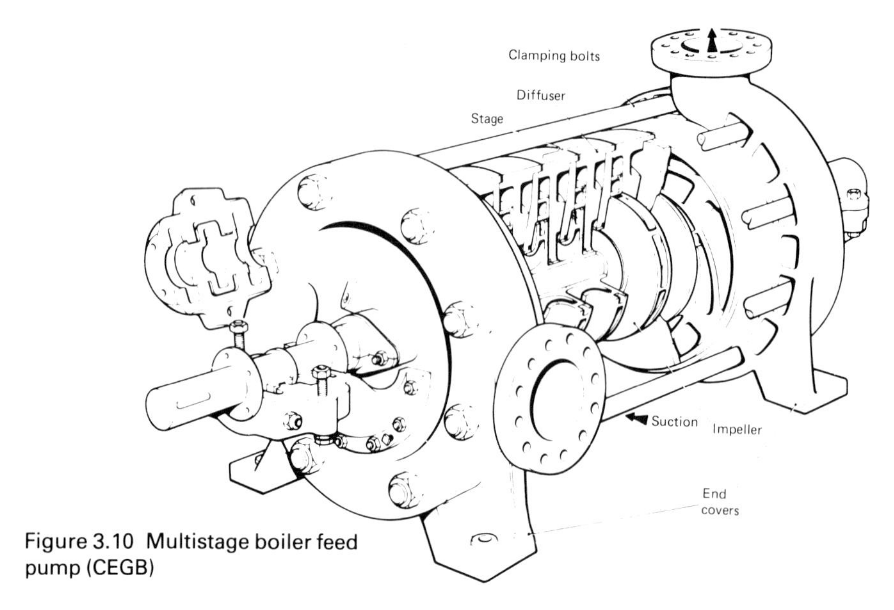

Figure 3.10 Multistage boiler feed pump (CEGB)

Generally there are three 'heads' in common use in connection with pumps:

(i) *Potential head.* Water at a vertical height of H metres above a datum level possesses potential energy equal to the product of its mass, height and acceleration due to gravity, i.e.

Potential energy = MgH
Where M is mass in kg, H is height in metres, and $g = 9.81$ m/s^2
The pressure exerted by a head of H metres is given by:
Pressure = water density × 9.81 × head
For cold water, pressure = 1000 × 9.81 × H newtons per square metre = 9 810 H N/m^2 = 0.0981 H bar, say 0.1 H bar.

(ii) *Velocity head.* If a particle of water, starting from rest, is allowed to fall freely, its velocity v after t seconds is given by:

$v = gt$ metres per second
The distance travelled will be equal to the average velocity multiplied by the time in seconds, i.e.

$$\text{Distance} = \frac{gt^2}{2} \text{ metres}$$

but $t = \dfrac{v}{g}$ and let the distance by H metres,

$$\text{then } H = \frac{v^2}{2g}$$

In other words H is the equivalent static water column of the moving liquid, and is known as the velocity head.

(iii) *Friction head.* This is the friction loss expressed as the head of an equivalent water column. Some resistance is inevitable whenever water flows, even in smooth pipes, but the loss is most pronounced when the water flows through valves, bends and constrictions.

The basic parameters which affect the friction loss are:

1. The loss is independent of the pressure of the water for practical purposes. So if the water is at a pressure of 1 bar or 100 bar the friction loss will be the same for the same flow in a given pipe.
2. If the flow is doubled the loss will increase four times. In other words the loss varies as the flow squared.
3. The loss increases as the internal surface of the pipe roughens.
4. The loss is directly proportional to the length of the pipe. Thus, doubling the length of the pipe will double the friction loss.
5. For the same flow the loss decreases directly as the pipe diameter increases. For example, if the diameter is doubled, the cross-sectional area of the pipe will increase four times. So for a given velocity of flow there will be a fourfold increase in the quantity of water. Also, doubling the diameter will double the circumference of the pipe and hence double the surface friction. So four times the flow causes the friction loss to double. Therefore for the original flow the friction loss is halved.

An approximate value of the head loss is given by the expression

$$h_f = \frac{fv^2L}{2gD} \text{ metres}$$

where h_f = the loss in metres
f = a coefficient that depends upon the pipe internal surface
v = mean velocity in metres per second
l = pipe length in metres
D = pipe diameter in metres

Some typical values of the coefficient f are:

New cast iron pipe 0.005
Old encrusted pipe 0.01
Cement pipes 0.003

For general purposes use a value of 0.007, although it should be remembered that the value varies with temperature, velocity, diameter of pipe and viscosity of the fluid.

For $f = 0.007$ the above formula becomes:

$$h_f = \frac{1428v^2}{d} \text{ m/km of pipe run}$$

where d = pipe diameter in millimetres

Normally the relevant data is obtained from a chart such as in *Figure 3.11(a)*

For example, consider a pipe of $d = 150$ mm, 500 metres long. The velocity of flow is 1.5 metres per second.

Assume the pipe is new cast iron.

$$h_f = \frac{4f\,v^2L}{2gD}$$

$$\frac{4 \times 0.005 \times 1.5^2 \times 500}{2 \times 9.81 \times 0.15}$$

$$= 7.65 \text{ m/500 m}$$

$$\therefore h_f = 15.3 \text{ m/km}$$

Velocity of flow. The velocity of flow through pipes is given by:

$$v = \frac{1.266 \times 10^6\, Q}{d^2} \text{ metres per second}$$

where Q = m^3/s
d = pipe diameter in millimetres

Total head

The 'total head' (sometimes called the 'virtual head') is the total capacity for work at any point per unit mass of the substance being considered.

Gross total head = potential head + kinetic head + losses

Figure 3.11(b) shows a layout with imaginary water columns to illustrate the total resistance to be overcome by the pump. If a gauge is connected to the suction of a pump it will register the total suction head, i.e., A + B + C. A gauge connected to the discharge branch of the pump will register the sum of components D + E. A gauge connected to a delivery air vessel should register the sum of all the components D + E + F, but because of the elasticity of the air and inertia fluctuations, it is almost impossible to get steady readings.

Note that with reciprocating pumps, on account of the presence of valves and the motion of the bucket or ram, the velocity energy which is generated by the pump in the suction pipe is destroyed when the stroke is reversed and has to be regenerated by the pump in the delivery pipe. Thus the velocity energy has to be created twice per cycle.

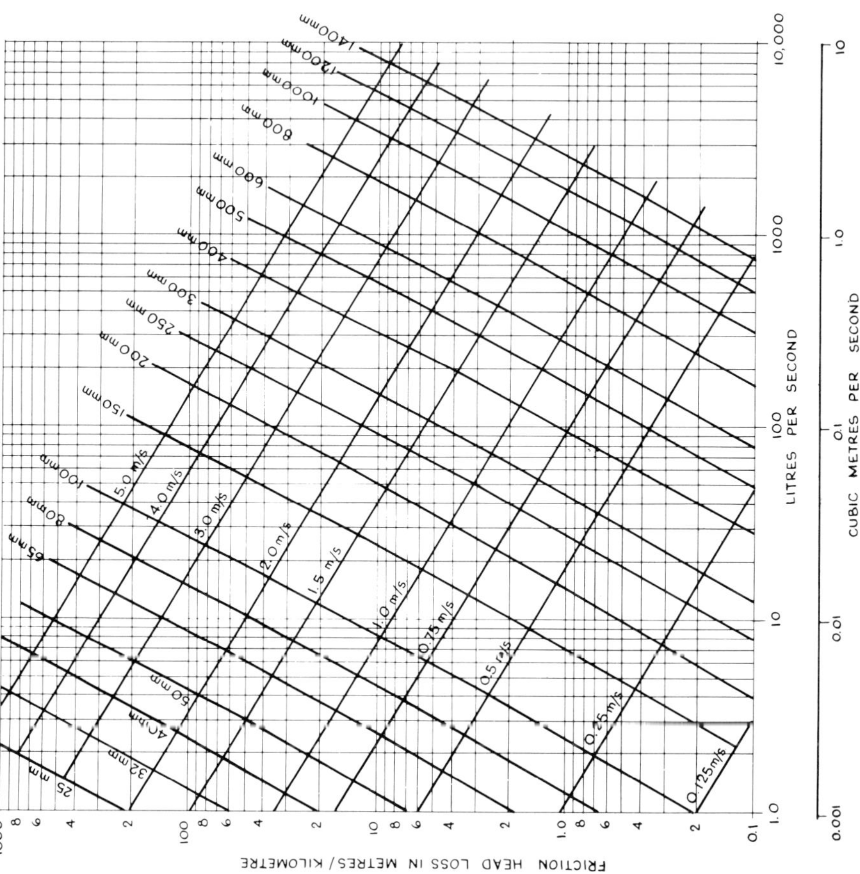

Figure 3.11(a) Chart of friction losses for water flow in straight pipes (CEGB)

Suction conditions

It is most important that the suction conditions are given due consideration

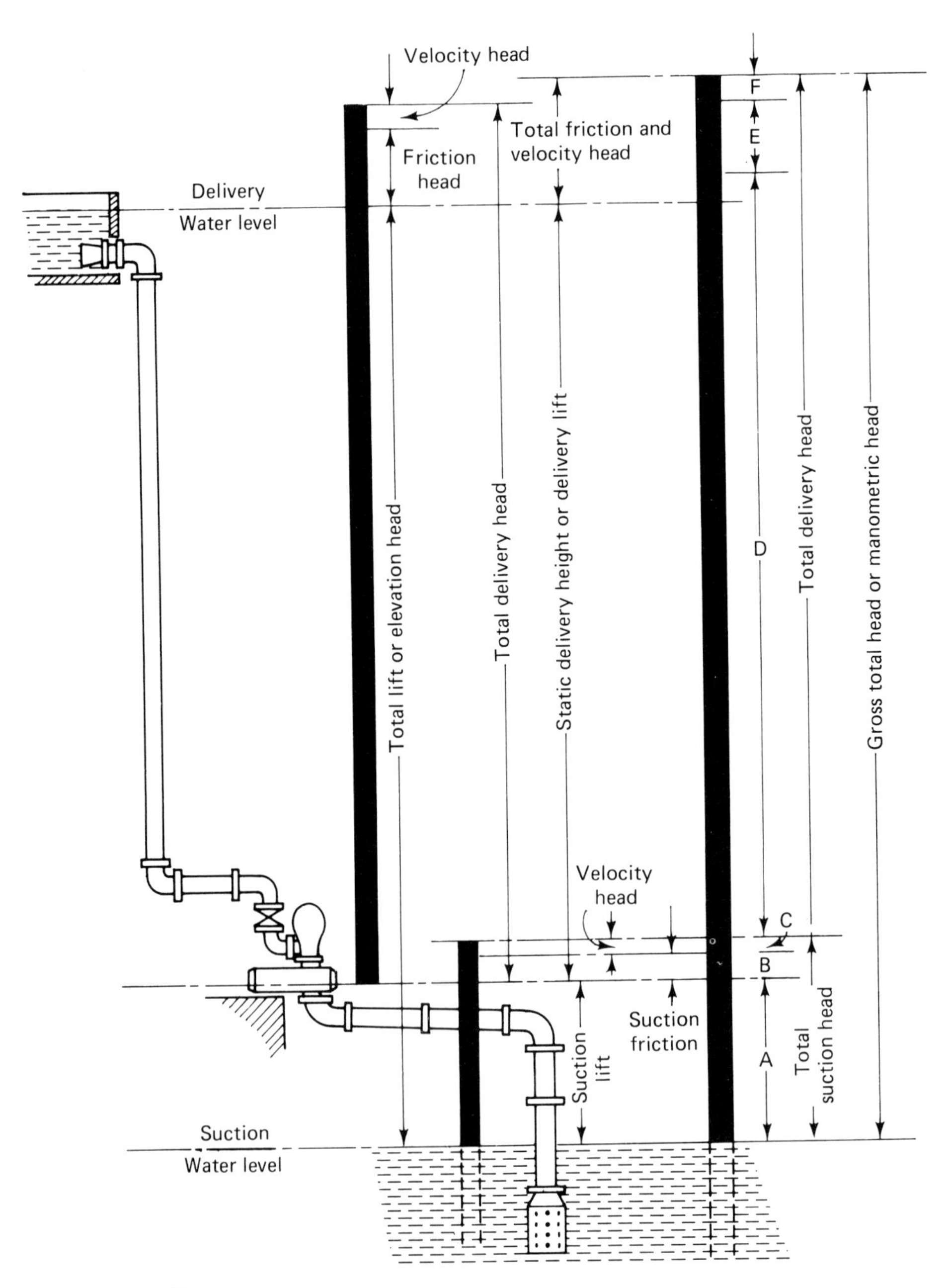

Figure 3.11(b) Diagrammatic representation of pumping heads

when considering pump layouts. A pump can do work only on the water that is *pushed* into it from the suction system. So if the suction layout is such that only a small quantity of water can get into the pump then that is all that can be discharged. It is a common fallacy that pumps somehow *pull* water into themselves – this is obviously impossible. All they can do is create suitable conditions within the pump body to enable some external agency, such as atmospheric pressure, to *push* the required water in.

There are three basic suction layouts to consider although the treatment of each case is identical.

Case 1. Pump supplied by water at its own level.

This situation is illustrated in *Figure 3.12*, the water being at the same level as the centre-line of the pump suction. The only pressure available to push the water into the pump is that due to the atmosphere acting upon the surface of the water. Thus, the total pressure is 1013 mbar absolute or about 10.3 m of water.

There are various losses involved in getting the water into the pump, including:

(a) Getting the water from the main tank into the supply pipe.
(b) Accelerating the water from rest to its velocity in the pipe.
(c) Supply pipe friction loss.
(d) Loss due to getting the water into the pump via the pump inlet passages.

These are shown diagrammitically in *Figure 3.12*. It can be seen that of the

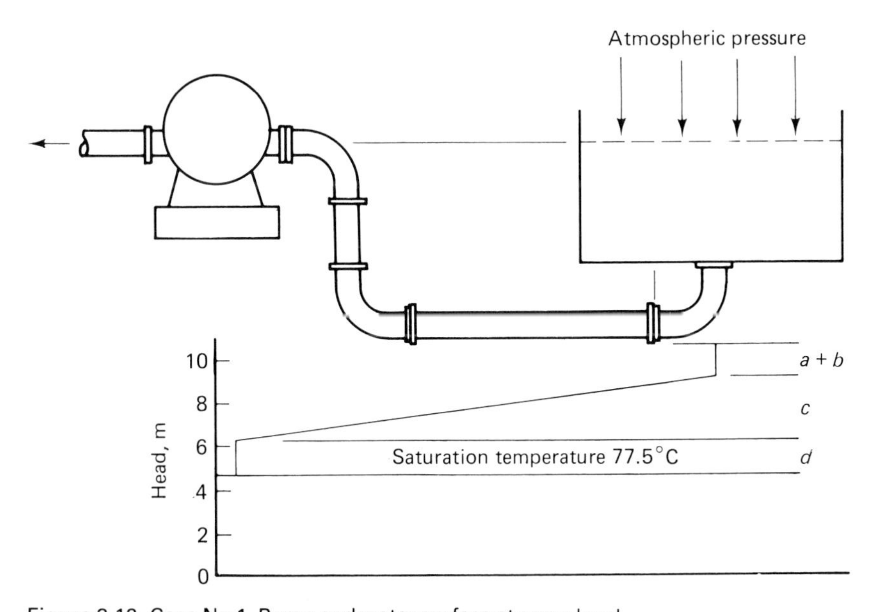

Figure 3.12 Case No 1. Pump and water surface at same level

original 10.3 m head, 5.9 is required to overcome the various friction losses, leaving the water at the pump at 4.4 m, i.e. 428.6 mbar absolute. The boiling temperature of water at this pressure is 77.5°C. Therefore, if the water in the tank were 77.5°C or above it would vaporize in the pump and so, for all practical purposes, no pumping would take place. Therefore it is essential that the water temperature is low enough to ensure that flashing will not occur.

Also notice that it was assumed that the equivalent head of atmospheric pressure was 10.3 m, but this is only true at sea level. At other altitudes the available head varies, as shown in *Figure 3.13*. So, for example, if the pump

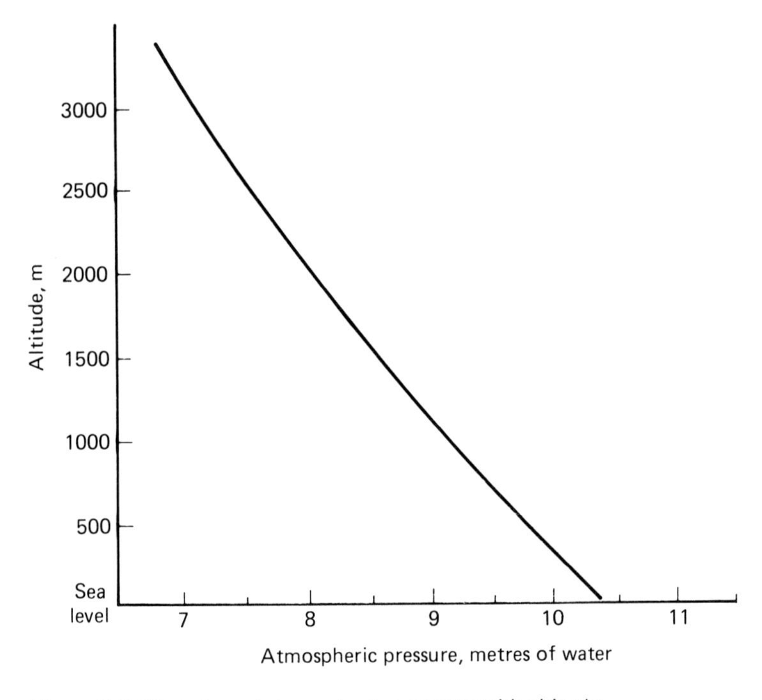

Figure 3.13 Variation of atmospheric pressure with altitude

were in Johannesburg, which is at an altitude of about 1700 metres above sea level, the atmospheric pressure would only be 8.4 metres of water. Therefore, the head of water at the inlet to the pump impeller would be $8.4 - 5.9 = 2.5$ metres. The equivalent boiling temperature is 64.5°C. Hence, the higher the altitude the lower the permissible water temperature to prevent boiling.

Case 2. Supply tank below pump suction

Next consider an installation at sea level where the pump is supplied from an open tank below the suction, as shown in *Figure 3.14*. Assume the surface of

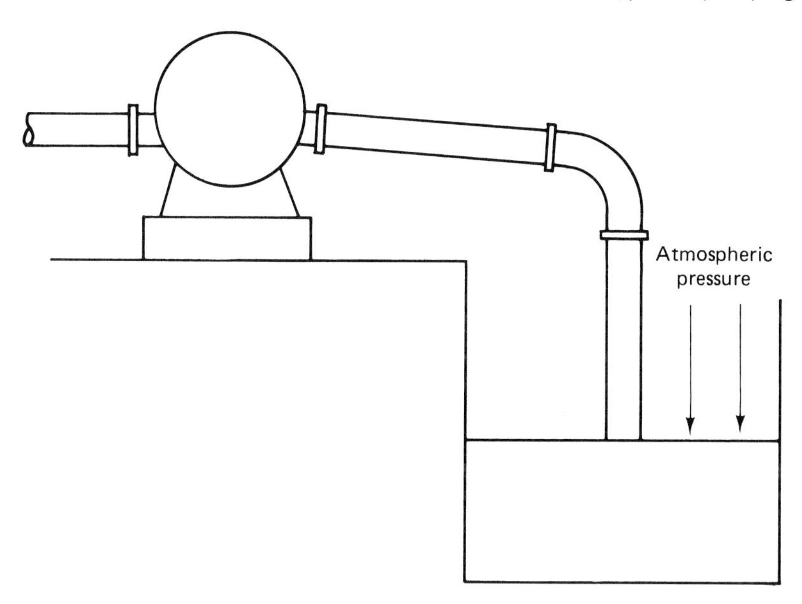

Figure 3.14 Case No 2. Supply tank below pump suction

the water is 3.0 m below the pump suction centre line. As in Case 1 the total head available to push the water into the pump is that of the atmosphere, i.e. 10.3 m. If the suction system has the same losses as in the previous case (5.9 m) there is 4.4 m left. But a further 3 m will be used in overcoming the suction lift, so the head at the pump impeller will be only 1.4 m. The associated boiling temperature is 52°C and so this is the theoretical maximum at which the pump will work.

Case 3. Supply tank above the pump

This case is shown in *Figure 3.15*. The surface of the water is, say, 3 m above the pump. By virtue of the elevation of the water supply there is a static head of 3 m *plus* the atmospheric pressure of 10.3 m available, i.e. 13.3 m. As in the previous cases assume the friction losses amount to 5.9 m. Then the head acting on the water at the pump impeller is 7.4 m, and the boiling temperature at that head is 90°C.

Notice how the maximum temperature of the water varies from case to case depending upon the suction supply conditions, as shown in *Table 3.2*.

If possible centrifugal pumps should be installed with a positive suction head to ensure ease of priming. If it is necessary to have a suction lift then it should never exceed 5 m.

Figure 3.16 shows the relationship between suction head and water temperature. Notice that in practice the maximum safe temperature is considerably less than the theoretical maximum. The information given assumes that the supply is from an open tank at sea level.

Case No	*Height of supply (m)*	*Max. Theor. Temp.(°C)*
1	0	77.5
2	(−) 3.0	52.0
3	(+) 3.0	90.0

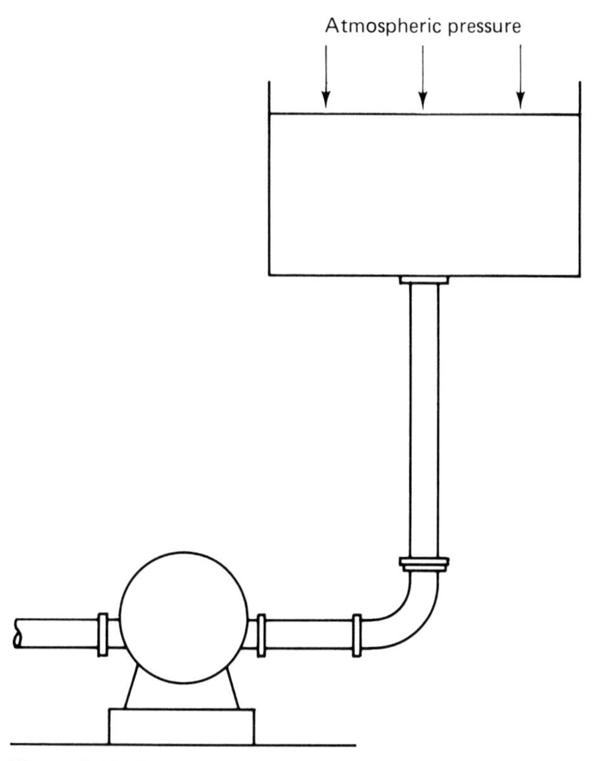

Figure 3.15 Case No 3. Supply tank above pump suction

Gas formation inside a pump

It has already been shown how steam can form if the temperature conditions are appropriate and so interfere with pumping. There is a further aspect to consider and it is best illustrated with reference to reciprocating pumps. *Figure 3.17(a)* shows two such pumps. The upper one has the lowest suction head and so, as the piston rises, the reduced pressure inside the barrel may become low enough to cause the water to flash. On the downstroke the vapour will be compressed and the pressure increase may cause the steam to

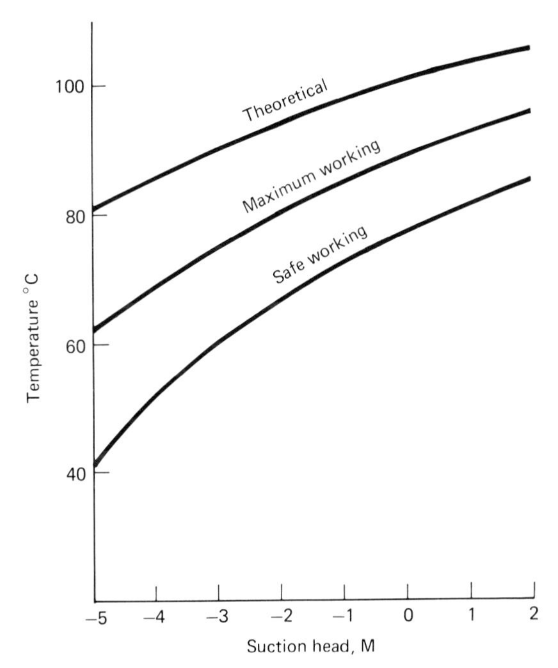

Figure 3.16 Pump suction conditions

condense. The resulting disturbance inside the pump will be considerable and the water quantity discharged will be small. It will be appreciated that with water at a suitably high temperature, steam will form before any water gets into the pump and so the piston will move up and down in an atmosphere of steam. Pumping will be virtually nil.

The solution is obvious – either reduce the temperature of the water, or lower the pump so that the positive suction head is sufficient to prevent flashing, as shown by the lower pump in *Figure 3.17(a)*.

Air is also troublesome if it gets into a pump as it collects at high points and so restricts the passage of the water. For example C.W. (particularly at cooling-tower stations) contains a lot of air. Some of it is detrained inside the C.W. pumps and collects at the top of the casing. Noisy running results and frequent venting is necessary. Cavitation may also be troublesome; it is caused by local boiling of the liquid being pumped, but is accentuated if the liquid contains dissolved gases such as air which are released at reduced pressure (or increased temperature).

Cavitation can cause serious erosion of an impeller. *Figure 3.17(a)* shows the phosphor-bronze impeller from a double-entry C.W. pump. Within a few years of operation it was so seriously eroded (*Figure 3.17(b)*)that it was replaced with one made of stainless steel.

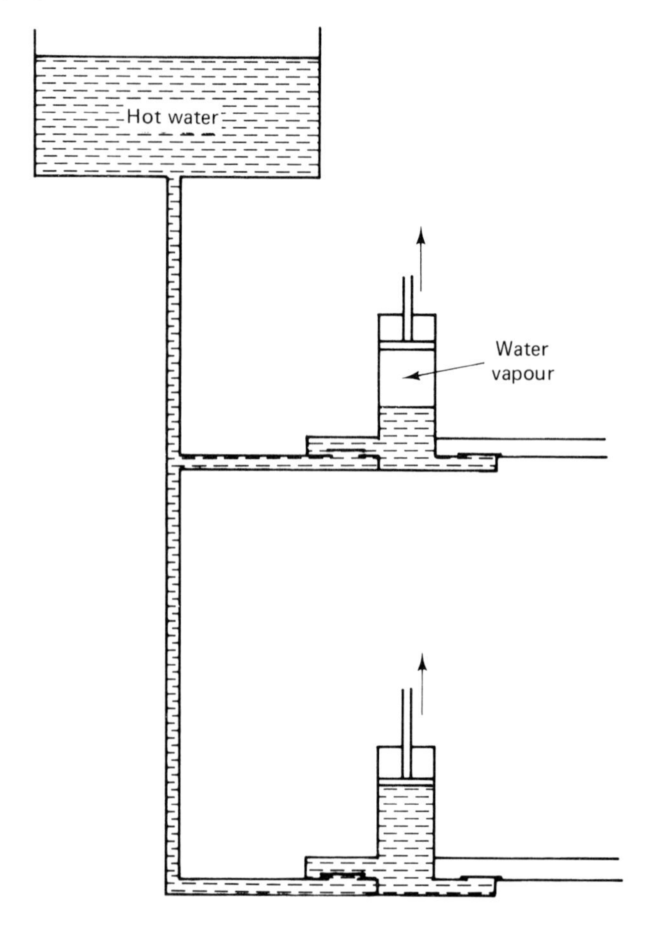

Figure 3.17(a) Effect of pump suction head upon vapour formation

Pump suction conditions

Example 1

An open tank contains water at 90°C. If the friction and other losses in the suction system total 5 metres, what is the minimum theoretical head of water required?

Atmospheric pressure at sea level.	1013 mbar abs.
Vapour pressure at 90°C (steam tables)	701 mbar abs.
Pressure in excess of vapour pressure	312 mbar abs.
Equivalent head	3.2 m
Pipe friction to be overcome	5.0 m
So positive suction head required = 5.0 − 3.2	(+) **1.8 m**

Figure 3.17(b) Phosphor-bronze impeller from a large CW pump (CEGB)

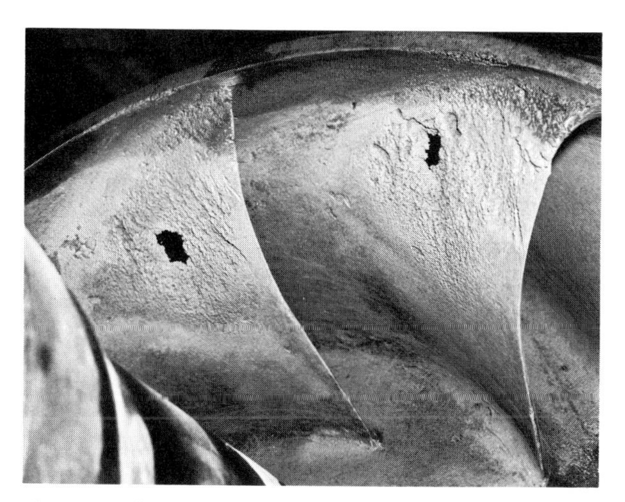

Figure 3.17(c) Cavitation damage to impeller (CEGB)

Example 2

If a pump draws water from an open tank 2 m below its level, what is the theoretical maximum temperature of the water for satisfactory operation? Pipe friction loss is 5 m.

Absolute pressure at sea level	1013 mbar
Allowance for pipe friction (5 m)	487 mbar
Equivalent head of 2 m	195 mbar
Pressure at impeller (1013 − 487 − 195)	331 mbar
Saturation temperature at 331 mbar	71°C

Exercises

1 A pump is installed in Johannesburg (altitude 1750 m). The open suction tank contains water at 50°C. Assume the friction loss is 5 m. What is the maximum theoretical suction lift at which the pump can be operated?
Answer: 2.0 m

2 Water at 90°C is supplied to a pump from an open tank at sea level. What is the theoretical minimum height the water must be at above the pump suction for satisfactory operation? Assume friction loss is 5.1 m.
Answer: 2.2 m

Pump supplied from a vessel containing boiling water

Whether the vessel is a condenser, deaerator, feed heater supplying a heater drains pump or some such, the arrangement is always similar, i.e. water at, or near, boiling temperature in the vessel is supplied to a pump for disposal.

Consider the case of a deaerator in which the pressure is 4 bar absolute, and the height of the water above the booster pump suction is 20 m. The total head acting upon the pump suction is thus 41 m (i.e. 4 bar abs.) + 20 m static head = 61 m. However, the water is boiling at 4 bar abs. and so the water at the pump impeller cannot be at a lower pressure than this. So, of the 61 m available, 41 m cannot be used, *leaving only the static head of 20 m to push the water into the pump and to overcome the pipe friction.* This is always the case when boiling water is considered.

Water supplied from a condenser is treated in a similar manner. Suppose a condenser is operating at 36.7 mbar abs. pressure, then the condensate will be at 27.5°C. Assume the pipe friction loss is 1 m and the condensate surface is 5 m above the extraction pump suction centre-line. As before, the only head available to push the water into the pump is that due to the static head of 5 m. After deducting the pipe friction loss from this the Net Positive Suction Head (NPSH) is 4.0 m.

The static head must be adequate, as otherwise the pipe friction loss may be sufficient to cause the water to flash to steam at the inlet to the pump, resulting in erratic pumping. For example, the very erratic operation of the evaporator blow-down pumps at one station was cured by merely relocating the pumps at a lower level.

Suction pipework layout

There are two basic criteria to be satisfied with suction pipe layouts:

1. The pipework must be erected in such a way that air pockets cannot form.
2. The friction loss should normally be as small as is economically possible, e.g. large-bore pipework with few bends or fittings is ideal.

Care should be taken to ensure that the situation depicted in *Figure 3.18*

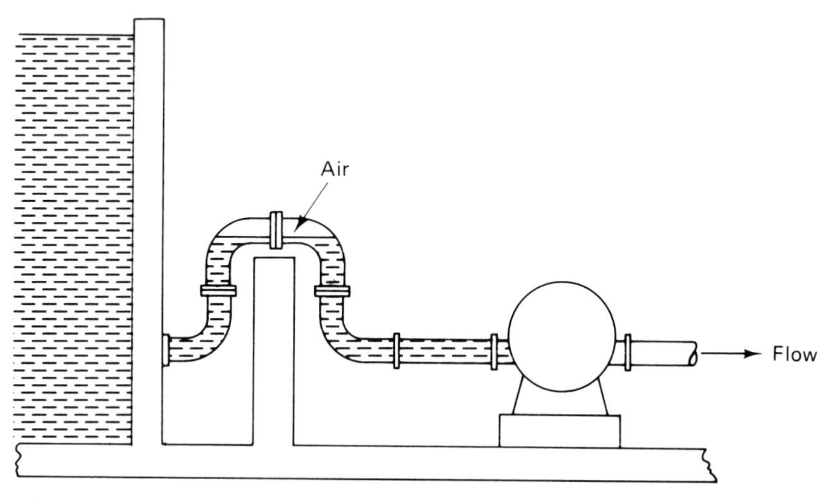

Figure 3.18 Incorrect suction pipe layout

does not occur. Where the air has accumulated in the 'hump' the pipe is severely restricted in effective area and the water only has the space beneath the air through which to flow. Variations of the same defect are shown in *Figures 3.19* and *3.20*. In *Figure 3.19* the suction pipe rises vertically but then

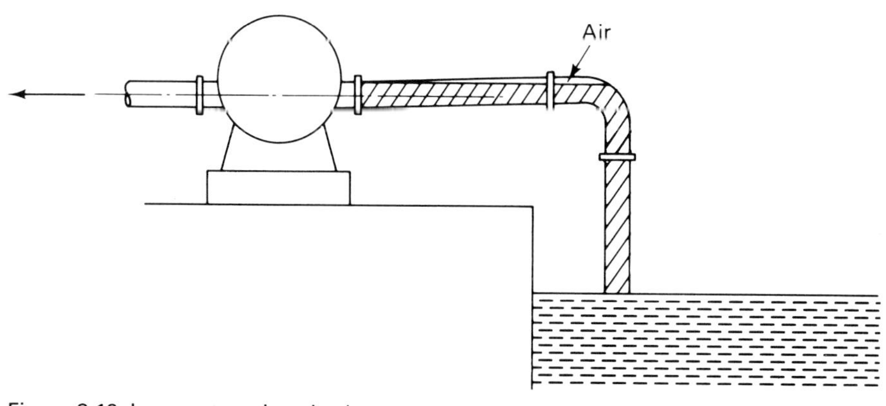

Figure 3.19 Incorrect suction pipe layout

falls towards the pump, so an air pocket will form at the bend. In *Figure 3.20* a pocket of air will collect at the hump after the suction strainer. The correct layouts are shown in *Figures 3.21* and *3.22,* where the suction pipe rises all the way to the pump.

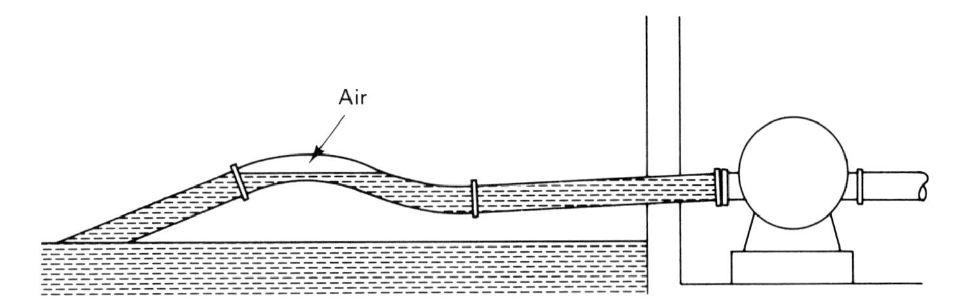

Figure 3.20 Incorrect suction pipe layout

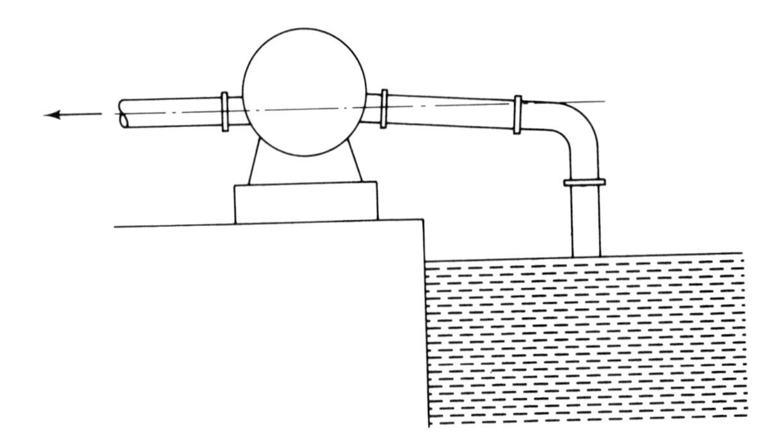

Figure 3.21 Correct suction pipe layout

There is no particular reason why the bore of the suction pipe should be the same as the bore of the suction branch of the pump. It should never be smaller, but very often it is larger. Thus, the problem of connecting the pipe to a smaller branch arises. It should never be done as illustrated in *Figure 3.23.* This is because the area indicated in the drawing will contain air and thus reduce the effective bore of the pipe. The correct way to do it is to use a taper as shown in *Figure 3.24* or *Figure 3.25.*

An arrangement whereby two or more pumps with a suction lift are supplied from a common suction line is not recommended. If such a case is unavoidable any places at which air can get into the system should be sealed, e.g. valve glands and standing pump glands should be sealed with water. The

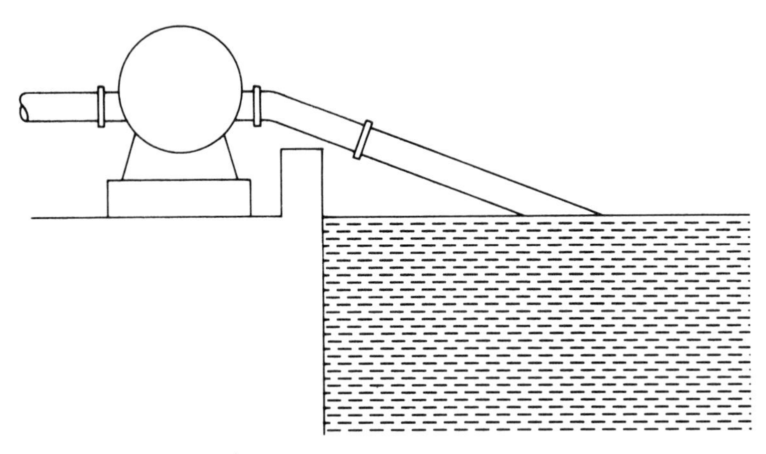

Figure 3.22 Correct suction pipe layout

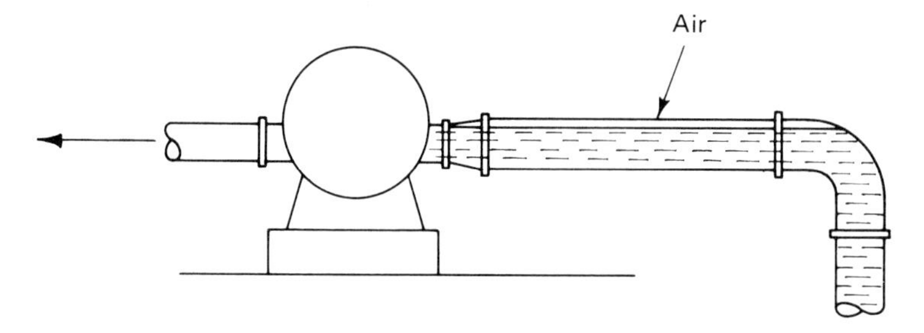

Figure 3.23 Incorrect method of joining a suction pipe to a smaller pump suction branch

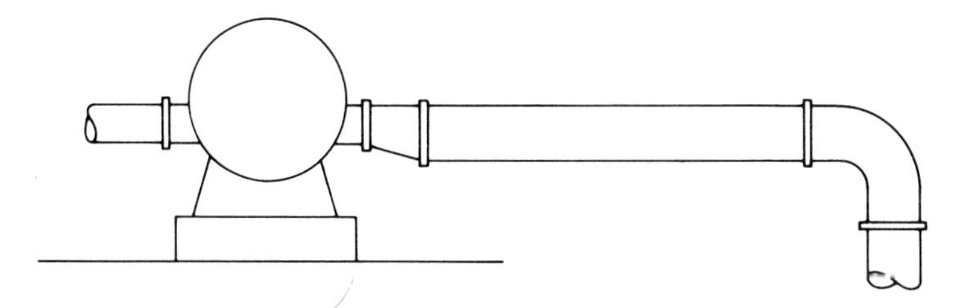

Figure 3.24 Correct connection of pipe to smaller suction branch

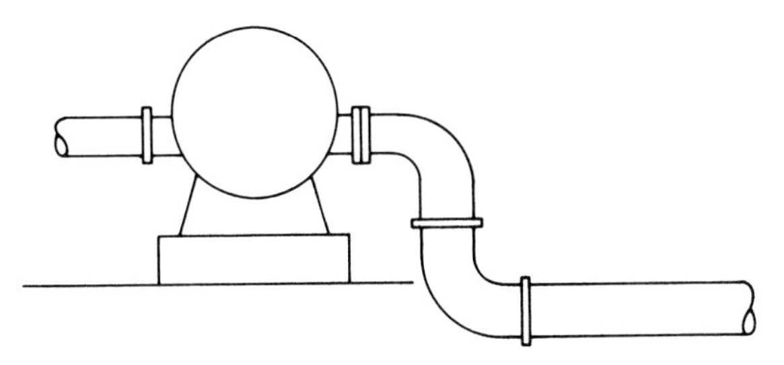

Figure 3.25 Alternative correct connection

area of a common suction pipe should be at least equal to the combined areas of the pump suction branches connected to it. For example, if there are two pumps with suction bores of 10 cm and 15 cm respectively then the bore of the common pipe should be at least:

$$(10 \times 10) + (15 \times 15) = \text{common pipe bore squared}$$
$$100 + 225 = 325\ \text{cm}^2$$
$$\text{So bore of supply pipe} = \sqrt{325} = 18\ \text{cm}$$

Determination of pipe sizes

Determination of the bore of the suction pipe

The basic requirements of the layout of suction systems has now been established. Next consider the determination of the required bore of the pipe. This is best done by using an example.

Suppose the arrangement is to be as shown in *Figure 3.26*. The pump

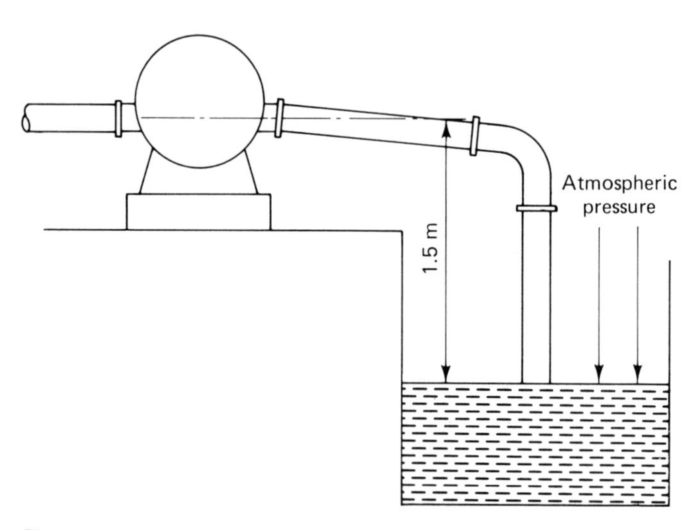

Figure 3.26 Layout of pump suction system

capacity is 50 litre/s and the suction lift is 1.5 m. The suction layout has:

7 m pipe; 1 medium radius bend; 1 foot valve; 1 strainer

Typical velocities for suction flows lie between 0.3 and 0.6 metres per second. In this case assume 0.5 m/s. At this velocity the required pipe bore to pass 50 litre/s is found from:

$$v = \frac{1.266 \times 10^6 Q}{d^2} \text{ m/s} \quad \text{where } Q = \text{m}^3\text{/s}$$
$$d = \text{pipe diameter mm}$$

$$\text{So } d = \sqrt{\left(\frac{1.266 \times 10^6 \times 0.05}{0.5}\right)} = 356 \text{ mm, say } \mathbf{350\ mm}$$

Next calculate the total suction lift using 350 mm pipe and, if it comes to more than 5 m, a new calculation must be carried out using a larger bore pipe and so on until a suitable value is established.

The equivalent pipe lengths of the fittings is determined from *Table 3.3*

Table 3.3 Equivalent pipe length of various fittings (m)

Fitting	m	Fitting	m
U-bend	70	45° elbow or contraction 4 to 1	16
Tee (side inlet or outlet)	65	Contraction 2 to 1	12
Elbow or enlargement 1 to 4	35	Gate valve (open)	8
Medium-radius bend	25	Globe valve (open)	300
Long-radius bend, Tee (on run) or enlargement 1 to 2	20	Angle valve (open)	160
		Non-return valve	80
Foot valve and strainer	120		

(Example: 150 mm diameter 45° elbow = 16 × 0.15 = 2.4 m equivalent straight pipe length.)

So equivalent suction pipe length is:
Suction pipe
1 medium-radius bend = 25 × 0.35
1 foot valve and strainer = 120 × 0.35 = 42.0m

Equivalent length = 57.8 m

Friction loss (from chart) = 0.55 m/km or 0.055%
friction loss = 0.055% of 57.8m
= 0.03
So total suction lift = 1.5 + 0.03 = 1.53, say 1.6 m

As this is less than the recommended maximum value of 5 m it is acceptable, provided the pipe bore is not less than the bore of the pump suction branch.

Size of delivery piping

For delivery piping the flow is usually between 2.4 and 3.0 m/s. In this case assume a speed of 2.8 m/s.

$$\text{Then the required pipe diameter } d = \sqrt{\left(\frac{1.266 \times 10^6 \times 0.05}{2.8}\right)}$$

$$= \mathbf{150\ mm}$$

Assume the water has to be elevated 70 m and consists of the following items, then the equivalent pipe length will be:

Straight pipe, say		100.0 m
1 Non-return valve	80×0.15	12.0 m
2 Gate valves	16×0.15	2.4 m
6 Long radius bends	120×0.15	18.0 m
2 Medium radius bends	50×0.15	7.5 m
Total equivalent pipe length		139.9 m

From chart, friction loss	= 44 m/km = 4.4%
So friction loss	= 6.2 m
Static lift	= **70.0 m**

Total discharge head	= 76.2 m
Total suction lift	= **1.6 m**
Total inclusive head	= 77.8 m

So the pump must be capable of delivering 50 litres of water per second against a total inclusive head of 77.8 metres.

Of course, other pipe bores could have been used, but it should be remembered that:

1. The larger the bore the smaller the friction loss, but the more expensive the pipework and fittings. Hence the friction loss affects the running cost and the size of the pipe the capital cost. The final economic decision will be affected by the load factor of the pump. If it is to be considerable then care must be exercised to keep the friction loss low.
2. The cost of the pump and motor is affected by the pump head, and this is affected by the size of the pipework.

Positive suction head

It has already been stated that it is advisable to operate centrifugal pumps with a positive suction head, and this can be considerable in some cases. For example, boiler circulation pumps have a very high suction pressure upon which the pump imposes only a very small extra amount.

On a 350 MW boiler the boiler circulation pumps have the following duty:

Suction pressure	192.8 bar
Discharge pressure	194.8 bar
Differential pressure	2.0 bar
Pumped quantity	0.979 m^3/s
Net positive suction head above vapour pressure	15 m

	Hot	Cold
Water temperature	363°C	
Specific gravity	0.518	
Power absorbed (kW)	242	466
Current at 415 V, 3-phase (A)	454	887

Thus, the pump casing has to be capable of withstanding 195 bar even though the pump only has to generate 2 bar.

Determination of pump efficiency

The pressure generated by a pump may be expressed as either a head h or a pressure p, where:

H = head in metres, and p = pressure in N/m^2 (i.e. bar $\times 10^5$)
To convert from one to the other use $p = h \rho g$
where ρ = density in kg/m^3, and $g = 9.81\ m/s^2$

For example, consider a boiler feed pump which generates a head of 2300 m when pumping feed water at 180°C (density 886 kg/m^3).

Equivalent pressure $p = 2300 \times 886 \times 9.81$
$= \mathbf{200 \times 10^5\ N/m^2}$, or **200 bar**

The pump throughput may be expressed either as a mass flow m or a volumetric flow Q, with m in kg/s and Q in m^3/s.
To convert from one to the other use $q = \dfrac{m}{\rho}$

So if the above pump had a mass flow of 600 kg/s, the volumetric flow would be:

$$Q = \frac{600}{\mathbf{886}} = \mathbf{0.677\ m^3/s}$$

The water power of a pump P_O (i.e. the output power) is given by $P_O - PQ$

where P is in N/m^2, PQ is in m^3/s, and P_o is in watts
Expressed in units, $P_o = N/m^2 \times m^3/s = Nm/s = J/s = W$

So for the above pump, $P_o = \dfrac{200 \times 10^5 \times 0.677}{10^3}$ kW
$= \mathbf{13\ 540\ kW}$

If the drive motor current is 1150 A at 11 kV, at 0.8 power factor and motor efficiency 0.95, then motor power consumption is:

$\sqrt{3} \times kV \times I \times \cos \phi = kW$
$\sqrt{3} \times 11 \times 1150 \times 0.8 = 17\ 528\ kW$

and the motor brake power = 17 528 × 0.95 = 16 652 kW

$$\text{Hence, the pump efficiency} = \frac{13\ 540}{\mathbf{16625}} = 0.813 = \mathbf{81.3\%}$$

Establishing pump characteristic curves

The characteristic curves usually show:

1. Pump discharge head against flow.
2. Power consumption against flow.
3. Pump efficiency against flow.

Normally the curves are determined from the results of a series of tests carried out at the manufacturers' works. For small capacities the pump on test has its discharge routed to a weigh-tank or a tank with a weir such as shown in *Figure 3.27*, while for higher flows a flow meter may be used. For

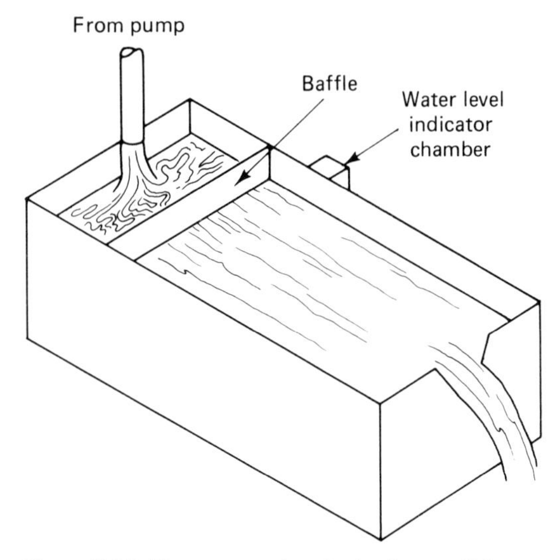

Figure 3.27 Flow measuring device for small flows

very large pumps it is necessary to carry out performance tests after installation at the power station. For example, CEGB Site Test Code No. 6 deals with site performance testing of condenser circulating water pumps.

The flow from the pump is regulated by the discharge valve setting. The method of testing is to run the pump with a series of different discharge valve settings, and usually at least one set of readings is taken with the valve shut.

At each one, the following information is recorded:

Pump speed
Suction gauge reading
Discharge gauge reading
Water flow
Water temperature
Motor power consumption

From this information a pump test record sheet such as the simplified one on page 122 can be completed.

Items 1 to 6 can be completed immediately.
Item 7 is calculated from $P_o = pQ = H \times \rho \times g \times Q$
In this case the water is at 15°C so its density is 1000 kg/m^3

$$\text{So } P_o = (4) \times 1000 \times 9.81 \times \frac{(5)}{1000}\ \text{W}$$
$$= (4) \times (5) \times 0.00981\ \text{kW}$$

Item 8 is calculated from $\text{kW} = \dfrac{\sqrt{3}VI\cos\phi}{1000}$

Item 9 is obtained from the motor test curves.
Item 10 is obtained from (8) × (9)

Item 11 is calculated from $\dfrac{(7)}{(10)}$

The information is plotted in *Figure 3.28*. It can be seen from the figure that information is given such as:

(a) The maximum head occurs when the discharge valve is shut, and is about 38 m.
(b) The output at any given head. For example at 35 m head the output is 125 litre/s.
(c) The power required by the pump for any flow. Thus, at 200 litre/s the power is 90 kW. Notice that at the maximum flow the power is still rising.
(d) The pump efficiency for any flow. For example, maximum efficiency occurs at 165 litre/s flow.

System resistance

The method of calculation of system resistance was given earlier when calculating the required size of pipe. It was shown that the static lift from the pump to the point of delivery was 70 metres and that the friction loss at a flow of 50 litre/s was 6.2 m. Now friction loss varies as the square of the flow, and so at 25 litre/s the friction loss would be 6.2 ÷ 4 = 1.55 m (i.e. for half flow the friction loss is one quarter). Thus the system resistance is as shown in *Figure 3.29*.

PUMP TEST RECORD FOR PUMP NO.

DATE OF TEST	CUSTOMER CEGB	PUMP CAPACITY 150 l/s
PUMP TYPE 1 STAGE HORIZONTAL	PUMP SPEED 745 rev/min	RATED HEAD 33 m
DIA. SUCTION BRANCH 200 mm	DIA. DISCHARGE BRANCH 200 mm	DIA. OF IMPELLER 62 cm
F.L. AMPS/VOLTS 210/415 V 3 ph	OTHER DATA	PURPOSE DUST PUMPING

(1)	(2)	(3)	(4)	(5)	(6)	(7)	(8)	(9)	(10)	(11)
Speed	*Suction gauge*	*Discharge gauge*	*Total head = (3) − (2)*	*Flow*	*Water temp.*	*Pump output power p_o*	*Motor imput power*	*Motor efficiency*	*Pump input power P_i*	*Pump efficiency*
rev/min	m	m	m	litre/s	°C	kW	kW	%	kW	%
745	(-) 0.6	36.4	37.0	65	15.0	23.6	57.3	95.8	54.9	43.0
745	(-) 1.6	31.2	32.8	165	15.0	53.1	77.4	96.2	74.5	71.3
745	(-) 1.2	34.1	35.3	115	15.0	39.8	64.9	96.1	62.4	63.8
745	(-) 2.2	27.4	29.6	205	15.0	59.5	93.4	96.3	89.9	66.2
745	(+) 0.3	38.7	38.4	0	15.0	0	41.9	95.5	40.0	0
745	(-) 2.6	19.9	22.5	240	15.0	53.0	110.4	96.4	106.4	49.8

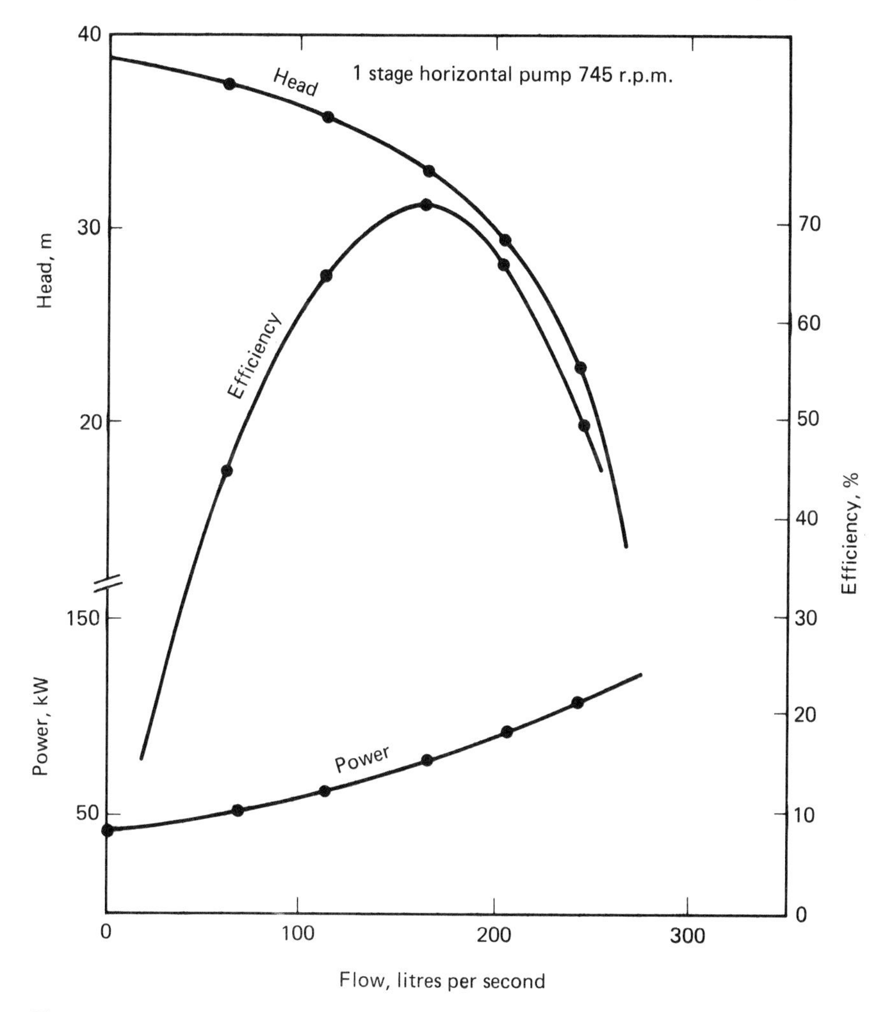

Figure 3.28 Characteristic curves for one stage horizontal pump

To determine the system resistance on an existing installation is also simple. Consider the dust line for use with the pump whose characteristic curves were determined. The pipeline is shown in *Figure 3.30*, the numbers denoting pressure measuring points along the line. The static head is determined by noting the pressure at the pump on the discharge side of the NRV with the pipeline charged but with zero flow, and in this case it is 10.5 m. The friction loss is determined by noting the discharge flow with the discharge valve wide open. In this case, when the pipework was new, it was 150 litre/s.

The discharge is determined by the flow at which the pump and system resistances intersect. The pump characteristic curves in *Figure 3.28* show that at a flow of 150 litre/s the head is 33.5 m; thus, the system resistance

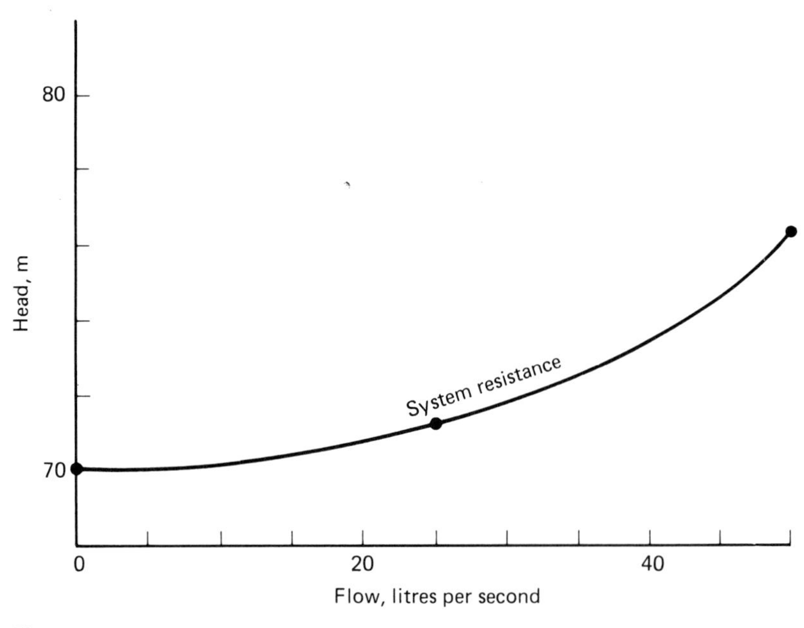

Figure 3.29 System resistance curve

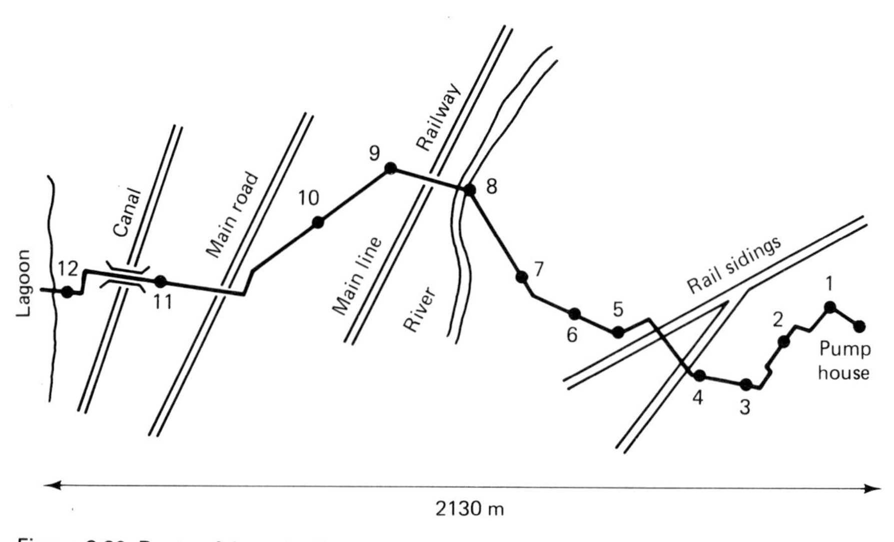

Figure 3.30 Route of dust pipeline showing measuring points

must also be 33.5. So the friction loss is 33.5 − 10.5 = 23 m at 150 litre/s. At 75 litre/s (i.e. at half flow), the friction loss will be a quarter, i.e. 23/4 = 5.7 m, and so on, as shown in *Figure 3.31*.

The pressure drop at each location along the line was noted when the

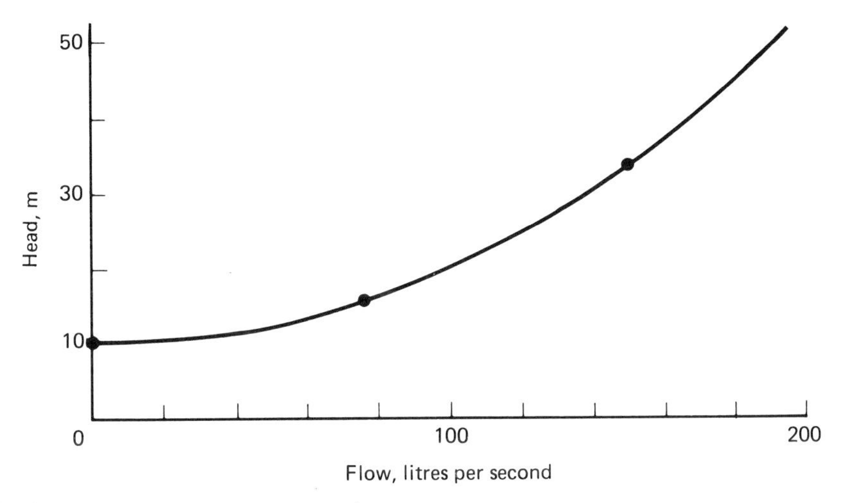

Figure 3.31 System resistance of dust pipeline

pipeline was first installed and the results are shown in *Figure 3.32(a)*. Some

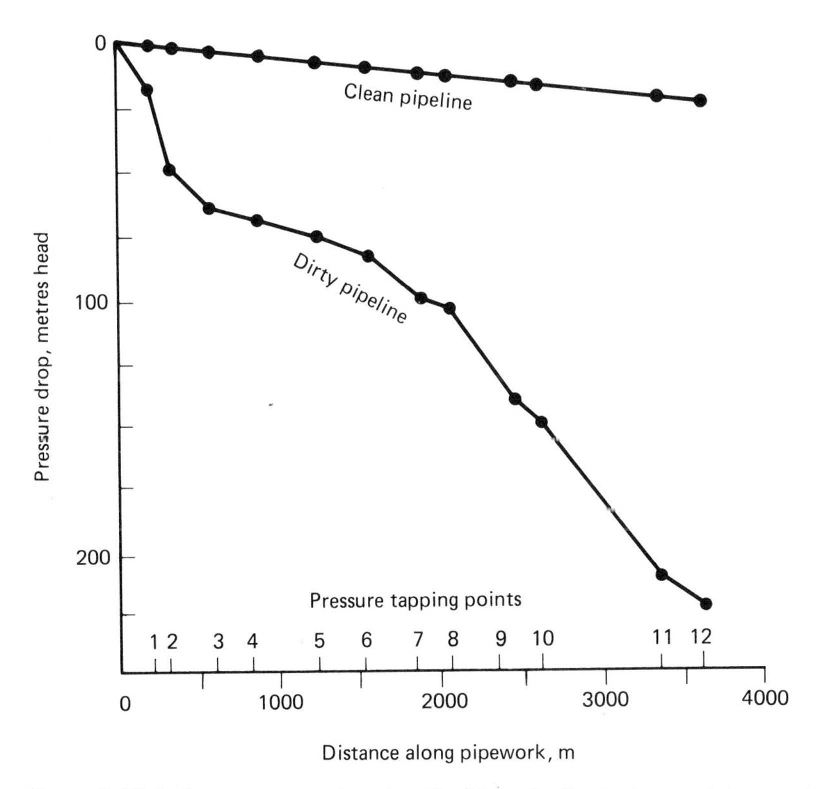

Figure 3.32(a) Pressure drops along length of dust pipeline in clean and dirty conditions

time later, when the pipe was fouled, a second set of readings was taken and the results referred back to the original flow of 125 litre/s. The results, when plotted on *Figure 3.32(a)* show clearly both the general effect of the fouling and also the sections of pipeline which are worst affected. *Figure 3.32(b)* shows the condition of a section of the fouled pipe.

Figure 3.32(b) Dust deposit inside pipeline (CEGB)

The fouled pipeline system resistance is determined in a similar manner to that for the clean condition. The static head remains unchanged. When the 'worn' pump discharge flow was 45 litre/s the head was 30.5 m and so this was also the system resistance at that flow. Therefore, the system resistance for various other flows can be calculated and plotted as shown in *Figure 3.33*. If a new pump was in service the flow would be determined by the inter-section of the 'as-new' pump and the dirty system resistance, i.e. 51 litre/s. On the other hand, an 'as-new' pump and a 'clean' pipe will produce a flow of 150 litre/s. It is clear that as the pipe fouls, the effect is to move the operating point on the diagram to the left.

Centrifugal pump affinity laws

It is shown in the Appendix that the following relationships are valid for a geometric change of size for a given speed.

$$Q \propto d^3 \qquad h \propto d^2 \qquad P \propto d^5$$

where Q = output, h = head, P = power, and d = impeller diameter. However, if only small diameter changes are involved it can be taken that:

$$Q \propto d \qquad h \propto d^2 \qquad P \propto d^3$$

Also, if a given pump is operated at a different speed the relationships will be:

$$Q \propto n \qquad h \propto n^2 \qquad P \propto n^3$$

where n = speed

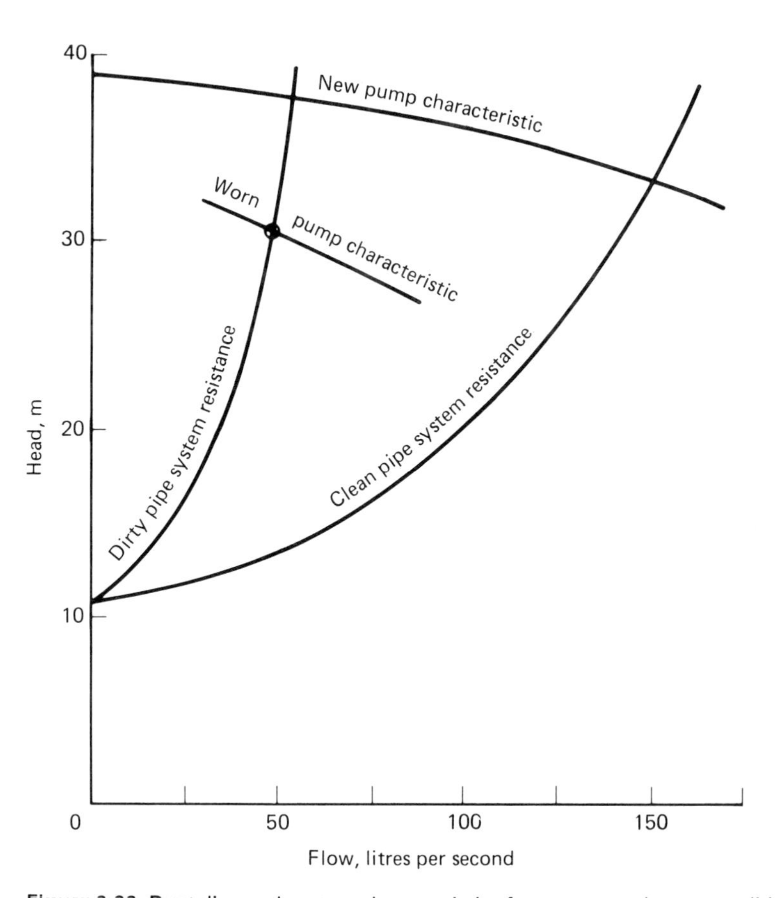

Figure 3.33 Dust disposal system characteristics for as-new and worn conditions

Change of impeller diameter

Consider a pump with, say, a 12 cm diameter impeller whose characteristics are as shown in *Figure 3.34*. If the impeller is turned down to 11 cm diameter the effect will be as shown. For example, at 15 litre/s output with the 12 cm impeller, the values with an 11 cm impeller will be:

$$Q_{11} = \frac{11.0}{12.0} \times 15 = 13.75 \text{ litre/s}$$

$$h_{11} = \left(\frac{11.0}{12.0}\right)^2 \times 88.8 = 74.6\text{m}$$

$$P_{11} = \left(\frac{11.0}{12.0}\right)^3 \times 100 = 77.0\,\text{kW}$$

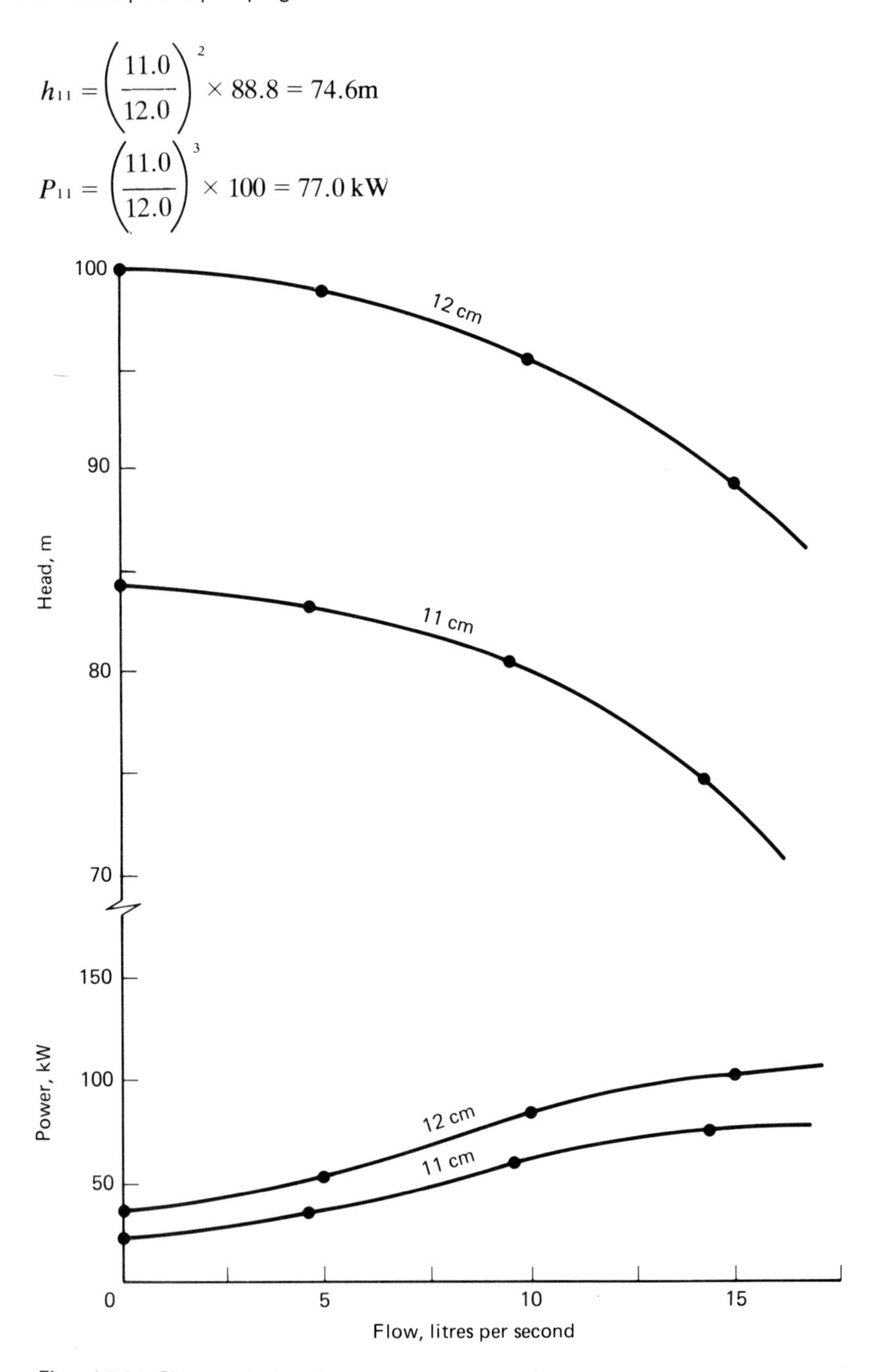

Figure 3.34 Characteristics of pump with 12 and 11 cm impeller

Change of speed

If the speed of a pump is changed the pump will have new characteristic curves. Consider the pump whose curves are shown in *Figure 3.35* as full

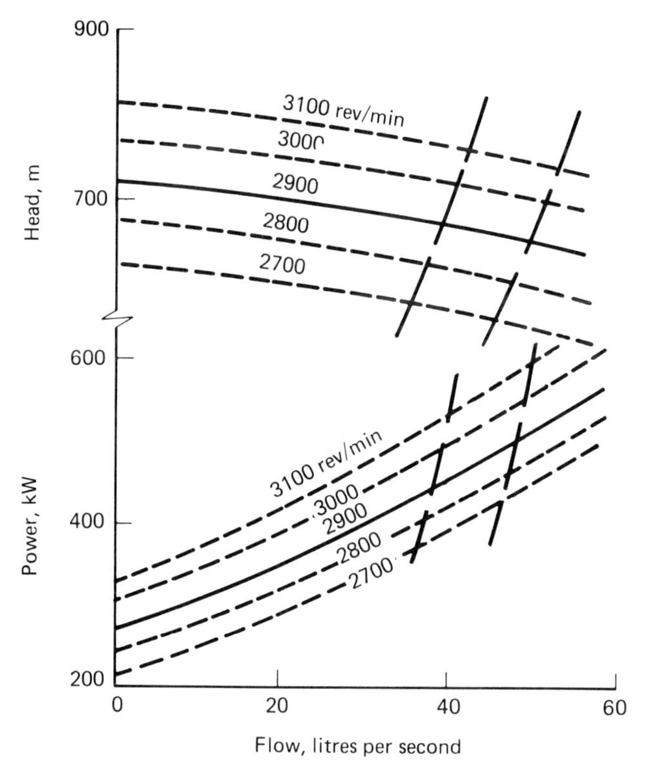

Figure 3.35 Centrifugal pump curves for various speeds

lines at 2900 rev/min. At other speeds the curves will be as shown by the short broken lines assuming the temperature of the fluid being pumped is unchanged.

For example, at 2900 rev/min the head is 700 m for a discharge flow of 25 litre/s, the power consumption being 375 kW. At say, 2700 rev/min the conditions would become:

$$\textit{Flow}\ Q_{2700} = \frac{2700 \times 25}{2900} = 23.3 \text{ litre/s}$$

$$\textit{Head}\ H_{2700} = \frac{2700^2 \times 700}{2900^2} = 607 \text{ m}$$

$$\textit{Power Consumption}_{2700} \quad \frac{2700^3 \times 375}{2900^3} = 303 \text{ kW}$$

The long broken lines in *Figure 3.35* indicate the locus of the operating point for variations of speed. For example, for a flow of 50 litre/s the head at 2900 rev/min will be 645 m and at 3100 rev/min it will be 740 m at a flow of 54 litre/s.

However, the various losses which occur in a pump do not vary in the same way, and so the affinity laws should be regarded as fairly accurate only if applied to within a reasonable range of known pump data.

Pump efficiency and speed

Theoretically the pump efficiency is independent of speed. In practice there is a small departure from this situation because, for example, changing the speed will alter the temperature of the fluid and, hence, its density.

Consider a pump with an efficiency of, say, 70% at a flow of 50 litre/s when running at 1000 rev/min. The theoretical efficiency will still be 70% if it is operated at 1500 rev/min, although it will now occur at a flow of $50 \times 1500/1000 = 75$ litre/s.

Effect of water temperature

When running at a set speed a pump discharges a definite volume of water. Hence, if the pump discharge head is measured in metres it will remain the same whatever the temperature. However, the specific volume of water varies with temperature (see Appendix II) and so the pump will discharge a greater mass of cold water in unit time than hot water. Therefore, if the pump discharge is measured in bars the value will be affected by the water temperature.

This effect is illustrated in *Figure 3.36*. The pump characteristic AB for pumping water at 10°C will become as shown by CD when handling water at 60°C. For example, at zero flow the pressure will drop from 100 bar to:

Density at 10°C = 1.0044; density at 60°C = 0.9864

$$\text{So discharge pressure at } 60°\text{C} = \frac{0.9864}{1.0044} \times 100$$

$$= \mathbf{98.2\ bar}$$

Boiler circulation pumps provide a good example of the necessity to be able to pump water at widely different temperatures. For example, the boiler circulation pumps on a 350 MW Unit have the following duty when pumping hot water.

Suction pressure	192.8 bar
Discharge pressure	194.8 bar
Differential pressure	2.0 bar
Pumped quantity	0.979 m^3/s

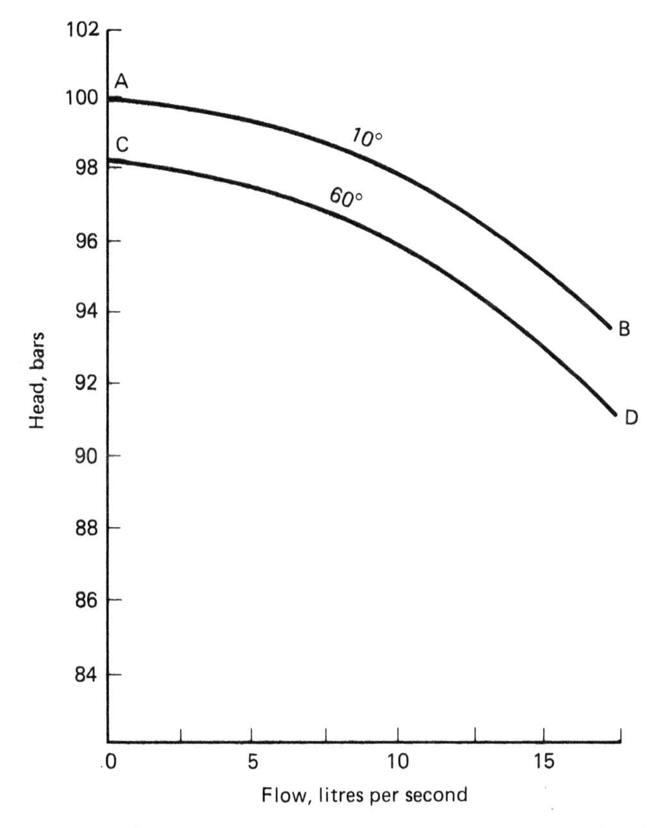

Figure 3.36 Effect of fluid temperature on pump characteristic

Water temperature	363°C
Water density	518 kg/m^3
Power absorbed	242 kW
Current at 415 V	454 A

When pumping cold water (density 1000 kg/m^3) the conditions become:

Differential head	$= \frac{1000}{518} \times 2 = 3.86$ bar
Power absorbed	$= \frac{1000}{518} \times 242 = 466$ kW
Motor current	= 887 A, allowing for motor efficiency

Specific gravity of fluid being pumped

This is similar to the water temperature change case just discussed. In both cases the essential factor is the change of density of the fluid.

$$\text{Specific gravity} = \frac{\text{mass of given volume of a substance}}{\text{mass of an equal volume of water}}$$

So if a pump absorbs, say, 100 kW when pumping water of specific gravity 1.0, it will absorb $100 \times 1.2 = 120$ kW when pumping a fluid of specific gravity 1.2 under the same operating conditions. On the other hand if it pumped, say, oil of s.g. 0.8 the power would only be 80 kW.

If a pump discharge is measured in metres head the specific gravity of the liquid can be ignored because the pump will deliver that head irrespective of the s.g. On the other hand if the discharge is measured in bars the s.g. must be considered. The relationship between the discharge measured in bars and measured in metres is given by:

$$\text{Bars} = \frac{\text{metres} \times 9.81 \times \text{s.g.}}{100}$$

For example, if the head is 200 metres when pumping a fluid of s.g. 1.0, the equivalent pressure will be:

$$\frac{200 \times 9.81 \times 1.0}{100} = 19.62 \text{ bar}$$

On the other hand if the s.g. was 0.8 the pressure would be:

$$\frac{200 \times 9.81 \times 0.8}{100} = 15.7 \text{ bar}$$

and the pump would probably need a smaller diameter impeller than in the first case. To avoid confusion it is preferable to always quote 'head' of fluid. If the pressure is quoted then so must the specific gravity.

Fuel oil is a case where the specific gravity varies considerably with temperature. There is an optimum temperature to which the oil should be raised for easy pumping, the value of which depends upon the class of oil.

Pumping with a free suction head

It has already been shown that a pump can only provide suitable conditions for some external agency to push water into the pump body. It follows that only such water that is pushed in can be discharged.

Consider an extraction pump which obtains its water from a condenser. The only head acting on the water at the pump suction is due to the difference in height between the centre-line of the suction and the surface of the water in the condenser shell – the greater the head of water the faster it can be pushed into the pump. The minimum suction head for any fraction of the pump capacity can be shown by a curve such as CD in *Figure 3.37*. AB is

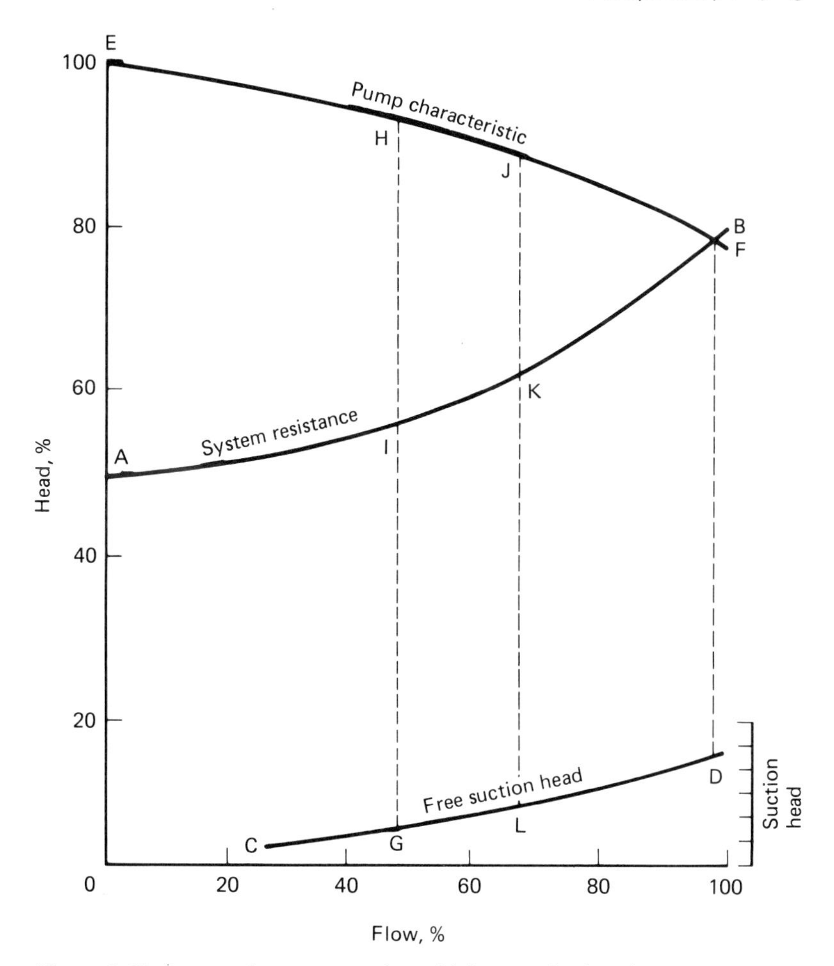

Figure 3.37 Curves of pump operating with free suction head

the system resistance and curve EF is the pump characteristic.

Provided the suction head is at least at level D the pump discharge will be determined by the intersection of the pump and system resistance curves, i.e. at the intersection of curves AB and EF. If, though, the suction head was only that represented by G then the pump would only deliver a maximum output represented by H. HI represents a zone of slack water within the early impeller stages. Similarly, if the suction head is L the output will be J.

This highlights one of the problems of operating with a free suction head, i.e. small changes of suction level can cause pronounced changes of output and so 'gulping' may occur.

Valve-controlled suction level

If the suction level is controlled by means of a valve on the pump discharge the conditions will be as shown in *Figure 3.38* and gulping is avoided. Variations of the valve opening alter the system resistance, as shown by the curves AB, AC, AD as the valve is progressively closed, AE representing the fully-closed position.

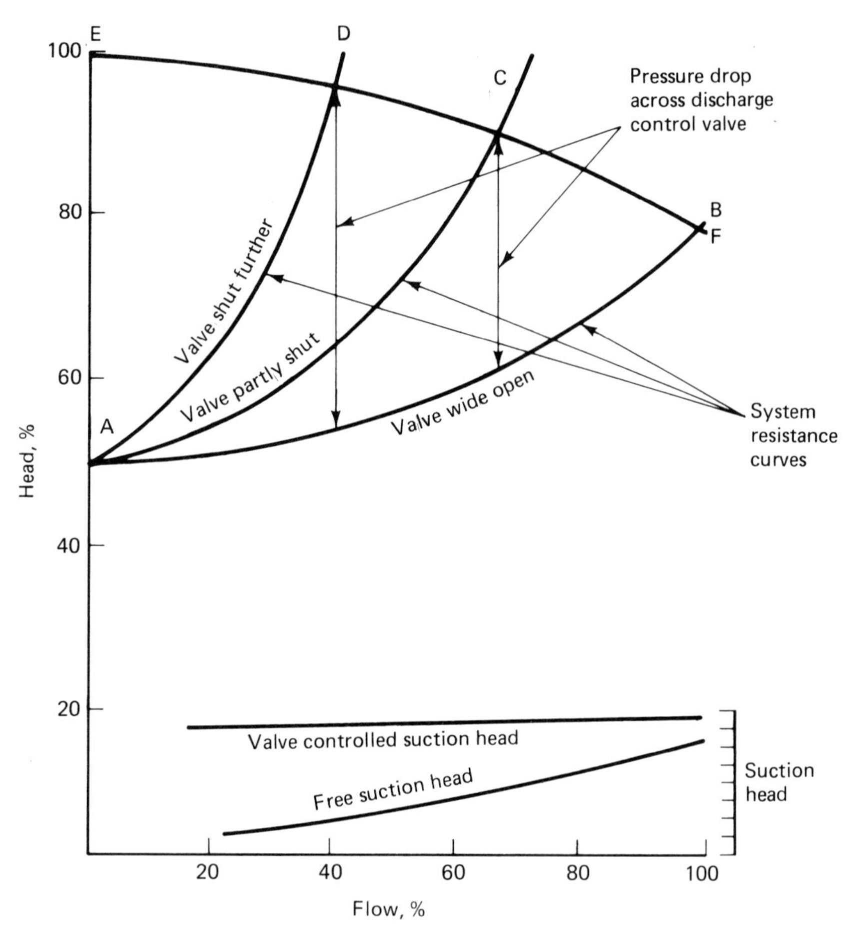

Figure 3.38 Curves of pump operating with controlled suction head

Series pumping

Often the discharge of one pump supplies the suction of another, i.e they operate in series. For example, consider a split feed system whereby a booster pump supplies the suction of the boiler feed pump. The various pressure/capacity characteristics are shown in *Figure 3.39*.The system resistance from the booster pump, through the HP heaters to the boiler feed pump suction is shown as curve AB. The pump characteristic is CD. Hence

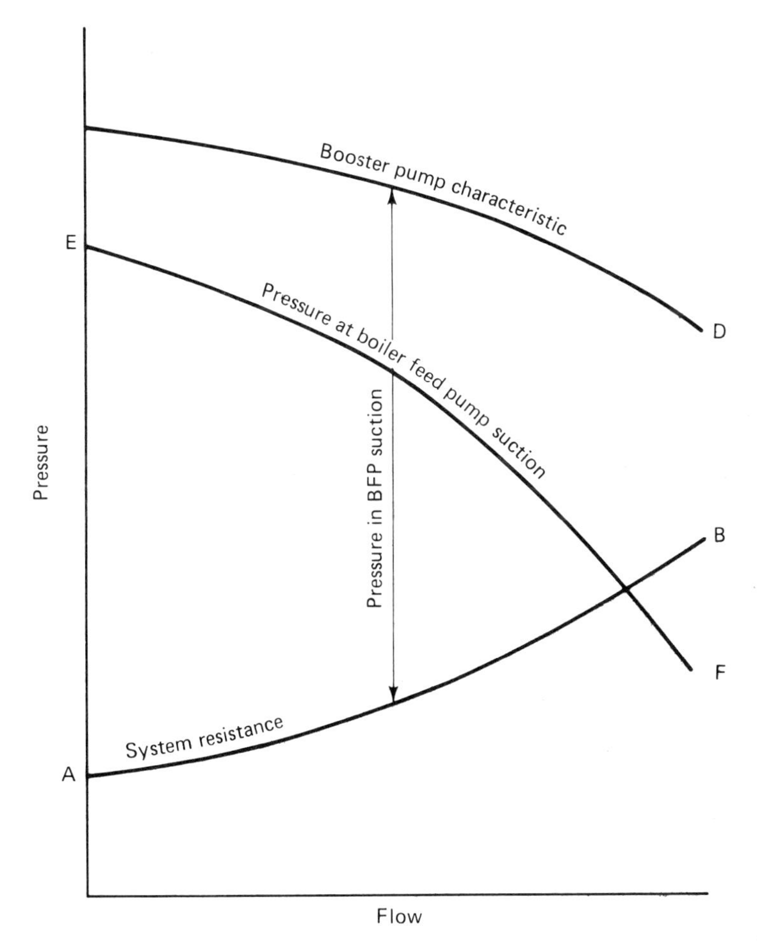

Figure 3.39 Series pumping

the pressure at the suction of the boiler feed pump is given by curve CD minus AB, and is shown as curve EF.

Parallel pumping

Centrifugal pumps often have a characteristic which rises and then falls as illustrated in *Figure 3.40.* A characteristic of this type is not suitable for some purposes. Reference to *Figure 3.40* shows that at certain heads (e.g. at A) there are two corresponding points on the characteristic curve at B and C. The pump could therefore operate at either point for the given head. Water is slightly compressible and this permits the pump discharge to surge from one point to the other and the reason is as follows. In moving from B to C the pressure increases until it is at a maximum at D, so sending a pressure

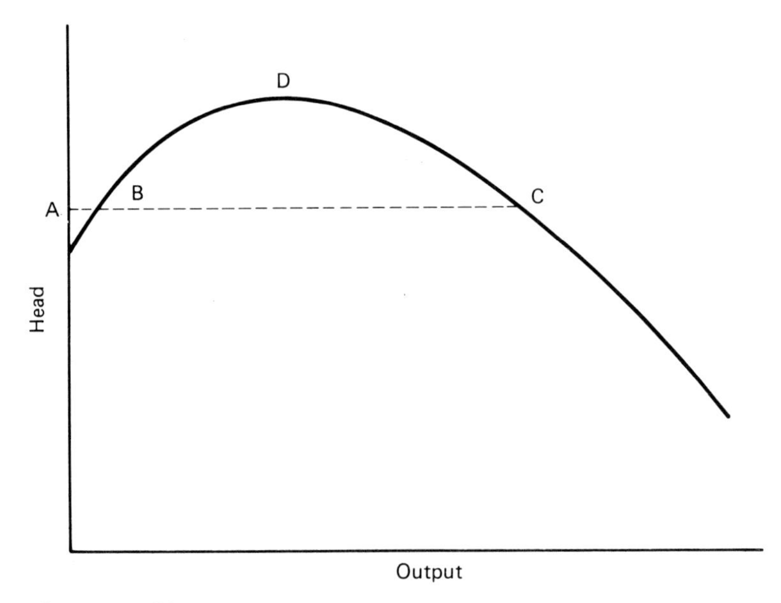

Figure 3.40 Rising and falling head characteristic

wave along the pipe line. After the output has gone beyond D the pressure falls. This allows the pressure wave to return along the pipeline to the pump and so reduce its output.

Thus, a cycle of fluctuating pressures and fluctuating outputs can be set up which is at best inconvenient and at worst could damage the installation. It should be noted that it is not necessary for the pump to have any appreciable flow for the above cycle of events to take place. Further, the surging from one capacity to the other may be rapid or slow.

Next, consider the implications of operating two pumps in parallel which have characteristic curves such as shown in *Figure 3.41 (a)*. Assume pump 1 is operating at 10% flow when 2 is started. The pressure at 1 will be 93% of maximum whereas at 2 it will be only 80%. Thus the excess pressure at 1 will prevent any delivery from 2. This will continue until the pressure due to 1 is at, or lower than, the pressure at 2. Hence it will be necessary to throttle the flow from 1, reduce the speed or increase the flow to more than 82% of the 1 pump capacity, to enable 2 to start to deliver.

Even if they could be operated at a certain load together, there are other difficulties. Suppose they are each supplying 10% flow. If, now, there is a demand for increased output such increase will be taken initially by the pump with the least friction resistance in its pipework. Suppose this applies to pump 1, then it will increase its flow to, say, 15% capacity and its discharge pressure will then be 98% of maximum. Meanwhile the flow from pump 2 will be opposed by the excess pressure from pump 1 and so its output will be reduced. This will cause pump 1 to deliver even more flow and this

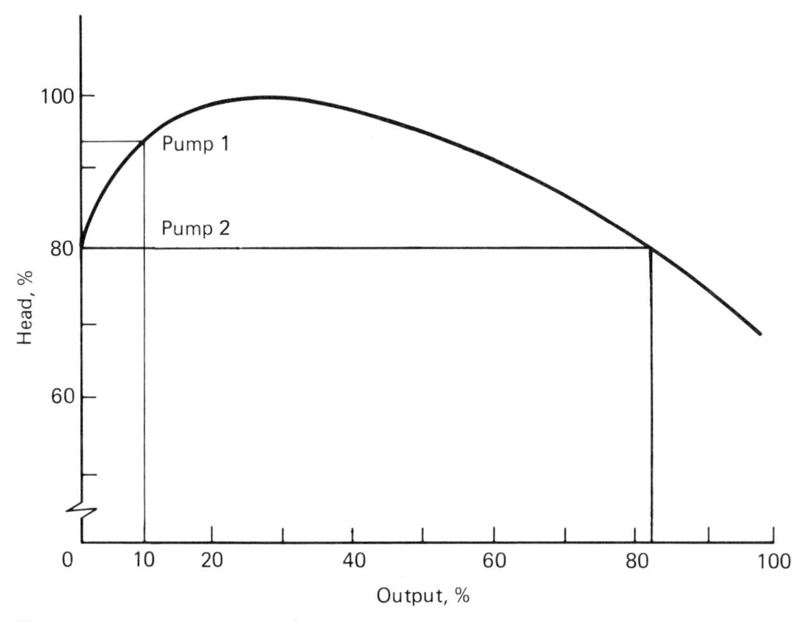

Figure 3.41(a) Characteristics of unstable pumps to be operated in parallel

state of affairs will continue until pump 2 is delivering zero flow and pump 1 is delivering it all. This will apply until pump 1 is supplying 82% of its capacity. Any further flow will be met by pumps 1 and 2 each delivering some flow, but of widely different values as shown in *Figure 3.41(b)*.

At 82% flow pump 1 will be operating at point F and pump 2 will be at point A, after which both pumps will deliver some flow until point D is reached. For example, when the total flow is determined by point G it will comprise the output of pump 1 at point J plus that of pump 2 at point H. For flows higher than that corresponding to point D both pumps will deliver the same quantity and be stable. Therefore the combined characteristic for the two pumps is given by A H B J F G D E.

For stable operation both pumps should normally have characteristics which fall continuously such as shown in *Figure 3.42(a)* by the curve EF. Two such pumps operating in parallel will have a combined characteristic as shown by the curve EK. It is obtained by doubling the flow for a series of different heads on EF.

Figure 3.42(b) shows the pump characteristics and system resistance for the complete CW pump installation at a power station. The output for any number of pumps operating in parallel is obtained by noting the flow at which the pump and system resistance curves intersect. Hence, with two pumps the output would be about 63%, and with three pumps it would be 85% with two culverts in use.

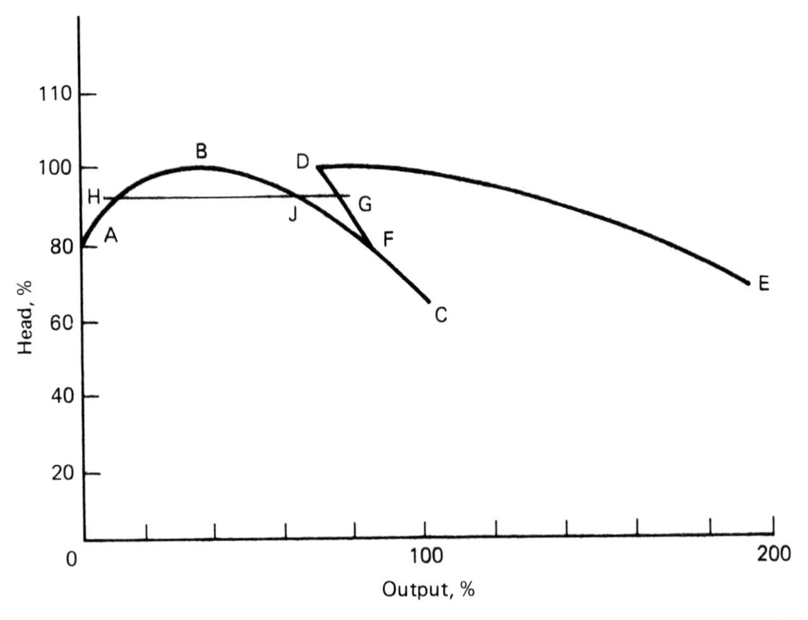

Figure 3.41(b) Combined characteristics of two unstable pumps being operated in parallel

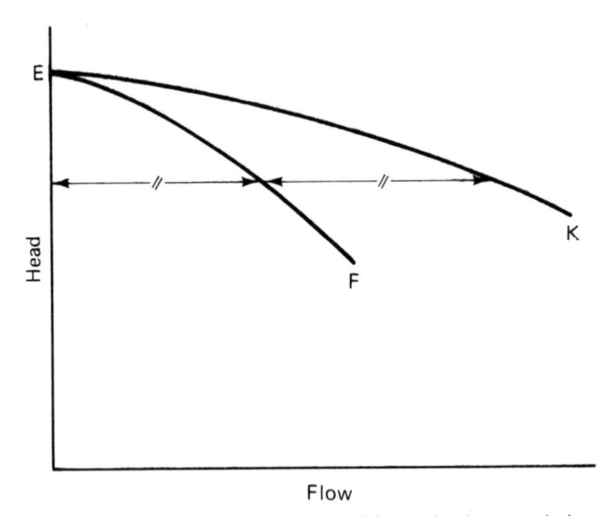

Figure 3.42(a) Parallel operation of two pumps with stable characteristics

Load sharing

Suppose two pumps with different characteristics are running in parallel as shown in *Figure 3.43*. The combined output is obtained by adding the individual outputs for a series of heads. If the system resistance is as shown the total discharge will be Q_{a+b} and the individual outputs will be Q_a and Q_b.

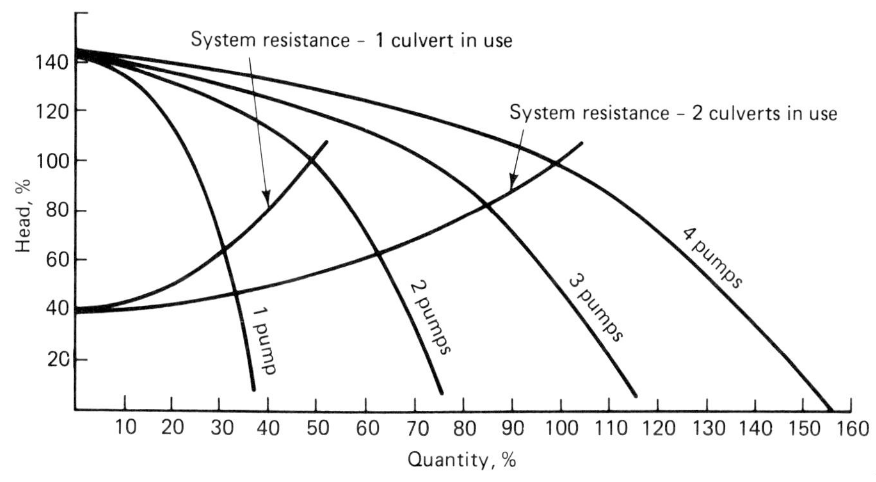

Figure 3.42(b) System resistance and pump characteristics for a complete CW, pump installation (CEGB)

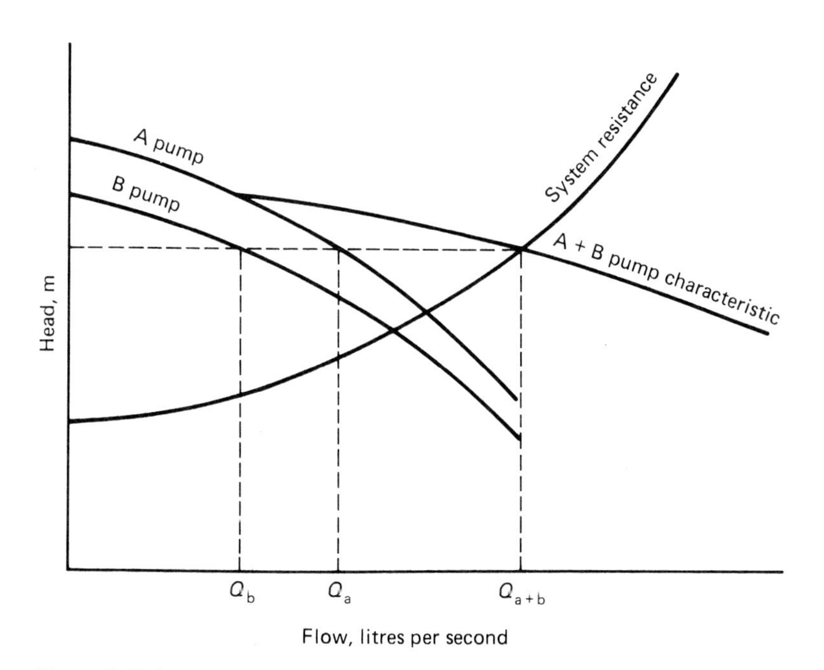

Figure 3.43 Load sharing of pumps with dissimilar characteristics

Pumping to two points

Consider the installation shown in *Figure 3.44*. The system resistance for the pipework to each tank is calculated as previously explained and plotted as shown. The combined system resistance is found by adding the capacities at

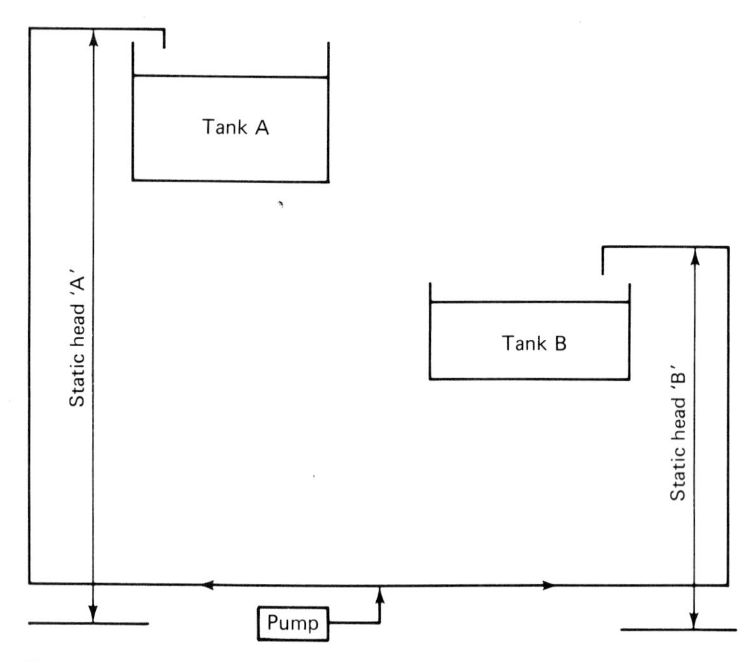

Figure.344(a) Diagram of installation for pumping to two points

any given head. The intersection of the pump characteristic and the combined system resistance determines the total flow Q_{A+B}. The individual flows are Q_A and Q_B. Should the supply to one system be stopped, say to tank A, then the total flow would be to tank B, and the quantity would be determined by the intersection of the pump characteristic with the system resistance for B, i.e. Q_X.

Pumping via twin discharge lines

Suppose a fire pump is in use supplying a single hose-pipe. What would be the effect of fitting a second hose? Consider the single hose first. Reference to *Figure 3.45* shows that the output of hose A will be Q_A and that the friction head is 40 − 10 = 30 bar. If now a second hose, identical to hose A is fitted, then at a total flow equal to Q_A each line will carry a half of Q_A, so the friction loss in each pipe will be a quarter of 30 bar = 7.5 bar. Thus the 2-hose system resistance will consist of a static head of 10 bar plus a friction loss of 7.5 bar, i.e. 17.5 bar for a total flow of Q_A. Notice that you do not add the 2-hose friction loss twice. Thus the 2-hose resistance will be as shown, and the total flow will be Q_{A+B}.

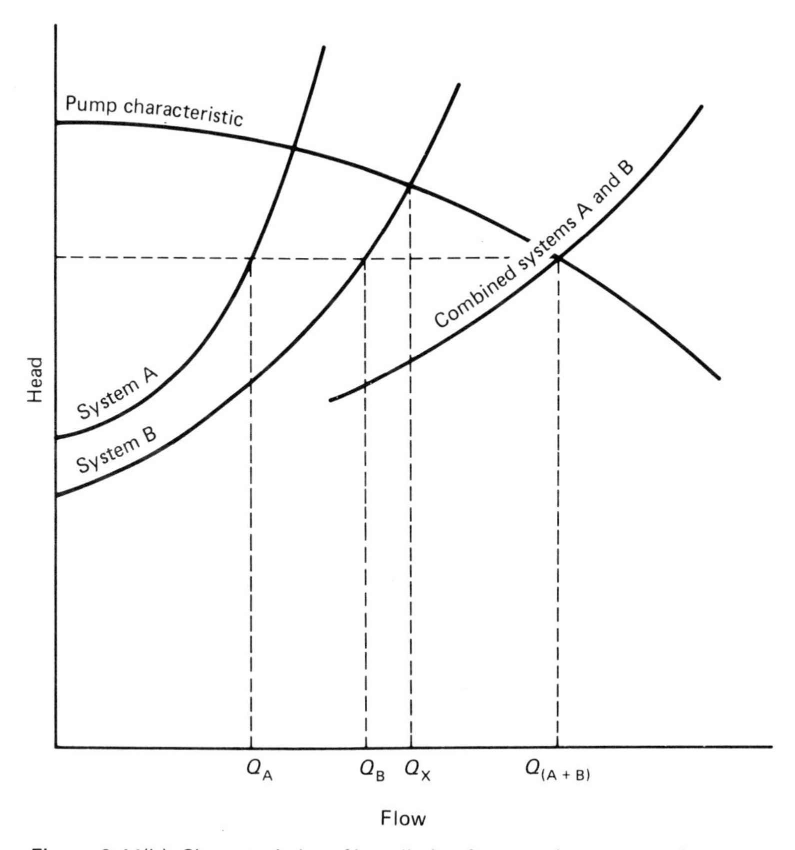

Figure 3.44(b) Characteristics of installation for pumping to two points

Variable suction and static head

Bearing cooling water is often supplied from a header tank. After passing through the bearings the water is collected and discharged into a lower tank. When the top tank level falls to a pre-set level a pump cuts in to pump the water back to the top tank. The arrangement is shown in *Figure 3.46(a)*. Thus at commencement of pumping the flow is Q_{START} and at the end it is Q_{END} as illustrated in *Figure 3.46(b)*.

Syphonic assistance

Sometimes advantage can be taken of the syphonic effect of a system layout, such as that shown in *Figure 3.47*. The static head *A* of the system when the pump is started is 15 m in the case illustrated. However, when the pump is running the static head falls to a much lower value due to syphonic assis-

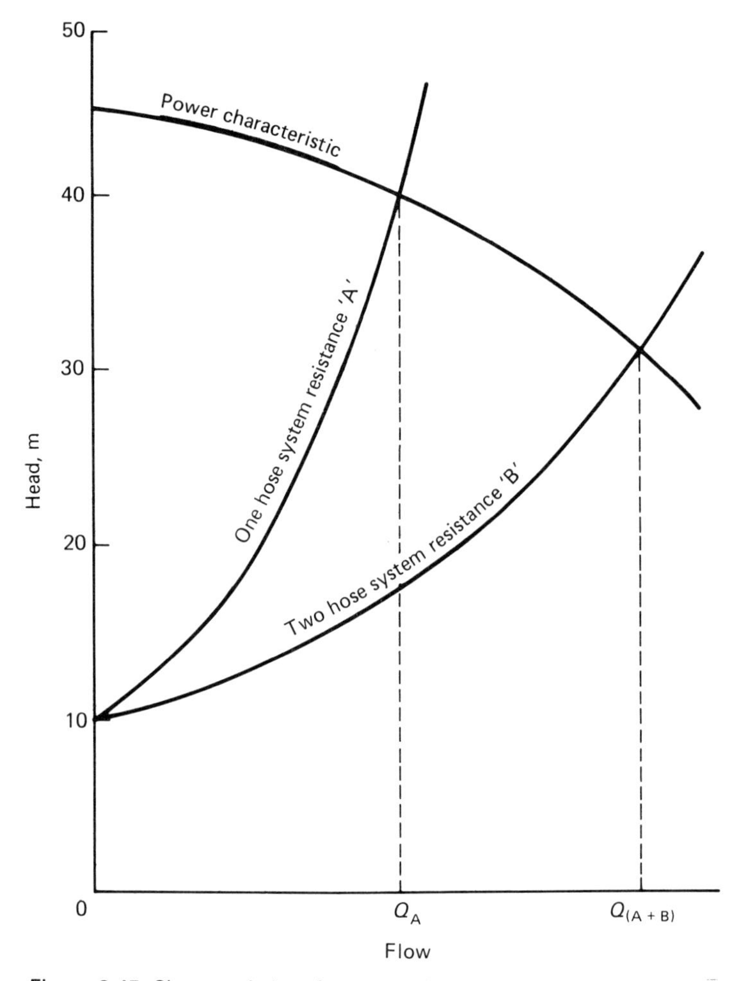

Figure 3.45 Characteristics of system using 1 and 2 pipelines in parallel

tance. Normally the running static head is assumed to be $A-0.8B$ where B is the height of the syphonic leg. In *Figure 3.47* it is 15 − 9 = 6 m. The maximum syphonic assistance is about 9 m.

Pump specific speed n_s

The specific speed is given by:

$$N_s = \frac{NQ^{0.5}}{H^{0.75}}$$

where N = shaft speed in rev/min
Q = capacity at maximum efficiency in m^3/h
H = discharge head in metres

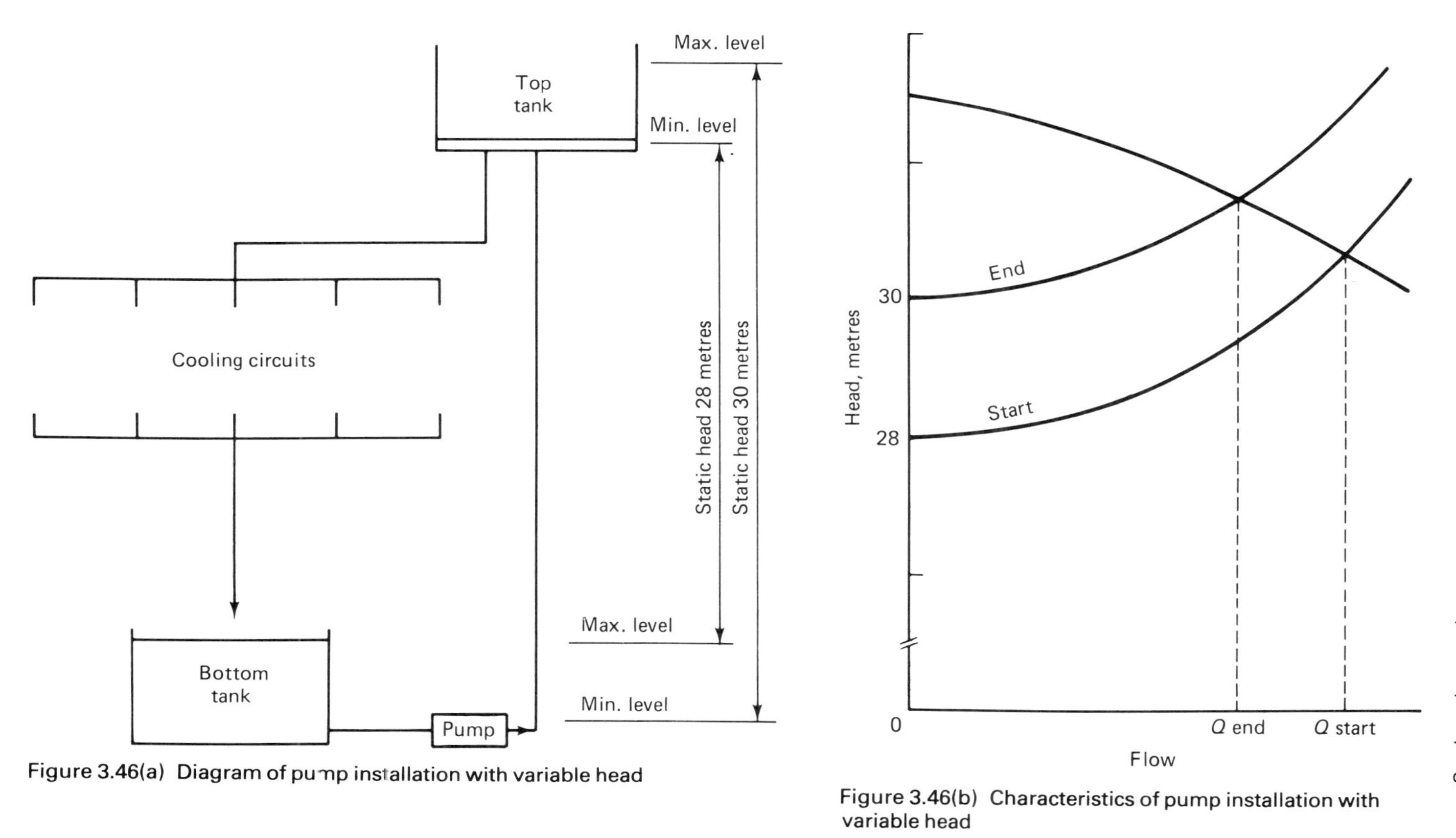

Figure 3.46(a) Diagram of pump installation with variable head

Figure 3.46(b) Characteristics of pump installation with variable head

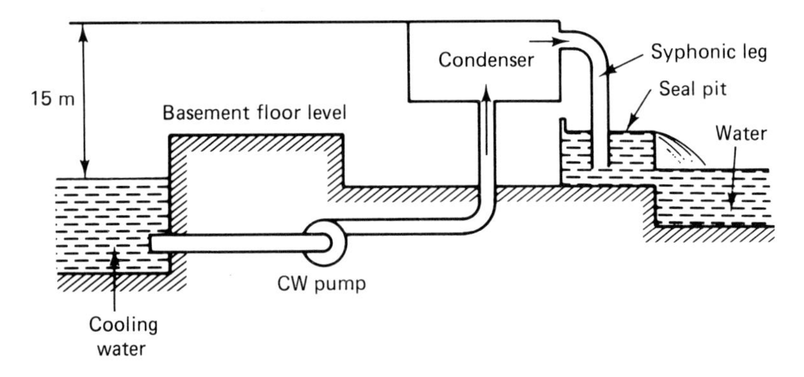

Static head (including syphonic recovery) 15 m − 9 m = 6 m

Figure 3.47 Diagram of installation utilising syphonic assistance (CEGB)

Specific speed is an indication of the pump *type* and is *not* synonymous with shaft rotational speed. *Figure 3.48* shows the general classification of pump types with the corresponding range of specific speeds. The power consumption/discharge capacity characteristics vary from one type to another as shown. For example, with axial-flow types the no-load power is greater than that at rated flow, hence the drive could be overloaded at very low flows so they should normally be started with the discharge valve open. *Table 3.5* shows the details of a CW pump and a boiler feed pump for a 350 MW unit.

A double-entry pump is really two single-entry pumps mounted back to back. The total flow is double that of a corresponding single-entry pump with a single impeller and the same discharge head. The specific speed of each side is $1/\sqrt{2}$ times that of the combined unit.

The specific speed N_S of the CW pump is:

$$N_S = \frac{333 \times \sqrt{30960}}{24.7^{0.75}} = 5288$$

The specific speed of each side is $\frac{5288}{\sqrt{2}} = 3739$

With multi-stage pumps the final head is given by the head per impeller times the number of stages S

$$\text{So } N_S = \frac{N \times \sqrt{Q}}{\left(\frac{H}{S}\right)^{0.75}}$$

The specific speed of the 100% boiler feed pump is:

$$N_S = \frac{4700\sqrt{1440}}{\left(\frac{1850}{4}\right)^{0.75}} = 1788$$

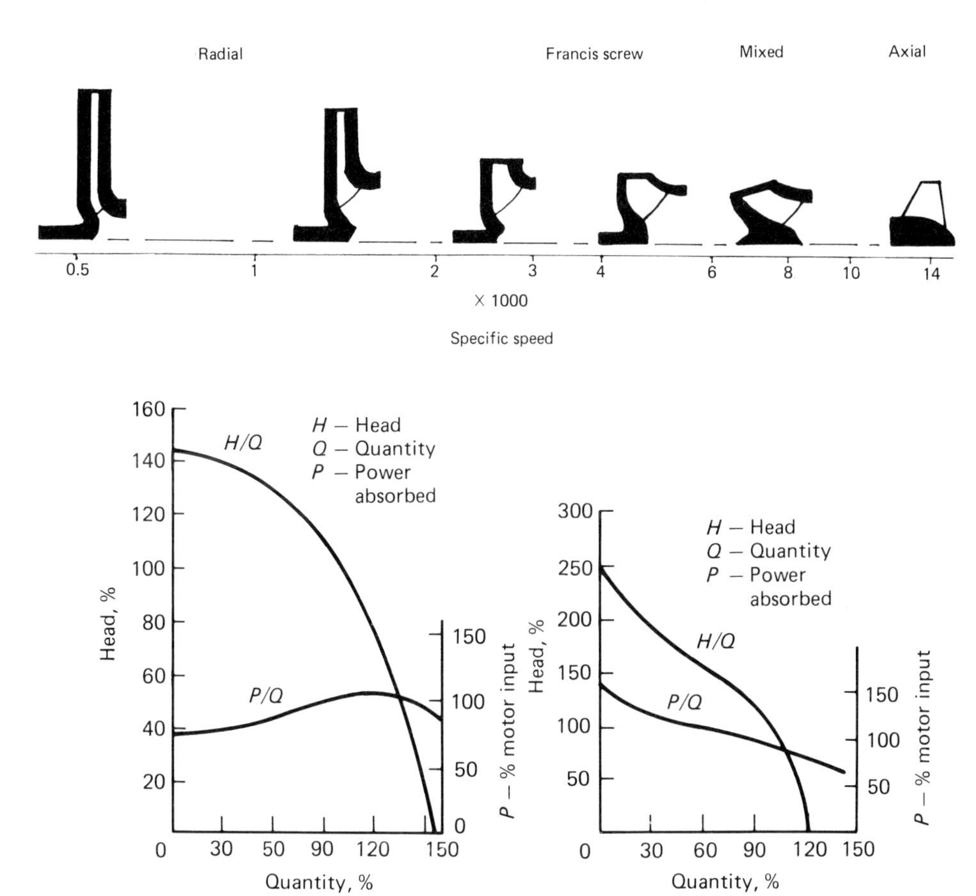

Figure 3.48 Impeller profiles and pump characteristics for various pump specific speeds

Table 3.5

	CW pump	*100% BFP*
No of stages	1	4
Liquid	CW	Boiler feed
Head (m)	24.7	1850
Efficiency (%)	90	85.5
Temperature (°C)	16.5	252
Classification	Double-entry	Multi-stage
Input power (kW)	2300	6600
Speed (rev/min)	333	4700
Capacity (m^3/h)	30 960	1440

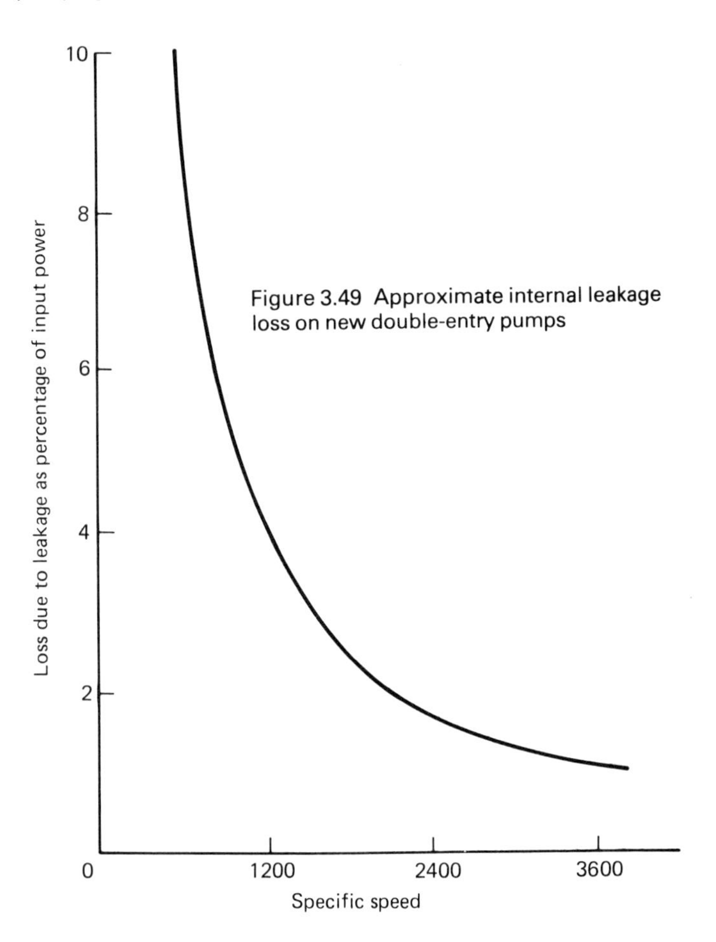

Figure 3.49 Approximate internal leakage loss on new double-entry pumps

Sometimes specific speed is given as a non-dimensional number by using the formula:

$$N_S = \frac{3.65 \times \text{rev/min} \times \sqrt{(\text{m}^3/\text{h})}}{m^{0.75}}$$

Generally pumps which operate at lower specific speeds have higher generated heads per stage. Thus, pump internal leakage is usually more pronounced on these as leakage rate varies as the square root of the differential pressure at the stage.

Figure 3.49 shows the order of internal leakage loss for double-entry pumps. Thus, a new pump with a specific speed of 600 would have leakage equal to about 9% of the input power, whereas one with specific speed of 2400 would have about 1.5%. Therefore, it is particularly important to keep the clearance as small as possible on pumps with low specific speed.

Figure 3.50 illustrates a pump characteristic for the 'as-new' and the 'worn' condition. At a particular head, say, h, the output of the new pump

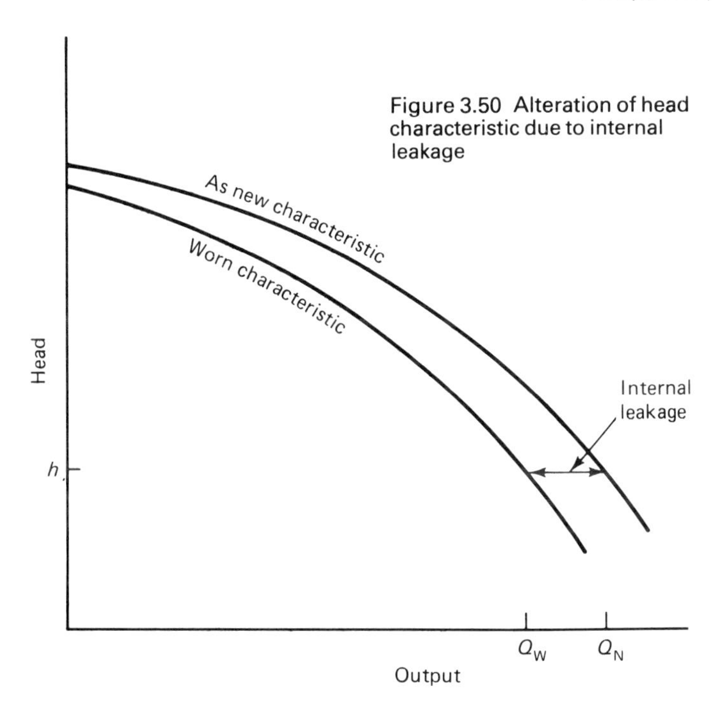

Figure 3.50 Alteration of head characteristic due to internal leakage

will be Q_N. As the clearances become greater with wear, the characteristic changes until it may become as shown in the diagram. In such a case the 'worn' output will be Q_W at head h. Hence, the leakage quantity will be represented by $Q_N - Q_W$.

Multi-stage pumps

These consist of two or more stages. Water enters the first impeller eye, passes through the impeller and then through the diffuser which surrounds the impeller. Its function is to transform as much of the velocity energy as is practicable into pressure energy. From there it is passed to the eye of the next impeller, and so on through the pump. Usually the increase in head is the same for each stage. Thus, if stage one generated head is 30 m then stage two will raise it to 60 m, stage three to 90 m and so on. Of course the same *quantity* of water flows through each stage. The internal inefficiency of a pump leads to an increase in the water temperature as shown in *Figure 3.51*.

Pump power consumption loss

The power consumption of the motor drives for feed pumps is considerable, as shown in *Table 3.6*. However, the pump power is not a complete loss as, with the exception of the small external losses, it is transferred to the water and so increases the energy of the water.

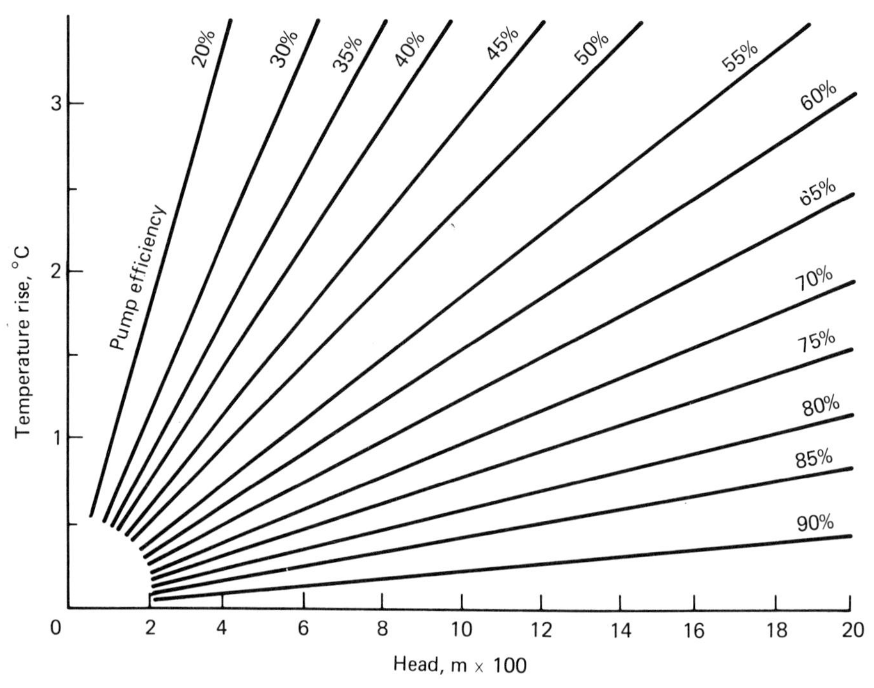

Figure 3.51 Water temperature rise due to pump inefficiency

Therefore, it may be argued that the power consumption of the pump is of little consequence as, no matter how high it is, it will be transferred to the feed water; but this is not so. For example, consider a unit whose boiler efficiency is 90%; turbo-alternator efficiency 41%; unit transformer efficiency 98%. Then the efficiency of producing electricity at the feed pump motor terminals will be $0.9 \times 0.41 \times 0.98 = 0.36$, or 36%. Thus for every 36

Table 3.6 Power consumption of feed pump drives

Unit size (MW)	*Boiler pressure (bar)*	*Pump power (MW)*	*Pump power (% of rating)*
60	62	0.6	1.0
100	103	1.5	1.5
350	158	8.0	2.3
500	158	12.5	2.5
660	158	16.5	2.5

units of heat consumed at the pump it has been necessary to supply 100 units to the boiler. So (100 − 36) units of heat are lost in the process.

If the pump supplies a 350 MW unit and the power consumption is 8.0 MW then the pump motor will consume 8.0/3500 = 0.023 of the alternator output at an efficiency of 36.0%.

So the *loss* = 0.023 (100 − 36) = 1.5% of the boiler heat input.

$$\text{In general terms, \% pump loss} = \frac{\text{Pump power}}{\text{Generated load}}\ (100 - \text{efficiency})$$

Example

Consider a 375 MW once-through supercritical unit. Two booster pumps must be run at all times when the unit is on load plus two 50% electrically driven boiler-feed pumps for high loads if the steam-driven pump is not in use.

Boiler efficiency	90%
T/A efficiency	44%
Transformer efficiency	98%
∴ Overall efficiency	= 38.8%
Pump power	= 20 MW
Generated load	= 375 MW

$$\text{So pump loss} = \frac{20}{375}(100 - 38.8)$$
$$= 3.3\% \text{ of boiler heat input}$$
$$\text{or} \quad \frac{20}{375}(100 - 44)$$
$$= 3.0\% \text{ of turbine heat input}$$

This is an unusually high figure because of the very high pump discharge pressure of 324 bar for this type of boiler.

End thrust

With a 'single-inlet' impeller the same hydraulic pressure acts upon the whole impeller surface. However, because of the impeller eye opening, the surface area is less on the suction than the downstream side. Accordingly, an out-of-balance force acts on the impeller in the direction of the suction. Thus, in a multi-stage pump with all the impellers facing the same way, there is a cumulative end-thrust in the direction of the suction. This end-thrust can be taken up by a mechanical thrust bearing or by a 'balance-disc', as shown in *Figure 3.52*.

Low-flow operation of centrifugal pumps

It is normally undesirable to operate a pump at zero or very low outputs for a

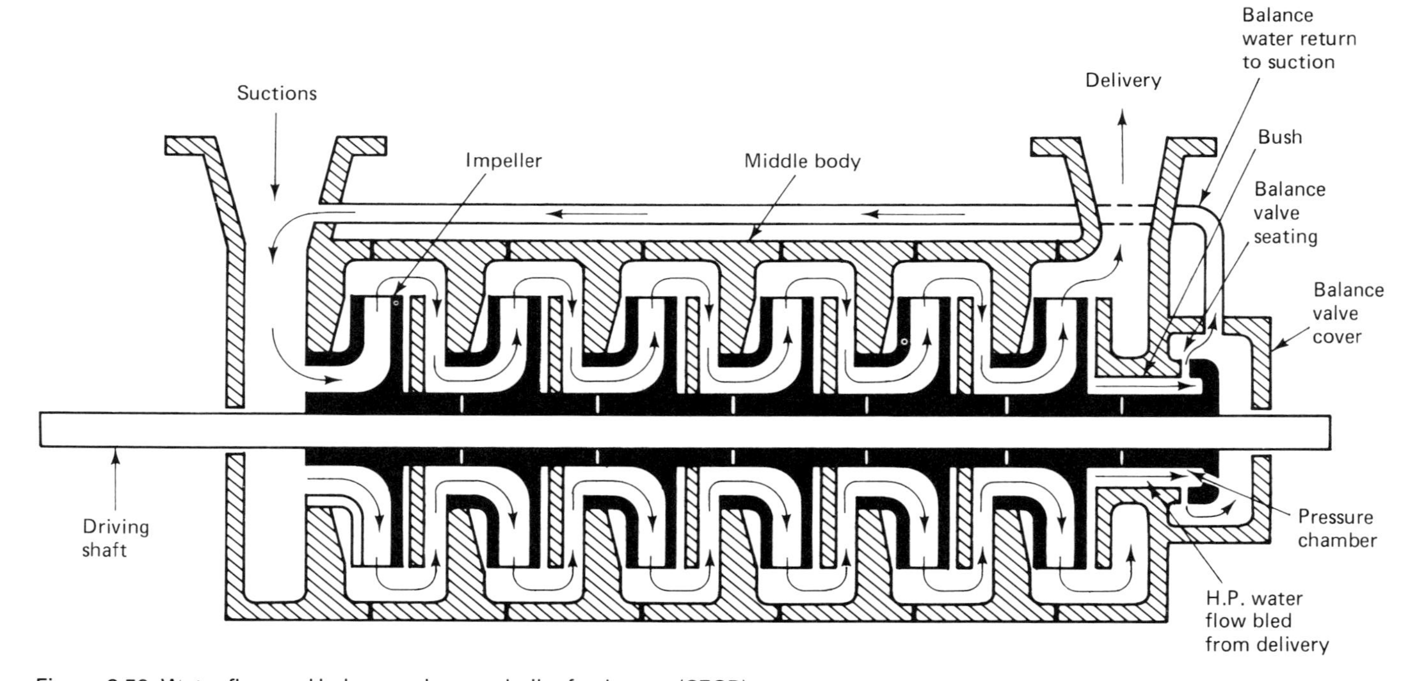

Figure 3.52 Water flow and balance valve on a boiler feed pump (CEGB)

prolonged period. The difficulties that can arise are, basically:

(a) *Water temperature rise*

Almost all the pump power manifests itself as an increase in the energy content of the water, and hence the temperature rises and, if allowed to go on increasing, could cause damage to the pump. Normally steps are taken to limit the rise.

As a rule of thumb a flow-rate of 3 litre/s for every 100 kW of input power to the pump will normally keep the temperature rise within acceptable limits.

Alternatively, use the formula:

$$\text{Temp. rise (°C)} = \text{head (m)} \times 0.00235\left(\frac{1}{\quad} - 1\right)$$

For example, suppose a particular pump has a minimum flow of 20 litre/s, determined by the rule-of-thumb method, and at that flow the efficiency is 25% and the head 300 m.

$$\text{Then the temperature rise} = 300 \times 0.00235\left(\frac{1}{0.25} - 1\right)$$

$$= 2.1\text{°C}$$

However, to save calculating the result it can be read directly from *Figure 3.51*.

(b) *Motor overload*

Reference to the section on specific speed indicates that pumps with specific speeds greater than 5000 have high power consumption at low flows. Pump protection at low flow in such cases depends upon pressure sensing which would initiate tripping if the discharge pressure became too high. For pumps with specific speeds less than 5000 temperature sensing can be used.

(c) *Mechanical problems*

A typical mechanical problem is that due to radial reaction. This is brought about because the volute is eccentric with regard to the impeller. Consequently, the pressure acting on the volute is not evenly distributed and this results in an out-of-balance force acting on it called 'radial-reaction'. The force increases at flows over or under the rated flow, and is most pronounced at zero flow. Further, the effect is more pronounced on pumps with overhanging impellers.

Boiler feed pumps

Figure 3.53 shows a modern boiler feed pump. This type of pump operates under quite arduous conditions, particularly with regard to thermal shock. For example, in a split pumping system if the standby feed pump is brought into service it will be handling hot feed water, so the temperature rise can be very rapid. At the same time, the pressure is very high and so the stress brought about by these conditions is also high. In particular, the bolting is a problem area as the bolts do not respond to temperature changes as rapidly as the rest of the casing. This causes the tension to change but, even so, the casing joints must remain tight.

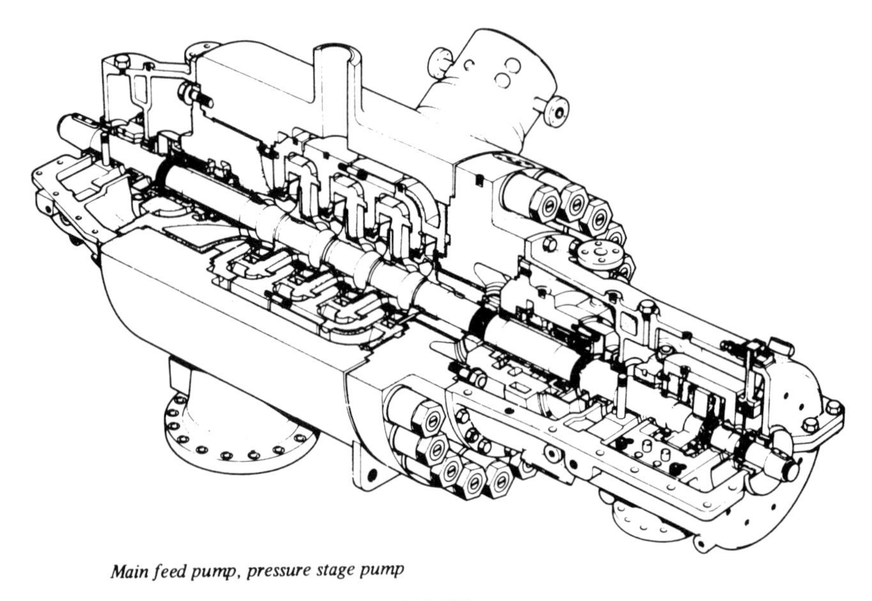

Main feed pump, pressure stage pump

Figure 3.53 Modern boiler feed pump (CEGB)

Thermal shock

Because of the arduous thermal conditions to which the pumps may be subjected, thermal shock tests are carried out at the manufacturers' works. The following are typical of such tests:

1. *Hot-to-cold shock*
   For this the temperature is lowered quickly through the range that could be encountered on site. For example, for one unit this is from 263°C to 138°C. The manufacturers could not test over this specific range of temperatures, so they tested over an equivalent range, i.e. from 168°C to 24°C.

During the test the inlet, discharge and balance chamber water temperatures were recorded frequently until conditions settled out at the reduced temperature. It took two minutes to go from hot to cold temperature conditions. The metal temperatures of the bolts, casing and end covers were recorded. Also strain gauges were fitted at selected points on the pump barrel.

2. *Cold-to-hot-shock*
   When the pump had stabilized at the lower temperature it was subjected to a very rapid water temperature rise, such that in one minute the temperature was raised from 21°C to 163°C.

During the above tests the pump had a substantial water flow (about 50 litre/s). Typical curves are shown in *Figure 3.54*.

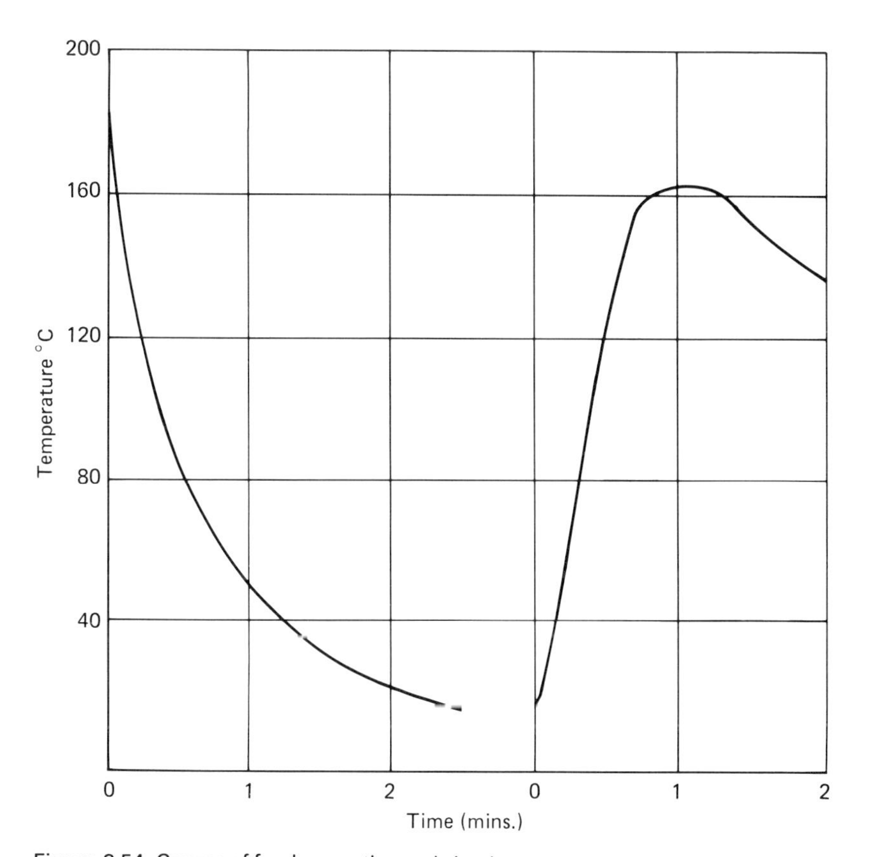

Figure 3.54 Curves of feed pump thermal shock test

Boiler feed pump leak-offs

The low flow leak-off water is returned to the deaerator, and provision must be made for effective isolation of the lines when carrying out turbine heat consumption tests if there is a possibility of the automatic leak-off valves passing (see *Figure 3.55*).

The balance-chamber leak-off water on smaller pumps is normally returned to the suction end of the pump, but modern practice is to return it to the deaerator because of the possibility of flash steam being generated if returned to the suction.

The pump gland leak-off water is returned to the deaerator. It is essential that provision is made for the measurement of both the gland supply and gland leak-off flows when carrying out a turbine heat consumption test.

Mechanical seals are now available which are satisfactory for feed pumps which operate at high pressures. From a testing point of view such seals are most desirable as they eliminate the necessity to measure the supply and return water flows associated with water sealed glands.

Pump size

Boiler feed pump capacity has increased in step with increased output of the main plant. Thus a 100% duty feed pump on a 120 MW unit will supply about 103 kg/s of feed on full load. On a 375 MW unit it will supply 315 kg/s, and on a 660 MW unit, 560 kg/s. However, the physical size of the pumps has gone down as the output has increased. For example, *Figure 3.56* shows the progressive reduction in physical size compared to Thorpe Marsh No. 1 pump for plant of roughly the same capacity as shown below.

	Boiler rating
Thorpe Marsh No. 1	445 kg/s
Ferry Bridge	435 kg/s
Thorpe Marsh No. 2	445 kg/s
Longannet	505 kg/s

The size reduction has been made possible by increasing the pump speed. For example, speeds of 3000 rev/min were normal on the smaller units, whereas 6000 rev/min and above is now possible.

Appendix I

Pump affinity laws

The pump variables are $Q, h, n, \rho, E, \mu, P, d$

where Q = volume flow $L^3 T^{-1}$

h = Head expressed as energy per unit mass of fluid $ML^2 T^{-2} M^{-1} = L^2 T^{-2}$

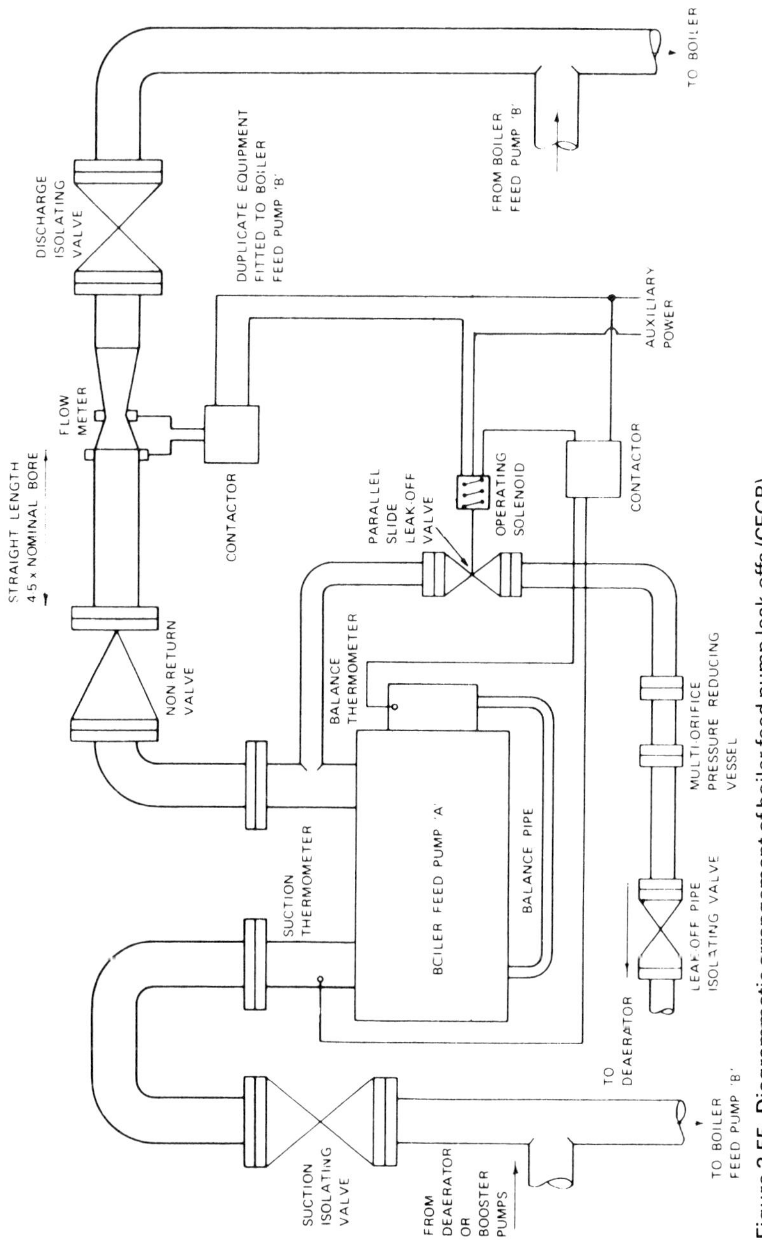

Figure 3.55 Diagrammatic arrangement of boiler feed pump leak-offs (CEGB)

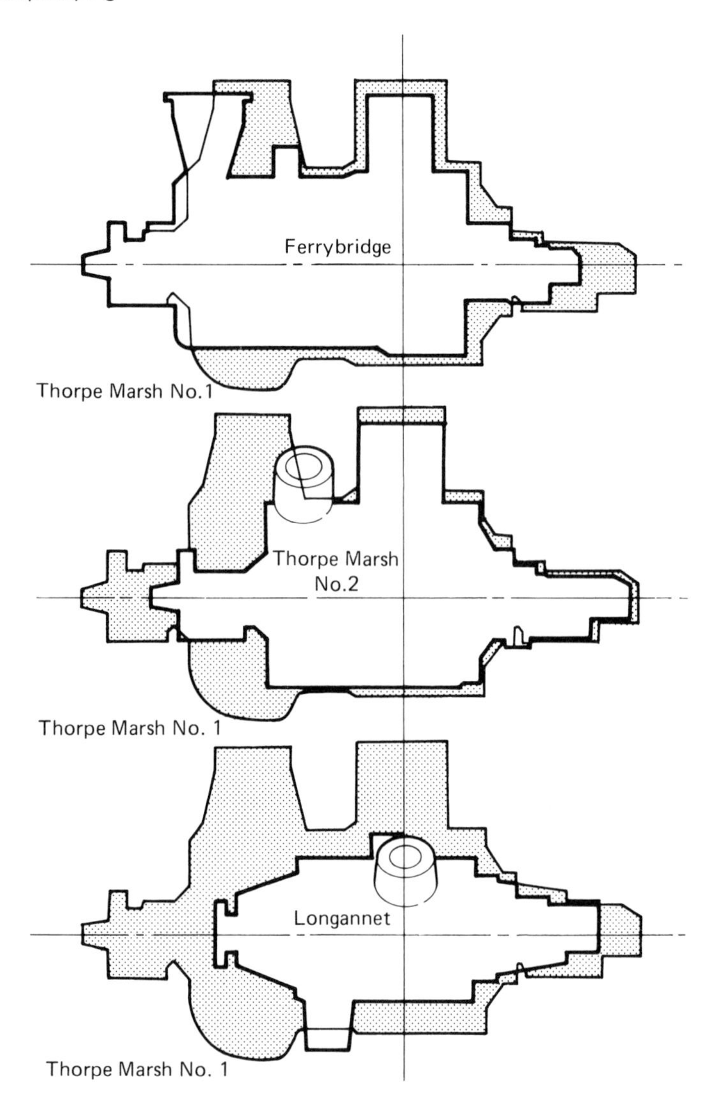

Figure 3.56 Comparison of size of boiler feed pumps (CEGB)

n = angular velocity in r.p.m.	T^{-1}
ρ = density of fluid	$FT^2 L^{-4}$
E = modulus of elasticity of the fluid	FL^{-2}
μ = kinematic viscosity of the fluid	$FL^{-2}T$
P = power	FLT^{-1}
d = impeller diameter	L

n, d and ρ are repeating variables.
Let the exponent of n be the arbitary constant (−) 1

Pump Fault Finding

	Up to speed but no delivery or discharge	Up to speed but pressure too low	Speed and head OK but discharge low	Excessive power consumption	Pump OK for a while and then stops delivering	Discharge head falls, vibration and overheating	Bearings hot	Rapid bearing wear	Irregular discharge	Excessive noise
Wrong oil or grease							●	●		
Not primed	●				●					
Shaft bent						●	●	●		●
Incorrect rotation	●	●	●							
Impeller diameter too small		●								
Suction pipe inlet not covered	●		●		●				●	●
Air ingress at suction system	●		●		●	●			●	●
Speed too low	●	●								
Internal blockage		●				●			●	
Speed too high				●			●			●
Misalignment with bearings or motor						●	●	●		●
Insufficient discharge head for system needs	●	●	●							
Suction strainer choked	●		●		●	●			●	
Delivery system restriction	●		●							
Excessive neck ring wear		●	●	●		●				
Damaged impeller		●	●	●						
Impeller diameter too large				●						
Glands too tight				●						
Balance disc wear						●				
Seal ring wear						●				
Leaking gaskets		●		●						
Defect at logging ring					●					
Pipework straining pump				●		●	●	●		●
Worn bearings						●	●	●		●
Holding-down bolts loose						●		●		●
Poor lubrication							●	●		

1. $n^{-1} \, d^{\alpha} \rho^{\beta} Q^{\gamma} = 0$

L: $\alpha - 4\beta + 3\gamma = 0$

T: $+ 2\beta - \gamma = 0$

F: $\beta = 0$

From F $\beta = 0$

T $\gamma = 1$

L $\alpha = -3$

$$\mathbf{n^{-1}\, d^{-3}\, Q = \frac{Q}{n^{-1}\, d^{3}}}$$

2. $n^{-1}\, d^{\alpha} \rho^{\beta} h^{\gamma} = 0$

L: $\alpha - 4\beta + 2\gamma = 0$

T: $1 + 2\beta - 2\gamma = 0$

F: $\beta = 0$

From F $\beta = 0$

T $\gamma = ½$

L $\alpha = -1$

$$\mathbf{n^{-1}\, d^{-1}\, h^{1/2} = \frac{h}{n^{2} d^{2}}}$$

3. $n^{-1} d^{\alpha} \rho^{\beta} P^{\gamma} = 0$

L: $\alpha - 4\beta + \gamma = 0$

T: $1 + 2\beta - \gamma = 0$

F: $\beta + \gamma = 0$

From F $\beta = -\gamma$

T $\beta = -1/3$ $\gamma = 1/3$

L $\alpha = -5/3$

$$\mathbf{n^{-1}\, d^{-5/3}}\, \rho^{-1/3}\, p^{1/3} = \frac{\mathbf{P}}{\mathbf{n^{3}\, d^{5}}\, \rho}$$

4 $n^{-1}\, d^{\alpha} \rho^{\beta} u^{\gamma} = 0$

L: $\alpha - 4\beta - 2\gamma = 0$

T: $1 + 2\beta + \gamma = 0$

F: $\beta + \gamma = 0$

From F $\beta = -\gamma$

T $\beta = -1$ $\gamma = 1$

L $\alpha = -2$

$$n^{-1}\, d^{-2} \rho^{-1}\, u = \frac{u}{n d^{2} \rho}$$

5. $n + d^{\alpha} \rho^{\beta} E^{\gamma} = 0$

L: $\alpha - 4\beta - 2\gamma = 0$

T: $1 + 2\beta = 0$

F: $\beta + \gamma = 0$

From: F $\beta = -\gamma$

T $\beta = -\frac{1}{2}$ $\quad \gamma = \frac{1}{2}$

L $\gamma = -1$

$$\mathbf{n}^{-1}\,\mathbf{d}^{-1}\,\rho^{-1/2}\,\mathbf{E}^{1/2} = \frac{\mathbf{E}}{\mathbf{n}^2\,\mathbf{d}^2\,\rho}$$

From the first three terms:

$Q \,\alpha\, n \qquad Q \,\alpha\, d^3$

$h \,\alpha\, n^2 \qquad h \,\alpha\, d^2$

$P \,\alpha\, n^3 \qquad P \,\alpha\, d^5$

Appendix II

Water data

Specific volume and density of water

(Volume in litre/kg; density in kg/litre)

Enthalpy of compressed water in kJ/kg

Pressure (Bar abs)	Temperature (°C) 10		50		100		150		200	
	Volume	Density	Volume	Density	Volume	Density	Volume	Density	Volume	Der[illegible]
1.0	1.0002	0.9998	1.0121	0.9880						
10.0	0.99977	1.0002	1.0117	0.9884	1.0432	0.9586	1.0904	0.9171		
20.0	0.99930	1.0007	1.0112	0.9889	1.0427	0.9590	1.0897	0.9177	1.156	0.8[illegible]
30.0	0.99883	1.00117	1.0108	0.9893	1.0422	0.9595	1.0890	0.9181	1.1550	0.8[illegible]
40.0	0.99836	1.0016	1.0103	0.9898	1.0417	0.9600	1.0883	0.9189	1.1540	0.8[illegible]
50.0	0.99789	1.0021	1.0099	0.9902	1.0411	0.9605	1.0877	0.9194	1.1529	0.8[illegible]
60.0	0.99743	1.0026	1.0094	0.9907	1.0406	0.9610	1.0870	0.9200	1.1519	0.8[illegible]
70.0	0.99696	1.0030	1.0090	0.9911	1.0401	0.9614	1.0863	0.9206	1.1509	0.8[illegible]
80.0	0.99650	1.0035	1.0086	0.9915	1.0396	0.9619	1.0856	0.9212	1.1500	0.8[illegible]
90.0	0.99604	1.00397	1.0081	0.9920	1.0391	0.9624	1.0850	0.9217	1.1490	0.8[illegible]
100.0	0.99558	1.0044	1.0077	0.9924	1.0386	0.9628	1.0843	0.9223	1.1480	0.8[illegible]
150.0	0.99329	1.0067	1.0055	0.9945	1.0361	0.9652	1.0811	0.9250	1.1432	0.8[illegible]
200.0	0.99103	1.0091	1.0034	0.9966	1.0337	0.9674	1.0779	0.9277	1.1387	0.8[illegible]
300.0	0.9866	1.0136	0.99927	1.0007	1.0289	0.9719	1.0718	0.9330	1.1300	0.8[illegible]

Enthalpy of Compressed Water in kJ/kg

Pressure (Bar abs)	Temperature (°C) 10	50	100	150	200	250	300	350
1.0	42.09	209.33	—	—	—	—	—	—
10.0	42.97	210.11	419.74	632.47	—	—	—	—
20.0	43.94	210.97	420.49	633.09	852.55	—	—	—
30.0	44.92	211.83	421.24	633.71	852.96	—	—	—
40.0	45.89	212.69	421.99	634.34	853.37	1085.8	—	—
50.0	46.86	213.55	422.74	634.96	853.79	1085.8		
60.0	47.84	214.41	423.49	635.58	854.21	1085.8	—	—
70.0	48.80	215.26	424.25	636.21	854.63	1085.8	—	—
80.0	49.77	216.12	425.00	636.84	855.06	1085.8	—	—
100.0	51.71	217.84	426.50	638.10	855.92	1085.8	1343.4	—
150.0	56.52	222.13	430.27	641.26	858.14	1086.2	1338.3	—
200.0	61.31	226.41	434.05	644.45	860.43	1086.7	1334.3	1647.2
300.0	70.81	234.95	441.62	650.90	865.20	1088.4	1328.7	1610.0

Questions

1 Describe the action of a lift pump.
2 Describe the action of a force pump. What is the advantage?
3 Describe the action of a ram pump.
4 What is a 'double-acting' pump?
5 How would you vary the output of a reciprocating pump?
6 Is it preferable to use a long- or short-stroke reciprocating pump? Why?
7 What are the two broad divisions of centrifugal pumps?
8 Define (i) potential head; (ii) velocity head; (iii) friction head; (iv) total head.
9 What are the essential requirements of a suction system?
10 What head is available to push water into a pump?
11 What is the effect of heating the water?
12 What is the effect of altitude?
13 What is the recommended maximum suction lift?
14 What is the cure for a pump which gives poor delivery when supplied with boiling water?
15 What is the head available to push boiling water into a pump?
16 What would be the bore of the common suction pipe supplying two pumps, each with a 100 mm bore pipe?
17 What determines the bore of a suction pipe?
18 How would you join a 100 mm pipe to an 80 mm suction branch?
19 What is the relationship between pressure P and head H?
20 What is the relationship between mass flow m and volumetric flow Q?
21 Define the output power P_o *of a pump, i.e. the water power.*
22 Define the input power P_i of a pump, i.e. the brake power.
23 What determines the discharge of a given pump installation?
24 What is the effect of throttling the pump discharge valve?
25 List the pump affinity laws.
26 Why is it common to have pump pressure gauges calibrated in metres rather than bars?
27 What characteristic causes unstable parallel operation of pumps?
28 How would you find the output of two pumps in parallel?
29 What is pump specific speed?
30 What use is specific speed?
31 Which would probably have the higher specific speed, a CW pump or a boiler feed pump?
32 State the formula for percentage pump loss.
33 What causes end thrust?
34 How would you protect a pump against damage due to low-flow operation?
35 What effects should be guarded against at low flows?
36 What special tests are carried out on boiler feed pumps?
37 A pump is running at speed but there is no delivery – what are possible causes?

38 Huncoat Power Station is a 'range' station with seven boiler feed pumps. On a certain station load four pumps are in service. As the loading increases the feed range pressure falls – why? How would you restore it?
39 Consider an extraction pump. What would happen to the suction and discharge heads and the pump motor current when:
(a) The suction valve was closed, all else normal?
(b) The discharge valve was closed, all else normal?
(c) A section of pipework near the discharge valve fell out completely?
40 What is the head available to cause flow into:
(a) An extraction pump? (b) A C.W. pump? (c) A sump pump with a suction lift?
41 In the event of a falling D/A level what is the final limiting factor which determines how far the level can be allowed to fall?
42 A pump has the following duty:
1000 rev/min; 100 litre/s; 100 m head; 48 kW.
What would the duty be at 500 rev/min?

Exercise 1

Draw the combined characteristic of two pumps in parallel, each of which has a characteristic as shown below. What is the minimum discharge at which stable operation is possible? What will be the head?

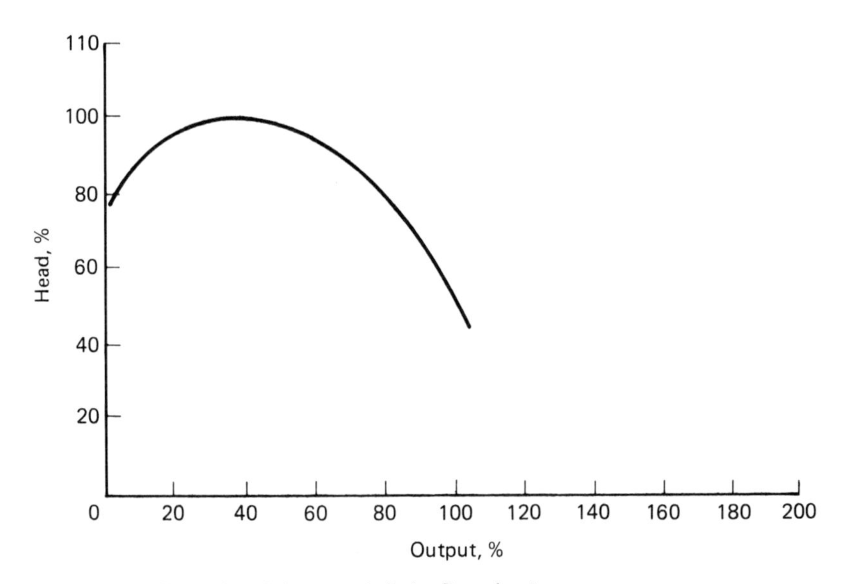

Figure 3.57 Pump head characteristic for Exercise 1

Exercise 2

At what speed must a single-stage, single-inlet pump of specific speed 2500 be run to discharge 3600 m^3/h of water at a head of 16 m?

Exercise 1 (Answer)

Output of each pump = 33%; head = 100%.

Exercise 2 (Answer)

$$2500 = \frac{n\sqrt{3600}}{(16)^{3/4}} = \frac{n\,60}{8}$$

$$\text{Thus } n = \frac{8 \times 2500}{60} = 333.3 \text{ rev/min}$$

Project 1

The pulverized fuel ash from a power station is mixed with water and the resulting slurry is pumped to an ash lagoon about 3.2 km distant via a pipeline. When first installed the flow rate was 150 litre/s. However, the rate became progressively less as the pipeline fouled, until it was down to 80 litre/s. Any further deterioration would result in the dust being produced at the station faster than it could be disposed of. The static head of the disposal system is the equivalent of 1 bar.

A second pipeline covers the same route and discharges into the same lagoon. It was provided for emergency dust disposal from a second power station on the same site and so is rarely used.

To improve the rate of dust removal various possibilities can be considered such as:

1. Increase the existing pump speed from its present 440 rev/min to 500 rev/min. The pump characteristic at 440 rev/min is shown (pump A) in *Figure 3.58*.
2. Operate the two pipelines in parallel using the 440 rev/min pump. For convenience consider that both pipelines are equally fouled.
3. Clean the fouled pipeline by chemical or mechanical means – for example put a 'pig' down the pipe (see *Figure 3.59*). The cost of this is, say, £10 000.
4. Install a new pump with a characteristic as shown (pump B).
5. Operate the existing pump in parallel with that from the emergency dust line, both discharging into the existing line. For convenience assume both pumps have identical characteristics.

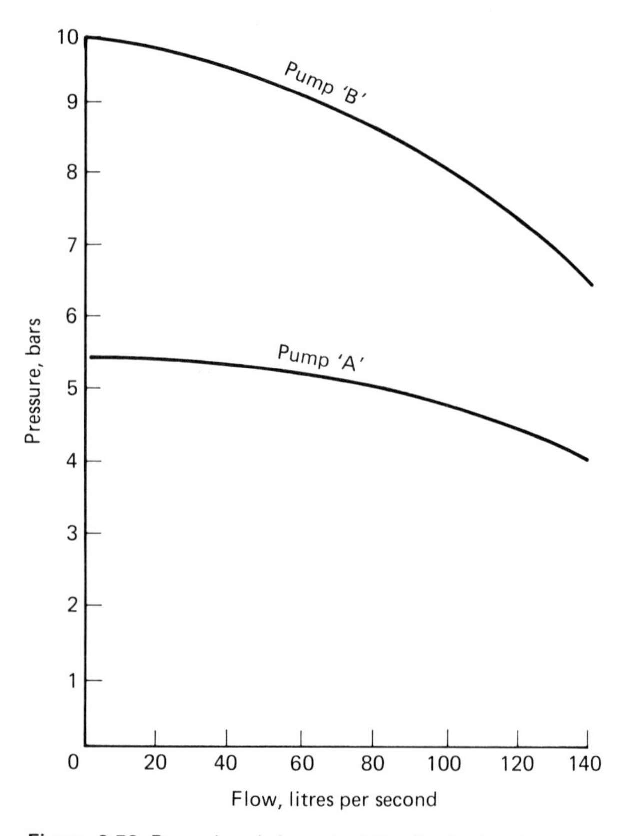

Figure 3.58 Pump head characteristics for Project 1

6. In addition to running the pumps in parallel (item 5) also operate both pipelines in parallel.
7. Replace the fouled pipeline. The cost of this is, say, £35 000.

Comment upon each of the options and give reasons for acceptance or rejection.

Project 1 (Answer)

Plot the system resistance. At zero flow this will be 1 bar. Also, at 80 litre/s it intersects the pump A curve, the pressure being 5 bar. So the friction loss is 4 bar. At a flow of 40 litre/s the friction loss will be a quarter of this, i.e. 1 bar, so at this flow the total pressure will be 2 bar. Knowing these three points the system resistance can be plotted. The possibilities can now be considered.

1. *Increase the speed from 440 to 500 rev/min*
   Care must be taken to ensure that the pump components can withstand

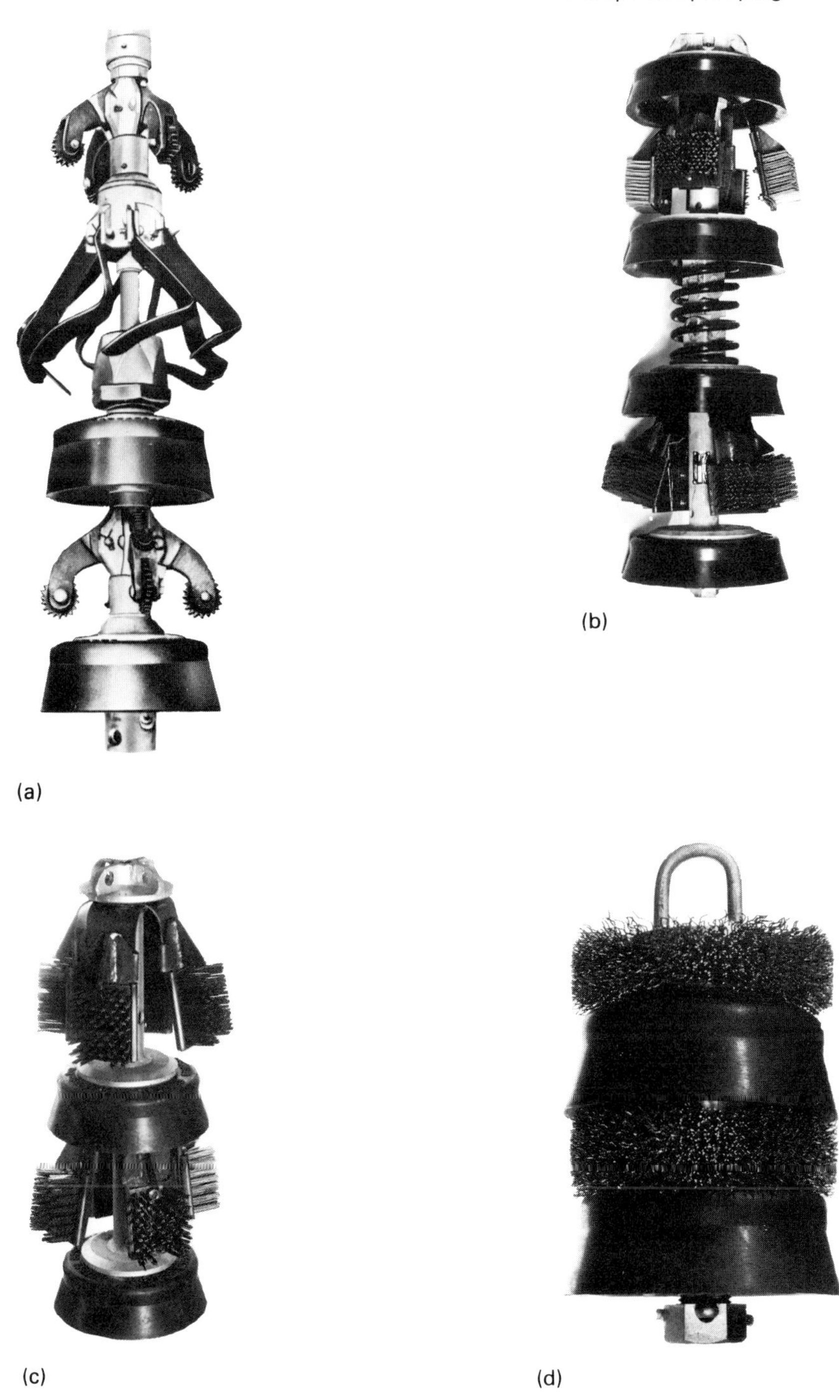

(a) (b) (c) (d)

Figure 3.59 Pigs for cleaning pipelines. (General Descaling Co. Ltd.)

(e)

(f)

Figure 3.59 (*continued*)

the new conditions and that the motor, switchgear and cables are adequate.

At the new speed the flow will be $Q_2 = 80 \times \frac{500}{440} =$ **91 litre/s**

The new discharge pressure will be $H_2 = 5 \times \left(\frac{500}{440}\right)^2 =$ **6.5 bar.**

The new flow and pressure are plotted at point C.

The new pump characteristic will be parallel to the old one and will pass through point C. The new pipe flow is determined from the intersection of the 500 rev/min pump curve and the system resistance, and it is seen that it is only 90 litre/s, a negligible increase (see *Figure 3.60*).

2. *Operate the two pipelines in parallel*
   If this is done the emergency dust disposal facility will be interfered with, possibly necessitating alternative arrangements. Also, the rate of fouling of the pipeline will increase because of the reduced volume flow in each.

   As the pipes are assumed to be identical the flows will be equal in each, so for a total flow of 80 litre/s each pipe will carry 40 litre/s. Thus the friction loss will be reduced to a quarter of its value at 80 litre/s, so it will be 1 bar. Therefore, the total pressure with a flow of 40 litre/s in each line will be 2 bar (i.e. 1 bar static head + 1 bar friction loss). At 160 litre/s it will be 5 bar. From this information the system resistance can be plotted. The flow obtained is given by the intersection of the 440 rev/min pump

characteristic and the 2-pipeline system resistance, and is 142 litre/s (see *Figure 3.61*).

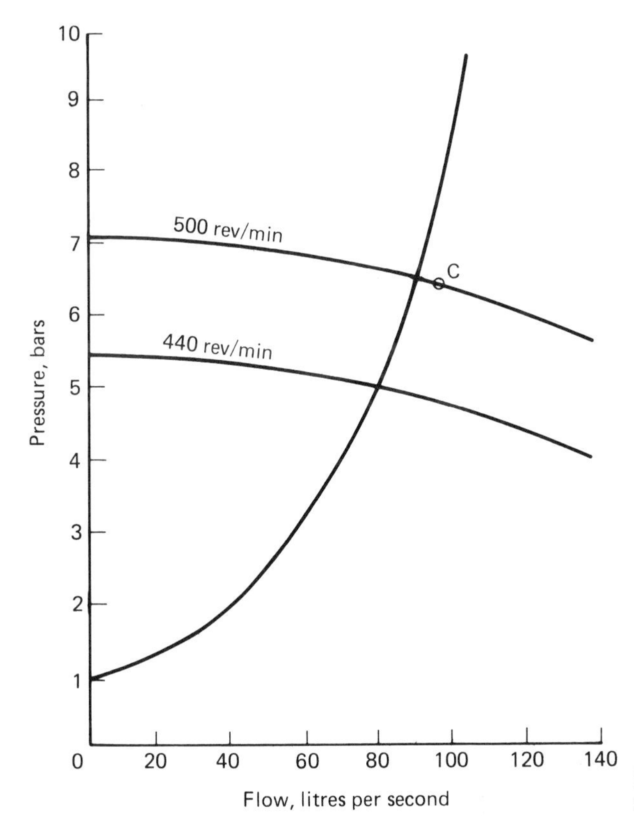

Figure 3.60 Project No 1—option No 1

3. *Clean the pipeline*
   Mechanical cleaning of the pipeline using 'pigs' (see *Figure 3.58* for typical types) was attempted. Unfortunately, though, the pipe had so many internal projections that the method was not practicable. Chemical cleaning was also attempted but only gave limited success. Thus this costly option gave no guarantee of acceptable cleanliness and was sure to have the line out of service for a long time. Thus, cleaning was not considered to be a practical option.
4. *Fit a new pump*
   Care must be taken that the pipeline will withstand the pressure. The capital cost (pump, motor, switchgear, etc.) will be high. With this option the flow will be given by the intersection of the pump characteristic and the system resistance, and amounts to 99 litre/s (see *Figure 3.62*).
5. *Operate the existing pump and emergency pump in parallel*
   This arrangement will give a flow of 83 litre/s (see *Figure 3.63*). In

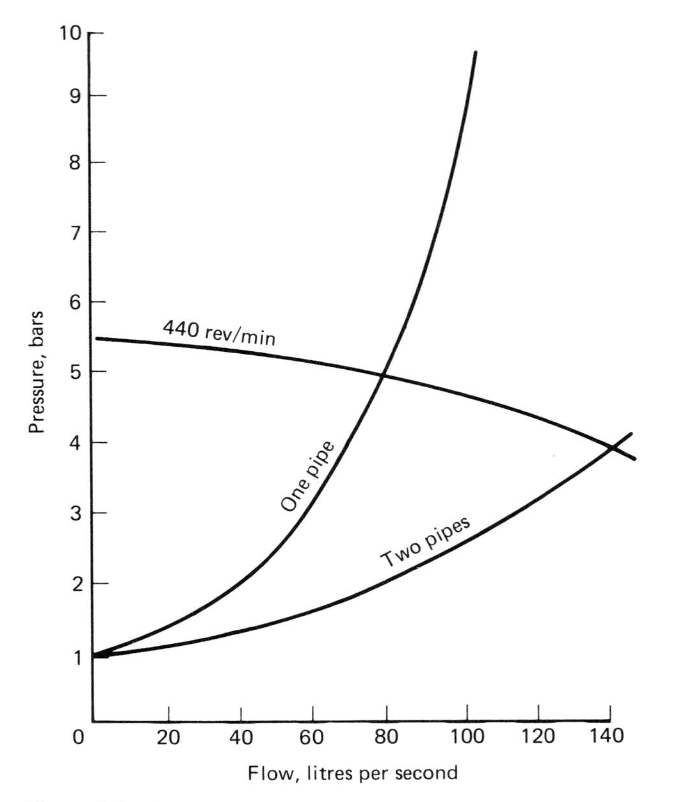

Figure 3.61 Project No 1 — option No 2

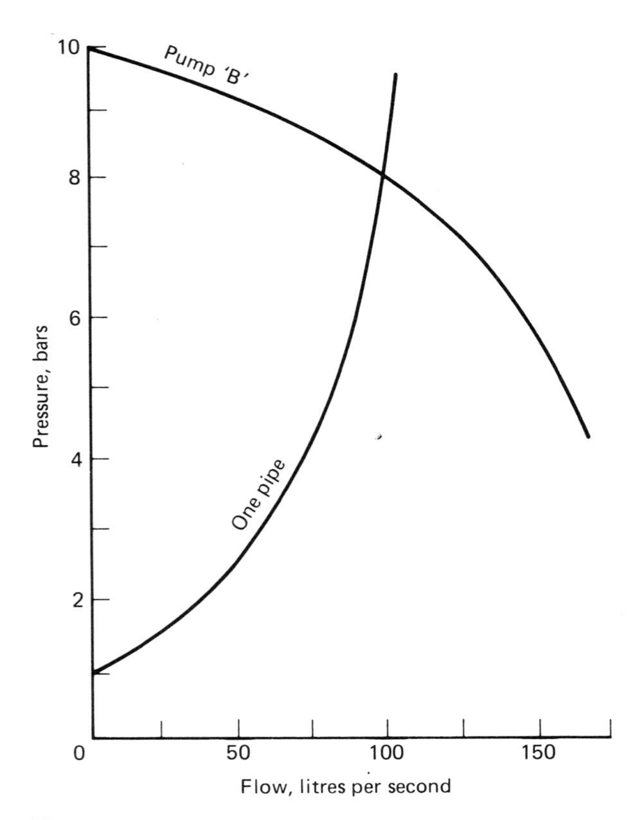

Figure 3.62 Project No 1 — option No 4

addition the emergency pump will be in regular use and so not being used for its intended purpose.

6. *As for Option 5, but with the two lines in parallel*
   This arrangement will result in a flow of 162 litre/s (see *Figure 3.63*). However, each line will carry only half the total flow and so the velocity will be low. This will permit rapid fouling of the pipelines.
7. *Replace the fouled pipeline*
   This option gives a guaranteed result, but is expensive in both time and money.

The only options which will restore the flow rate to its original value are numbers 2, 6 and 7. However, numbers 2 and 6 each involve the pipelines carrying low flows and so fouling would continue. Hence, even though alleviation of the problem occurred for a time it would re-appear soon.

Accordingly the option adopted was number 7.

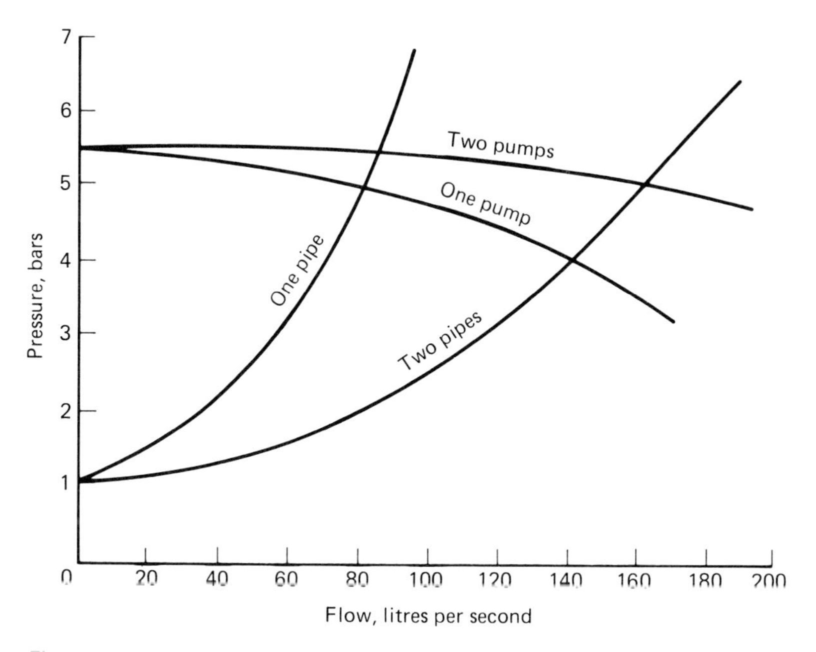

Figure 3.63 Project No 1 — option Nos 5 and 6

Project 2

Main boiler feed pump

Cold water tests

Pump details and specified duty:

Output 328 kg/s
Suction pressure 78 bar(g)
Pumping pressure 225 bar
Suction temperature 263°C
Discharge pressure 303 bar(g)
Speed 4500 rev/min

			1	*2*	*3*	*4*	*5*
1	Corrected output	litre/s	71.3	121.0	174.3	227.3	273.4
2	Speed	rev/min	2 995	3 020	3000	2 990	3 020
3	Discharge pressure	bar	204	207.9	199	197	190
4	Suction pressure	bar	48	51	48	51	48
5	Pumping pressure	bar					
6	Water temperature	°C	54	53	73	63	72
7	Pump output power	kw					
Motor							
	Current	A	292.8	336	379.2	418.8	466.8
9	Voltage	V	11 400	11 200	11 250	11 250	11 200
10	kW	kW	4 206	5 196	6 036	6 840	7 650
11	Efficiency		0.634	0.642	0.638	0.636	0.643
12	Output power	Kw					
13	Gearbox power consumption	kW	40	44	46	48	51
14	Pump input power	kW					
15	Pump efficiency	%					
16	Calculated output at 3000 rev/min	litre/s					
17	Calculated output at 4500 rev/min	litre/s					
18	Calculated pump head at 3000 rev/min	m					
19	Calculated pump head at 4500 rev/min	m					

Plot curves of pressure and efficiency against flow in litre/s for 3000 rev/min and 4500 rev/min.

Project 2 (Answer)

Consider test 2

Pumping pressure = (3) − (4) = 207.9 − 51.0 = 156.9 bar
So $p = 156.9 \times 10^5$ N/m^2 (if velocity head ignored).
Pumped quantity Q = 119.6 kg/s ÷ 986.5 kg/m^3 = 0.121 m^3/s
where density of water at 53°C = 986.5 kg/m^3
and weigh tank quantity = 119.6 kg/s

So pump output $P_O = p \times Q$
$= 156.9 \times 10^5 \times 0.121$ W
$= 1898490$ W
$= 1898.49$ kW

Motor input power $= 5196$ kW
Motor output power $= 5196 \times 0.642 = 3335.8$ kW
Pump input $= 3335.8 - 44.0$
$= 3291.8$ kW

$$\text{Pump efficiency} = \frac{1898.49 \times 100}{3291.8} = 57.7\%$$

$$\text{Pump output at 3000 rev/min} = 0.121 \times \left(\frac{3000}{3020}\right) = 0.120\ \text{m}^3/\text{s}$$

$$\text{Pump output at 4500 rev/min} = 0.121 \times \left(\frac{4500}{3020}\right) = 0.180\ \text{m}^3/\text{s}$$

$$\text{Pump pressure at 3000 rev/min} = 156.9\left(\frac{3000}{3020}\right)^2 = 154.8\ \text{bar}$$

$$\text{Pump pressure at 4500 rev/min} = 156.9\left(\frac{4500}{3020}\right)^2 = 348.4\ \text{bar}$$

Project 2 (Answer)

Test No		1	2	3	4	5
Pumping pressure p	bar	156	156.9	151	146	142
Pumped quantity Q	m³/s	0.0713	0.121	0.1743	0.2273	0.2734
Pump output pQ	kW	1 112.3	1 898.49	2 631.9	3 318.6	3 882
Motor input power	kW	4 206	5 196	6 036	6 840	7 650
Motor output power	kW	2 666.6	3 335.8	3 851.0	4 350.2	4 919
Pump input power	kW	2 626.4	3 291.8	3 805.0	4 302.2	4 868
Pump efficiency	%	42.3	57.7	69.2	77.1	79.8
Pump output at 3000 rev/min	litre/s	71.4	120.2	174.3	228.1	271.6
Pump output at 4000 rev/min	litre/s	107.1	180.3	261.4	342.1	407.4
Pump pressure at 3000 rev/min	bar	156.5	154.8	151.0	147.0	140.1
Pump pressure at 4500 rev/min	bar	352.1	348.4	339.8	330.8	315.2
Pump input power at 4500rev/min	kW	8 909	10 891	12 842	14 666	16 105

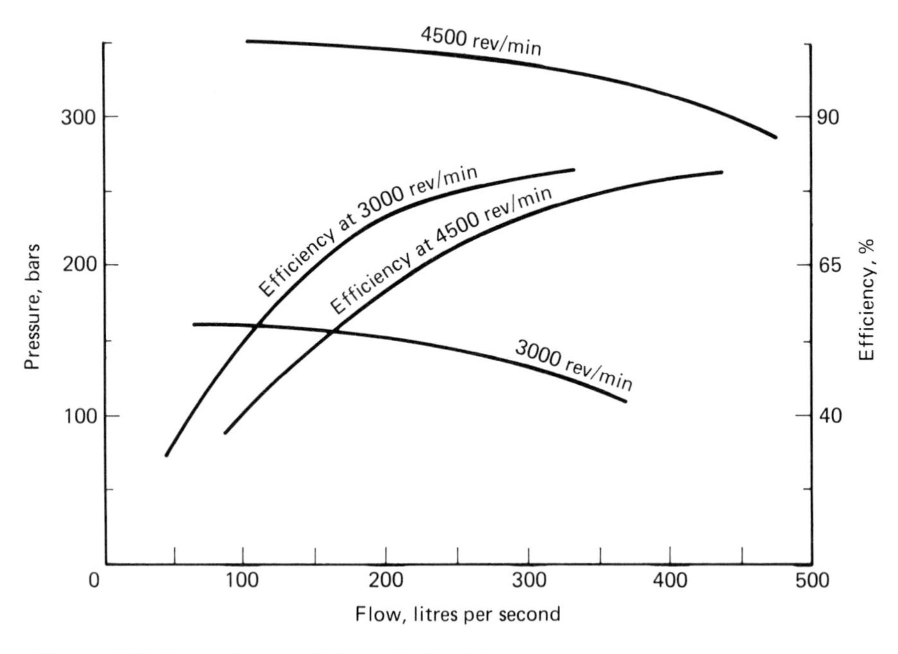

Figure 3.64 Pump characteristics — Project No 2

Additional Reading

1 CEGB Site Test Code No. 1 – *Boiler Feed Pumps.*
2 CEGB Site Test Code No. 6 – *Circulating Water Pumps.*
3 BS 599: *Methods of Testing Pumps.*
4 ANDERSON, H.H. 'Design of Modern Boiler Feed Pumps'Proc. I. Mech. E., **175**, No. 12 (1961)
5 HILLIER, H., 'Suction Supply Conditions for Pumping Installations', *Trans. Inst. Marine Engs,* Vol. LXIV, No. 11 (1952)
6 BS 5316: *Acceptance Tests for Centrifugal, Mixed-flows and Axial Pumps* (2 parts).

Part II

Measurement

6 **Gas flow**

7 **Water flow**

4 Temperature measurement

The temperature-sensing devices normally used in a test department consist of:

1 Thermocouples.
2 Mercury-in-glass thermometers.
3 Pyrometers.
4 Miscellaneous instruments.

Thermocouples

Thermocouples consist of two wires, each of a different suitable material, which are joined at the ends. If heat is applied to one junction a small voltage is produced, the value of the voltage increasing as the temperature of the junction increases. Thus, if a suitable voltage measuring device is connected to the other end of the wires the readings obtained can be used to indicate the temperature at the 'hot' junction above the temperature of the 'cold' junction. *Figure 4.1* shows the circuit of an elementary thermocouple.

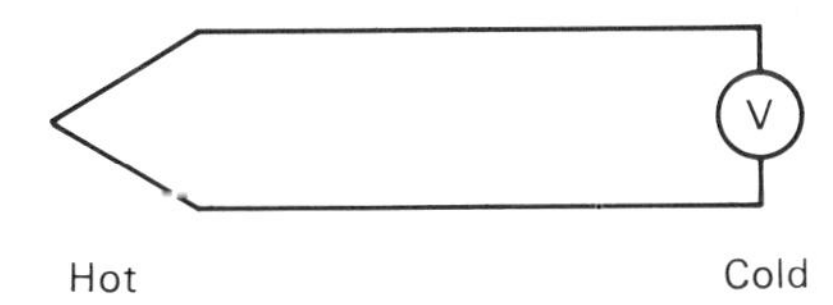

Figure 4.1 Diagrammatic arrangement of basic thermocouple

Laws of thermocouples

There are two basic laws which are of extreme importance for thermocouple work:

(a) The Law of Intermediate Temperatures.
(b) The Law of Intermediate Metals.

(a) *The Law of intermediate temperatures*

Consider an arrangement of thermocouples such as shown in *Figure 4.2*. The

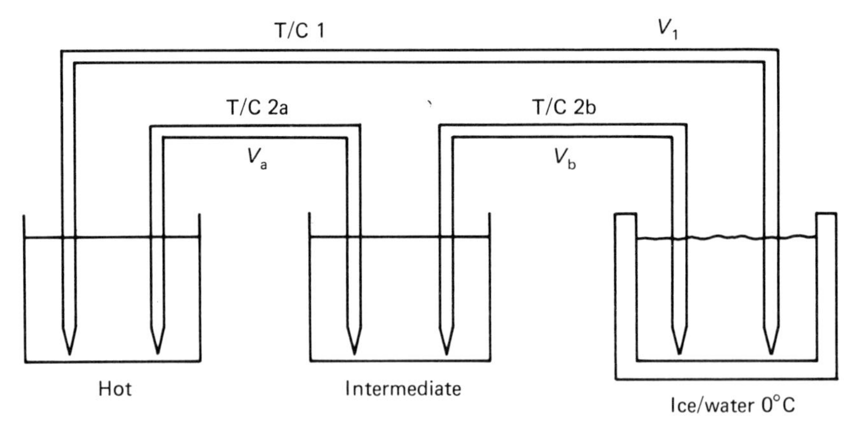

Figure 4.2 Law of intermediate temperatures

temperature at the hot end, T_1, is the same for both thermocouple arrangements as also is the cold end temperature T_3. This will cause an e.m.f. V_1 to flow in the top thermocouple circuit T/C1. The other thermocouple arrangement, T/C 2, has the same hot and cold junction temperatures as T/C 1 but in addition there is an intermediate temperature T_2. The voltage that will flow in T/C 2a is, say, V_a while that in T/C 2b is V_b.

The Law of Intermediate Temperature states that $V_1 = V_a = V_b$

This is a very convenient relationship. For example, we normally wish to know the temperature of the hot junction relative to a cold junction at 0°C. But instead of keeping T_3 at °C it is possible to have the cold junction T_2 at ambient temperature. It is then merely necessary to add the voltage equivalent of the ambient temperature with reference to 0°C to the voltage in T/C 2a. For example, suppose the temperature at T_1 is 300°C and the voltage 12.21 m V if the cold junction is at 0°C. The same result could be obtained by measuring the voltage if T_1 is at 300°C and the cold junction T_2 at an ambient temperature of, say, 26°C, i.e. 11.17 mV.

The voltage equivalent of the ambient temperature above 0°C is 1.04 mV. So $T_1 = 11.17 + 1.04 = 12.21$ m V, the same as in the previous case.

(b) *The Law of intermediate metals*

To measure the voltage in a thermocouple circuit it is necessary to insert a detecting instrument such as a potentiometer. This will have, say, brass terminals, copper connections, plus components made of various metals (see *Figure 4.3*).

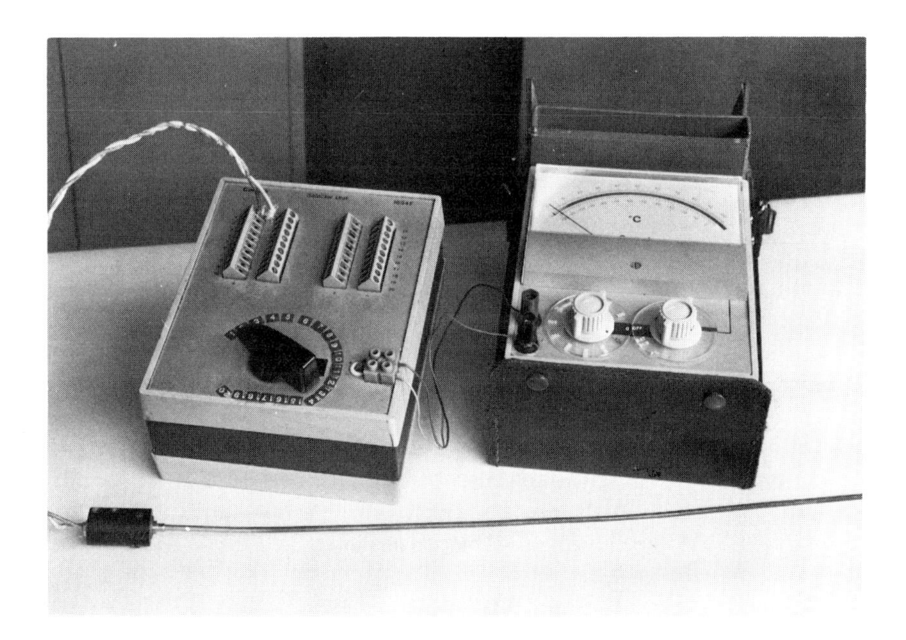

Figure 4.3 Law of intermediate metals (CEGB)

The Law states that *provided* the two thermocouple wires at the switchbox are at the same temperature T_2 the thermocouple voltage will be the same as if there was no detector in the circuit.

Thermocouple wires

It has been found that certain combinations of metals give very good results. These can be split conveniently into two groups, i.e. rare metal and base metal (see *Tables 4.1* and *4.2*.) Thermocouples from the base metal groups are used in power stations.

Table 4.1 Rare metal thermocouples

Positive wire	*Negative wire*	*Max working temp. (°C)*
90% Platinum 10% Rhodium	Platinum	1400
87% Platinum 13% Rhodium	Platinum	1400

Table 4.2 Base metal thermocouples

Positive	*Negative*	*Continuous Working Temp. (°C)*		*Colour code UK*	*USA*
Copper	Constantan	(−) 185–300	±	White Blue	Blue Red
Iron	Constantan	(+) 20–700	±	Yellow Blue	White Red
Chromel, T_1	Alumel, T_2	0–1100	±	Brown Blue	Yellow Red
Chromel	Constantan	0–800	±	Brown Blue	Purple Red

Table 4.3 gives the voltage equivalent of a range of temperatures with 0°C reference temperature for $T_1 - T_2$ (chromel-alumel) thermocouples. Of course, the appropriate tables must be used if other couples are used.

Location of the cold junction

The measuring instrument may be a considerable distance from the hot junction. Extension leads are used to join the hot junction thermocouple to the cold junction. Suitable leads are given in *Table 4.4* and *Figure 4.4* shows a typical arrangement.

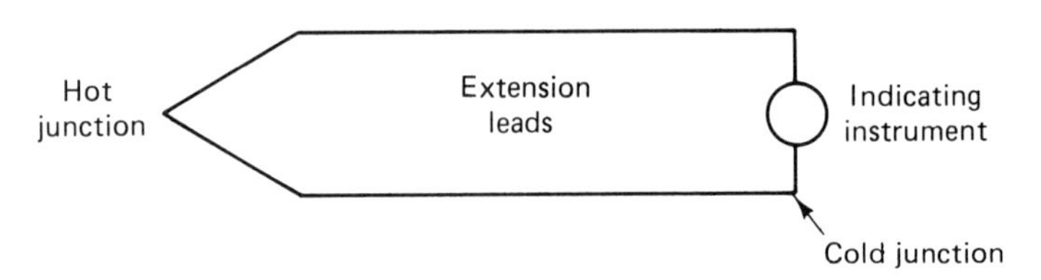

Figure 4.4 Thermocouple with extension leads

If it is required to have the cold junction at 0°C a suitable arrangement is shown in *Figure 4.5* The cold junction should be located in a thermos flask

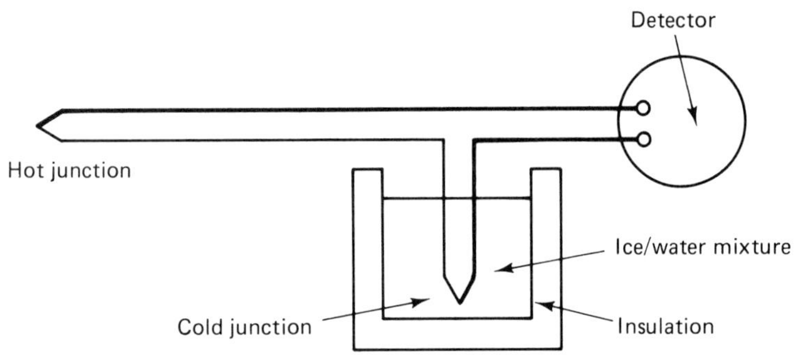

Figure 4.5 Thermocouple with zero cold junction

Table 4.3 T1 – T2 or Chromel – Alumel

°C	0°	100°	200°	300°	400°	500°
			mV			
0	0	4.10	8.13	12.21	16.30	20.64
2	0.08	4.18	8.21	12.29	16.47	20.73
4	0.16	4.26	8.29	12.37	16.55	20.81
6	0.24	4.34	8.37	12.45	16.64	20.90
8	0.32	4.42	8.45	12.53	16.73	20.08
10	0.40	4.51	8.53	12.62	16.82	21.07
12	0.48	4.59	8.61	12.70	16.90	21.15
14	0.50	4.67	8.69	12.78	16.99	21.24
16	0.64	4.75	8.77	12.86	17.07	21.32
18	0.72	4.83	8.85	12.95	17.16	21.41
20	0.80	4.92	8.93	13.04	17.24	21.49
22	0.88	5.00	9.01	13.12	17.32	21.58
24	0.06	5.08	9.09	13.20	17.41	21.66
26	1.04	5.16	9.17	13.28	17.49	21.75
28	1.12	5.24	9.25	13.30	17.58	21.83
30	1.20	5.33	9.34	13.45	17.00	21.02
32	1.28	5.41	9.42	13.53	17.74	22.00
34	1.38	5.40	9.50	13.01	17.83	22.09
36	1.44	5.57	9.58	13.09	17.91	22.17
38	1.52	5.05	9.65	13.78	18.00	22.26
40	1.61	5.73	9.74	13.87	18.08	22.34
42	1.09	5.81	9.82	13.05	18.10	22.43
44	1.77	5.80	9.90	14.03	18.25	22.52
46	1.85	5.97	9.95	14.11	18.33	22.60
48	1.93	6.05	10.06	14.20	18.42	22.68
50	2.02	6.13	10.15	14.29	18.50	22.77
52	2.10	6.21	10.23	14.37	18.58	22.80
54	2.18	6.29	10.31	14.45	18.66	22.04
56	2.20	6.37	10.30	14.53	18.75	23.03
58	2.34	6.45	10.47	14.62	18.84	23.11
60	2.43	6.53	10.56	14.71	18.93	23.20
62	2.51	5.61	10.64	14.79	19.02	23.28
64	2.59	6.69	10.72	14.88	19.11	23.37
66	2.67	6.77	10.80	14.96	19.20	23.45
68	2.76	6.85	10.89	15.05	19.28	23.54
70	2.35	6.93	10.97	15.13	19.36	23.62
72	2.93	7.01	11.05	15.21	19.44	23.71
74	3.01	7.09	11.13	15.30	19.53	23.79
76	3.09	7.17	11.21	15.38	19.61	23.88
78	3.17	7.25	11.29	15.47	19.70	23.96
80	3.26	7.33	11.38	15.55	19.70	24.05
82	3.34	7.41	11.46	15.63	19.87	24.14
84	3.42	7.49	11.54	15.72	19.95	24.22
86	3.50	7.57	11.62	15.80	20.04	21.31
88	3.59	7.65	11.71	15.80	20.12	24.39
90	3.68	7.73	11.80	15.97	20.21	24.48
92	3.76	7.81	11.88	16.05	20.30	24.56
94	3.84	7.89	11.90	16.14	20.38	24.65
96	3.92	7.97	12.01	16.22	20.47	24.73
98	4.01	8.05	12.12	16.31	20.55	24.82
100	4.10	8.13	12.21	16.39	20.64	24.90

(Courtesy Negretti & Zambra Ltd)

Table 4.4 Thermocouple extension leads

Thermocouple		*Extension leads*	
Positive	*Negative*	*Positive*	*Negative*
Copper	Constantan	Copper	Constantan
Iron	Constantan	Iron	Constantan
Chromel	Alumel	Chromel	Alumel
Chromel	Alumel	Iron	Copper–nickel alloy
Platinum–rhodium	Platinum	Copper	Copper–nickel alloy

which contains a mixture of crushed, melting ice made from distilled or demineralized water. The modern alternative is to use an electrically controlled reference temperature such as an Ice-stat or Frigistor. If an automatic scanner is used a compact reference temperature attachment can be used which fits neatly to the rear of the scanner.

The average of several temperatures

By connecting the thermocouples T/C1, T/C2, T/C3, etc. in series as shown in *Figure 4.6*, the total voltage produced will be the sum of the individual

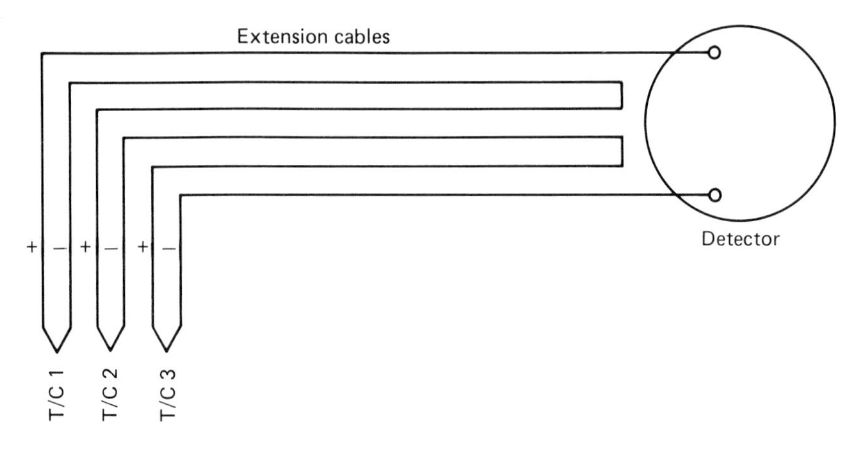

Figure 4.6 Diagram of layout for average temperature

voltages. Therefore, the arithmetic average voltage is given by:

$$V\text{ average} = \frac{V_1 + V_2 + V_3 + \dots}{\text{Number of T/Cs}}$$

Hence, the voltage detector reading should be divided by the number of thermocouples involved. It is important that the individual extension leads should be brought back to the detecting instrument.

Determination of temperature difference

It is desired to measure the difference in temperature between T/C1 and T/C2 in *Figure 4.7*. If each temperature is measured independently the hot

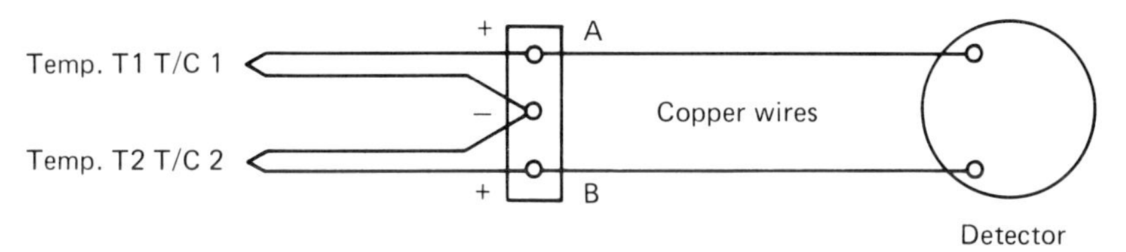

Figure 4.7 Diagram layout for temperature difference

junction temperatures will be T_1 and T_2 and the common cold junction T_0. The voltage will be V_1 and V_2 respectively.

$$\text{So } V_1 - V_2 \propto (T_1 - T_0) - (T_2 - T_0)$$
$$\therefore V_1 - V_2 \propto (T_1 - T_2)$$

Therefore the arrangement shown in *Figure 4.7* only needs copper wires from the connecting block AB to the detector.

Multi-point installations

Often it is required to measure a number of temperatures, e.g., when checking feed heaters. In such a case a multi-point switch-box is used. *Figure 4.8* shows an installation with single-pole and with double-pole switching. In addition to the manually operated switch-boxes it is possible to purchase electrically operated ones. Typical models are made by 'Comark', shown in *Figure 4.9*.

It is best to arrange for adjacent switch points to be in ascending or descending order of millivolts if possible, purely for the convenience of the observer. The contact resistance of the switches is obviously very important as the available voltage is so small. Also note that double-pole switching is preferred because a fault on the common lead affects all the others with the single-pole arrangement.

Voltage detectors

Potentiometers

For many years the standard device used to measure the voltage in thermocouple circuits was the potentiometer. Potentiometers work on the null-

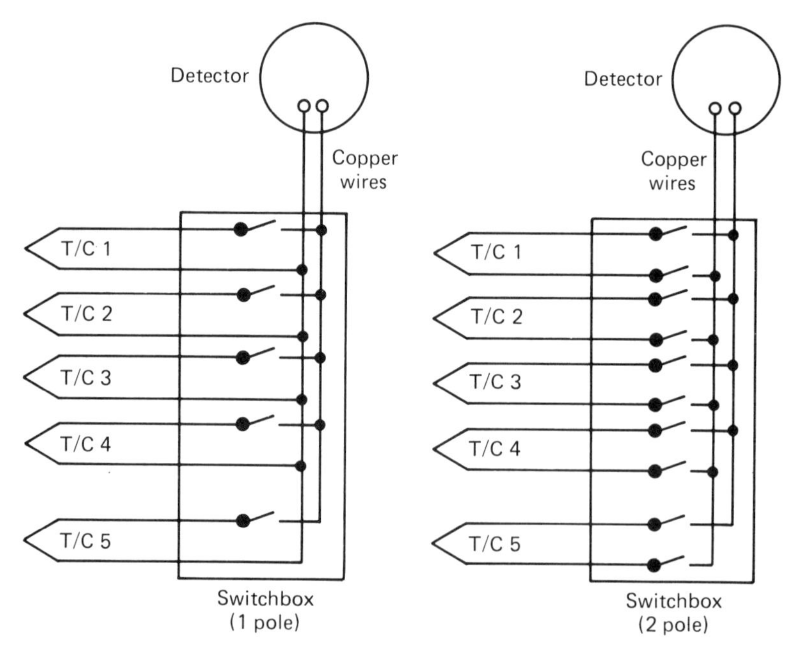

Figure 4.8 Multi-point thermocouple switch boxes (diagrammatic)

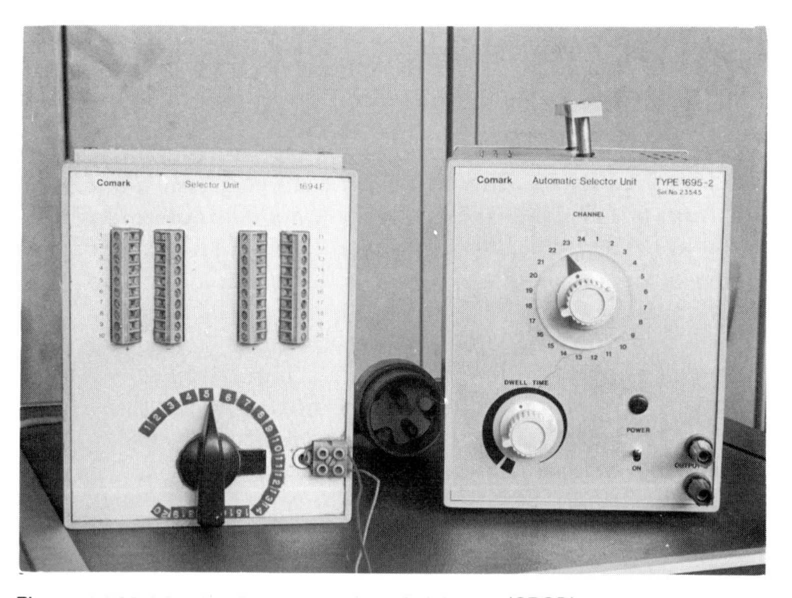

Figure 4.9 Multi-point thermocouple switch boxes (CEGB)

balance principle as this avoids errors due to resistance changes in wires or at the junctions with the thermocouple. *Figure 4.10(a)* shows a diagram of an

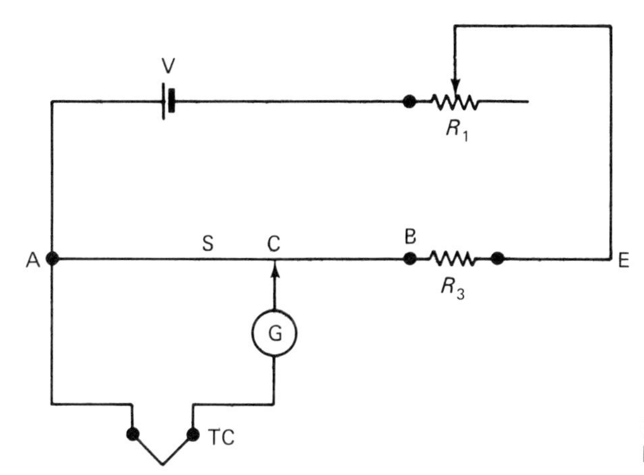

Figure 4.10(a)
Basic potentiometer circuit

elementary potentiometer.

The output voltage of battery V is adjusted by the variable resistance R_1 to give a pre-determined value across the wire AB and the resistance R_3. The purpose of R_3 is to give the effect of a considerably longer wire AB. If the wire is uniform and homogeneous there will be a constant voltage drop per unit length. For example, if the voltage is 0.05 and the distance 100 cm, then the voltage drop will be 0.05/100 = 0.0005 V/cm, or 0.5 mV/cm, and so the distance can be calibrated in terms of millivolts.

Suppose the thermocouple TC is generating a voltage of 20 mV, the reading on galvanometer G will be zero when the potentiometer and thermocouple are in electrical balance, i.e. when the balance point C is 40 cm from point A, and the millivolt reading on the potentiometer scale will be $40 \times 0.5 = 20$ mV. A practical potentiometer is shown in *Figure 4.10(b)*. If only one type of thermocouple is to be used with the instrument, then it can be scaled directly in terms of temperature, such as has been done with the electronic thermometer shown in *Figure 4.3*.

Digital voltmeters

For quite a number of years now it has been common to use digital voltmeters instead of potentiometers. They are much easier to use as the thermocouple circuit millivolts are displayed as a digital read-out (see *Figure 4.11*). These instruments are usually called DVMs.

Flue-gas temperature measurement

When measuring the flow of flue gas it is necessary to determine the gas temperature. For this purpose it is usual to employ suitable thermocouple extension wires with the hot ends twisted together. For example, a length of $T_1 - T_2$ extension wire may be passed through a suitable

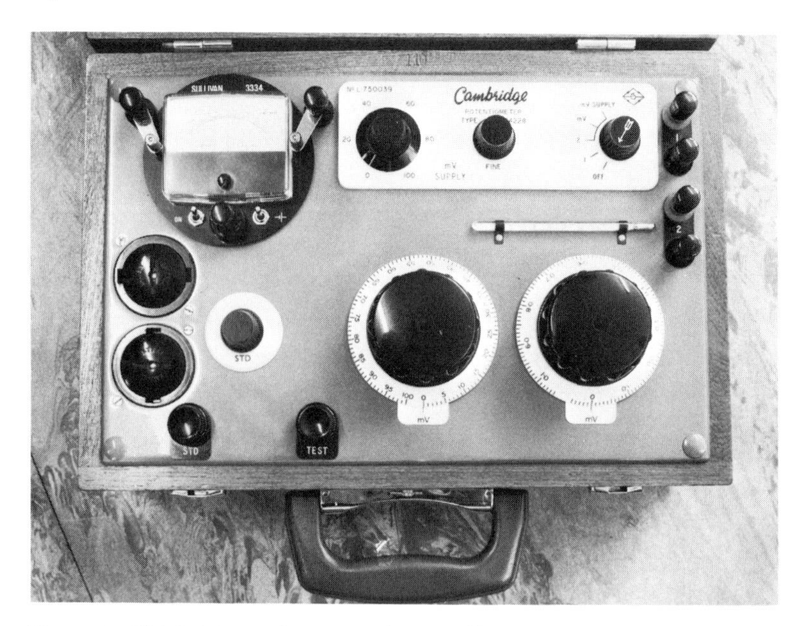

Figure 4.10(b) Quick reading potentiometer (CEGB)

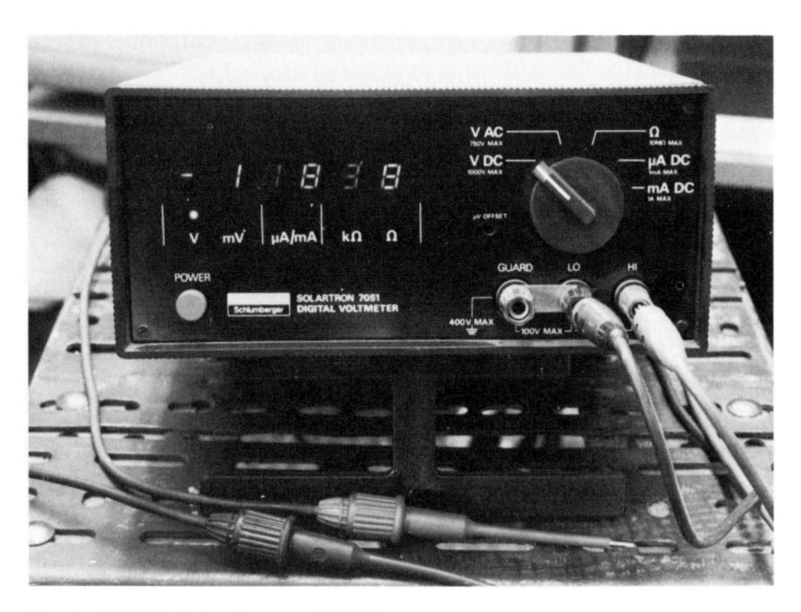

Figure 4.11 Digital voltmeter (CEGB)

length of metal tube with the hot end exposed so that it can be placed well into the gas stream. The other ends are connected to a suitable detector, such as a Comark electronic thermometer.

Sometimes the wires in the gas stream become electrostatically charged and this causes the readings to be false. In addition to the spurious readings there are considerable fluctuations of the indicated temperature. The remedy is to earth the system by connecting the negative terminal of the detector to suitable metalwork.

Some typical causes of faulty operation of thermocouples are listed below:

Thermocouple installation defects

Low millivolts

1. Incorrect immersion of T/C.
2. T/C damaged.
3. Wrong type of T/C.
4. Poor connection at terminals.
5. Extension cable insulation defective.
6. Wrong extension cables.
7. Polarity of extension cables wrong:
   (Wrong at both ends – reading is wrong).
   (Wrong at one end – reading is backwards).
8. Incorrect zero.

High millivolts

1. Flame touching T/C.
2. Wrong type of T/C.
3. Wrong extension cables.
4. Incorrect zero.

Mercury-in-glass thermometers

These can be used for temperatures up to about 600°C. Of course, there are also other liquids beside mercury which can be used, some of which are shown in *Table 4.5*.

Table 4.5 Thermometer liquids

	Range (°C)
Alcohol	− 80 to + 70
Toluene	− 80 to + 100
Pentane	− 200 to + 30
Creosote	− 5 to + 200

However, for normal power station work only mercury thermometers are used. The boiling point of mercury is 358°C, but thermometers can be made for higher temperatures than this by introducing nitrogen under pressure. As the temperature rises the mercury expands and so further pressurizes the gas. Thus the boiling point of the mercury is raised. For mercury thermometers in the range − 20°C to 110°C 'lead' glass is used. For other temperature ranges other glasses are used, e.g. 'Normal' grade, Corrosilicate and Supermax.

Before reading a thermometer ensure that the temperature is steady, and also be careful to avoid parallax error. If extreme accuracy is required it is necessary to refer to the immersion length which will be found etched on the back of the glass. Immerse the thermometer to this depth and correct for the emergent stem error.

Wet and dry bulb (or hygrometer) type

This type consists of two matched mercury-in-glass thermometers. One has its bulb covered with muslin, the other end of the fabric being immersed in distilled water. Thus the fabric is always damp, and evaporation from it governed by the humidity of the air, results in its temperature being reduced. Thus, the difference in temperature between the 'wet' and the 'dry' thermometers is a measure of the relative humidity.

The instrument should be exposed to the air but shaded from sunlight. In one type the two thermometers are surrounded by metal jackets with substantial clearance between the jacket and the thermometer. A clockwork driven fan causes a flow of air over the thermometers. The difference between the dry and wet readings is called the depression of the wet bulb, from which the relative humidity can be determined, (see *Figure 4.12.)*

Calibration

Calibration of thermocouples and thermometers should preferably be carried out in specialist laboratories such as at the CEGB Calibration Centre at Hams Hall. Temperature sensing devices are calibrated by:

(a) the Fixed-Point Method;
(b) the Comparison Method.

With method (a) the device is calibrated at any of the fixed points on the International Temperature Scale (see *Table 4.6.*) With method (b) the device is compared with a suitable sub-standard.

Fixed-Point methods

(i) *Ice Point*

A mixture of crushed ice and water (both derived from pure water) is contained in a vacuum flask. The thermometer is immersed in the mixture.

Figure 4.12 Wet and dry bulb thermometer. (Assmann hygrometer) (CEGB)

Table 4.6 International Temperature scale (fixed points of some substance at a pressure of 1013 mbar)

Fixed point	*°C*	*K*
Hydrogen boils	− 252.87	20.28
Neon boils	246.048	27.102
Oxygen boils	− 182.692	90.188
*Water freezes	0.0	273.15
Water boils	100.0	373.15
Zinc freezes	419.58	692.73
* Sulphur boils	444.60	717.82
Silver freezes	961.93	1235.08
Gold freezes	1064.43	1337.59

* Secondary points

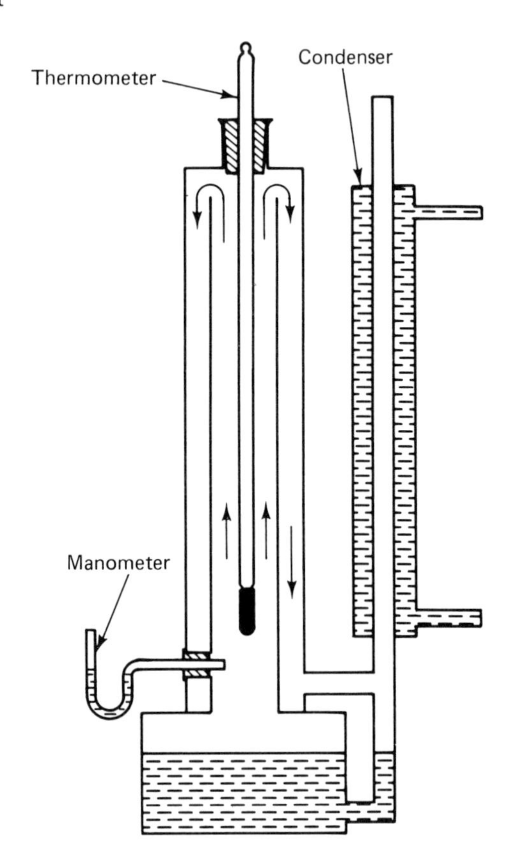

Figure 4.13 Hypsometer apparatus (CEGB)

(ii) *Steam Point*

A hypsometer (see *Figure 4.13*) is required for this. The thermometer is immersed in steam whose temperature is that of the saturation temperature of the water at atmospheric pressure. Therefore regular readings of the pressure are taken during the test. When these readings have been fully corrected (refer to notes on the Fortin barometer) the corresponding saturation temperature can be obtained. The manometer is provided on the apparatus to enable the observer to satisfy himself that there is no pressure difference from the inside of the equipment to the outside.

(iii) *Sulphur Point*

The apparatus is shown in *Figure 4.14*. The thermometer to be tested is inserted in the glass tube and the sulphur is heated until it boils. The tube is open at the top and it acts as a condenser, so a clear condensation line will appear on the glass. The thermometer is surrounded by a metal shield to minimize radiation loss.

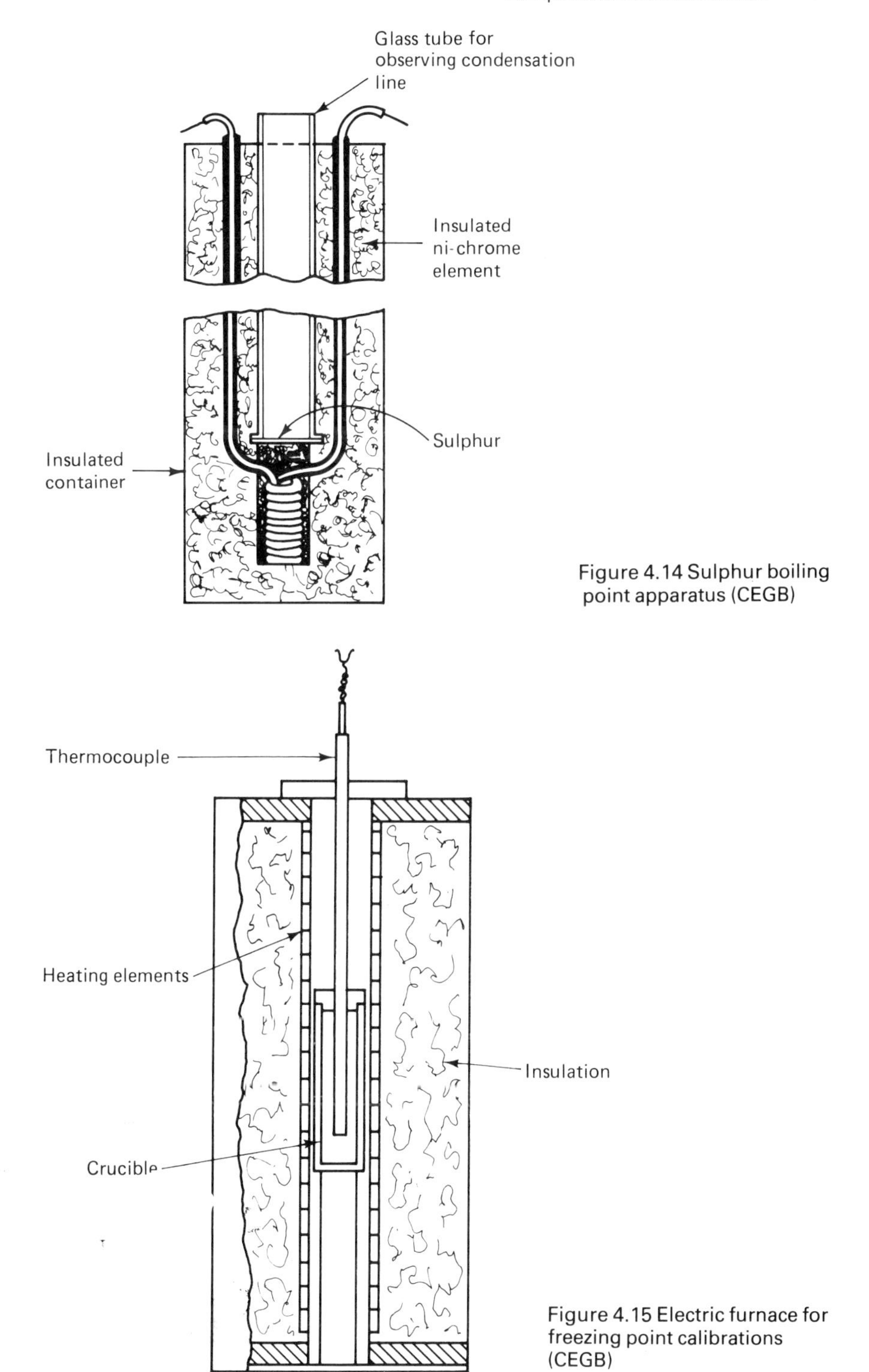

Figure 4.14 Sulphur boiling point apparatus (CEGB)

Figure 4.15 Electric furnace for freezing point calibrations (CEGB)

(iv) *Freezing-Point method*

The apparatus is shown in *Figure 4.15*, and it is usually used for thermocouple calibration. Tests can be carried out up to 1100°C with suitable equipment. The thermocouple is protected by a sheath of suitable material and immersed to a depth at least eight times its diameter when the metal melts. The apparatus is then allowed to cool and, as the metal freezes, the thermocouple voltage will remain constant. Normally this will last for several minutes. The metal is then re-heated and the thermocouple removed.

Comparison methods

For these a bath such as shown in *Figure 4.16* is required. Electric heating

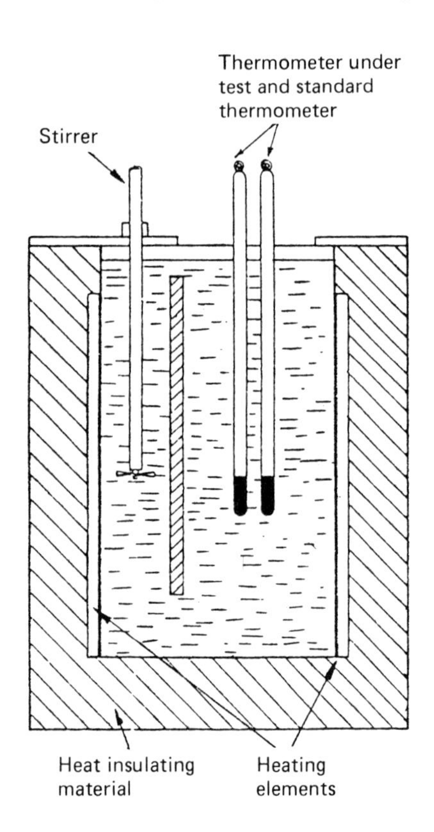

Figure 4.16 Water, oil or salt bath for comparison tests (CEGB)

coils raise the temperature of the liquid and constant stirring is necessary to ensure the even distribution of heat. Various liquids can be used, but usually they are:

(a) Pure water for temperatures in the range 0–100°C.
(b) Special liquid paraffin oil for the range 100–200°C.

For temperatures between 200 and 600°C a salt bath is used. It is imperative that every care is taken when using such a bath because:

1 The salt is highly oxidising.
2 The salt, although molten, does not appear to be hot.
3 Should water be spilt into the salt an explosion will result.

Various salts are used, the most common being a mixture of sodium nitrate and potassium nitrate.

Pockets

If the temperature of a pressurized substance is required (e.g. feed water), it is necessary to use a pocket. Various types are available, the prime reason for the development of different pockets being the desirability of reducing the response time for a change of temperature. This is not a particularly important consideration for testing purposes as one would expect the conditions to be steady for a substantial time before testing commenced (see *Figure 4.17*).

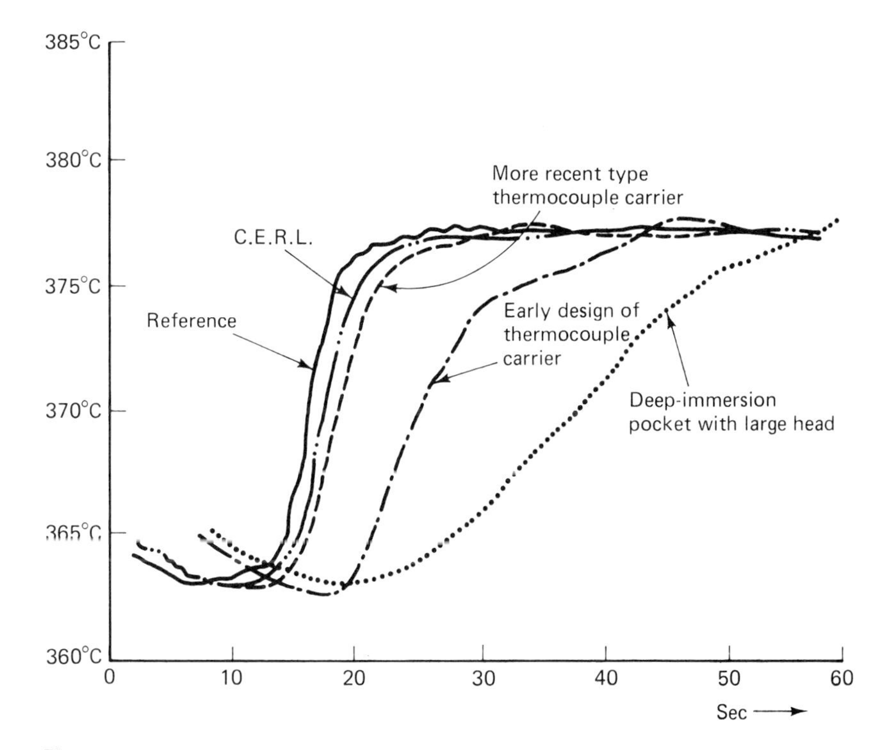

Figure 4.17 Comparison of time lags of different pockets (CEGB)

However, various errors can be caused by a poor design of pocket and also by poor installation of the sensing element. The most common errors are shown in *Figure 4.18*, and the remedies are obvious. One troublesome

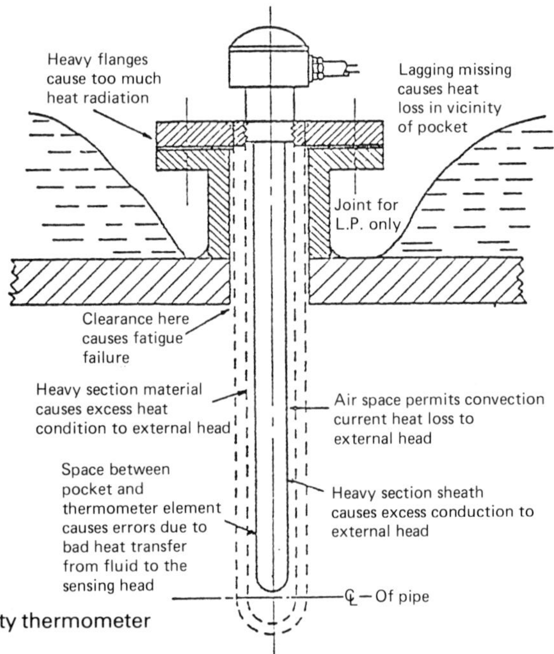

Figure 4.18 Errors due to faulty thermometer pocket installation (CEGB)

aspect of pockets is that dirt and debris lodges in them. One way of removing such debris is to fasten a suitably sized *blunt* metal drill securely to a piece of stiff wire. Insert the drill in the pocket and rotation of the wire by hand will entangle the debris with the drill flutes and so enable it to be removed. Another way to clear a pocket of debris is to direct a jet of compressed air into the pocket.

All test pockets should have a suitable cap secured to them by a short length of chain so that when the pocket is not in use the cap can be put on to keep out debris. *Figure 4.19* shows a suitable design of pocket for test purposes.

Pyrometers

For measuring the temperature of, say, the flame or gas in a combustion chamber the normal instrument to use is the *pyrometer*. There are two basic types:

(a) The disappearing-filament type.
(b) The suction type.

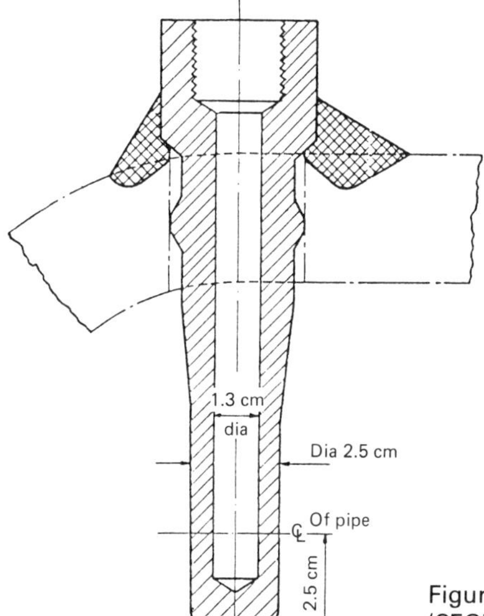

Figure 4.19 High pressure thermometer pocket (CEGB)

The disappearing-filament pyrometer

With this type the flame is viewed through an optical system. Also viewed is an electrically heated filament which is part of the apparatus. The filament can be raised to various temperatures by variation of a built-in resistance in the electrical circuit. The method of use is to view the flame with the filament relatively cool, when it will look black against the flame, as shown in *Figure 4.20*.

Operation of a knob on the instrument causes the filament to heat further and eventually its brightness will match that of the flame, at which time the filament will seem to disappear. The temperature is then read directly from a scale on the instrument.

The great advantage of this type of instrument is that it is very convenient and portable.

The suction pyrometer

This type consists of a shielded thermocouple which is inserted into the high temperature zone. Heat is supplied to the thermocouple by drawing a stream of gas over the couple. The probe is water cooled (see *Figure 4.21*.) A venturi pneumatic pyrometer is used if the gas contains a high dust burden.

Figure 4.20 Disappearing filament pyrometer (CEGB)

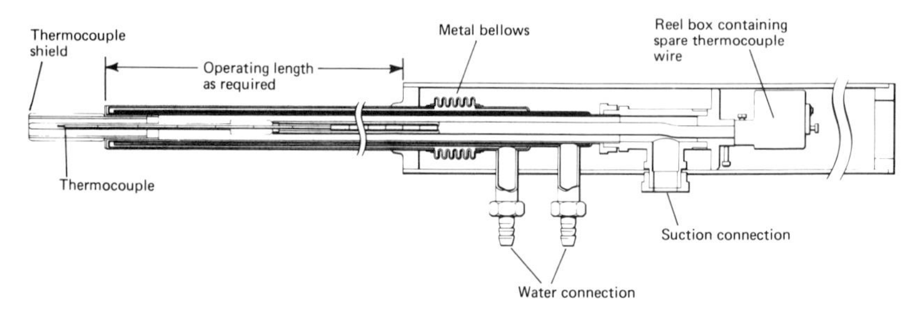

Figure 4.21 Suction pyrometer (Land Combustion Ltd.)

Miscellaneous instruments

Electronic thermometers

Routine testing does not always require an extremely high degree of precision when measuring temperatures. In these cases convenience coupled with acceptable accuracy is the basic necessity. A range of instruments is in this category.

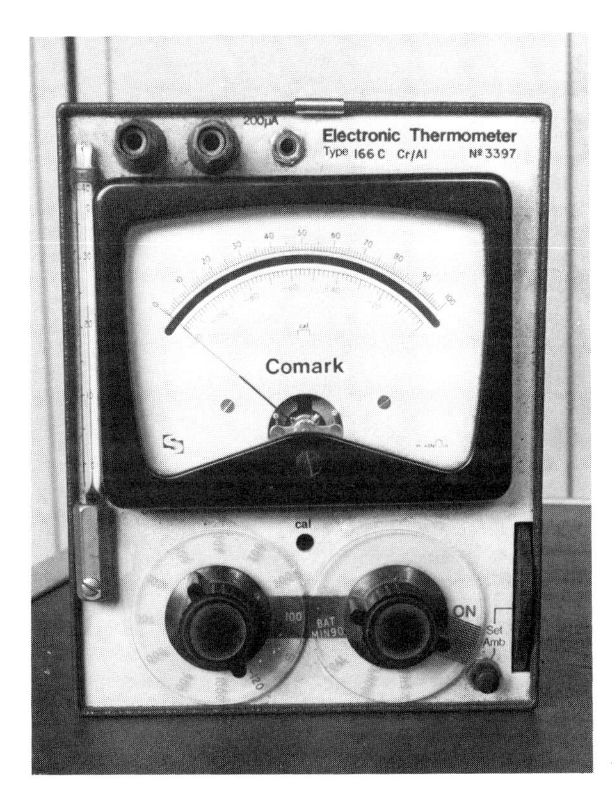

Figure 4.22 Electronic thermometer (CEGB)

One of the most convenient and useful is the Comark electronic thermometer as shown in *Figure 4.22*. The model illustrated has manual ambient temperature compensation, although these have been superseded for some time by models which incorporate automatic compensation. The instrument is really a potentiometer scaled in temperature units. Therefore it is important that the instrument is compatible with the thermocouple being used. Electronic thermometers are compact, robust and light instruments.

Digital electronic thermometers

These are often small and easily used instruments such as the model shown in *Figure 4.23*. They are useful for obtaining surface temperatures. The temperature is displayed as shown.

Mechanical types

It should not be forgotten that there is still an important need for the older established mechanical types, such as the Rototherm dial type temperature indicator. One version of this has a small copper disc which is applied to the

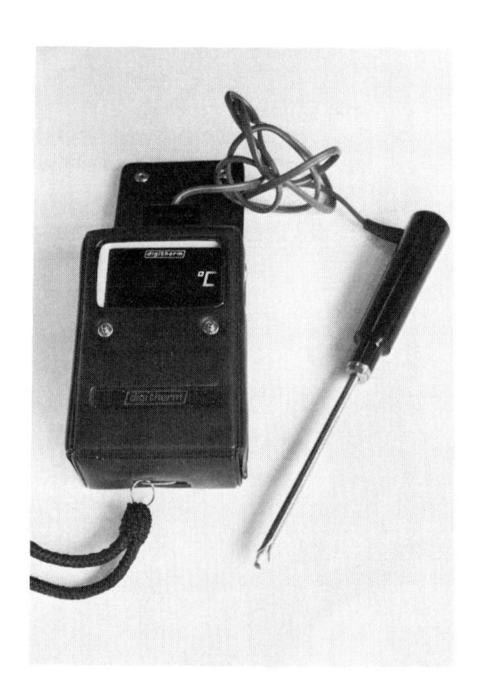

Figure 4.23 'Digitherm' digital thermometer (CEGB)

surface to be measured and the heat flow through the disc operates the pointer on the face of the indicator.

Temperature strips

These are self-adhesive strips (e.g. Tempatch), marked with a temperature scale. Each strip contains a calibrated range of sealed heat-sensitive elements which change colour at a given calibrated temperature. When each white indicator is exposed to heat at its calibrated temperature it turns permanently black. The strips are accurate to ± 1% and the various ranges covered span + 37°C to + 260°C. They have the advantage that they can be fastened to rotating and other parts which normally are difficult to measure.

Infra-red thermometers

These measure the quantity of infra-red radiation from a heat source. One such instrument can be located between 15 cm and 4 m from the temperature source, and temperatures between 0°C and 1000°C can be measured. The instrument is very light (750 grams) and is completely self contained.

Questions

1 State the two basic laws of thermocouples.
2 Name suitable combinations of metals for thermocouples. Which is the positive wire?

Figure 4.24 Rototherm thermometer (CEGB)

3 What extension wires would you use with a chromel-alumel T/C?
4 What would you use for a cold junction?
5 How would you determine the average of several temperatures using T/Cs?
6 How would you determine temperature difference using T/Cs?
7 How would you connect a number of temperature points to a potentiometer?
8 What is the advantage of a DVM compared to a potentiometer?
9 What precautions should be taken when using a mercury in glass thermometer?
10 What are the main ways of calibrating thermometers?
11 Name some fixed points.
12 What is a hypsometer?
13 What substances are used for comparison tests?
14 What precautions are necessary when using a salt bath?
15 What is 'thermometer pocket response time'?
16 What errors can arise when using a pocket?
17 How would you clean a pocket of debris?
18 How would you measure flame temperature?
19 What is the effect of connecting the positive wire of a T/C extension

wire to the negative of the T/C?

20 What would cause a T/C output to be low?

21 What would cause a T/C output to be high?

Exercise 1

During a turbine test the following potentiometer readings were obtained using $T_1 - T_2$ thermocouples:

> TSV 21.62 mV; HP cylinder exhaust 14.41 mV; temperature of the cold junction 16°C.
> What were the TSV and exhaust temperatures?

Exercise 2

Sketch the connections for several thermocouples to be connected to a digital voltmeter via a selector box.

Exercise 1 (Answer)

Cold junction equivalent = 0.64 mV
So TSV = 21.62 + 0.64 = 22.26 mV
HP exhaust = 14.41 + 0.64 = 15.05 mV

The equivalent temperatures are, from *Table 4.3*, 538°C and 368°C.

Exercise 2

Refer to text.

Additional Reading

1 JONES, E.B., *Instrument Technology Vol. 1*, Butterworths.
2 BS 1041: *Code for Temperature Measurement* (7 Parts).
3 BS 284: *Whirling Hygrometers.*
4 BS 4937: *International Thermocouple Reference Tables* (7 Parts).
5 MORGAN, E.S., and ROUGHTON, J.E., 'Dynamic Performance of Various Thermometer Pockets for Steam Temperature Measurement' *CERL Report*, Laboratory Note No. RD/L/N59/63.
6 ROUGHTON, H.E., 'Design of Thermometer Pockets for Steam Mains', *Proc. I.E.E.*, **180**, Part 1.
7 LENK, J.D., *abc's of Thermocouples*, W. Foulsham & Co.

5 Pressure measurement

Bourdon tube pressure gauges

These pressure gauges are the most common type, named after Eugéne Bourdon, the French instrument maker who developed the original instrument in the nineteenth century.

Test pressure gauges, such as shown on the right of *Figure 5.1*, are

Figure 5.1 'Comparative, type gauge tester with a standard test gauge and a gauge under test (CEGB)

potentially accurate to within $^1/_4$% of full-scale deflection (FSD), while commercial instruments may have an accuracy better than 1%. When selecting a gauge it is usual to specify a range such that the normal working pressure is 60% – 70% FSD. Normally the instruments indicate 'gauge' pressure although, if the tube is contained within an evacuated case, absolute pressure can be measured.

Other types include differential gauges (*Figure 5.2(a)*), used for purposes such as indicating the pressure drop across strainers; also there are

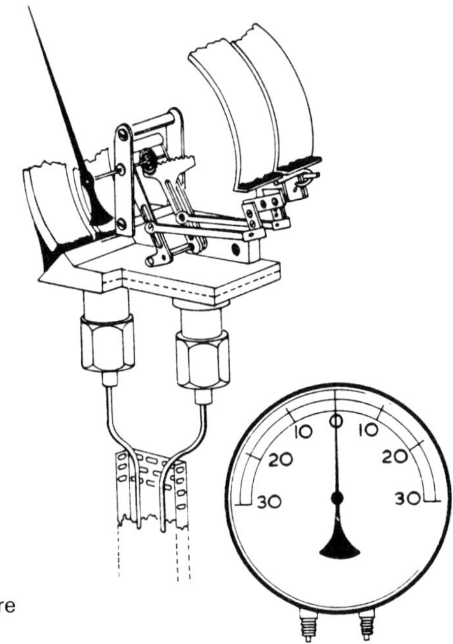

Figure 5.2 (a) Differential pressure Bourdon tube gauge (CEGB)

compound gauges which indicate values above and below atmospheric pressure. Standard atmospheric pressure is 1.013 bar.

Typical tube materials are phosphor-bronze; beryllium-copper and alloy steel for duty with a medium that will not cause attack. Where the pressure medium is corrosive it is common to use 'K' monel; carbon steel and stainless steel. Provided the elastic limit of the tube material is not exceeded the deflection of the tube is proportional to the applied pressure. The deflection is very small and so it is necessary to actuate the pointer via a quadrant, pinion and magnifying linkage as shown in *Figure 5.2(b)*. A hair spring is

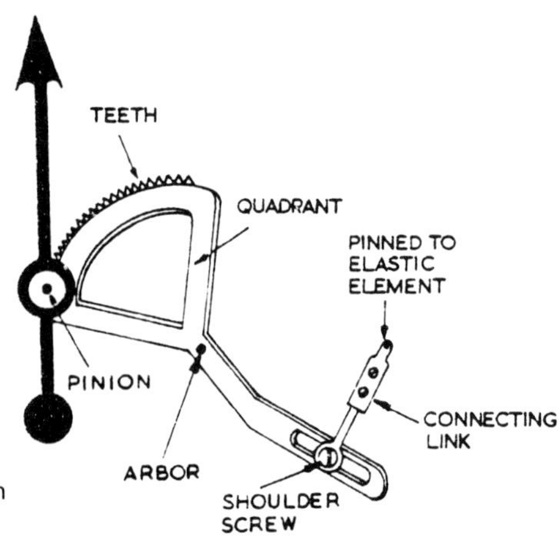

Figure 5.2(b) Magnification mechanism used in Bourdon tube gauges (CEGB)

included to take up any backlash between the quadrant and the pinion.

Gauge errors

The usual errors encountered with Bourdon tube gauges are:

(1) *Zero error*, which results in a constant displacement over the whole range of the gauge. It is corrected by repositioning the pointer. See *Figure 5.3*.

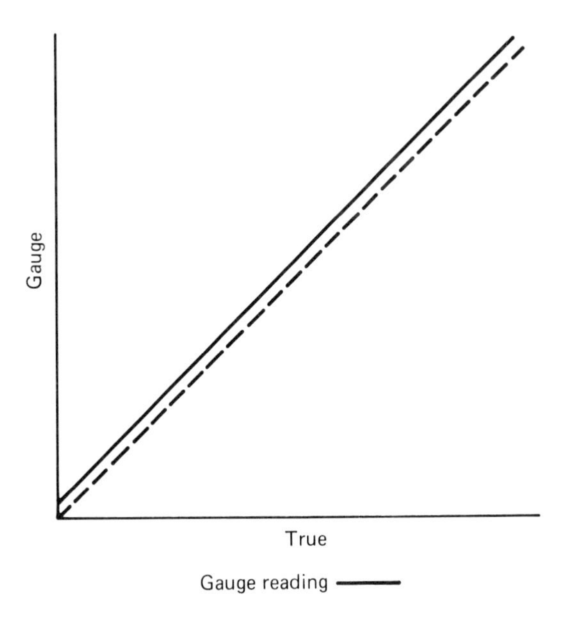

Figure 5.3 Zero error

(2) *Hysteresis error*. If the indicated readings are different when ascending pressures are applied to those obtained at the same pressures when descending, there is a hysteresis error (see *Figure 5.4*).
(3) *Multiplication error*. If the gauge reads progressively higher or lower than true as pressure is applied, the instrument has a multiplication error (see *Figure 5.5*).
(4) *Angularity error* is present when the top and bottom indications are correct but the mid point is high or low (see *Figure 5.6*).

Deadweight testers

The gauges are tested by using a *deadweight tester*. The gauge is connected to the tester by means of a pressure-tight union (see *Figures 5.7(a)* and *(b)*). Weights are added to the table to obtain the desired pressure. The screw press is wound in to pressurize the oil until the weight carrier rises, at which

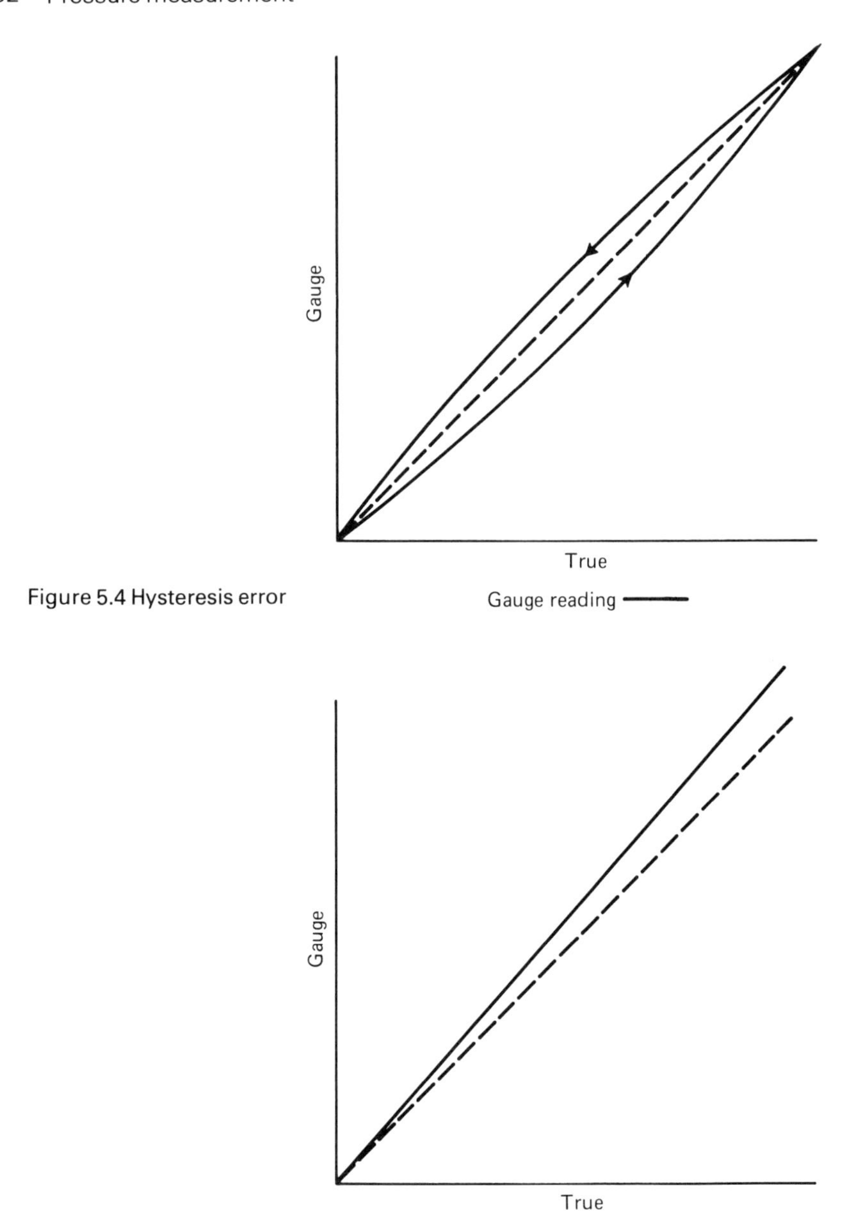

Figure 5.4 Hysteresis error

Figure 5.5 Multiplication error

point the pressure corresponding to the weights is transmitted to the gauge. The weight carrier should be spun slowly to eliminate friction. Care should be taken when unwinding the screw press as it is possible to create a slight vacuum. The weights are marked in terms of the pressure they will produce.

Where it is required to have one tester to cover a considerable range of

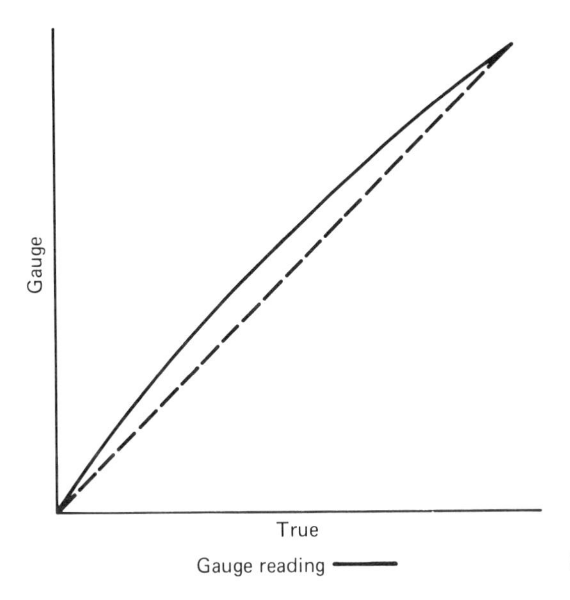

Figure 5.6 Angularity error

pressures it is possible to use a *dual range tester*, a type patented by Messrs Budenberg. The general arrangement is shown in *Figure 5.8*. Essentially the dual-range piston unit contains three pistons (auxiliary, low pressure and high pressure). When used at low pressures the oil acts on the underside of the LP piston. As the auxiliary piston rests on top of the LP piston both are lifted as the screw press is operated, so raising the weight carrier until the weight carrier skirt exposes the LP (blue) band.

As pressure is increased further the LP piston rises until a flange at the bottom of the piston engages with the bottom of the LP cylinder. The oil pressure then causes the HP piston to lift and this lift is communicated via the ball to the weight carrier. At the correct pressure the weight carrier skirt will expose the HP band (red). The auxiliary weight is lifted by a landing on the weight carrier as the carrier rises. The auxiliary weight is necessary to compensate for the loss of weight from the carrier system of the LP piston. The vent is provided to avoid a pressure build-up above the LP piston as it rises. *Figure 5.8* shows the piston unit in the high-pressure position.

The dead-weight gauge

The dead-weight gauge is used for high-accuracy pressure measurement. The introduction of pressure transducers has reduced the scope for these instruments, but they remain worthy of consideration. The arrangement is shown in *Figure 5.9*. Basically it is a modified dead-weight tester and both have a similar method of lifting the dead-weights by means of pressure applied to the underside of the piston of the weight-carrier. However, in the case of the dead-weight pressure gauge the pressure is measured by adding

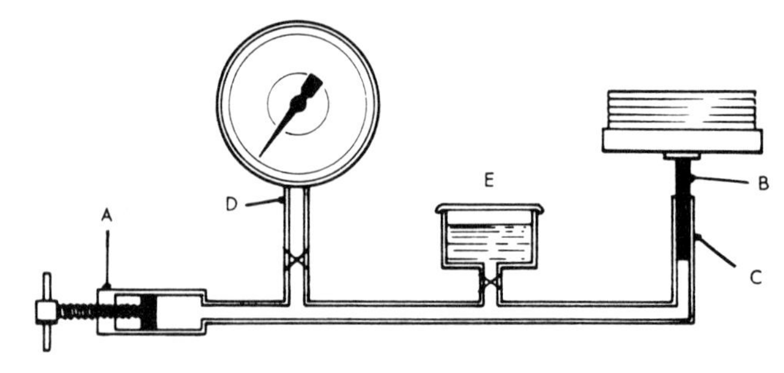

(a) Illustrating action of tester

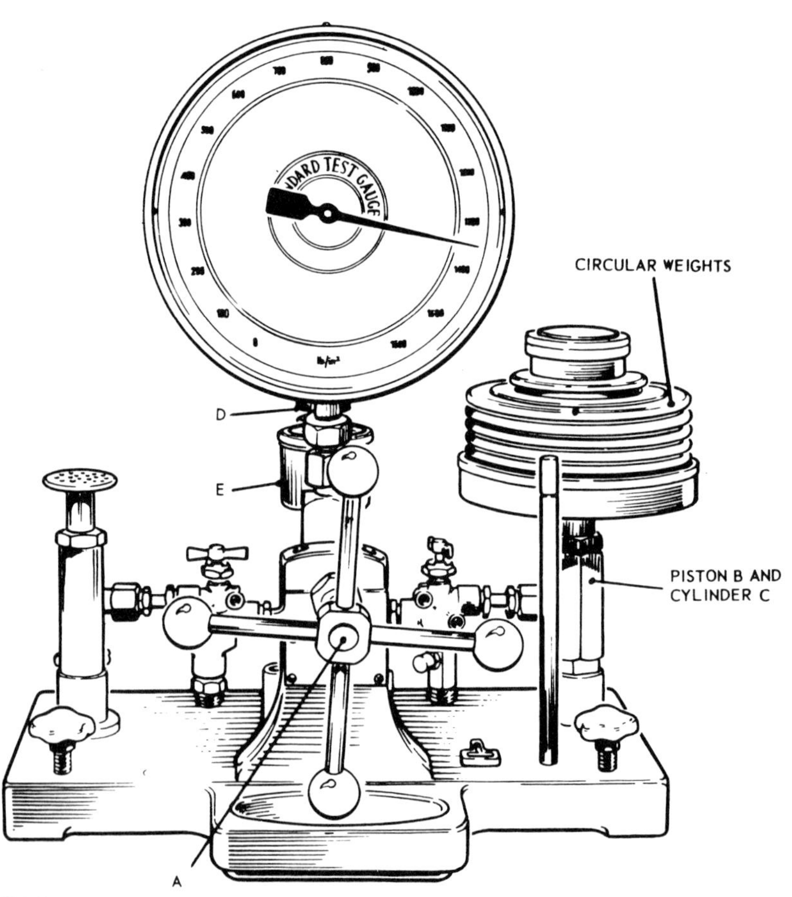

(b) General arrangement showing pressure gauge being calibrated

Figure 5.7 Dead weight tester (CEGB)

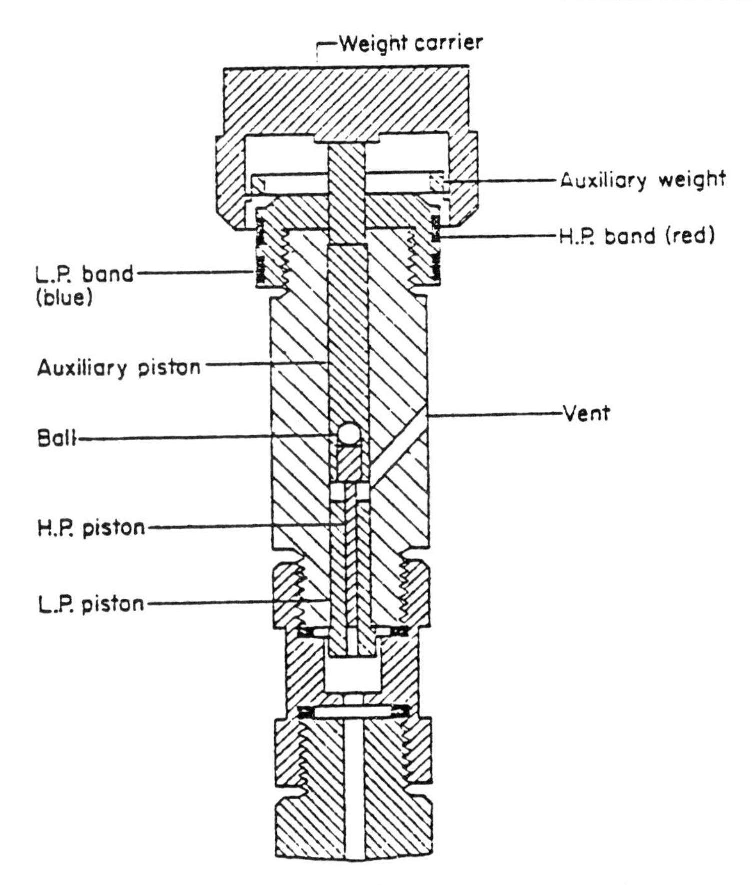

Figure 5.8 Dual range piston unit (Budenberg Gauge Co. Ltd.)

weights to the carrier until it just exceeds the applied pressure from the system under test.

The small extra pressure required to lift the weights is applied to the underside of the auxiliary piston by means of the hand pump. This additional pressure is also transmitted to a precision gauge which is specially calibrated in such a way that the required total pressure is the sum of the pressure due to the weights plus that shown on the gauge.

Testing vacuum gauges

A mercury column tester such as the one shown in *Figure 5.10* is convenient for testing vacuum gauges. Operation of the hand pump will produce a vacuum of up to 0.95 bar, i.e. 0.06 bar absolute.

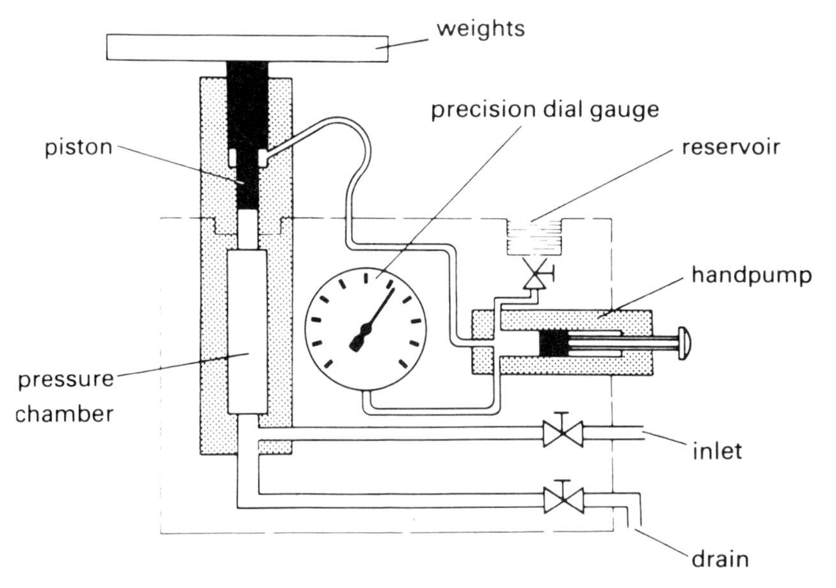

Figure 5.9 Dead weight pressure gauge (Budenberg Gauge Co Ltd)

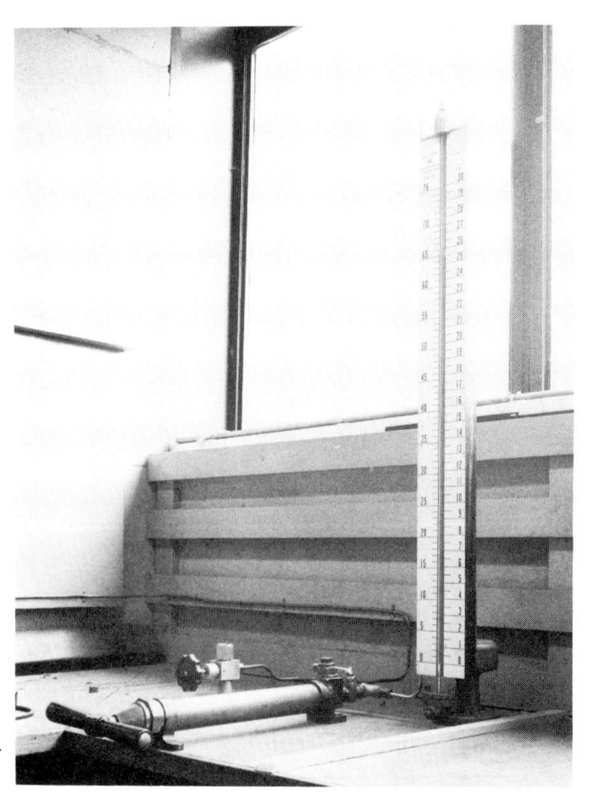

Figure 5.10 Mercuy column tester (CEGB)

Testing Bourdon tube pressure gauges

The procedure is as follows (refer to *Figure 5.11*):

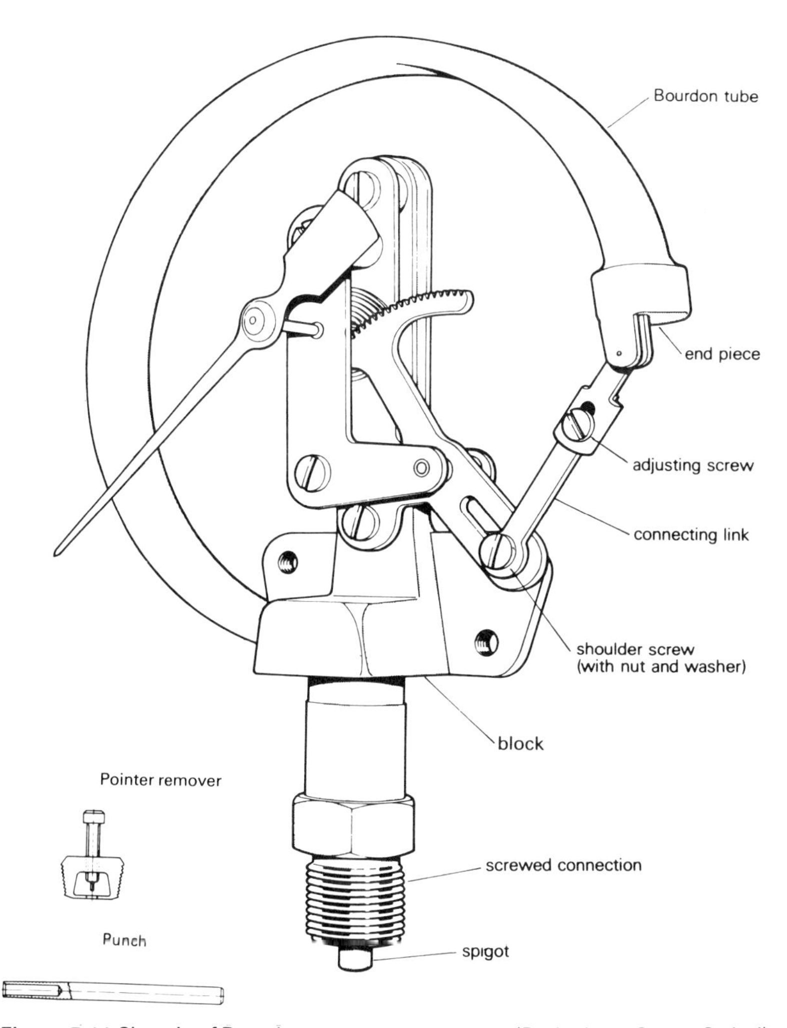

Figure 5.11 Chassis of Bourdon tube pressure gauge (Budenberg Gauge Co Ltd)

∴1 Before carrying out any adjustments note the instrument reading when on a deadweight tester at about 10%, 30%, 50%, 70% and 90% of full-scale pressure with the pressure rising and then falling.

2 Apply about 10% pressure and, if the gauge reading is incorrect, remove the pointer with a pointer remover and re-position it correctly (using a pointer punch) to eliminate the *zero error*. Flick the pointer gently and check that it returns to the correct position. If it fails to do so it may be

that the tube is defective.

3 Raise the pressure to about 90% of the scale pressure. If the reading is incorrect alter the position of the shoulder screw and linkage. Move the screw towards the quadrant pivot to increase the range, or away from the pivot to decrease it.

4 Repeat steps 2 and 3 until the gauge is correct at both points.

5 Adjust for angularity if necessary. Apply 50% pressure and move the angularity adjusting screw until the connecting link and the quadrant arm are at right angles.

6 Note the readings at the five points with both ascending and descending pressures as in step 1.

7 Plot the readings to check for hysteresis error. If the gauge has been subjected to overpressure the loop may be 'open', in which case it has a permanent set. If the set is not excessive it is possible that the gauge can be recalibrated and function satisfactorily.

8 Assemble the gauge taking care that the pointer does not foul the glass.

9 Prepare a calibration curve such as that shown in *Figure 5.12*. An error is

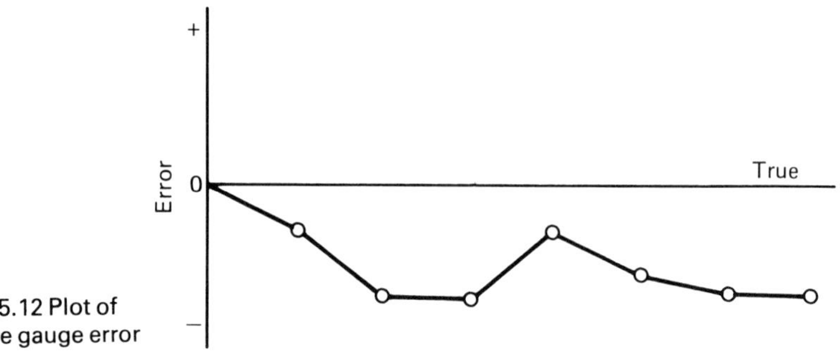

Figure 5.12 Plot of pressure gauge error

positive when the gauge reading is greater than the true reading.

$$\text{Percentage error} = \frac{\text{error} \times 100}{\text{true reading}}$$

10 Attach a label to the gauge with details of the date of test, maximum percentage error and the name of person carrying out the test.

Head errors

If a pressure gauge is mounted above or below the level of the measuring point an error is applied to the gauge if the connecting pipework is full of liquid as this head is transmitted to the gauge. Consider *Figure 5.13(a)* and *(b)*. In (a) the measuring point is 30 m above the gauge and so the head error is given by (if the liquid is water)

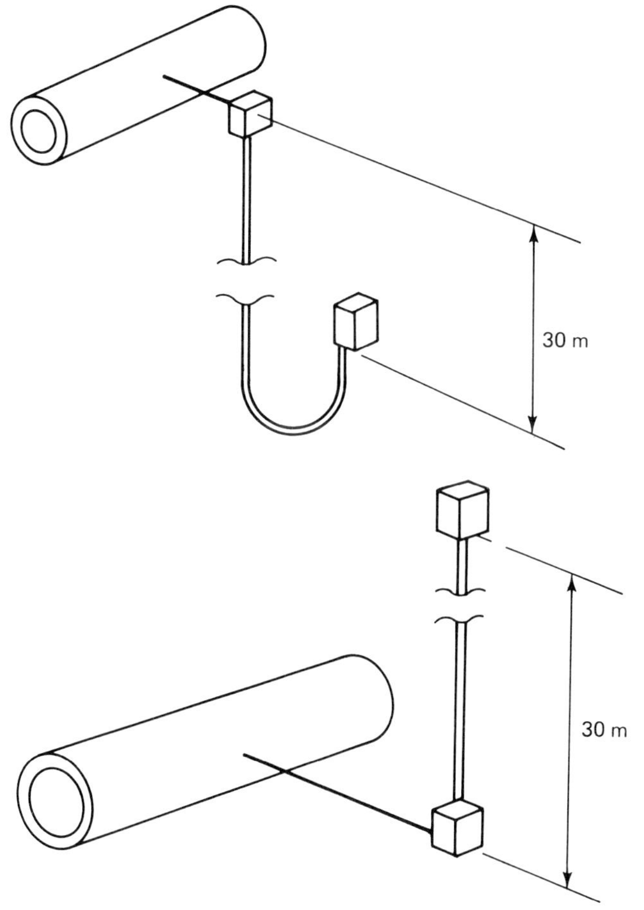

Figure 5.13(a) Positive pressure gauge head error; (b) Negative pressure gauge head error (CEGB)

$$g \rho \ H = 9.81 \times 1000 \times 30 \ \text{N/m}^2$$
$$= 294.3 \ \text{kN/m}^2$$
$$= 2.943 \ \text{bar high}$$

where $g = 9.81 \ \text{m/s}^2$

ρ = density in kg/m^3

H = head in metres

Note. N/m^2 are often called Pascals (Pa).

In (b) the gauge is 30 m above the tapping point and so the head error will be 2.943 bar low.

If such gauges were to be part of a permanent installation they should have the errors removed by offsetting the pointer and the scale plate marked

'Calibrated 30 m slow' or 'Calibrated 30 m fast' for (a) and (b) respectively.

Installation of pressure gauges

Connecting pipe runs should be as short as possible and of ample strength for the highest pressure they are likely to encounter. Copper or steel are the usual materials, although sometimes plastics can be used. If a liquid pressure is being measured the connecting pipe must contain cold liquid before the pressure is applied to the gauge. Steam or hot water must not be allowed to enter the Bourdon tube. A coil (*Figure 5.14*) is a simple device to seal the

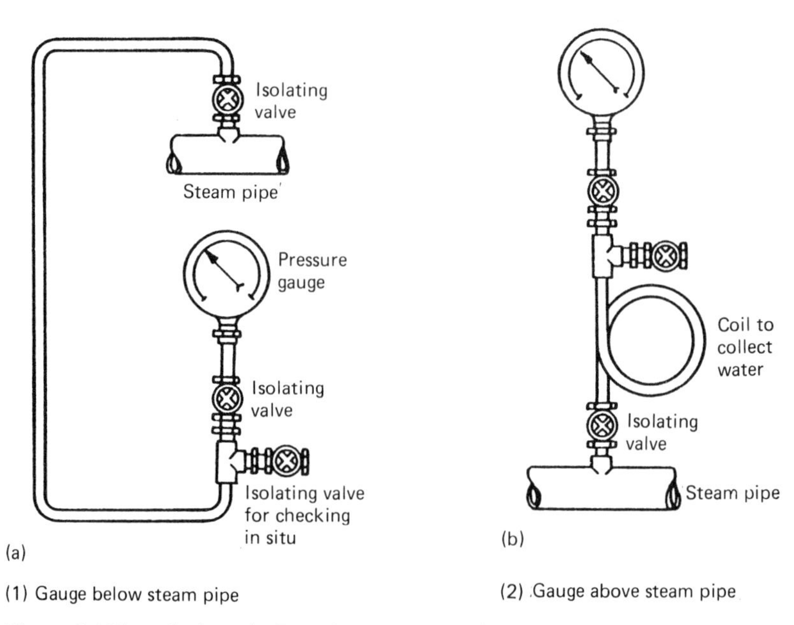

Figure 5.14 Installation of a Bourdon tube gauge (CEGB)

gauge. Where the system to be measured is subject to rapid pulsations the gauge should be protected by a *snubber*, see *Figure 5.15*. This damps out the pulsations and the gauge indicates the average pressure.

Corrosion fatigue cracking inside steam pipes can be caused by water dripping from pressure gauge lines which act as reflux condensers. However, the damage may not occur in the immediate vicinity of the gauge tapping. The droplets can be carried for a considerable distance by the steam flow before being projected against the pipe wall at a bend or other item causing a change in the direction of flow. Thus, it may be difficult to relate the cause of the pipe damage to the effect. To overcome the problem the take-off pipework should be nestled alongside the steam pipe underneath

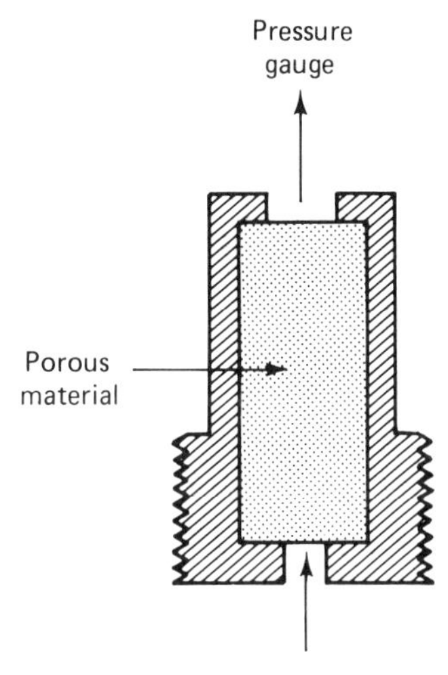

Figure 5.15 Snubber: for dampening pressure fluctuations.
Note. Snubbers often incorporate a tapered needle to achieve the desired throttling effect

the lagging before being routed to the gauge. This will permit the re-evaporation of drips in the gauge pipework before they can enter the main pipe.

Pressure transducers

It is now common to measure pressures by means of transducers, a typical pressure transducer being shown in *Figure 5.16*. For one particular type the

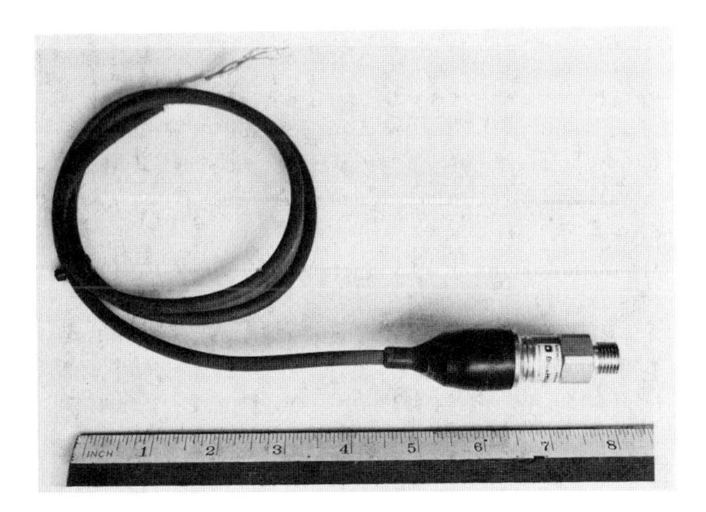

Figure 5.16 Pressure transducer (CEGB)

input is 10 volts d.c. and the input leads are coloured red (+) and white (−). The output leads (often referred to as the 'signal' leads) are coloured yellow (+) and blue (−). Other manufacturers use different colour codes.

Some transducers work off 28 volts d.c. The higher voltage has the advantage that voltage drop along the connecting wires from the supply is not normally critical. On the other hand if a 10 V supply is used the drop may be such that with only 2 or 3 m of connecting wire the transducer must be calibrated with the connecting wire in circuit as the voltage drop may be significant.

Calibration

Calibration is carried out using a dead-weight tester. The arrangement is shown in *Figure 5.17*. Note that the connecting cable is included in the

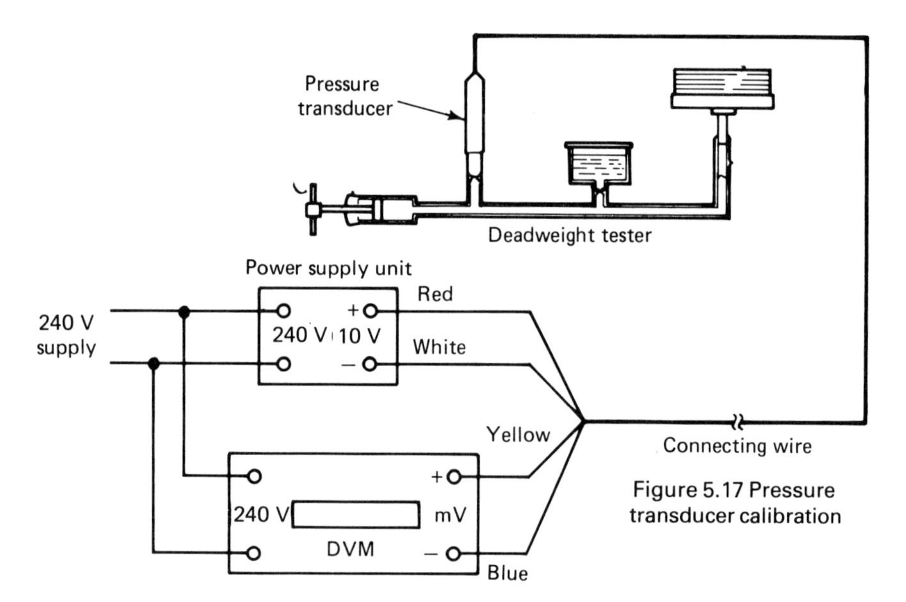

Figure 5.17 Pressure transducer calibration

circuit. Before the transducer is screwed into the dead-weight tester the DVM reading is noted – this is the no-load millivolts. It is then connected to the tester and a series of pressures applied which span the range of the transducer. For each new pressure applied to the tester the output millivolts is noted. A series of increasing pressures is applied first, followed by another set as the pressure is reduced. A pro-forma for calibration purposes is shown at the end of this section.

When the results are plotted they should lie on a straight line. However, the test values will not be exact and so there will be a slight scatter of points. This means that the line of best fit must be calculated by regression analysis, either manually or by computer. For example, the following results were obtained when a 10 V pressure transducer (including the connecting wire of about 5 m) was tested.

No. of points	*Applied pressure (bar g)*	*Ascending pressure (mV)*	*Descending pressure (mV)*
1	0	0.96	1.02
2	6	2.74	2.78
3	60	18.68	18.73
4	70	21.64	21.68
5	80	24.61	24.65
6	90	27.58	27.61
7	100	30.55	30.57
8	110	33.52	33.53
9	115	35.00	—

To determine the best line manually, proceed as follows:

The line of best fit will pass through X and Y

$$\text{where } \bar{X} = \frac{\Sigma X}{N} \quad \text{and } x = X - X$$

$$\bar{Y} = \frac{\Sigma Y}{N} \quad \text{and } y = Y - Y$$

N = number of readings

(1) Point no.	*(2) X (bar g.)*	*(3) Y (mV)*	*(4) x*	*(5) y*	*(6) xy*	*(7) x^2*
1	0	0.96	− 67.47	− 19.97	1 347.4	4 552.2
2	6	2.74	− 61.47	− 18.19	1 118.1	3 778.6
3	60	18.68	− 7.47	− 2.25	16.8	55.8
4	70	21.64	2.53	0.71	1.8	6.4
5	80	24.61	12.53	3.68	46.1	157.0
6	90	27.58	22.53	6.65	149.8	507.6
7	100	30.55	32.53	9.62	312.9	1 058.2
8	110	33.52	42.53	12.59	535.5	1 808.8
9	115	35.00	47.53	14.07	668.7	2 259.1
10	110	33.53	42.53	12.60	535.9	1 808.8
11	100	30.57	32.53	9.64	313.6	1 058.2
12	90	27.61	22.53	6.68	150.5	507.6
13	80	24.65	12.53	3.72	46.6	157.0
14	70	21.68	2.53	0.75	1.9	6.4
15	60	18.73	− 7,47	− 2.23	16.7	55.8
16	6	2.78	− 61.47	− 18.15	1 115.7	3 778.6
17	0	1.02	− 67.47	− 19.91	1 343.3	4 552.2
$N = 17$	$\Sigma X = 1{,}147$ ∴ $\bar{X} = 67.47$	$\Sigma Y = 355.85$ $\bar{Y} = 20.93$	—	—	$\Sigma xy = 7\,721.3$	$\Sigma x^2 = 26\,108.3$

The slope of the line, m is given by:

$$m = \frac{\Sigma \times y}{\Sigma \times^{2}}$$

So $\overline{X} = 67.47$, and $\overline{Y} = 20.93$

$$\text{Slope} = \frac{7721.3}{26\ 108.3} = 0.2958$$

The calibration curve is plotted in *Figure 5.18*.

Note how tedious the manual calculation is. Therefore it is best to use a computer or calculator to obtain the information. Thus, for the information obtained from the transducer test the computerized results are:

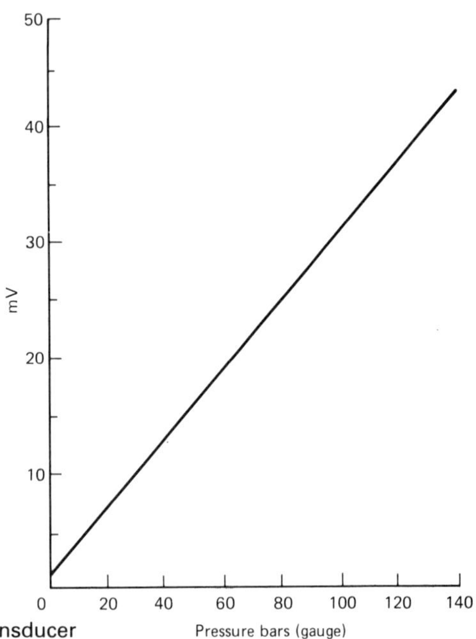

Figure 5.18 Calibration of pressure transducer

Intercept with Y axis, $Z = 0.979$ mV
Slope m $= 0.296$
The law of the transducer is derived from the straight line: $y = mx + Z$ where y is in mV, x is in bar (gauge), m is slope of line, and Z is the interecept with the Y axis.

$$\therefore x = \frac{1}{m}(y - Z)$$

$$\frac{1}{m} = s = 3.378$$

Then $x = s\,(y - Z)$
So bar $= s\,(mV - Z)$

For example, what is the pressure when the millivolt reading is 38.0?

$$x = 3.378\,(38.0 - 0.979) = 3.378 \times 37.021 = \mathbf{125.06\ bar\ (g)}$$

Transducer Calibration

Type ____________________ Range ________ Serial No. ____________

Tested on ___/___/198__ by ____________________________

______ metres of connecting cable included.

No.	*Applied pressure (bar a or g)*	*Ascending (mV)*	*Descending (mV)*
1			
2			
3			
4			
5			
6			
7			
8			
9			
10			
11			
12			
13			
14			
15			
16			
17			
18			
19			
20			

(1) Intercept $Z =$ _____mV
(2) Slope of line $m =$ ________ $\therefore s =$ ________

Law of transducer $x = s\,(mV - Z)$

$\therefore$ Pressure = ____ $(MV -$ ____ $)$ bar (a) or (g)

Questions

1 What are the gauge errors? How would you recognize them?
2 How does a dual-range tester work?
3 How would you test a Bourdon tube pressure gauge?
4 Why does a Bourdon tube gauge have a hair spring?
5 What is meant by head error?
6 What would it be if the tapping point were 10 m above the gauge?
7 What are the main requirements of a gauge installation?
8 What is the purpose of a snubber?
9 What is a suitable range for a pressure gauge to measure 60 bar?
10 Define positive error
11 What is the law of a pressure transducer?

Exercise 1

What is the head correction of the pressure gauge shown in *Figure 5.19*.

Answer: (−) 67.7 m

Exercise 2

What is the equivalent water gauge reading of the mercury manometer shown? (Refer to section on head errors)
There is no water above the mercury, the temperature is 20°C and the density of the mercury is 13545.9 kg/m^3

Answer: 81.275 cm w.g.

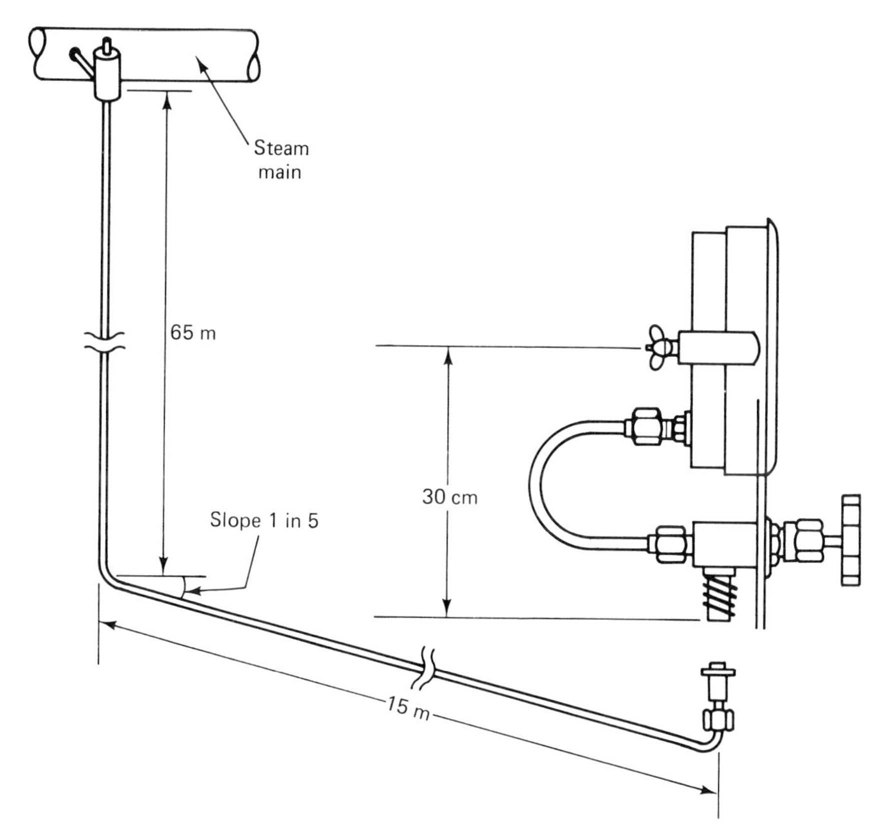

Figure 5.19 Pressure gauge pipework. Exercise No 1 (CEGB)

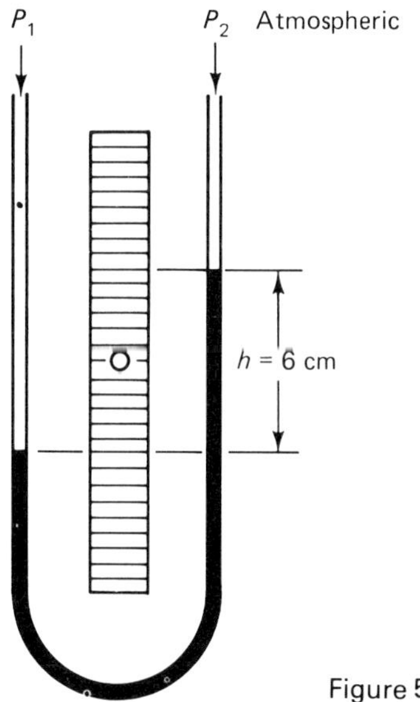

Figure 5.20 Manometer. Exercise 2

Project 1

A Bourdon tube pressure gauge is to be installed permanently to measure the pressure in a pipe carrying hot oil. The pressure range is 0–3000 kN/m^2 and the oil is supplied from a reciprocating pump. The oil density is 900 kg/m^3 and the gauge is to be located 10 m above the tapping point.

(a) What range of instrument is required?
(b) State the location and purpose of all cocks and fittings.
(c) What is the head correction and how would the gauge be adjusted?

Project 2

A Bourdon tube pressure gauge was tested on a deadweight tester and the results obtained were:

True Pressure (bar)	*Indicated Pressure (bar)*	
	Rising	*Falling*
10.0	15.0	15.0
30.0	36.5	36.5
50.0	57.0	57.0
70.0	78.0	78.0
90.0	99.0	99.0

Comment upon the results.

Project 1 (Answer)

(a) $$\frac{300\ \text{kN/m}^2}{0.6} = 5000\ \text{kN/m}^2 = 50\ \text{bar}$$

So range of instrument = 0–50 bar.

(b) At the tapping point there would be an isolating valve.
In the vicinity of the gauge the pipe would be formed into a coil or pigtail and there would be an isolating valve for the gauge. The gauge itself would be in a vibration-free location and fitted with a 'snubber'.
(c) Head correction = $9.81 \times 900 \times 10 = 88\ 290\ \text{N/m}^2$

= 0.88 bar fast

(*Note:* The *error* is slow so the correction is fast). The head error would be corrected by re-positioning the pointer and marking the dial accordingly.

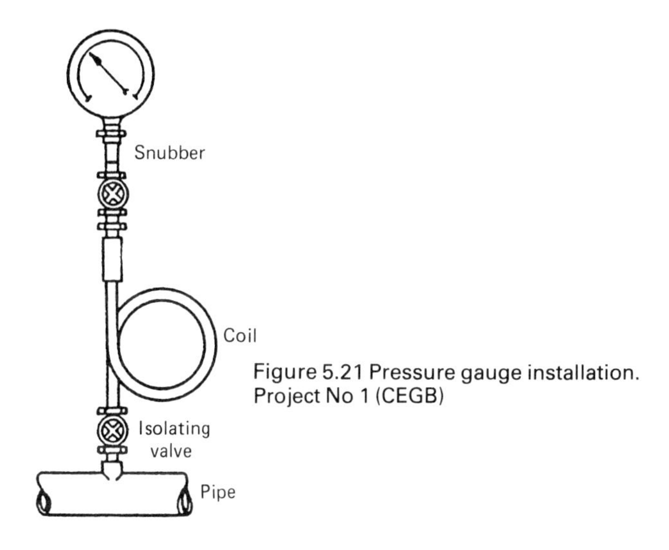

Figure 5.21 Pressure gauge installation. Project No 1 (CEGB)

Project 2 (Answer)

The results are plotted in *Figure 5.22*.
It is apparent from the tabulated results that there is no hysteresis or angularity error. From the graph it is seen that the error consists of a zero error (amounting to (+) 5.0 bar) and a multiplication error which is zero at zero pressure and + 5.0 bar at full pressure of 100 bar.

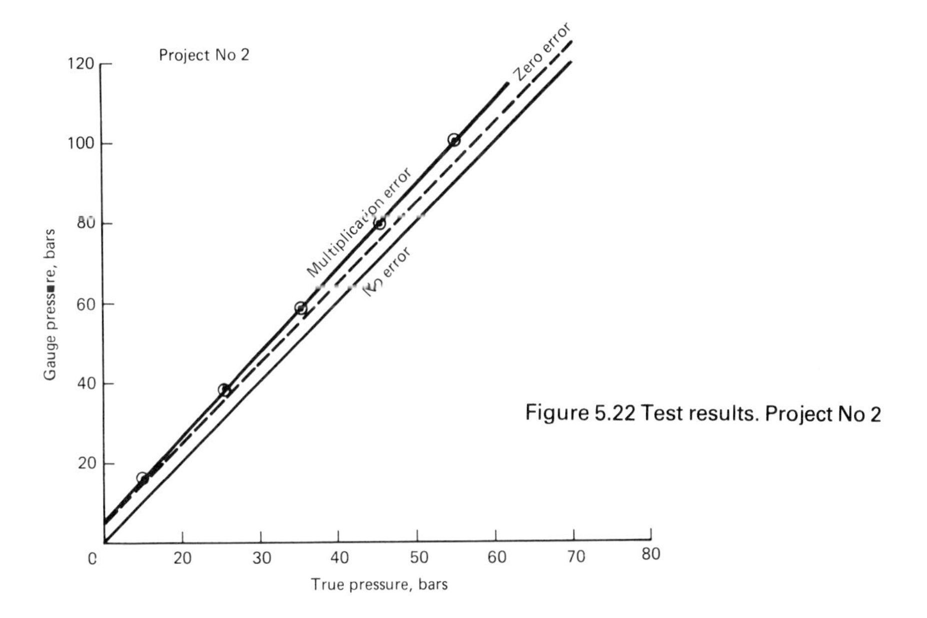

Figure 5.22 Test results. Project No 2

Project 3

Determine the law

Transducer Calibration

Type Pressure Range 60 – 115 bar Serial No. L170334

Tested on / / 198 by

3 metres of connecting cable included.

No.	*Applied (bar g)*	*Ascending pressure (mV)*	*Descending (mV)*
1	0	0.992	1.037
2	6	2.582	2.614
3	60	17.215	17.256
4	70	19.967	20.000
5	80	22.716	22.744
6	90	25.472	25.490
7	100	28.272	28.237
8	110	30.973	30.985
9	115	32.349	32.356
10			
11			
12			
13			
14			
15			

(1) Interecept $Z =$ ____ mV
(2) Slope of line $s =$ ________
Law of transducer $x = s\ (mV - Z)$

$\therefore x =$ (mV −) bar (g) or (a)

Project 3 (Answer)

(1) Intercept $Z = 0.609$ mV
(2) Slope of line $= 0.275$ ∴ $s = 3.636$
Law of tranducer $x = s(mV - 0.609)$ bar (g)
Law of transducer $x = s$ (mV $- Z$)
∴ **x = 3.636 (mV − 0.609) bar (g)**

Project 4

This project relates to a pressure transducer connected to a pipeline containing water which was subsequently exposed to freezing conditions. Usually, the consequent damage to the transducer would render it useless; but sometimes, as in this case, it merely alters the calibration of the device.

The test results are given in the table. Determine the calibration before and after the freezing conditions. What would have been the percentage error at 51 bar absolute if it had not been re-calibrated? A pro-forma for manual calculation is given.

Transducer Calibration

Type Pressure Range 26 – 52 bar(a) Serial No. L162892

__________ by __________

5 metres of connecting cable included.

No.	*Bar (a)*	*Before (mV)*	*After (mV)*
1	26.40	14.180	9.810
2	31.40	16.890	12.490
3	36.40	19.590	15.160
4	41.40	22.300	17.840
5	46.40	25.000	20.500
6	51.40	27.690	23.188
7	51.40	27.700	23.188
8	46.40	25.020	20.510
9	41.40	22.320	17.850
10	36.40	19.630	17.170
11	31.40	16.920	12.500
12	26.40	14.210	9.810

No.	X Bar (a)	mV	x	y	xy	x^2
1	26.40					
2	31.40					
3	36.40					
4	41.40					
5	46.40					
6	51.40					
7	51.40					
8	46.40					
9	41.40					
10	36.40					
11	31.40					
12	26.40					
N = 12	Σ = 466.8 X = 38.9	ΣY = Y =	– –	– –	$\eta\ \Sigma$y =	Σx^2 =

Project 4 Answer

Before the freezing conditions:
$S = 1.8516 \qquad Z = -0.06$
So calibration = 1.8516 (mV + 0.06) bar absolute

After the freezing conditions:
$S = 1.8699 \qquad Z = -4.30$
So calibration = 1.8699 (mV + 4.30) bar absolute.
Thus, at 51 bar absolute applied pressure the readings would be:
Before, 27.484 mV
After, 22.974 mV

$$\therefore \text{ Error} = \frac{(27.484 - 22.974)\ 100}{22.974}$$

$$= +\ \mathbf{19.6\%}$$

Additional Reading

1 JONES, E.B., *Instrument Technology Vol. 1* (Butterworths).
2 BS 759, *Valves, Gauges and Other Safety Fittings for Application to Boilers and to Piping Installations for and in Connection with Boilers.*
3 BS 1780: *Bourdon Tube Pressure and Vacuum Gauges* (2 Parts).
4 BUDENBERG. C.F.,'The Bourdon Pressure Gauge' *Trans. Soc. Instr. Technology,* **8**, No. 2.
5 BUDENBERG, C.F., 'Current Practice in the Measurement of Fluid Pressure', *Control and Instrumentation* (May 1971).

6 Gas flow

Consider first the case of air and then the more general case of flue gas flow. The flow of air is from a high pressure zone to one of lower pressure. It is the difference of pressures which causes the flow, but its rate is determined by the resistance it encounters. As the air moves it exerts a pressure upon obstacles in its path – the higher the speed the greater the pressure exerted. It is a common experience that when in a high wind a considerable pressure is applied to your body. The pressure caused by air movement is called *velocity pressure* and denoted by h_v.

The effect of obstacles in the path of the moving air is to cause the air speed to become less. Even the friction of the air against the sides of a duct has this effect. As the resistance increases so the velocity falls but the *static pressure* increases. The static pressure maintains the air velocity against the system resistance and is denoted by h_S.

Pressure measurements

To measure the static pressure in a duct, a tube called a *side tube* can be used. The opening of the side tube is at right-angles to the flow and so it is not subjected to any velocity pressure. The opening of the tube is flush with the duct wall and free of any irregularities, see *Figure 6.1*. When considering the performance of fans it is usual to employ the static pressure it can produce as one of the design criteria.

Of course in all practical cases of flow there are both velocity and static pressure components present simultaneously. The precise value of each depends upon the circumstances. The sum of the velocity and static pressure components is called the *total pressure* and is denoted by h_t.

Therefore total pressure = velocity pressure + static pressure.

The total pressure can be measured by means of a *facing tube* such as shown in *Figure 6.2*. It consists of a tube facing directly into the stream of air.

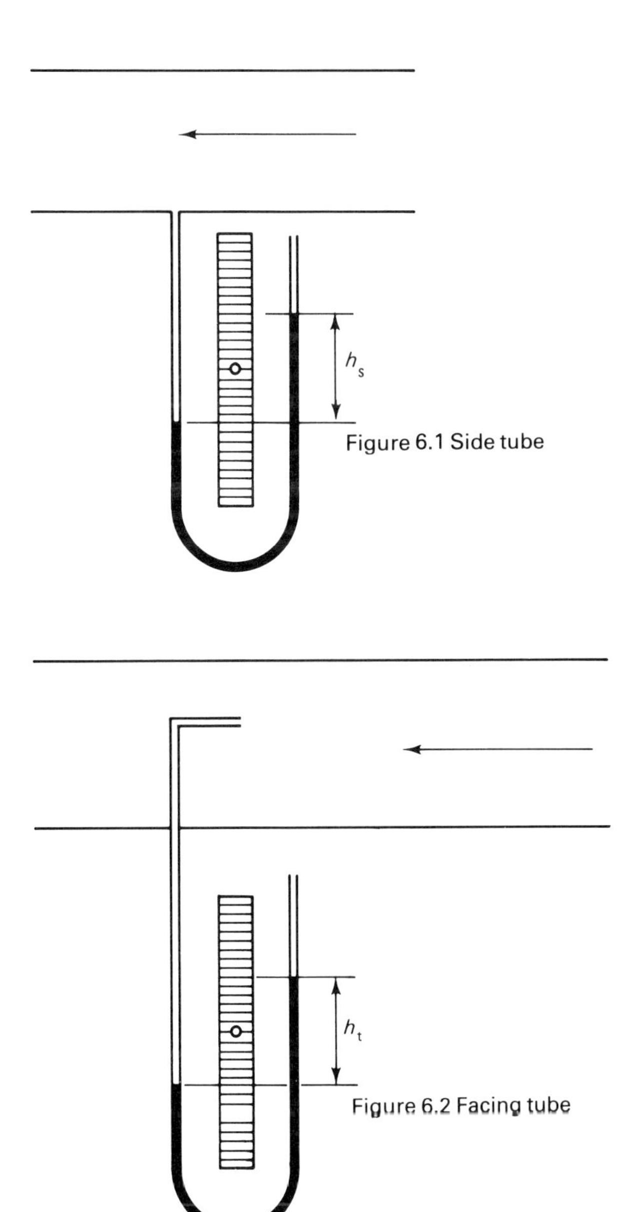

Figure 6.1 Side tube

Figure 6.2 Facing tube

To sum up, there are three different aspects of pressure due to flow to consider:

(a) Velocity pressure, produced by the air speed and denoted h_V.
(b) Static pressure which maintains the air flow against the system resistance, denoted h_S.

(c) Total pressure, which is the sum of the previous two and is denoted h_t.

It follows that by connecting a facing tube (measuring total pressure) and a side tube (measuring static pressure) differentially as shown in *Figure 6.3*,

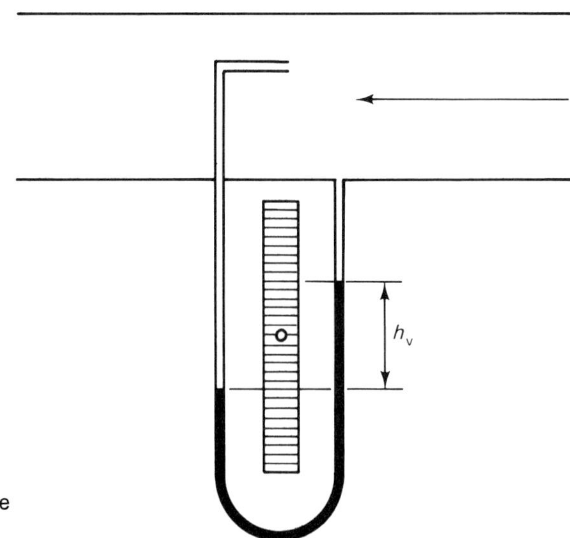

Figure 6.3 Combined side and facing tubes

the indicator will measure the difference between the two, i.e. velocity pressure h_V.

Because the values involved are small it is usual to use units of millimetres of water gauge (mm w.g.) to measure pressures due to flow. It is important that it is clearly understood that this is synonomous with a 'pressure' and is *not* just a head of water.

Imagine a cylinder which contains a 'piston' of water, say 10 mm deep supported on a very light tray. If the static pressure from a fan acted on the underside of the piston and held it steadily in suspension the fan would be developing a pressure of 10 mm w.g., see *Figure 6.4*.

Manometers

U-tube manometers

Of course the method of measurement described above is quite impractical, so instead manometers are used. The simplest form of manometer consists of a U-tube which is partly filled with water as shown in *Figure 6.5*. The U-tube is made of glass or other suitable material. The diameter is not important provided it is not so small that capillary action may lead to errors of measurement. Usually the diameter is at least 5 mm.

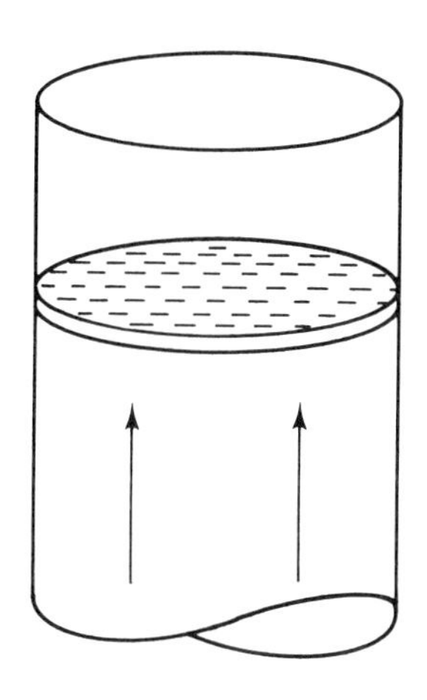

Figure 6.4 Illustration of static pressure

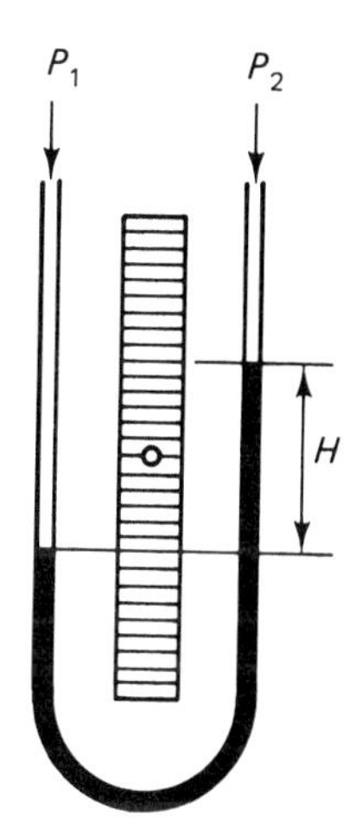

Figure 6.5 The simple U-tube manometer

Reference to *Figure 6.5* shows that the pressure P_1 is sufficient to balance pressure P_2 plus the liquid column. The force exerted by the column is known as the 'Controlling Force'.

The pressure due to the liquid column is given by ρHg newtons per square metre or Pascals,

where ρ = liquid density in kg/m^3
H = height of liquid in metres
g = gravitational acceleration = 9.81 m/s^2

Thus in *Figure 6.5* $\quad P_1 = \rho gH + P_2$

So $P_1 - P_2 = \rho gH$

and $H = \dfrac{P_1 - P_2}{\rho g}$

Example. If the liquid column is water and the displacement is 10 mm w.g. what is the differential pressure?

The density of water is 1000 kg/m^3

$$P_1 - P_2 = 1000 \times \frac{10}{1000} \times 9.81$$

$$= 98.1 \text{ N/m}^2$$

Newtons per square metre is a very small unit and so it is common to convert the answer to millibars (mbar) by dividing by 100 or to kilo Pascals by dividing by 1000.

So 98.1 N/m^2 = 0.981 mbar or 0.0981 kPa.

As the displacement of the liquid in the manometer is usually expressed as 'h' mm w.g. the equivalent differential pressure is given by:

$$P_1 - P_2 = \rho Hg \quad N/m^2$$

$$\text{But } H \text{ metres} = \frac{h \text{ mm}}{1000}$$

$$\rho \text{ (water)} = 1000 \text{ kg/m}^3$$

$$\text{So } P_1 - P_2 = \frac{1000 \times h \times 9.81}{1000}$$

$$= 9.81\, h \text{ N/m}^2$$

A liquid with a high density, such as mercury, will be displaced less than one with a low density, such as water. Therefore for low pressure differentials low-density liquids are used. Actually, water itself is not particularly convenient as it evaporates and needs to be coloured for ease of reading. Liquids such as transformer oil and paraffin oil are much better and are in common use. It is obviously most important that whatever fluid is used its density must be accurately known. Similarly, if a manometer requires 'topping-up' it must be done with the correct fluid – there is no point in topping-up a manometer which contains, say, transformer oil with paraffin as the resulting mixture will be of unknown density.

Irrespective of the fluid used the scales are usually graduated, with due regard to the density of the fluid, in millimetres water gague (mm w.g.) except where mercury is used, in which case the scale will be in millimetres of mercury (mm Hg). Alternatively, they may be graduated in Pascals or millibars. The meniscus of liquids which wet the glass (such as water) are concave, whilst that of mercury is convex. The reading of the mercury level is taken at the top of the meniscus and at the bottom for the others. The liquid used must be clean. If the meniscus is mis-shapen it is probably because either the fluid or the glass is dirty.

One problem with the simple U-tube is that the scale has a centre zero and to obtain the total displacement of the liquid the displacement in each limb should be measured separately and added. To overcome this problem a single-limb manometer can be used, and these instruments will now be considered.

The single-limb manometer

If the area of one of the manometer limbs is considerably greater than the other, then the depression of the liquid level in the large area limb will be small compared to the rise in level in the other. With reference to *Figure 6.6*, the liquid displaced from the reservoir is equal to area A_1 multiplied by the distance d by which the level had been lowered. The column of liquid in the

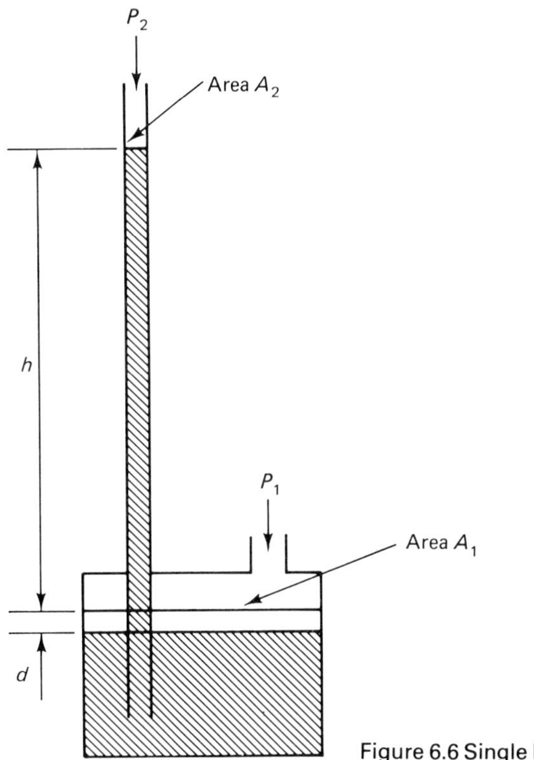

Figure 6.6 Single limb manometer — diagrammatic

tube is equal to the area A_2 multiplied by the height of the column h and is equal in volume to that displaced from the reservoir.

So $A_1 d = A_2 h$

$$\therefore \quad d = \frac{A_2}{A_1} h$$

It was shown earlier that for a U-tube, $P_1 - P_2 = \rho\, gH$
From *Figure 6.6* it is seen that the height $(h + d)$ is the equivalent of H.

$$\text{So } P_1 - P_2 = \rho\, g\,(h + d)$$

$$= \rho g \left(h + \frac{A_2}{A_1} h \right)$$

$$= \rho\, gh \left(1 + \frac{A_2}{A_1} \right)$$

$$\therefore \quad h = \frac{P_1 - P_2}{\left(1 + \dfrac{A_2}{A_1} \right) \rho\, g}$$

Example

Figure 6.7 shows an instrument which contains mercury. Assume the

Figure 6.7 STL single limb manometer (CEGB)

diameter of A_1 = 150 mm and that of A_2 = 6 mm. The density of the mercury is 13 500 kg/m^3. What will be the value of h if the pressure difference $P_1 - P_2$ = 700 mbar?

$$P_1 - P_2 = 700 \text{ mbar} = 70\,000 \text{ N/m}^2$$

$$\therefore h = \frac{70\,000}{\left[1 + \left(\frac{6}{50}\right)^2\right] \times 13\,500 \times 9.81}$$

$$= \frac{70\,000}{1.0016 \times 13\,500 \times 9.81}$$

$$= 0.528 \text{ m Hg} = 528 \text{ mm Hg}$$

To allow for the change in level d in the reservoir as height h increases, it is necessary to graduate the scale in 'Contracted Units', i.e.

$$\text{Contracted Units} = \text{Normal Units} \times \frac{A_1}{A_1 - A_2}$$

This type of instrument has the advantage, compared with the U-tube, that only one reading is required and, that the scale is more open, such that, say, a 100 mm Hg pressure difference between the reservoir and the limb will result in almost 100 mm change of level in the single limb, whereas with a U-tube there would only be 50 mm change in each leg. *Figure 6.7* shows the front view of a single-limb instrument – note the levelling screws at the front of the supports.

The 'Slim-Jim' manometer

A variation of the single-limb manometer, known as 'Slim-Jim', is manufactured by Airflow Developments Ltd and is used extensively for power station test work. The instrument is illustrated in *Figure 6.8*. The liquid level is zeroed by rotating the knurled ring on the low pressure connection, and this alters the level of the reservoir container. The zero can be checked by blowing gently across the top of the connectors and checking that the liquid level returns to zero.

The fluids have used the following specific gravities:

0.787 (coloured red) at 15.6°C
1.58 (coloured yellow) at 15.6°C

Manometers often contain liquid of one density but are scaled in relation to another. The 'Slim-Jim' is a typical example. The fluid density is, say, 787 kg/m^3, but the scale is in millimetres of water. The problem is one of determining the heights of two liquid columns of different density when the pressure is identical. Let subscripts $_1$ and refer $_2$ refer to liquids 1 and 2 respectively.

Then $h_1 \rho_1 g = h_2 \rho_2 g$
so $h_1 \rho_1 = h_2 \rho_2$

For example, what is the actual distance between 10 mm water gauge

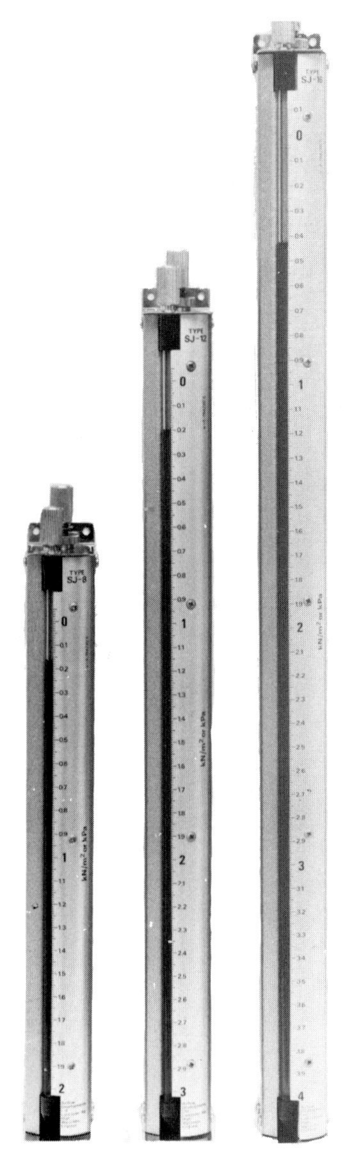

Figure 6.8 'Slim-Jim' single limb manometers (Airflow Developments Ltd)

divisions on a manometer whose liquid density is 787 kg/m^3?

$$10 \times 1000 = h \times 787$$

$$h = \frac{10\,000}{787} = 12.7 \text{ mm}$$

The Inclined manometer

Very small pressure differences can be measured with this type of instrument. The general arrangement is shown in *Figure 6.9*.

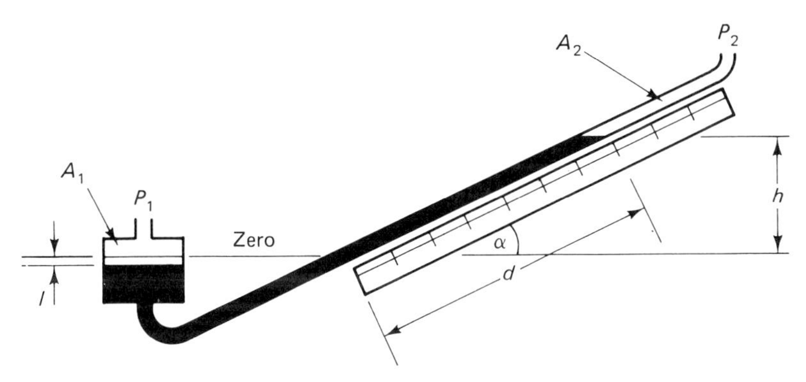

Figure 6.9 Inclined manometer — diagrammatic

Let the lowering of the reservoir level from zero be l metres.

Then $A_1 l = A_2 d$

So $l = \dfrac{A_2 d}{A_1}$

but the vertical height of the fluid column is h metres.

So $h = \sin \alpha \; d$

It has previously been established that

$P_1 - P_2 = \rho \; gH$

In the present case $(l + h)$ is the equivalent of H

$\therefore P_1 - P_2 = \rho \; g(l + h)$

$$= \rho g \left(\frac{A_2}{A_1} d + \sin \alpha \, d \right)$$

$$= \rho g d \left(\frac{A_2}{A_1} + \sin \alpha \right)$$

$$\therefore d = \frac{P_1 - P_2}{\rho g \left(\dfrac{A_2}{A_1} + \sin \alpha \right)} \quad \text{N/m}^2$$

Example

Suppose in *Figure 6.9* the reservoir has a diameter of 100 mm and the diameter of the inclined limb is 6 mm. The fluid density is 787 kg/m^3 and is displaced up the tube a distance d of 20 mm, the tube being inclined 30° to the horizontal.

What is the pressure differential $P_1 - P_2$?

$$\frac{A_2}{A_1} = \frac{6^2}{100^2} = 0.0036$$

$$\begin{aligned} P_1 - P_2 &= \rho g d\,(0.0036 + \sin 30°) \\ &= 787 \times 9.81 \times 0.02 \times 0.5036 \\ &= 77.76 \text{ N/m}^2 \\ &= 0.778 \text{ mbar} \end{aligned}$$

Airflow Developments test set

Messrs Airflow Developments Ltd manufacture a portable testing set which utilizes an inclined manometer, see *Figure 6.10*. The inclined limb is movable and can be used in the vertical position or in any one of three inclined positions. Thus the ranges available are:

0–12.5 mm w.g.
0–25.0 mm w.g.
0–50.0 mm w.g.
0–250.0 mm w.g.

The scale is graduated from 0–250 mm w.g. and gives a direct reading only when in the vertical position. When used in any of the three inclined positions the scale reading must be multiplied by the appropriate factor marked on a label fixed to the inside of the lid. The fluid is a dyed blend of paraffin having a specific gravity of 0.787 at 15.6°C.

The gauge may be used for positive, negative or differential readings as shown in *Figure 6.11*. The manometer base must be carefully levelled before use and for this purpose spirit levels are incorporated in the set.

The Pitot tube

The most accurate device for determining the velocity head of a flow of gas is the Pitot tube if the velocity is above about 5 m/s. It comprises a double tube bent at right angles as shown in *Figure 6.12*. The inner tube faces directly into the gas stream and so is subjected to the total pressure, while the outer

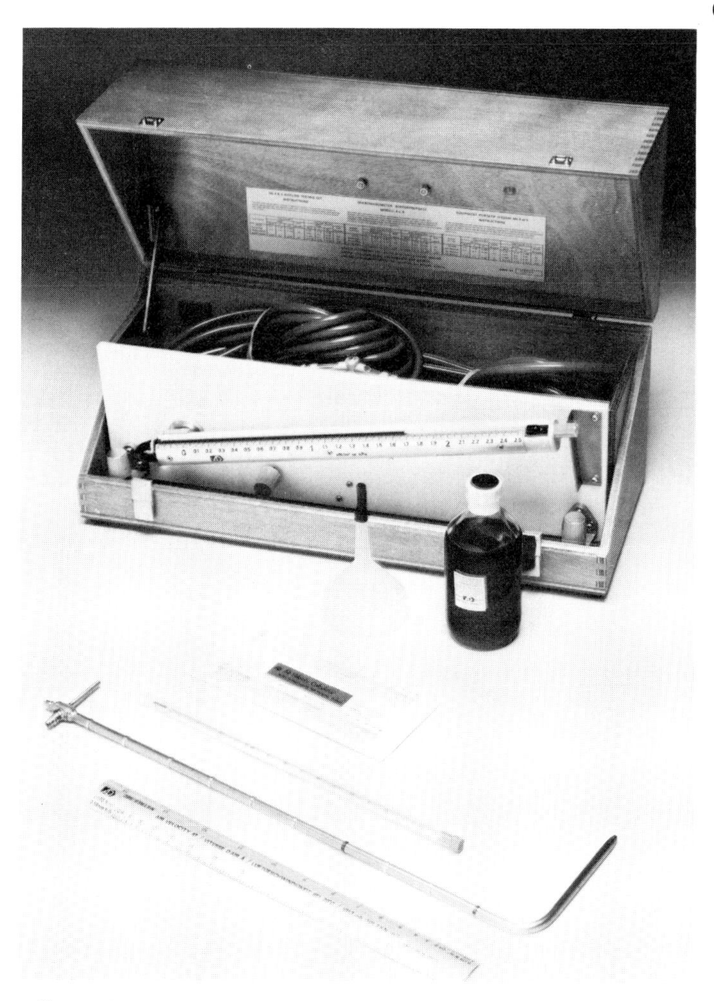

Figure 6.10 Portable testing set (Airflow Developments Ltd.)

tube is sealed at the end but has small holes in the side which thus communicate static pressure to the tube.

If the Pitot tube is connected to a manometer as shown in *Figure 6.13* the resultant displacement of fluid is a measure of the velocity pressure.

$$\text{Velocity pressure} = P_1 - P_2 = \tfrac{1}{2}\,\rho\, v^2$$

$$\text{So } v = \sqrt{\frac{2(P_1 - P_2)}{\rho}} \text{ m/s}$$

where ρ = density of gas

But $P_1 - P_2 = \rho_w gH$

where ρ_w = density of water in manometer = 1000 kg/m^3

H = height of water column in metres

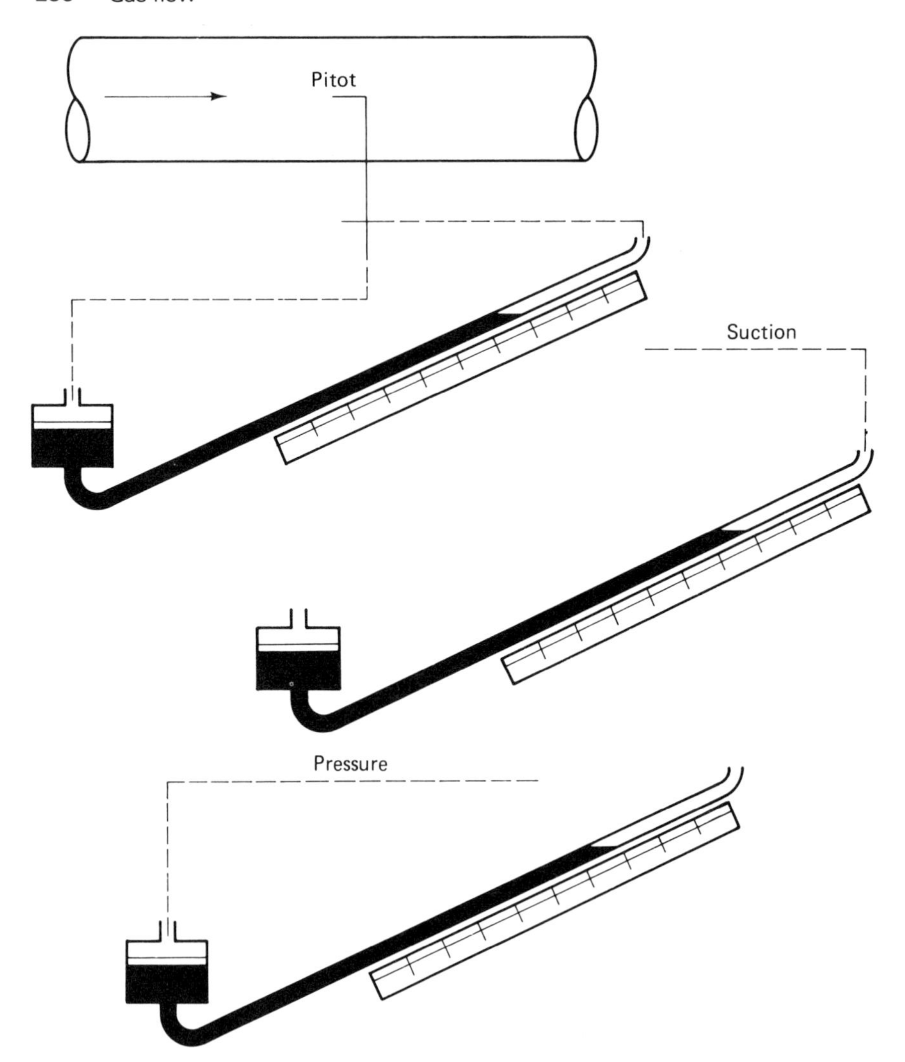

Figure 6.11 Uses of an inclined manometer

g = gravitational constant = 9.81 m/s²

$$\therefore v = \sqrt{\frac{(2\ w Hg)}{\rho}} = \sqrt{\frac{(2 \times 1000 \times H \times 9.81)}{\rho}} \text{ m/s}$$

but the height of the liquid column is usually expressed in millimetres of water h_V.

So $H = \dfrac{h_V}{1000}$

$$\therefore v = \sqrt{\frac{2 \times 1000 \times \frac{hv}{1000} \times 9.81}{\rho}} \text{ m/s}$$

So velocity of flow = $4.43 \sqrt{\dfrac{hv}{\rho}}$ m/s

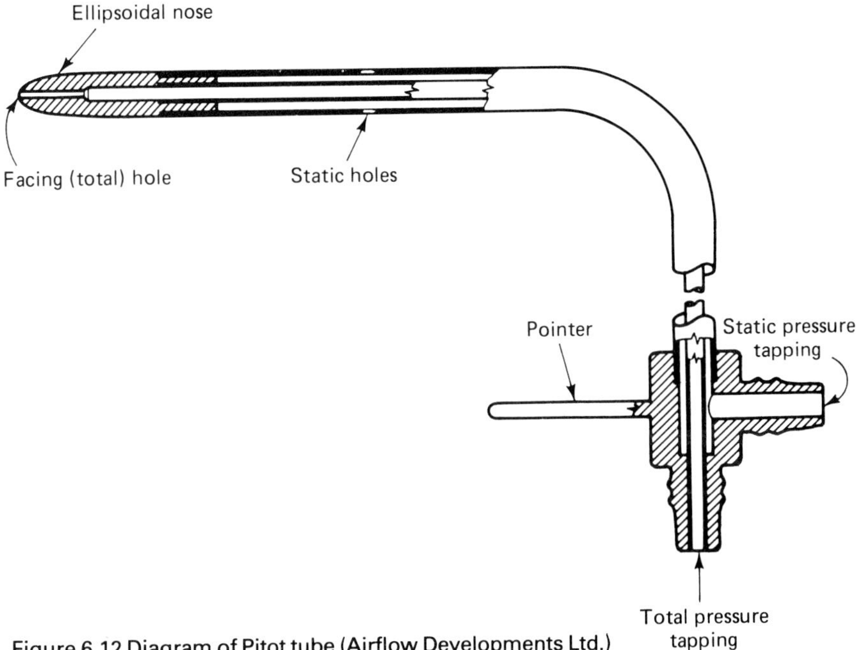

Figure 6.12 Diagram of Pitot tube (Airflow Developments Ltd.)

For example, what is the velocity of flow of air when the velocity head is 14.0 mm w.g. and the density of the air is 1.2334 kg/m^3?

$$v = 4.43\sqrt{\frac{14.0}{1.2334}} = 14.93 \text{ m/s}$$

Note: It is good practice to compress the connecting tubes when inserting a Pitot tube into the gas stream.

Establishing the air velocity

In the above example it was stated that the air density is 1.2334 kg/m^3. However, in practice the density is affected by temperature and by static pressure and so it necessitates knowing the air density at some reference temperature and pressure, and then applying corrections to obtain the value at the test condiitons.

The density of air at 1.013 bar and 0°C is 1.29 kg/m^3 and it varies inversely as the absolute temperature and directly as the absolute pressure.

The density ρ for any temperature and pressure condition is thus given by:

$$\rho = 1.29 \times \frac{273}{T} \times \frac{10363 + h_s}{10363} \times \frac{B}{760}$$

where 1.29 = density of air at 0°C, 1.013 bar, in kg/m^3
T = air temperature K

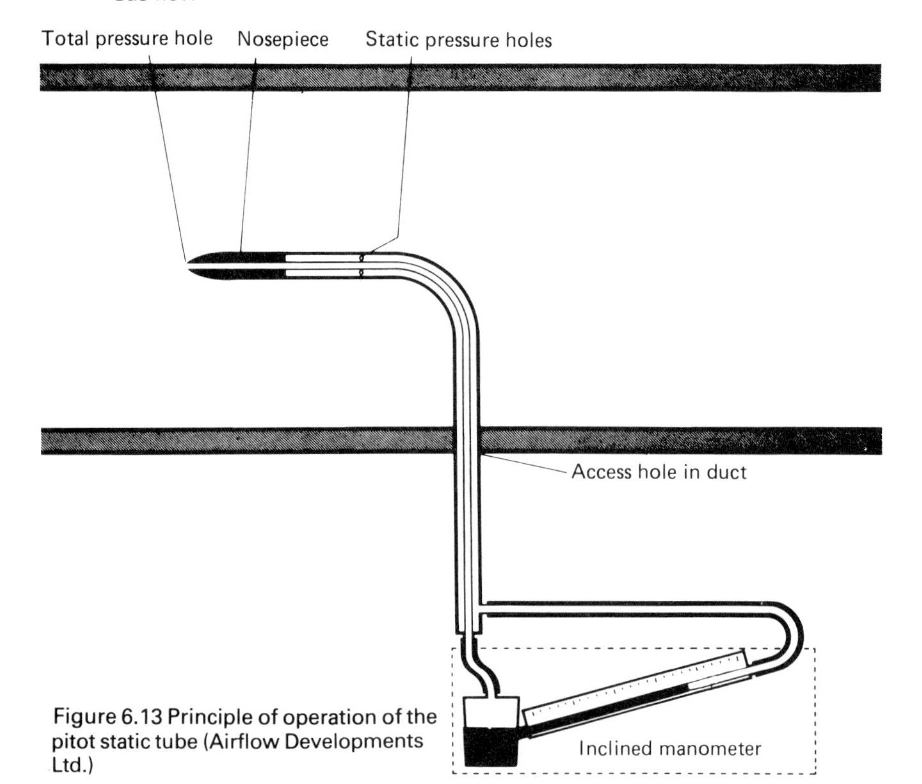

Figure 6.13 Principle of operation of the pitot static tube (Airflow Developments Ltd.)

h_S = static pressure in duct in mm w.g.
B = barometric pressure in mm Hg
10363 = standard pressure in mm w.g.

Example
The air in a duct is at 98°C. The static pressure of the air is (−) 25 mm w.g. and the barometric pressure is 762 mm Hg. The cross-sectional area (CSA) of the duct is 1.5 square metres. What is the mass flow of the air if the velocity head is 10 mm w.g.?

$$\text{Velocity} = 4.43 \sqrt{\frac{h_V}{\rho}} \text{ metres per second}$$

$$\rho = 1.29 \times \frac{273}{371} \times \frac{10338}{10363} \times \frac{762}{760}$$

$$= 0.949 \text{ kg/m}^3 \text{ at duct conditions.}$$

$$\text{So Velocity} = 4.43 \sqrt{\frac{10.0}{0.949}} = 14.38 \text{ m/s}$$

Volume flow = velocity × cross-sectional area of duct.
= 14.38 × 1.5

$$= 21.57 \text{ m}^3/\text{s}$$

$$\text{Mass flow} = \text{volume flow} \times \text{air density}$$
$$= 21.57 \times 0.949$$
$$= \mathbf{20.47\ kg/s}$$

The barometric pressure is usually obtained from a Fortin type barometer, normally located in or near the main control room. The method of use is described later. Portable barometers are also available. These are of the aneroid type and are of a high standard of precision. They are checked against the Fortin barometer before use. An excellent precision aneroid barometer is manufactured by Mechanism Ltd, Croydon, which gives a digital read-out (see *Figure 6.14*).

Figure 6.14 Precision aneroid barometer (CEGB)

Obtaining representative values

The air or gas distribution in a duct is normally far from uniform. Therefore it is necessary to take the average of a number of readings as the representative value. For example, during commissioning tests on a 660 MW unit the I.D. fans were run to determine the velocity distribution in the I.D. fan discharge ducts when using cold air. The results of the Pitot traverse are shown in the table on page 240, the figures obtained being the velocity pressures in mm w.g. i.e. h_v. The average velocity pressure is 0.789 mm w.g. Notice the considerable variations from this value in the various subsections. Therefore the precautions to take to obtain reasonably accurate figures are that the measurements of velocity pressure should be obtained at a position in a straight length of duch as far downstream as possible from any blend or obstruction so that fairly even flow may be expected. Conditions

Units (mm w.g.)

'A' I.D. Fan Discharge

	1	2	3	4	5	6	7	8
A	0.96	1.12	1.14	1.32	1.27	0.97	0.76	0.74
B	0.56	0.76	0.94	1.04	1.02	0.69	0.53	0.51
C	0.46	0.69	0.94	0.97	0.94	0.58	0.28	0.38
D	0.28	0.48	0.69	1.17	0.97	0.41	0.36	0.30
E	0.76	0.81	0.71	1.45	1.37	0.66	0.84	0.69

should be acceptable six duct diameters or more on the downstream side of a single bend or damper, or the equivalent distance in rectangular ducts.

The root mean velocity pressure is determined by taking the average of a series of $\sqrt{h_V}$ readings over the area of the duct. The measuring positions should be calculated in accordance with the relevant British Standards (BS 848 is the Fan Test Code), if a high degree of accuracy is required.

For circular airways having a diameter less than 1.5 metres, traverse two diameters at right angles. If the diameter is greater than 1.5 metres traverse four diameters at 45° as shown in *Figure 6.15(a)*.

For rectangular ducts the diagram indicates the division of the airway into a number of geometrically similar smaller areas. For normal purposes a reading should be taken at the centre of each small area, but if extreme accuracy is required extra readings should be obtained as indicated:

Up to 1.5 m^2 airway – take 16 readings
Up to 7 m^2 airway – take 25 readings
Over 7 m^2 airway – take 36 readings

If flow conditions are uneven or the duct is very large, it is desirable to take an increased number of readings.

The vane anemometer

If it is necessary to measure the flow of cooling air to the intake of an electric motor or some similar application it is convenient to use a vane anemometer. There are various excellent models available, the one described here being marketed by Messrs Airflow Developments Ltd, see *Figure 6.16*. This instrument is mains or battery operated and has a range of 0.25–25 metres per second. It also has a 0 –1 mA output socket so that, for example, a recorder can be operated from it.

Rotation of the aluminium vanes is sensed by a capacitance transducer which actuates the read-out. When measurements are taken the instrument must face directly into the air stream and the operator should stand as far away as possible so as not to interfere with the air flow.

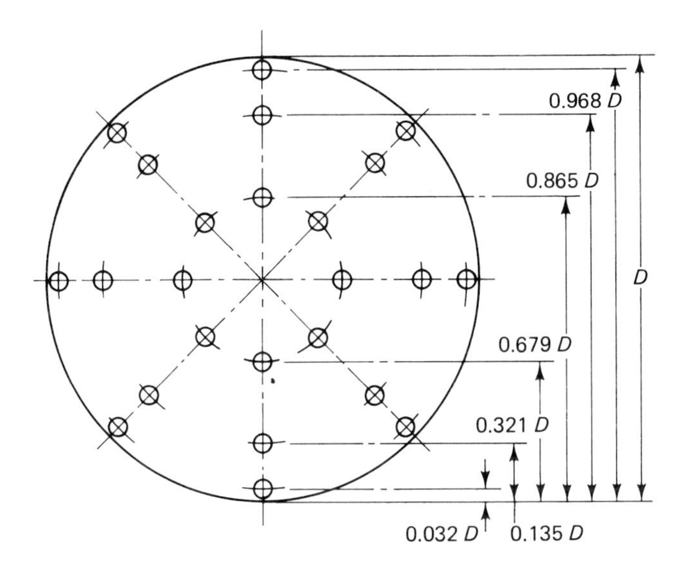

Figure 6.15(a) Positions in circular airways when using log linear rule

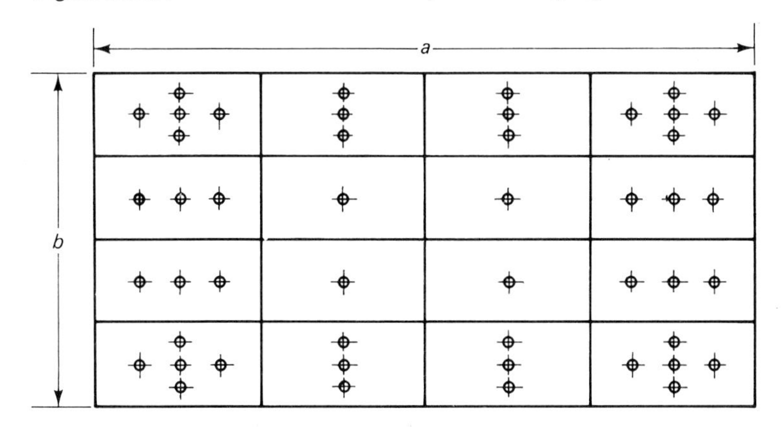

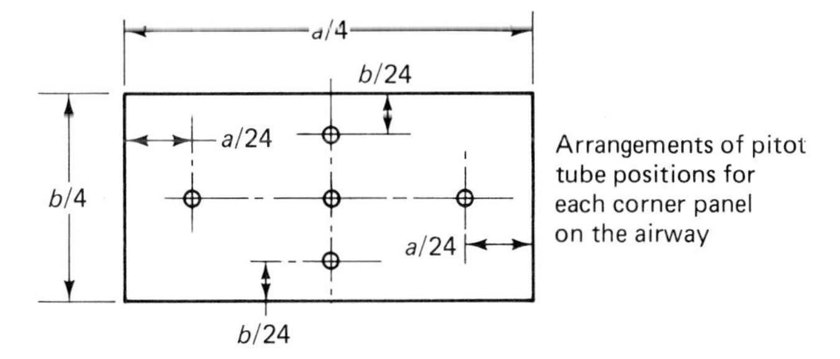

Figure 6.15(b) Positions in rectangular airways for pitot measurements

Figure 6.15 Pitot tube measuring points (Airflow Developments Ltd.)

Figure 6.16 Vane anemometer (Airflow Developments Ltd.)

Examples of air-flow calculations

A station has medium-speed suction mills. The amount of inleakage air should be less than 10% of the total air at the mill outlet. Tests were undertaken to establish the amount of inleakage by operating the mill with cold air. The inleakage was determined by calculating the mass flow of air at inlet to the mill and at outlet.

Air flow at mill inlet

Air temperature	= 11.5°C = 284.5 K
Velocity pressure h_V	= 14.0 mm w.g.
Barometer	= 747.6 mm Hg
Duct cross-sectional area	= 0.444 m^2
Static pressure h_S	= (−) 32.3 mm w.g.

$$\rho = 1.29 \times \frac{273}{284.5} \times \frac{10330.7}{10363} \times \frac{747.6}{760}$$

$$= 1.214 \text{ kg/m}^3$$

$$\text{So Velocity} = 4.43\sqrt{\frac{14}{1.214}} = 15.0 \text{ m/s}$$

Volume flow = 15.0 × 0.444 = 6.66 m^3/s
Mass flow = 6.66 × 1.214 = **8.09 kg/s**

Air flow at mill outlet

Air temperature	= 11°C = 284 K

Velocity pressure h_V = 38.252 mm w.g.
Barometer = 747.6 mm Hg
Duct area = 0.40 m^2
Static pressure h_S = (−) 396.7 mm w.g.

$$\rho = 1.29 \times \frac{273}{284} \times \frac{9966.3}{10363} \times \frac{747.6}{760} = 1.173 \text{ kg/m}^3$$

$$\text{Velocity} = 4.43\sqrt{\frac{h_V}{\rho}} = 4.43\sqrt{\frac{38.252}{1.173}} = 25.30 \text{ m/s}$$

Volume flow = 25.3 × 0.40 = 10.12 m^3/s
Mass flow = 10.12 × 1.173 = 11.87 kg/s
Hence inleakage air = 11.87 − 8.09 = 3.78 kg/s

$$\text{So percentage inleakage} = \frac{3.78 \times 100}{11.87} = \mathbf{31.8\%}$$

Boiler flue gas measurement

It is often necessary to measure the flow of flue gas, for example while carrying out precipitator emission tests. The basic formula is the same as that for air, viz:

$$\text{Velocity} = 4.43\sqrt{\frac{h_V}{\rho}} \text{ metres per second}$$

Obtaining the value of ρ presents some difficulty. It is determined from a knowledge of the flue gas composition and the method is best illustrated by an example.

Example
A test was carried out to determine the gas flow at airheater outlet on a 120 MW boiler, the following results being obtained:

CO_2 = 13.05%. Flue gas average temperature = 129°C = 402 K
Static pressure h_S = (−) 277 mm w.g. Velocity pressure h_V = 5.1 mm
Barometer = 761 mm Hg.
Dry flue gas analysis:
CO_2 13.05% (by Orsat apparatus)
O_2 6.40% (from CO_2/O_2 conversion, see *Figure 6.17*)
N_2 80.55% (i.e. 100 − CO_2% − O_2%)

The moisture in the wet flue gas can be determined from the ultimate analysis of the fuel. Failing this a value can be assumed, based upon experience. In this case the moisture is 7.35% by volume of the wet flue gas.

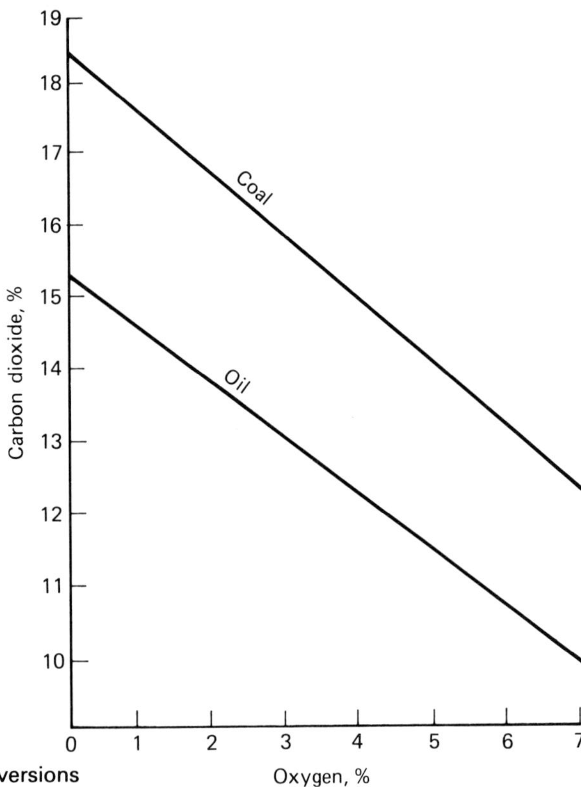

Figure 6.17 CO_2/O_2 conversions

Now the total percentage wet flue gas is $CO_2\% + O_2\% + N_2\% + H_2O\% =$ 100%

So $CO_2\% + O_2\% + N_2\% = 100 - H_2O\% = 100 - 7.35$
$= 92.65\%$

So the wet volume of each constituent will be 92.65% of its dry volume, i.e.

	Dry analysis %		*Wet analysis %*
CO_2	13.05×0.9265	=	12.09
O_2	6.40×0.9265	=	5.93
N_2	80.55×0.9265	=	74.63
		+	7.35
			100.00

The relative mass of the gas is obtained by multiplying each constituent of the wet gas by its molecular mass as follows:

	Wet analysis	*Molecular mass*	*Relative mass*
CO_2	0.1209	44	5.3196
0_2	0.0593	32	1.8976
N_2	0.7463	28	20.8964
H_20	0.0735	18	1.3230
			29.4366

From Avagadro's hypothesis, the kg mol of any gas occupies 22.4 cubic metres at 0°C, 1.013 bar absolute.

$$\text{So the density of the flue gas} = \frac{29.44}{22.4} = 1.314 \text{ kg/m}^3$$

at 0°C and 1.013 bar (abs.)

At other values of temperature and pressure the density is corrected as in the case for air, i.e.

$$\rho_{gas} = (\text{Density at } 0°\text{C, 1.013 bar}) \times \frac{273}{T} \times \frac{10363 + h_S}{10363} \times \frac{B}{760}$$

where the symbols have the same meaning as before.

$$\text{So density at duct conditions} = 1.314 \times \frac{273}{402} \times \frac{10086}{10363} \times \frac{761}{760}$$

$$= 0.870 \text{ kg/m}^3$$

$$\text{So velocity} = 4.43\sqrt{\frac{5.1}{0.870}} = \mathbf{10.73\ m/s}$$

Specific gravity of mixtures of gases

Sometimes a knowledge of the specific gravity of flue gas at 0°C and 1.013 bar abs. is required. Let subscripts 1, 2, 3, etc. refer to different gases present in the flue gas. Then the specific gravity of the mixture, relative to air, is given by:

$$S = \frac{(M_1 V_1 + M_2 V_2 + M_3 V_3 + \ldots\ldots \text{etc.})}{28.96}$$

where S = specific gravity of the mixture
M = molecular mass of the component gases
V = percentage by volume of the component gases
28.96 = molecular mass of dry air

For example, what is the specific gravity of flue gas in a PF boiler whose CO_2 is 12.5% by using Orsat apparatus) and whose wetness is 7.0% by volume?

	Dry gas volume			*Wet gas volume*
CO_2%	12.5 × 0.93	=		11.63
0_2%	6.7 × 0.93	=		6.23
N_2%	80.8 × 0.93	=		75.14
		+	H_20%	7.00
				100.00

	Wet gas volume, V	*Molecular mass M*	*Relative mass MV*
CO_2	0.1163	44	5.117
0_2	0.0623	32	1.994
N_2	0.7514	28	21.039
H_20	0.0700	18	1.260
			29.410

$$\text{So } S = \frac{29.410}{28.960} = 1.0155$$

Duct traverses

When carrying out a traverse of a flue gas duct it is common practice to determine the gas velocity, temperature and percentage CO_2 at the specified sampling points – normally a minimum of 24 points. Each gas temperature is multiplied by the gas velocity at the same point and the average product determined. The average product is then divided by the average gas velocity to obtain the true average temperature. Similarly each CO_2 percentage should be multiplied by the corresponding gas velocity, and the average of the products divided by the average gas velocity to give the true average CO_2 percentage.

However, many tests have been carried out of flow distributions in large boiler ducts, and these indicate that velocity weighting of the gas composition and temperature is not normally justified. It is found that the arithmetic mean value adequately represents the true mean value and, of course, it is much easier to obtain. So this is the recommended method for normal traverses. For example, refer to *Site Testing of Power Station Regenerative Air Heters* by P. Humphries (CEGB, 1968) To give an idea of the small loss of accuracy that results from using the arithmetic mean, seven tests on different plants were analysed by Humphries involving a total of 126 sampling points.

The ratio of $\frac{\text{Weighted mean}}{\text{Arithmetic mean}}$ varied between the limits of 1.002 to 0.999.

Having found the mean CO_2 % and gas temperature, several symmetrically spaced points should be determined, such that their average is representative of the traverse average, and these points can then be used for testing purposes. For routine tests, samples are taken from a location in the duct known to be near the mean, using a multi-probe. This is a tube, sealed at the remote end, about 2.5 cm diameter. It has 2.5 mm holes along its length at intervals of about 30 cm. Any holes not in the gas stream must be sealed.

The Fortin barometer

A Fortin barometer should be installed at every power station to enable accurate determinations of the atmospheric pressure to be made. The instrument is housed in a glass case and must be located in a suitable position – normally the main control room is a good place. The instrument is mounted vertically and, once installed, should never be moved. If it is necessary to determine the pressure at some other location then corrections should be applied to the observed reading as will be explained later.

Figure 6.18(a) shows the general construction of the instrument. A fixed scale is engraved upon the upper part of the metal case and indicates heights above the datum level, i.e. above the tip of the ivory pointer. Usually the scales are graduated in centimetres or millibars. The cistern, which contains the reservoir of mercury, has a glass window through which the surface of the mercury and the ivory pointer can be viewed. To zero the instrument the screw at the bottom is operated. This alters the volume of the chamois leather bag and so varies the level of the mercury reservoir. The instrument is zeroed when the tip of the pointer just makes contact with the surface of the mercury. There is a small hole in the top of the cistern to allow the atmospheric pressure to be communicated to the inside.

The height of the mercury column is read against the fixed scale. To enable this to be done accurately a small plate engraved with a vernier scale is provided. The vernier scale plate can be moved up or down by turning a knob on the side of the barometer. Correct alignment is achieved when the bottom of the plate appears to be sitting on top of the mercury meniscus, as shown in the inset. In the case illustrated the reading is between 76.0 and 76.1 cm. The interpolation is determined by noting the graduation on the vernier scale which is exactly aligned with a fixed scale graduation. In the case illustrated it is '6', therefore the observed reading is 76.06 cm Hg or 760.6 mm Hg.

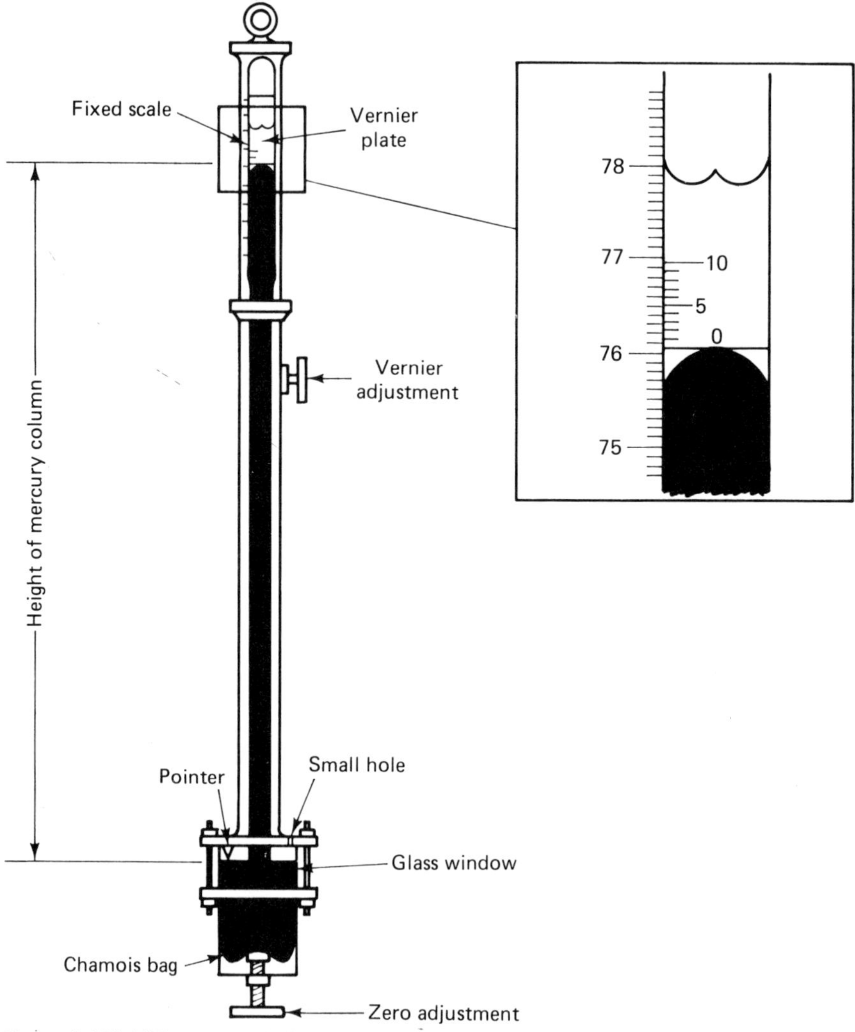

Figure 6.18(a) The Fortin barometer (CEGB)

Scale conversions

To convert from one set of units to another use *Table 6.1*.

Table 6.1 Barometer pressure units

	kN/m²	*mbar*	*mm Hg*	*in Hg*
1 kN/m² =	1.0	10.0	7.50062	0.2953
1 mbar =	0.1	1.0	0.750062	0.02953
1 mm Hg =	0.1333224	1.333 224	1.0	0.0393701
1 in Hg =	3.38639	33.8639	25.4	1.0

Figure 6.18(b) Exterior view of Fortin barometer (CEGB)

So an observed reading of 760.6 mm Hg is equal to:

$760.6 \times 0.1333224 = 101.405\ \mathrm{kN/m^2}$
$760.6 \times 1.333224 = 1014.05\mathrm{mbar}$
$760.6 \times 0.0393701 = 29.94$ in Hg

Correction to standard conditions

There are various corrections which should be applied to the observed reading if extreme accuracy is required and reference should be made to BS 2520, *Barometer Conventions and Tables*. However, there are only three which need concern the reader. These are due to:

1 Variation of temperature.
2 Variation of latitude.
3 Variation of altitude.

1 *Variation of temperature.* The reference temperature is 0°C. If the temperature of the instrument is other than this a correction should be applied to the observed barometric height as shown in *Table 6.2.* The

Table 6.2 Barometer correction for temperature (Reference temperature 0°C)

Temp (°C)	*Barometer reading (mm Hg)*			
	720	*740*	*760*	*780*
10.	1.17	1.21	1.24	1.27
20	2.34	2.41	2.47	2.54
30	3.51	3.61	3.71	3.80
40	4.68	4.82	4.95	5.07
50	4.85	5.02	5.19	6.14

correction should be subtracted from the observed reading.

2 *Variation of latitude.* The reference latitude is 45°. Therefore, if the barometric height is determined at some other latitude a correction should be applied to the reading as indicated in *Table 6.3.*

Table 6.3 Barometer correction for latitude (Standard latitude 45°, gravity 980.665 cm/s²)

Latitude N or S	*Barometer reading (mm Hg)*			
	720	*740*	*760*	*780*
80	+ 1.75	+ 1.80	+ 1.85	+ 1.90
70	+ 1.42	+ 1.46	+ 1.50	+ 1.54
60	+ 0.91	+ 0.94	+ 0.97	+ 1.99
50	+ 0.29	+ 0.30	+ 0.31	+ 0.32
40	− 0.37	− 0.38	− 0.39	− 0.40
30	− 0.98	− 1.01	− 1.04	− 1.07
20	− 1.49	− 1.53	− 1.57	− 1.61
10	− 1.82	− 1.87	− 1.92	− 1.97
0	− 1.93	− 1.99	− 2.04	− 2.10

For example if the previous reading of 760.6 mm Hg was obtained when the temperature was 20°C. at a location 30°N, the barometric height corrected for temperature and latitude would be:

Observed reading	760.6 mm Hg
Temperature correction	(−) 2.47 mm Hg
Latitude correction	(−) 1.04 mm Hg
Corrected reading	757.09 mm Hg

3 *Variation of altitude.* Gravitational attraction also varies with height above

sea level. Thus, if the reading is obtained at a location considerably above sea level, a further correction should be applied as shown in *Table 6.4*.

Table 6.4 Barometer correction for altitude (reference altitude mean sea level)

Height (metres)	500	1 000	2 000	3 000	4 000
Correction (mm Hg)	– 0.11	– 0.21	– 0.38	– 0.50	– 0.58

So if the previous reading was obtained at a location 2 000 metres above sea level, the corrections would be:

Observed reading	760.6 mm Hg
Temperature correction	(–) 2.47 mm Hg
Latitude correction	(–) 1.04 mm Hg
Altitude correction	(–) 0.38 mm Hg
Corrected reading	756.71 mm Hg

Variation of pressure from barometer to some other level

If it is necessary to determine the pressure at a location above or below the barometer, a correction of 0.089 mm Hg should be applied per metre of vertical height measured from the reservoir of the barometer. For heights above the barometer the correction is (–) and if below it is (+). The correction given above is applicable if the pressure is 760 mm Hg and for other pressures is proportional.

So if the pressure is required at, say, a condenser situated 10 metres below the barometer then:

Observed reading	760.6 mm Hg
Temperature correction	(–) 2.47 mm Hg
Latitude correction	(–) 1.04 mm Hg
Altitude correction	(–) 0.38fimm Hg
Displacement correction	(+) 0.89 mm Hg
Pressure at condenser	757.60 mm Hg

Example

A barometer reading of 725.0 mm Hg is obtained at a location 500 metres above sea level. The temperature is 30°C and the latitude 10°S. What is the pressure at a point 30 metres above the instrument?

$$\text{Temperature correction} = 3.51 + 5 \times \left(\frac{3.61 - 3.51}{20} \right) = 3.53 \text{ mm Hg}$$

Observed reading	725.0 mm Hg
Temperature correction	(−) 3.53 mm Hg
Latitude correction	(−) 1.82 mm Hg
Altitude correction	(−) 0.11 mm Hg
Displacement correction	(−) 2.67 mm Hg
	716.87 mm Hg

Exercise 1

New Delhi, India, is situated in latitude 29°N at an elevation of 300 metres above sea level. At a time when the temperature was 30°C the observed reading of a Fortin barometer was 76.26 cm Hg. What is the corrected pressure at a location 4 metres below the instrument?

Answer: 758.08 mm Hg.

Procedure for obtaining a reading from a Fortin barometer

1 Note the temperature on the thermometer attached to the body of the barometer before opening the instrument case.
2 Gently tap the upper part of the instrument.
3 Gently tap the cistern and adjust the zero setting until the ivory pointer is just touching the top of the mercury.
4 Operate the vernier scale plate adjusting screw until the bottom of the vernier plate appears to rest upon the top of the mercury meniscus.
5 Read the vernier.
6 Correct the reading for temperature, latitude and altitude.

Transportation of a Fortin barometer

As mentioned earlier, the barometer, once installed, should not be moved but, should it be necessary to transport the instrument, the following notes are given:

(a) Remove the barometer from its mounting board and slowly slope it to an angle of about 45° with the cistern end lowest.
(b) Screw in the adjustment screw at the bottom of the instrument until it is seen that the glass cistern is completely filled with mercury.
(c) Slowly lower the top of the barometer until the instrument is inverted.
(d) It can now be carried in a sloping position with the cistern end uppermost. Special carrying cases are available for this purpose.

When the instrument is to be re-installed the procedure is as follows:

(a) Remove the barometer from its packing case with the cistern uppermost, and slowly bring the instrument to an angle of about 45° with the cistern end lowest.
(b) Unscrew the adjustment screw as far as it will go without straining it when the stop is reached.
(c) The barometer can now be brought slowly to the vertical position, mounted on the wooden backing board and held by the three clamping screws in the ring at the lower end of the board.

Appendix I

Air flow calculation sheet *(with speciment calculation)*

UNIT 10 LOAD: 320 MW PLANT Mill TEST NO. 2 DATE / /198

(Units: h_V = mm w.g. h_S = mm w.g. T = °C + 273 B = mm Hg)
Barometer = 762 mm Hg CSA = 1.5 m²

	$\sqrt{h_v}$	h_s	T
Average	3.16	− 25	371

$$\rho = 1.29 \times \frac{273}{T} \times \frac{10363 + h_S}{10363} \times \frac{B}{760}$$

$$= 1.29 \times \frac{273}{371} \times \frac{10338}{10363} \times \frac{762}{760}$$

$\therefore \rho = 0.949$ kg/m³ $\therefore \sqrt{\rho} = \mathbf{0.974}$

$$\text{Velocity} = 4.43\sqrt{\frac{h_V}{\rho}} = 4.43 \times \frac{3.16}{0.974} = \mathbf{14.37\ m/s}$$

Volume flow = velocity × CSA = 14.37 × 1.5 = **21.56 m³/s**
Mass flow = volume flow × ρ = 21.56 × 0.949 = **20.46 kg/s**

REMARKS:

Signed ____________________

Appendix II

Gas flow calculation sheet *(with speciment calculation)*

UNIT	LOAD	MW	PLANT	TEST	DATE / /198

(Units: h_V = mm w.g. h_S = mm w.g. T = °C + 273 B = mm Hg O_2 = % by vol.)

Barometer = 761 mm Hg   CSA = 4.0 m²

	$\sqrt{hv}$	*hs*	*T*	CO_2%	O_2%	N_2%	H_2%
Average	2.26	− 277	402	13.05	6.4	80.55	7.40

	Dry vol.		*Wet vol.*		*RW*
% CO_2	13.05 × 0.926	=	12.09 × 44	=	531.96
% O_2	6.4 × 0.926	=	5.92 × 32	=	189.44
% N_2	80.55 × 0.926	=	74.63 × 28	=	2089.64
% H_2O	— —	=	7.40 × 18	=	133.20
			100.00		2944.24

$$\rho = \frac{RW}{2240} \times \frac{273}{T} \times \frac{10363 + h_S}{10363} \times \frac{B}{760}$$

$$= \frac{2944.24}{2240} \times \frac{273}{402} \times \frac{10086}{10363} \times \frac{761}{760}$$

$\therefore \rho$ = 0.8696 kg/m³ $\sqrt{\ }$ = **0.9327**

$$\text{Velocity} = 4.43\sqrt{\frac{h_V}{\rho}} = 4.43 \times \frac{2.26}{0.9325} = \mathbf{10.73}$$

Volume flow = velocity × CSA = 10.73 × 4 = **42.92 m/³s**
Mass flow = volume flow × ρ = 42.92 × 0.8699 = **37.3 kg/s**

REMARKS:

SIGNED: ____________________

Questions

1 What is velocity pressure? Static pressure? Total pressure?
2 What would you use to measure each?
3 What is the 'controlling force'?
4 With a simple manometer what is the formula for head h?
5 What will be the probable cause of a mis-shapen meniscus?
6 What is the advantage of an inclined manometer?
7 In a Pitot tube, which connections go to the tappings?
8 What precaution must be taken when inserting a Pitot tube into a gas stream?
9 What is the formula for velocity of flow?
10 How would an average flow be obtained across the cross-sectional area of a duct?
11 Name some typical uses of an anemometer?
12 How would you determine the density of flue gas?
13 How would you convert a dry flue gas analysis to wet?
14 How would you determine the specific gravity of a flue gas?
15 How would you obtain a reading from a Fortin barometer?
16 What corrections are necessary to be applied to a Fortin barometer reading?
17 How would you transport a Fortin barometer?
18 What is the relationship between the head and density of different fluids?

Exercise 1

The fluid in the manometer illustrated has a specific gravity of 0.75. What is the absolute pressure P_1 in millibars?

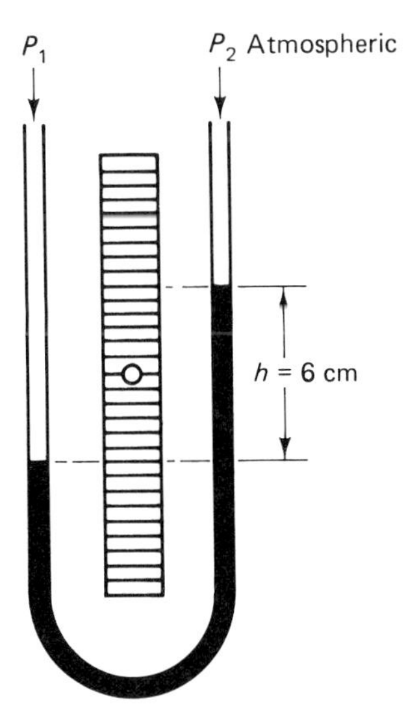

Figure 6.19 U-tube. Exercise 1

Exercise 2

A single-limb manometer is scaled in millimetres water gauge when using a fluid of density 600 kg/m^3. However, the correct fluid is not available and one of density 900 kg/m^3 is used instead. By what factor must the scale reading be multiplied to obtain the water gauge reading?

Exercise 3

What is the density of the fluid in a single-limb manometer if it rises 400.2 mm when a pressure difference of 0.53 bar is applied? The diameter of the reservoir is 150 mm and that of the limb 6 mm.

Exercise 1 (Answer)

$$\begin{aligned}\text{Pressure } P_1 &= h\,\rho\,g = 0.06 \times 750 \times 9.81 \\ &= 441.5 \text{ N/m}^2 \text{ gauge} \\ &= 441.5 + 101\,300 = 101\,741.5 \text{ N/m}^2 \text{ absolute} \\ &= \mathbf{1\,017 \text{ m bar absolute}}\end{aligned}$$

Exercise 2 (Answer)

Let subscripts $_1$ and $_2$ refer to fluids 1 and 2 respectively.

Then, for the application of a given pressure

$h_1\ \rho_1 g = h_2 \rho_2 g$

So $h_1\ \rho_2 = h_2 \rho_2$

Let $\rho_1 = 600$ kg/m^3 and $\rho_2 = 900$ kg/m^3

$$\text{Then } h_1 = \frac{900\ h_2}{600} = 1.5\,h_2$$

In other words the height of the liquid column with the correct fluid will be 1.5 times that with the alternative and so the scale reading should be multiplied by a factor of 1.5.

Exercise 3 (Answer)

$$\rho = \frac{P_1 - P_2}{\left(1 + \dfrac{A_2}{A_1}\right)hg} = \frac{53\,000 \text{ N/m}^2}{\left(1 + \dfrac{6^2}{150^2}\right) \times 0.4002 \times 9.81}$$

$$\rho = \frac{53\,000}{1.0016 \times 0.4002 \times 9.81} = \mathbf{13\,478 \text{ kg/m}^3}$$

Project 1

(a) The air ducts at the FD fan inlets on a 350 MW unit measure 4.57 m × 2.4 m in cross-section, and there are two per boiler. Calculate the total air flow in the ducts in kg/s at these design conditions:

Barometer 747 mm Hg; air temperature 32°C; duct static pressure (−) 127 mm w.g.; velocity pressure h_V 2.65 mm w.g.

(b) On the same boiler the design flue gas conditions at the two airheater outlet ducts are:

Gas temperature 121°C; static pressure h_S (−) 241 mm w.g.; CO_2 by vol. of dry gas 14.4%; moisture by vol. in wet gas 7.0%; velocity pressure 2.2 mm w.g.; duct cross-section 8.5 m × 2.75 m.

Calculate the gas flow in kg/s.

Project 1 (Answer)

(a) $$\rho = 1.29 \times \frac{273}{305} \times \frac{10236}{10363} \times \frac{747}{760} = 1.121 \text{ kg/m}^3$$

So velocity $$= 4.43\sqrt{\frac{2.65}{1.121}} = 6.8 \text{ m/s}$$

Volume flow = 6.8 × 4.57 × 2.4 = 74.58 m³/s per duct
Mass flow = 74.58 × 1.121 = 83.6 kg/s per duct
(Note: This is over 5 tonnes of air per minute)

(b)

	Dry products	*Wet products*	*Relative mass*
CO_2	14.4	13.4	5.896
O_2	4.6	4.3	1.376
N_2	81.0	75.3	21.084
		7.0	1.260
			29.616

So density $$= \frac{29.616}{22.4} = 1.322 \text{ kg/m}^3 \text{ at } 0°\text{C, } 1.013 \text{ bar}$$

Density at duct conditions $$= 1.322 \times \frac{273}{394} \times \frac{10122}{10363} \times \frac{747}{760}$$

$$= 0.8794 \text{ kg/m}^3$$

Velocity $$= 4.43\sqrt{\frac{2.2}{0.8794}} = 7.0 \text{ m/s}$$

Volume flow = 7.0 × 8.5 × 2.75 = 163.6 m³/s per duct
Mass flow = 163.6 × 0.8794 = 143.9 kg/s per duct
(Note: This is over 8.5 tonne/min)

Project 2

The following information was obtained from the hot air supply to a mill. Calculate the airflow in kg/s.

Barometer = 766.3 mm Hg; velocity pressure h_V = scale reading × 0.2
The sample points were as shown:

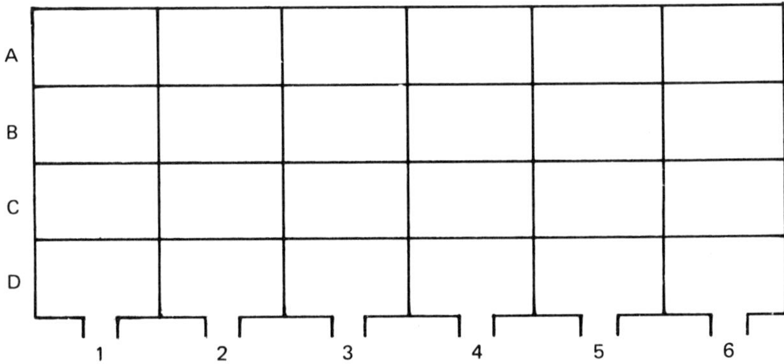

Location of test points in duct. (Duct cross-sectional area = 0.44 m²)

The following scale readings of velocity pressure were obtained using an inclined manometer (mm w.g.)

Point	*1*	*2*	*3*	*4*	*5*	*6*
Depth A	30.5	36.8	63.5	96.5	107.2	116.8
Depth B	31.8	39.4	73.7	91.4	118.4	127.0
Depth C	29.2	35.6	61.0	85.1	104.1	102.1
Depth D	30.5	34.3	59.7	57.2	98.6	101.6

Static pressure *hs* and temperature
(The value of *hs* in mm w.g. is shown in brackets)

Point	*1*	*2*	*3*	*4*	*5*	*6*
A	*205*	*205*	*210*	*211*	*208*	*207*
	(– 23.0)	(– 17.9)	(– 15.4)	(– 10.3)	(– 7.7)	(– 7.1)
B	203	207	212	209	210	209
	(– 22.9)	(– 17.9)	(– 15.5)	(– 10.3)	(– 7.8)	(– 7.2)
C	203	204	210	208	205	204
	(– 22.9)	(– 17.9)	(– 15.2)	(– 10.2)	(– 7.6)	(– 6.9)
D	205	204	204	204	205	204
	(– 22.8)	(– 17.9)	(– 15.1)	(– 10.0)	(– 7.3)	(-6.8)
Average	204	205	209	208	207	206
	(– 22.9)	(– 17.9)	(– 15.3)	(– 10.2)	(– 7.6)	(– 7.0)

So average temperature = 206.5°C, and average static pressure = (–) 13.5 mm w.g.

Project 2 (Answer)

Value of $\sqrt{(\text{Rdg} \times 0.2)}$ for each sample point:

	2.47	2.71	3.56	4.39	4.63	4.83
	2.52	2.81	3.84	4.28	4.87	5.04
	2.42	2.67	3.49	4.13	4.56	4.52
	2.47	2.62	3.46	3.38	4.44	4.51
Column average	2.47	2.70	3.59	4.05	4.63	4.73

So average $\sqrt{h_V}$ = 3.70

Average static pressure h_S = (−) 13.5 mm w.g.;
Average air temperature = 206.5°C = 479.5 K

$$\text{Velocity} = 4.43\sqrt{\frac{h_V}{\rho}}$$

$$\rho = 1.29 \times \frac{273}{479.5} \times \frac{10349.5}{10363} \times \frac{766.3}{760.0} = 0.740\ \text{kg/m}^3$$

$$\sqrt{\rho} = 0.860$$

$$\text{So velocity} = 4.43 \times \frac{3.70}{0.860} = 19.059\ \text{m/s}$$

Volume flow = velocity × duct cross-sectional area
= 19.059 × 0.44 m^2 = 8.4 m^3/s
Mass flow = Volume flow × density = 8.4 × 0.740 = 6.2 kg/s

Additional reading

1 **BS 250:** *Barometer Conventions and Tables.*
2 BS 1042: *Methods for the Measurement of Fluid Flow in Pipes* (3 Parts).
3 BS 587: *Methods for Measurement of Fluid Flow in Closed Conduits Using Tracers* (2 Parts).
4 *Woods Practical Guide to Fan Engineering* (Woods of Colchester Ltd.).
5 *The Efficient Use of Fuel* (HMSO)
6 JONES, E.B., *Instrument Technology Vol. 1,* Butterworths.
7 OWER and PARKHURST., *The Measurement of Air Flow*, Pergamon Press.

7 Water Flow

Usually, for power station testing purposes, the main flows to be measured are of water in pipes. For example, feed water, pump sealing water supply and return, feed pump gland leak-off and so on need to be measured. In addition it may be necessary to measure flows other than water from time to time, such as the steam flow to a bled steam turbine.

For the above and similar applications it is usual to have one of the following as the primary element for flow measurement:

(a) Venturi tube; (b) Nozzle; (c) Orifice plate.

In each case the pipe must run 'full' and the pressure drop across selected points at the primary element is a function of the flow. Hence they are commonly called 'Pressure Difference' devices. There is always an irrecoverable loss of pressure of the fluid as it passes the primary element.

Primary elements

Venturi tubes

The general construction of a venturi tube is shown in *Figure 7.1*. The inlet bore tapers to a throat, after which it diverges usually to the original size. Pressure tappings are provided at the inlet and at the throat as shown. The tubes must be manufactured accurately and they are expensive. On the other havd this type has the smallest irrecoverable pressure loss of all the standard devices, an important consideration if the primary element is to be left in-line for long periods. Dall tubes and other 'low loss' devices can have an even lower irrecoverable head loss.

Nozzles

These are used extensively in the USA and Europe and, to a lesser extent, in the UK. Care is required in their manufacture and they are quite costly. The irrecoverable loss is greater than for a venturi tube. A typical application is

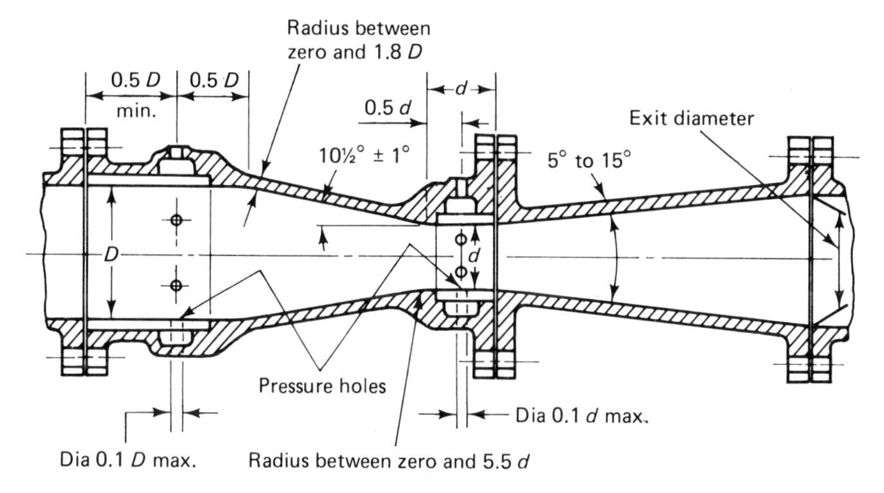

Figure 7.1 Venturi tube (From BS Code 1042: Part 1: 1964)

the measurement of steam flow to bled steam turbines. It is necessary to 'spring' the pipes a considerable amount to install a nozzle, as can be seen from *Figure 7.2*. The ASME throat tap nozzle is very accurate and is used for turbine heat consumption tests in the USA.

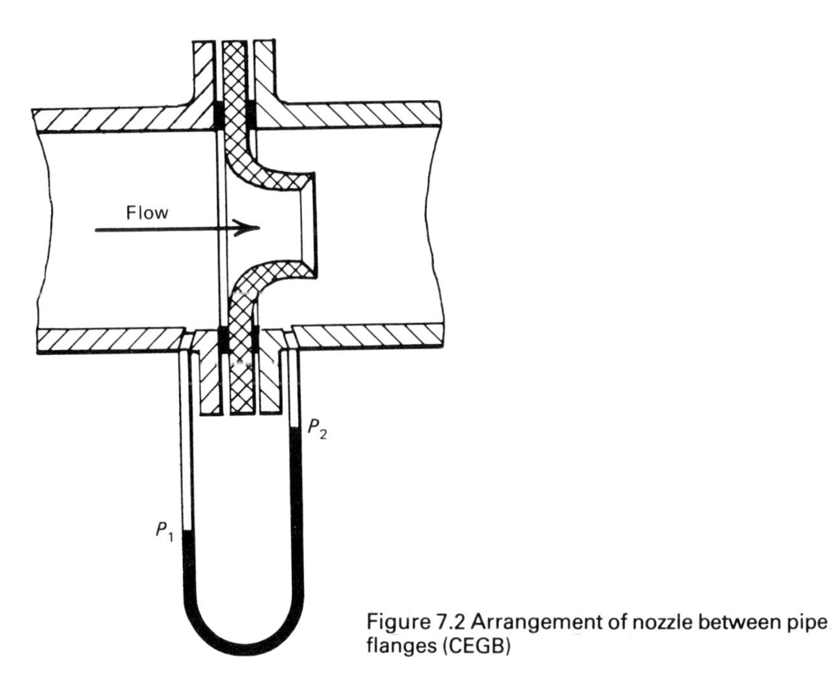

Figure 7.2 Arrangement of nozzle between pipe flanges (CEGB)

Orifice plates

Care must be taken but the manufacture of the devices presents little difficulty. The finished product must conform to BS 1042: 1981 Section 1.1. *Fluid Flow in Closed Conduits.* The pressure tappings are usually one of the following: (a) Corner; (b) Flange; (c) D and D/2.

The same general considerations apply to them all, but there are differences of detail. A carrier ring orifice plate is shown in *Figure 7.3.* The irrecoverable head loss is high but the cost of manuacture is least.

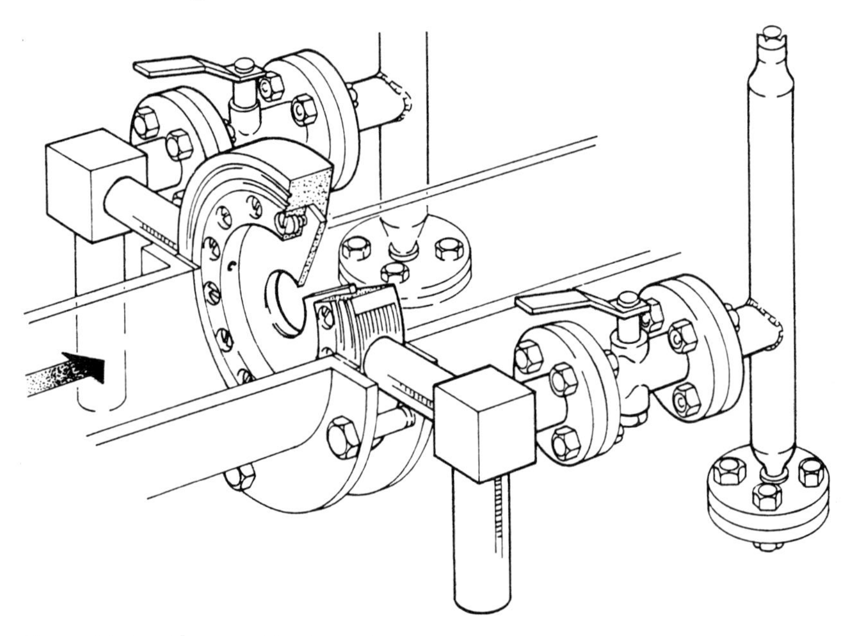

Figure 7.3 Carrier ring orifice (CEGB)

Detailed information about all the primary elements is given in BS 1042: 1981. It is sometimes necessary to design and manufacture a primary element at a power station and the only one that can easily be made is the orifice plate. When a plate has been made it should be calibrated if possible, which involves determining the mass flow rates of water through the device and the corresponding differential pressures. If calibration facilities are not available, but the plate has been constructed in strict conformity with the requirements of BS 1042, then the flow can be calculated, as will be shown later.

Calibration of flow measuring devices

The CEGB has excellent test facilities at the Hydraulic and Temperature

Calibration Centre, situated at Hams Hall. A flow measuring device of any capacity used within the CEGB can be calibrated, the general layout being shown in *Figure 7.4*. Typical calibration results are given in *Table 7.1* for an orifice plate with D and $D/2$ tappings.

Also given with the calibration results is a plot of discharge coefficient against Reynolds number. An explanation of the meaning of 'coefficient of discharge' and Reynolds number is given later.

Orifice plates with D and D/2 tappings

General rules for design and installation

1 *Figure 7.5* shows the dimensions and tolerances to which the complete installation must comply.
2 The minimum pipe diameter (D) is 2.5 cm bore
3 When determining the flow of a gas it is desirable to keep the differential in mm w.g. to less than 2000 times the upstream pressure in bars.
4 It can not be used to measure viscous fluids.
5 The D and $D/2$ tappings must be free from burrs.
6 The thickness of the plate should be sufficient to resist distortion:

For pipe diameters D up to 15 cm use a plate 2 mm thick.
For pipe diameters D up to 30 cm use a plate 3 mm thick.
For pipe diameters D up to 75 cm, use a plate 5 mm thick.
For pipe diameters D up to 120 cm, use a plate 6 mm thick.
For pipe diameters D over 120 cm use a plate 10 mm thick.

7 The downstream edge of the orifice has a bevel only if the plate thickness exceeds 1/10 of the orifice diameter d.
8 The upstream edge of the orifice must be sharp and the bore must be at a right-angle to the face of the plate.
9 The minimum orifice diameter varies with circumstances, but is between 0.5 and 1.5 cm.
10 A drain hole is normally drilled in the plate if $D > 100$ mm. It is located at the top of the main if water is being measured, to allow any gas or air to escape, and at the bottom, if gas is being measured, to allow any moisture to drain. The hole must be displaced at least 90° from the pressure tappings.
11 The orifice plate should have an identification tongue.
12 The orifice is located centrally in the pipe by the flange bolts, as shown in *Figure 7.6*.
13 Concentricity is important. It is an advantage if the ratio of d/D is less than 0.5. In any case it should not exceed 0.75.

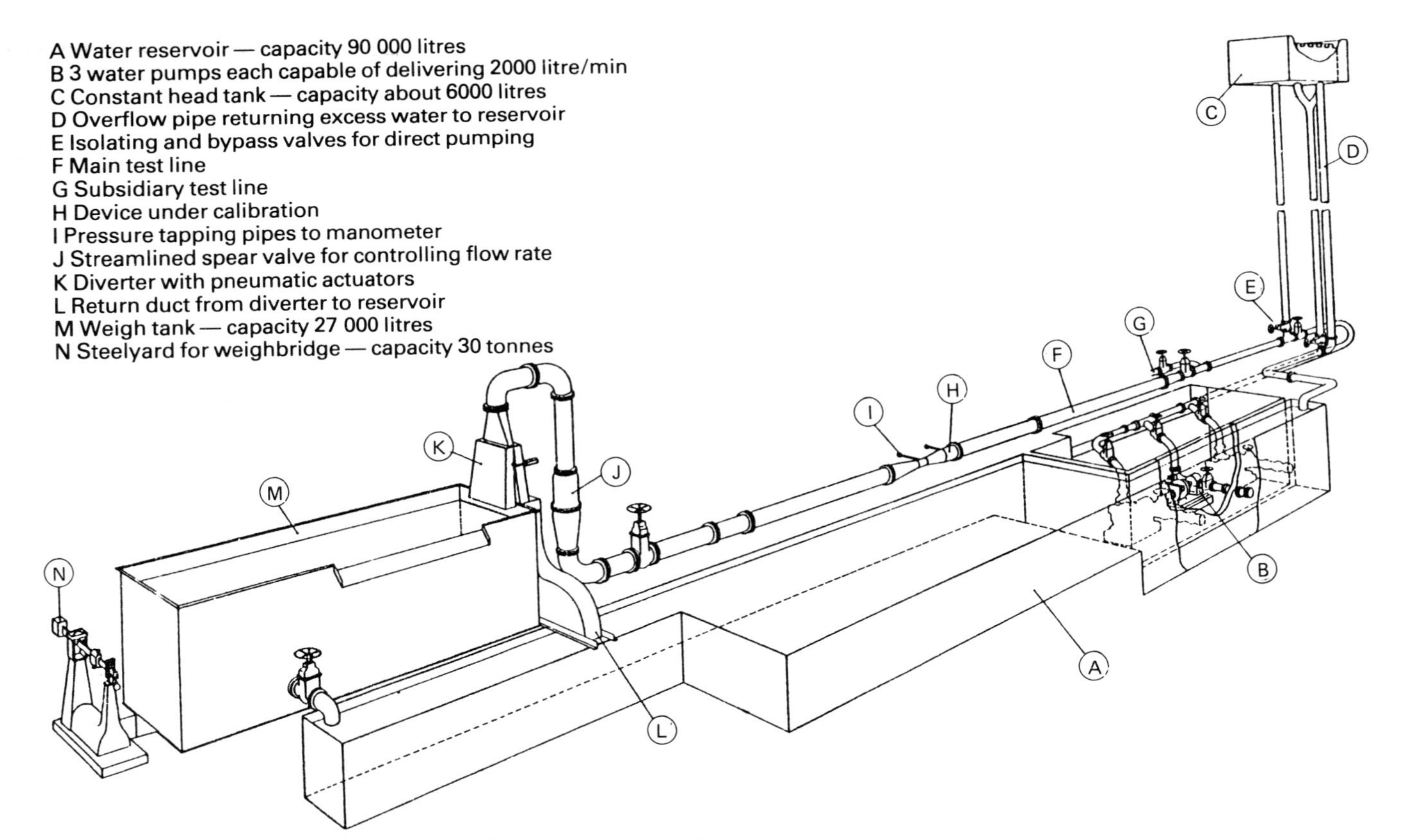

Figure 7.4 Perspectivs view of water flow calibration equipment (CEGB)

Table 7.1 Calibration results

Test No.	Weight of water (kg)	Water temp. (°C)	Divers on time (s)	Manometer Hg under water (mm)	Mano. temp. (°C)	Diff. pressure (mb)	Mass flowrate (kg/s)	Coeff. of disch. (C)	Reynolds number R_{ed} ($\times 10^{-6}$)	$R_{ed}^{0.5}$ ($\times 10^{3}$)
1	4647	27.4	111.063	56.26	20.6	69.26	41.89	0.6213	0.428	1.528
2	4272	27.4	72.300	112.05	20.8	137.95	59.15	0.6217	0.605	1.286
3	5347	27.4	68.951	193.07	20.8	237.69	77.63	0.6216	0.794	1.122
4	6029	27.4	62.603	297.47	20.9	366.21	96.40	0.6218	0.986	1.007
5	7677	27.3	66.283	429.86	21.0	529.19	115.94	0.6222	1.183	0.919
6	8133	27.3	60.583	577.55	21.0	711.01	134.39	0.6221	1.368	0.855
7	9349	27.2	60.474	766.79	21.0	943.97	154.76	0.6218	1.575	0.797
8	10556	27.3	60.826	965.36	21.0	1188.42	173.73	0.6221	1.772	0.751
9	11604	27.3	60.330	1186.46	20.9	1460.64	192.54	0.6219	1.964	0.714
10	11654	27.4	56.280	1421.98	20.9	1750.58	210.84	0.6221	2.156	0.681
11	9350	27.4	60.348	776.37	21.0	955.77	155.75	0.6219	1.592	0.792
12	5181	27.6	67.251	190.38	21.4	234.36	77.12	0.6219	0.792	1.124

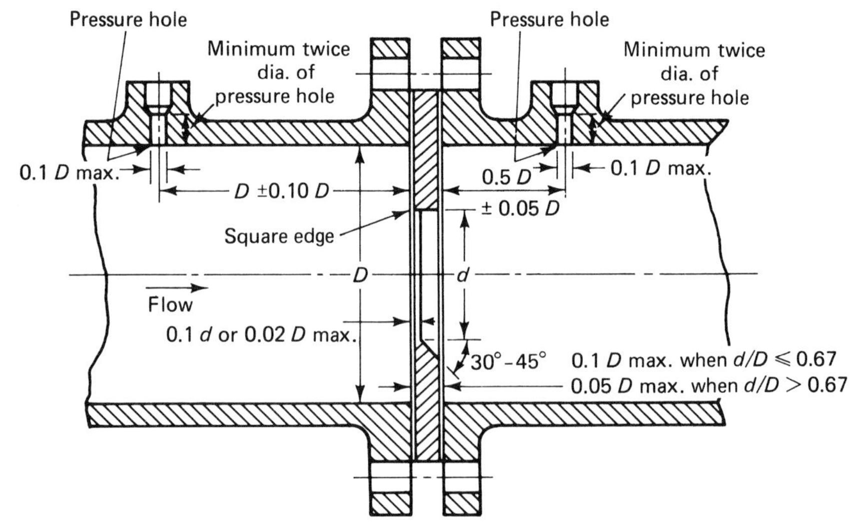

Figure 7.5 Orifice plate with D and D/2 tappings (From BS Code 1042: Part 1: 1964)

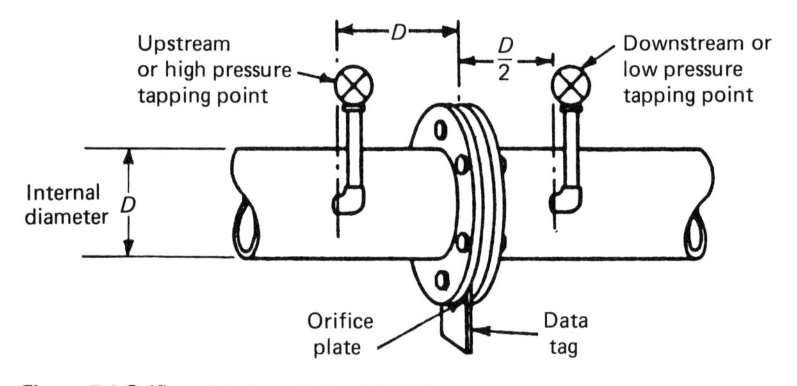

Figure 7.6 Orifice plate installation (CEGB)

14 If the flow is pulsating it will cause serious errors. This is because the mean differential pressure will be indicated on the measuring device, whereas the actual rate of flow is a function of the square root of the pressure difference. Hence, the instrument will read high.

The ratio $\frac{\text{True flow}}{\text{Apparent flow}}$ is called the 'Pulsation Factor'

15 An essential requirement for a suitable flow pattern is that there should be an adequate length of straight pipe between the measuring device and any upstream valve, bend, tee or other such items which will cause interference with the flow pattern. *Figure 7.7* shows some typical situations and the necessary straight lengths of upstream pipework.

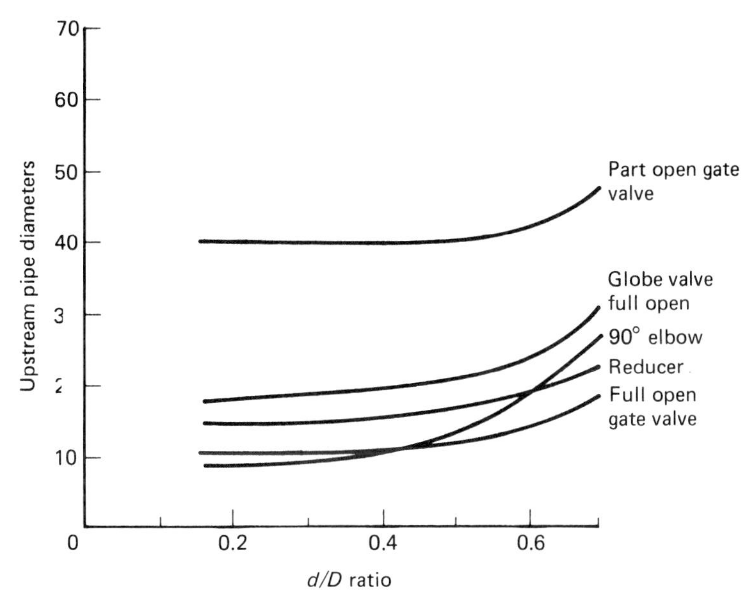

Figure 7.7 Typical upstream pipe lengths for various fittings before an orifice plate

16 Materials used for orifice plates include:

For water – Gun metal, bronze, stainless steel
For steam – Stainless steel, Monel
For air – Mild steel, Monel, gun metal

17 *Figures 7.8* and *7.9* show the connections between the orifice plate tapping and the metering device.

Discharge coefficient 'C'

When the stream of fluid leaves a pressure reducing device such as an orifice plate, the area reduces. Thus, at the vena contracta the area of the stream may only be about 60% of that at the orifice. One of the advantages of using orifice plates is that the flow conditions at the orifice can be predicted accurately when allowance is made for the local conditions. Consequently the discharge coefficient can be determined.

$$\text{Discharge coefficient } C = \frac{\text{Actual flow}}{\text{Theoretical flow}}$$

The value of the discharge coefficient depends upon various factors such as:

(a) The ratio of the area of the orifice to that of the pipe, the area ratio d^2/D^2 being denoted by m, or β^2

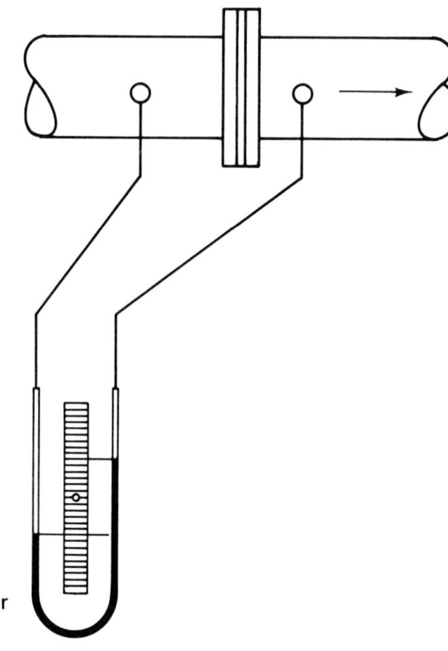

Figure 7.8 Installation of manometer below the pipe

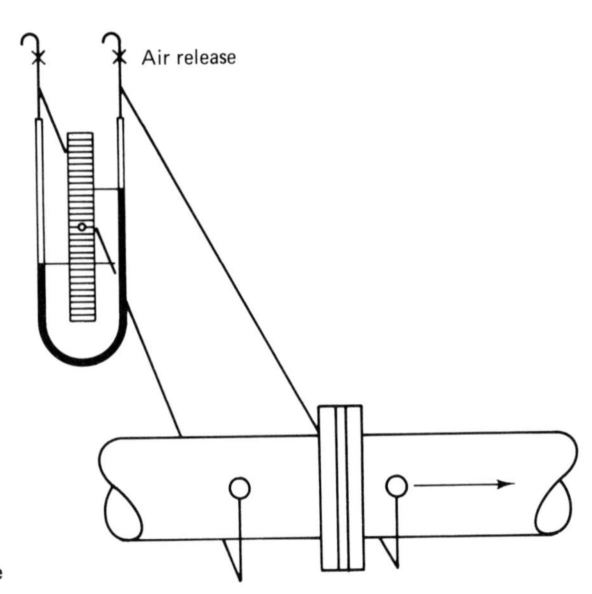

Figure 7.9 Installation of manometer above the pipe

(b) The type of primary element.
(c) The Reynolds number.
(d) The pressure tappings.

In *Figure 7.14* the value of the discharge coefficient C is plotted against the area ratio m.

The value of C may be modified for low values of Reynolds number and the size and roughness of the pipe. These correction factors are denoted by Z_{Re} and Z_D. They are combined into one factor Z, where:

$$Z = Z_{Re} \times Z_D$$

Hence, the modified coefficient of discharge is given by CZ.

When a flow measuring device is calibrated, the discharge coefficient is the most important item calculated.

A suitable formula for water is:

$$\text{Discharge coefficient } C = \frac{90\,032\,q}{d^2 E\sqrt{(\Delta p \times \rho_w)}}$$

where q = mass flowrate in kg/s
d = throat or orifice bore in mm
E = velocity of approach factor = $\dfrac{1}{\sqrt{(1 - m^2)}}$
Δp = differential pressure across device in mbar
ρ_w = density of water in the calibration line in kg/m^3

Calculation of orifice size

The basic flow equation is derived in Appendix 1 and is:

$$W = 0.01252\ CZeEd_w^2\sqrt{h\rho}$$

where W = mass flow rate in kg/h
C = discharge coefficient
e = expansibility factor = 1.0 for liquids
E = velocity of approach factor = $\dfrac{1}{\sqrt{(1 - m^2)}}$
d_w = orifice diameter in mm at working temperature
h = differential pressure at orifice in mm H_2O
ρ = density of fluid in kg/m^3
Z = correction factor for pipe size and Reynolds number

For complete details of the calculations required for various pressure difference devices and substances, reference should be made to BS1042. Here only the most common calculation will be performed, i.e. for an orifice plate with D and $D/2$ tappings on a pipe carrying water. It is best illustrated by an example.

Example

Calculate the size of orifice required to meter the gland sealing water supply to the boiler feed pump on a 120 MW unit. The conditions are:

> Flow = 22 460 kg/h at 127°C, 46.5 bar abs; h = 7600 mm H_2O;
> $\therefore \sqrt{h} = 87.18$
> The plate is to be made of stainless steel, square edged with D and $D/2$ tappings. The pipe is made of clean cold-drawn mild steel and the average of several measurements of the internal diameter is 76.20 mm.

The basic equation can be slightly modified by substituting $d^2 = D^2m$
So $W = (0.01252)\ CZeED^2m\sqrt{(\rho h)}$
Let subscript 'a' refer to ambient and 'w' to working conditions.
Step 1

$$\text{Calculate } N \text{ from } N = \frac{W}{0.01252 \times D_w^{\ 2}\ \sqrt{(\rho h)}}$$

where D_W = pipe diameter at working temperature in mm.

$D_w = D_a\ [1 + \alpha\ (t_W - t_a)]$

where α = mean coefficient of linear expansion per °C

t = temperature of fluid in °C

If it is assumed that t_a = 15°C, then use *Figure 7.10*.

So $D_w = 76.20 \times 1.0013 = 76.299$ mm

The density of the fluid is obtained from *Figure 7.11* or steam tables and is 939 kg/m³, so $\sqrt{\rho} = 30.64$

$$\therefore N = \frac{22\ 460}{0.01252 \times 76.299^2 \times 87.18 \times 30.64} = 0.11536$$

Step 2

$W = (0.01252)\ CZeED^2m\sqrt{(\rho\,\mathrm{h})}$

$$\text{So } \frac{W}{0.01252D^2\sqrt{(\rho h)}} = N = \mathrm{CZeEm}$$

$$\therefore CmE = \frac{N}{Ze}$$

As the fluid is water, $e = 1.0$

$$\therefore CmE = \frac{N}{Z}$$

For the present assume $Z = 1.0$, but if it is subsequently found to be some other value a recalculation can be carried out.

Refer to *Figure 7.12* and against $CmE = 0.115$, read $m = 0.180$

So, $\sqrt{m} = 0.426$

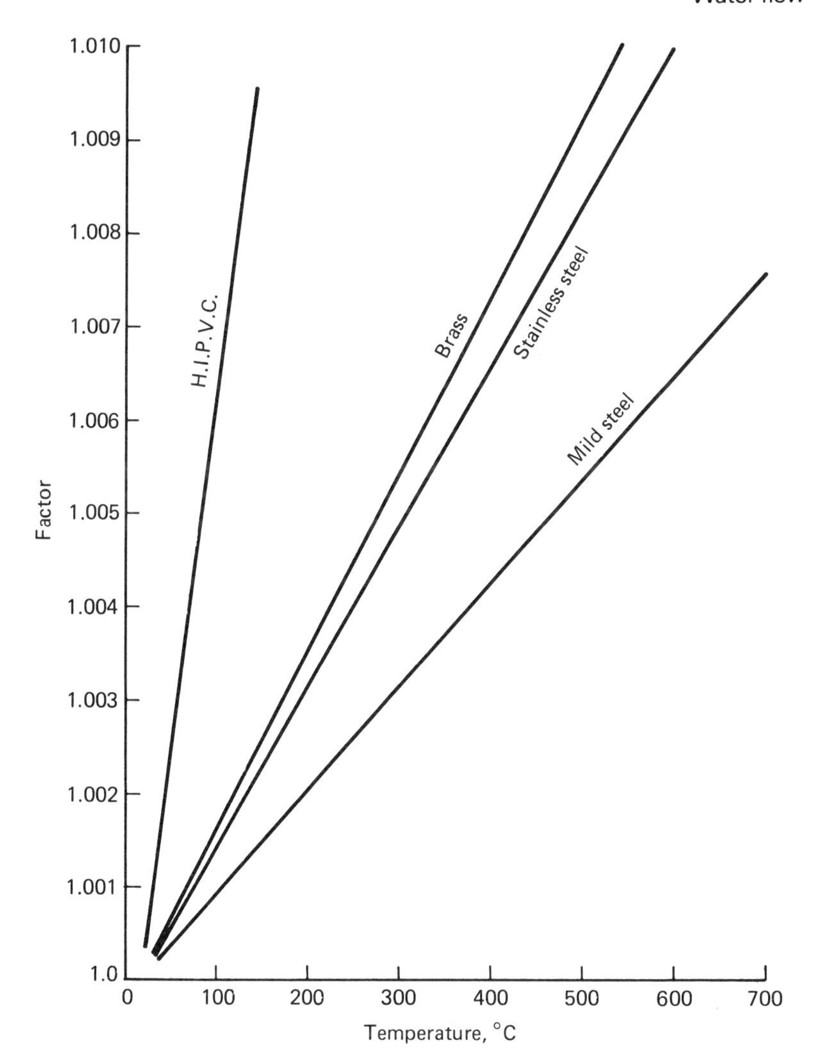

Figure 7.10 Expansion factor vs temperature for various materials

Step 3

The value of m can now be used to calculate the approximate Reynolds number Re.

$$Re = \frac{3.54\,W}{\mu\, d} = \frac{3.54\,W}{\mu\, D\sqrt{m}}$$

where μ = dynamic viscosity in poise or g/cms (Note: 10 poise = 1 kg/ms)
= 0.0021 from *Figure 7.13*.

$$\text{So } Re = \frac{3.54 \times 22460}{0.0021 \times 76.299 \times 0.42} = 1.2 \times 10^6$$

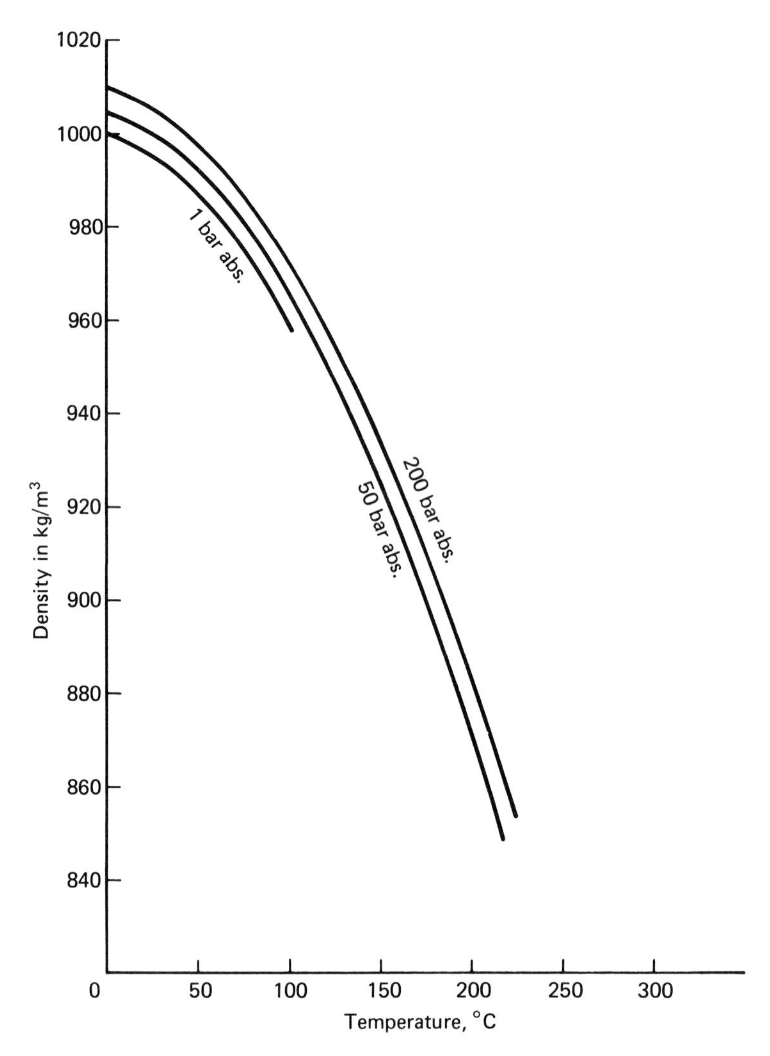

Figure 7.11 Density of water in kg/m³ (Derived from steam tables)

Reference to BS 1042 shows that this value of Reynolds number is so high that $Z_{Re} = 1.0$. Also, for $m = 0.18$ and $Dw = 76.299$ mm, the value of $Z_D = 1.002$.

However, the value of Z_D may require modifying, depending upon the bore of the pipe, its material and its condition. If the diameter of the pipe is over 50 mm $Z_D = 1.0$.

So $Z = Z_{Re} Z_D = 1.0$

Therefore, the value of m found in Step 2 from $CmE = N/Z$ remains 0.18. If the value of Z had been other than 1.0 it would have been necessary to find a

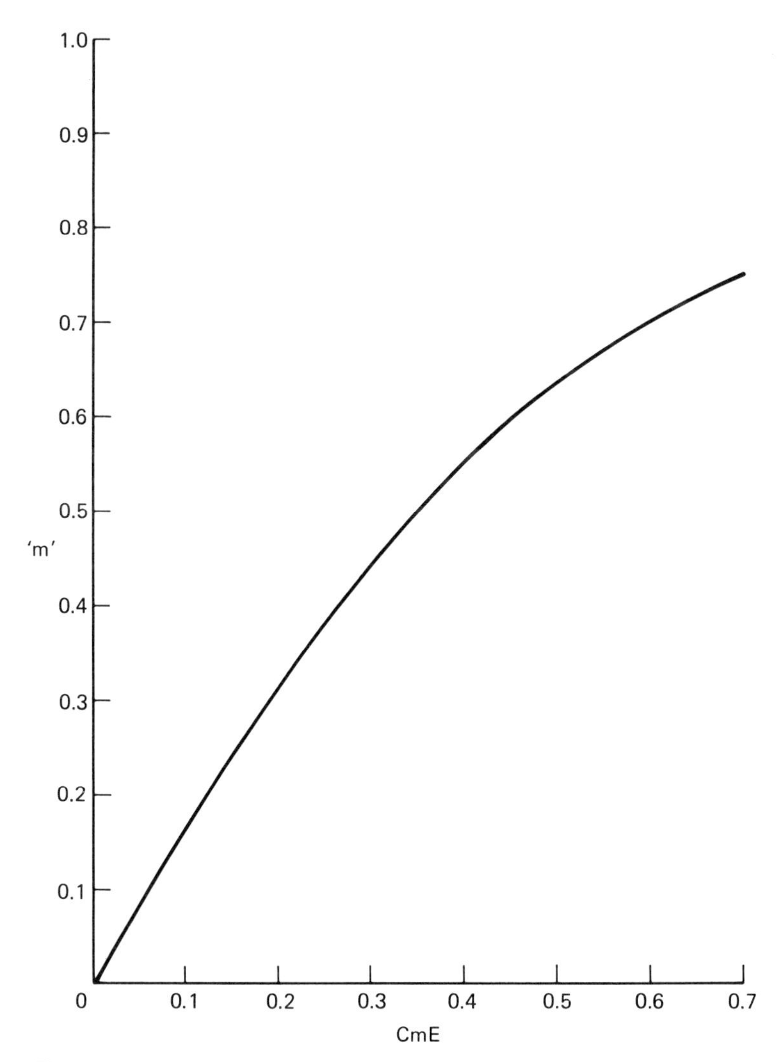

Figure 7.12 Area ratio 'm' vs '*CmE*'

new value of CmE and then a new value of m.

Step 4

Reference to *Figure 7.14* shows that for $m = 0.18$ the value of $C = 0.6032$.

$$\text{Now } CmE = 0.115, \text{ so } mE = \frac{0.115}{0.6032} = 0.191$$

Reference to *Figure 7.15* shows that for $mE = 0.191$ the value of $\frac{d}{D} = 0.435$

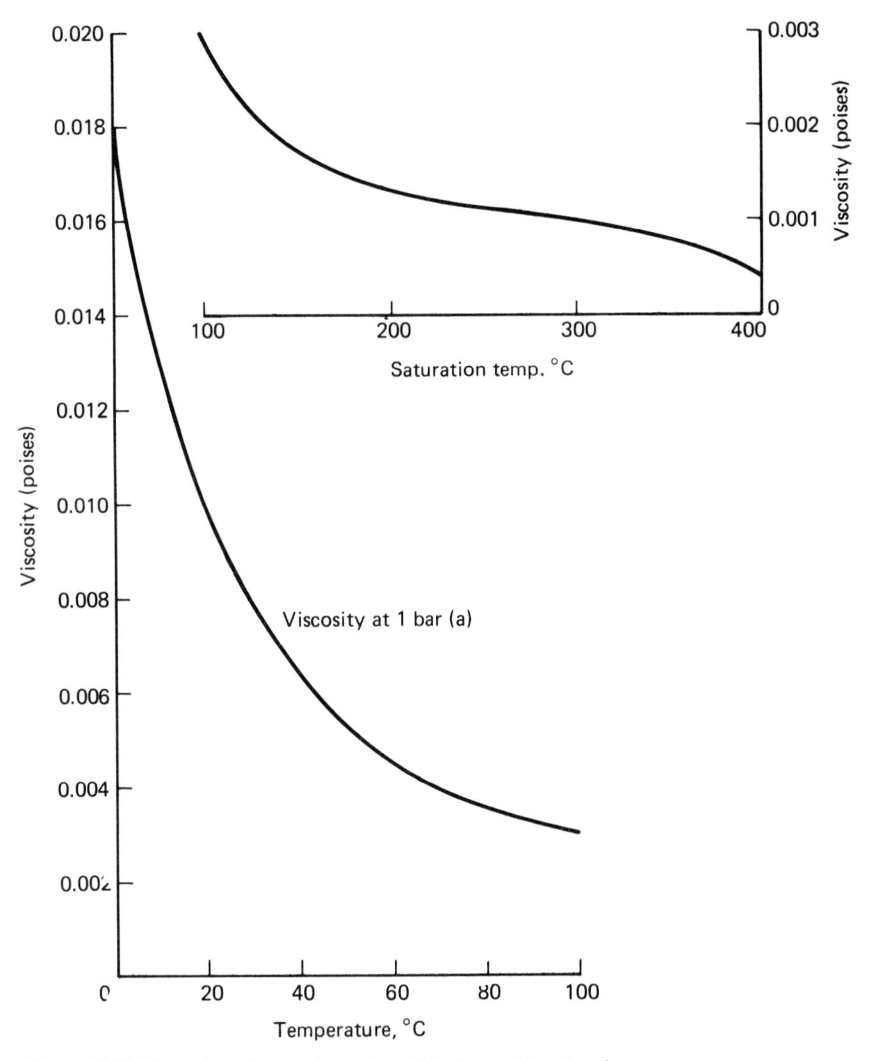

Figure 7.13 Viscosity of water in poises (1 kg/ms = 10 poises)

So $d_W = 0.435 \times 76.299 = 33.19$ mm

$$\therefore d_a = \frac{33.19}{1.0019} = 33.127 \text{ mm, say } 33.13 \text{ mm}$$

The value 1.0019 is obtained from *Figure 7.10*.

Check

$$\begin{aligned} W &= 0.01252CZeEd_w^2\sqrt{(h\ \rho)} \\ &= 0.01252 \times 0.6032 \times 1.0184 \times 33.19^2 \times 87.18 \times 30.64 \\ &= 22\ 630 \text{ kg/h, so the size is acceptable.} \end{aligned}$$

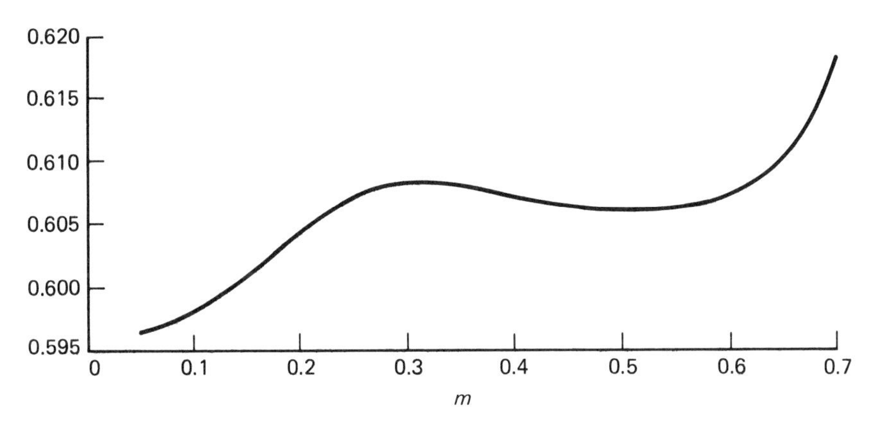

Figure 7.14 Coefficient 'C' vs area ratio 'm' (From BS Code 1042: Part 1: 1964)

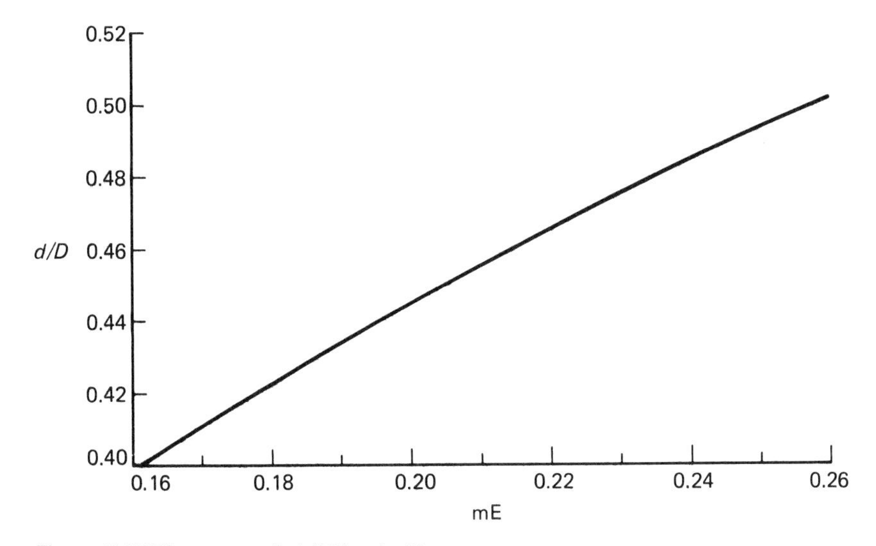

Figure 7.15 Diameter ratio '*d/D*' vs '*mE*'

Note: $m = (d/D)^2 = 0.435^2 = 0.1892$

$$E = \frac{1}{\sqrt{(1-m^2)}} = \frac{1}{\sqrt{(1-0.1892^2)}} = 1.0184$$

The thickness of the plate will be 5 mm. The orifice diameter is 33.19 mm and requires a bevel if the thickness is more than $0.1d$, so in this case a bevel is necessary.

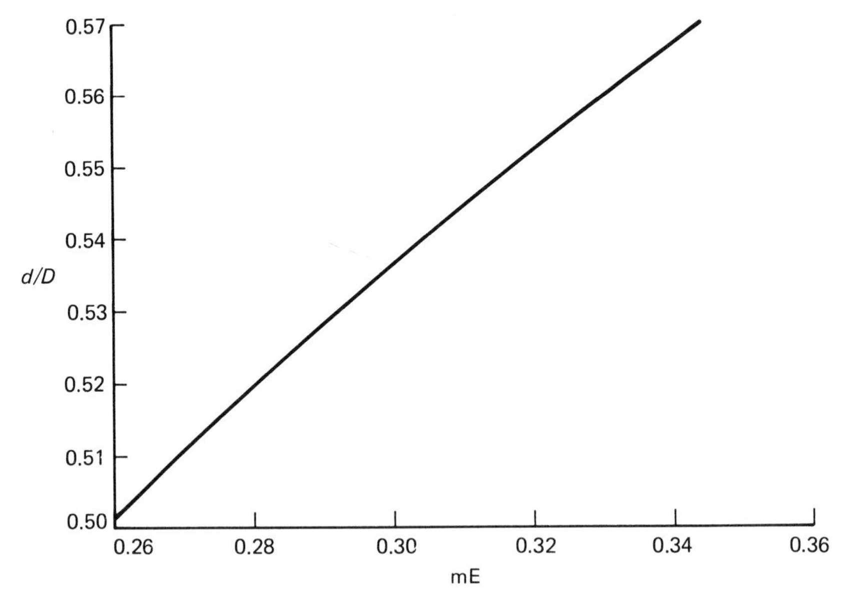

Figure 7.16 Diameter ratio '*d/D*' vs '*mE*'

Allowance for drain hole

The diameter of the orifice should be corrected to allow for the drain hole if there is one. Normally a hole is not required if the pipe diameter is less than 100 mm. When there is a drain hole in an orifice plate in a pipe carrying liquid, it should be at the top to prevent the accumulation of air.

The diameter of the drain hole is usually $0.1d_W$, and its area must be deducted from the area of the orifice so the diameter of the orifice at working temperature d_m will be

$$\sqrt{d_w^2 - (0.1\,d_w)^2}$$

$$\therefore \quad d_m = 0.9950\,d_w$$

Flow constant K

It will be observed that in the expression $W = (0.01252)\,CZeEd^2\,\sqrt{(\rho h)}$ for any given set of conditions every term is a constant except W, h and ρ. Given the water conditions ρ is also a constant.

Therefore $W = K\sqrt{h}$

For example, for the above orifice plate operating at design conditions we have:

$$22\,630\text{ kg/h} = K\sqrt{(7600\text{ mm})}$$

So $K = \dfrac{22\,630}{\sqrt{7600}} = 259.6$. Therefore $W = 259.6\sqrt{h}$ kg/h

Actually the value of K for a given installation varies slightly with flow similar to the variation of C with Reynolds number. In fact it is common to include with the results of the calibration of a flow measuring device, a graph of how the value of $W/\sqrt{h}$ varies with $\sqrt{h}$. For example some calibration results were given on page 265. The calculated values of K for the twelve tests are:

Test	1	2	3	4	5	6	7	8	9	10	11	
$W/\sqrt{h} = K$	5675.7	5679.9	5677.9	5680.8	5683.3	5683.8	5680.4	5683.1	5681.0	5682.6	5681.4	56

where W = flow in kg/h, and h = manometer head in mm H_2O at 4°C. The results are plotted in *Figure 7.17.* The magnitude of the variation of 'K' is, considering the lowest and the highest values in the table:

$$\frac{(5683.8 - 5675.7)\,100}{5675.7} = \mathbf{0.14\%}$$

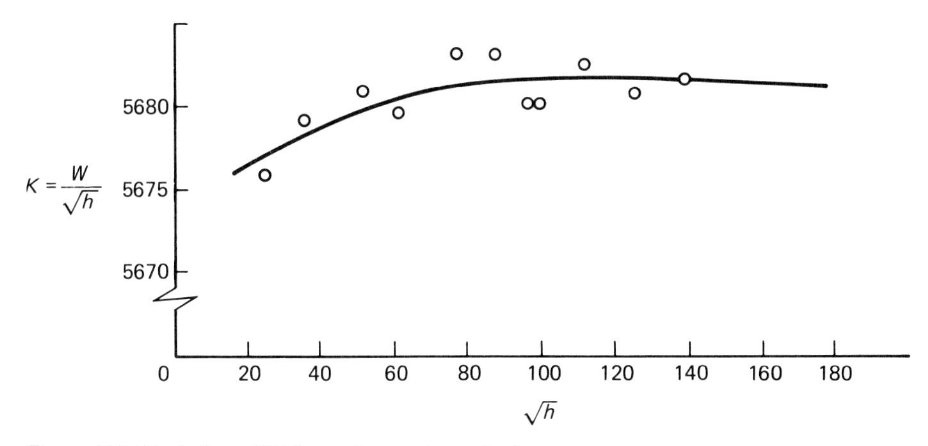

Figure 7.17 Variation of 'K' for various values of $\sqrt{h}$

Rapid calculation of approximate orifice size

The following method is suitable for determining the approximate size of orifice required and is best illustrated by an example using the same data as in the previous case.

Example

Calculate the approximate size of orifice required for a square-edged orifice plate made of stainless steel for the following conditions:

Flow = 22460 kg/h at 127°C, 46.5 bar abs.; h = 7600 mm H_2O; Pipe bore = 76.20 mm, material mild steel; D_W = 76.299 mm.
The pressure tappings to be D and $D/2$.

Step 1

Calculate N, from $$N = \frac{W}{0.01252\ D_W^2\ \sqrt{\rho\ h})}$$

$$= 0.115 \text{ (from previous calculation)}$$

Step 2

$CmE \quad = N$
Assume $C = 0.606$

$\therefore mE \quad = 1.65\ N = 1.65 \times 0.115 = 0.190$

Step 3

From *Figure 7.15*, $d_w/D_w = 0.432$ for mE $= 0.190$
So $d_w = 0.432 \div 76.299 = 32.889$ mm, say 32.9 mm

Measuring the pressure differential

For test work it is usual to connect a mercury manometer across the orifice plate to measure the differential. Alternatively, it is now common to use an electrical differential pressure transducer.

Consider a mercury manometer used to measure the differential pressure in a pipe carrying water. Both connecting pipes will be full of water above the mercury. For a given differential in mm of mercury under water the equivalent differential in mm of water is given by:

$$h_W = \frac{h_m\ (\rho_m - \rho_W)}{\rho_W} \quad \text{(see Appendix 2)}$$

where h_w = differential head in mm w.g.
h_m = differential head in mm mercury
ρ_m = density of mercury
ρ_w = density of water

For example, what would be the value of h_w if the differential reading was 600.0 mm Hg under water when the ambient temperature was 15.0°C? Refer to *Table 7.2*.

$$h_W = \frac{600.0\ (13558.2 - 999.1)}{999.1} = 7542 \text{ mm w.g.}$$

Normally the equivalent differential head in millimetres water gauge is referred to a standard ambient temperature of 4°C. Thus the previous formula needs to be slightly modified:

Table 7.2 Density of Mercury and water

Ambient Temp. (°C)	Density (kg/m³) Mercury	Water	Ambient Temp. (°C)	Density (kg/m³) Mercury	Water
12	13 565.5	999.49	22	13 540.7	997.77
13	13 563.2	999.37	23	13 538.3	997.53
14	13 560.8	999.24	24	13 534.5	997.29
15	13 558.2	999.10	25	13 533.2	997.04
16	13 555.9	998.94	26	13 530.6	996.78
17	13 553.4	998.77	27	13 527.9	996.51
18	13 550.9	998.59	28	13 525.5	996.23
19	13 548.4	998.40	29	13 522.9	995.94
20	13 545.9	998.20	30	13 520.3	995.64
21	13 543.3	997.99	31	13 517.6	995.34

$$h_w \text{ at } 4°\text{C} = \frac{h_m(\rho_m - \rho_w)}{999.971}$$

For example, in the previous case the reading was 600 mm Hg under water when the ambient temperature was 15.0°C.

$$\text{The equivalent head at } 4°\text{C is } h_w = \frac{600(13558.2 - 999.1)}{999.971}$$

$$= 7536 \text{ mm w.g.}$$

Table 7.3 lists the conversion factors for various ambient temperatures, i.e.

$$\text{Conversion factor} = \frac{\rho_m - \rho_w}{999.971}$$

The information in *Table 7.3* is given also in *Figure 7.18*.

Table 7.3 Conversion factor mm Hg under water at a certain temperature to mm H_2O at 4°C

Temp. (°C)	Conversion factor	Temp. (°C)	Conversion factor
12	12.5664	22	12.5433
13	12.5642	23	12.5411
14	12.5619	24	12.5388
15	12.5595	25	12.5365
16	12.5573	26	12.5342
17	12.5550	27	12.5318
18	12.5527	28	12.5296
19	12.5504	29	12.5273
20	12.5481	30	12.5250
21	12.5457	31	12.5226

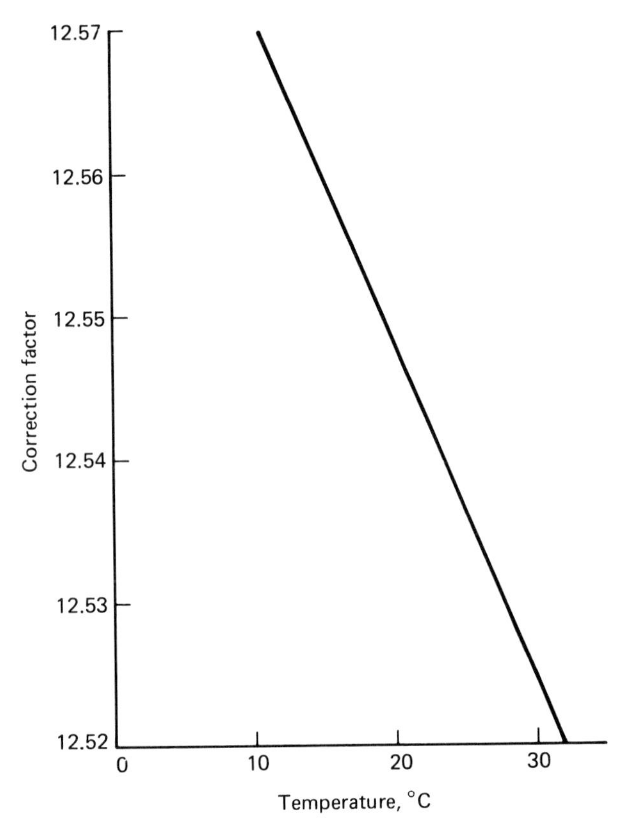

Figure 7.18 Manometer conversion (millimetres mercury under water to millimetres water at 4°C)

Sizing of control valves

Often it is desirable to fit a control valve in a line in which the valve is smaller than the pipe. One method adapted is to calculate a suitable size of orifice and stipulate a valve with the same bore.

Example

On a 375 MW unit the control of the CW flow through the main oil coolers was too coarse. It was decided to fit a regulating valve in the common CW pipe from the coolers. The installation details are as follows:

Pipe bore = 432 mm; CW flow = 1 000 000 kg/h; CW temperature = 32°C; CW pressure = 6.3 bar; CW density = 1000 kg/m^3

$$N = \frac{W}{0.01252\ D^2\ \sqrt{\rho h})} = \frac{1\ 000\ 000}{0.01252 \times 432^2\ \sqrt{(1000)} \times \sqrt{h}} = \frac{13.53}{\sqrt{h}}$$

Prepare a table of values of h that are acceptable and select a suitable value of d from the table. In this case, say, 'R' 2200 is acceptable.

Table 7.4

h (mm)	$\sqrt{h}$	N	$mE = 1.65N$	$\frac{d}{D}$	d (mm)
1600	40.0	0.338	0.558	0.698	301
1800	42.4	0.319	0.526	0.682	295
2000	44.7	0.303	0.500	0.669	289
2200	46.9	0.288	0.476	0.655	283

A 300 mm valve was selected as the nearest standard size valve which would given an acceptable pressure drop of 1.6 m.

Reynolds number (Re)

The significance of the Reynolds number is not always appreciated, so a few words about it will not be out of place.

The flow in a pipe is not uniform across the whole of the cross-sectional area. In *Figure 7.19* consider the flow rates along the diameter AB. It is found that the value at the centre is highest and reduces sharply as the pipe wall is approached, as shown in the graph. If the true flow is required it follows that great care must be exercised to determine the true average velocity. With turbulent flow and a fully developed velocity profile it is about 0.82 of the maximum for water. However, the ratio varies significantly with Reynolds number as shown in *Figure 7.20*.

Notice that at values of Reynolds number above about 40 000 there is not much change in the ratio of average to maximum speed. It follows that for flow measurement high values of Reynolds number are desirable. Flow with Reynolds numbers less than 2000 is regarded as streamline and over 10 000 as turbulent. The higher the viscosity of the fluid the higher the *Re* number at which turbulent flow commences.

Just in passing it may be mentioned that if the flow is streamline, then heat transfer rate is proportional to the cube root of the velocity,

i.e. HTR $\propto$ $(\text{Vel})^{0.33}$ – streamline flow.
If the water is turbulent it is proportional to the power 0.8 of the velocity,
i.e. HTR $\propto$ $(\text{Vel})^{0.8}$ – turbulent flow.

Hence, better heat transfer rates are achieved if the flow is turbulent, as one would expect.

Reynolds Number '*Re*' can be expressed in many forms, and is dimensionless provided consistent units are used throughout. Thus, to determine the Reynolds number for the flow in a pipe a suitable formula is:

$$R_{eD} = \frac{v\,D\,\rho}{\mu}$$

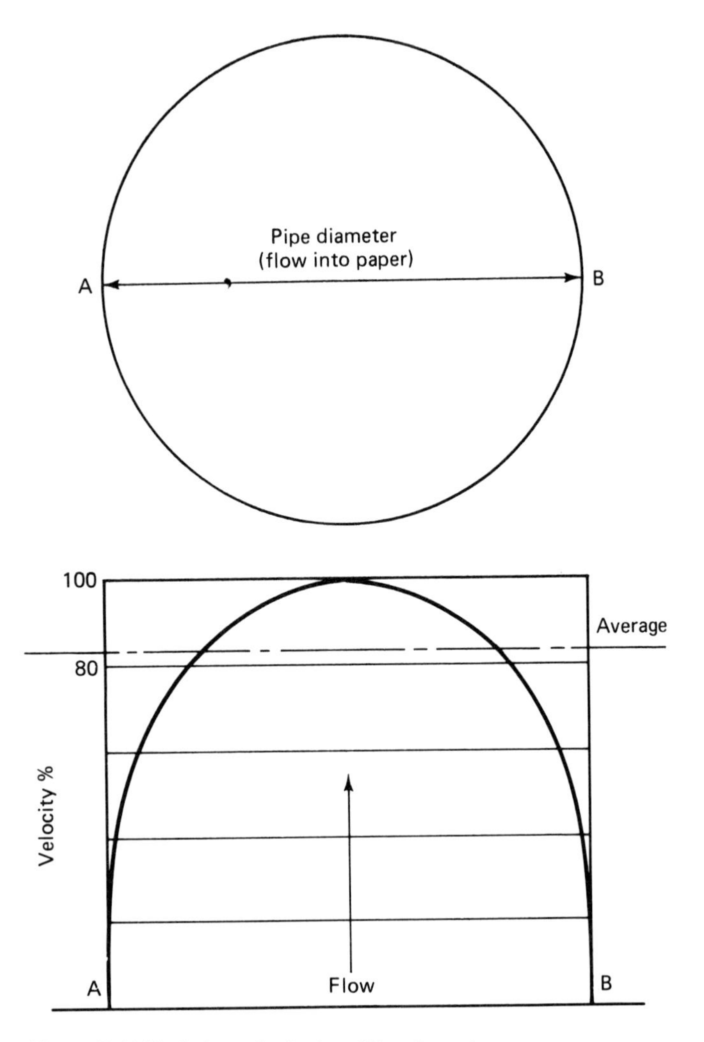

Figure 7.19 Variation of velocity of flow in a pipe

where v = velocity of flow in m/s
D = pipe diameter in metres
ρ = density of fluid in kg/m^3
μ = viscosity of the fluid in kg/ms

When calculating orifice sizes a useful formula is:

$$R_{ed} = \frac{3.54\,W}{\mu d}$$

where W = mass rate of flow in kg/h
μ = dynamic viscosity in g/cms or poises (10 poises = 1 kg/ms)
d = size of orifice in mm

$$\text{or } Re = \frac{3.54\,W}{\mu\, D\sqrt{m}}$$

Note: Since $d^2/D^2 = m$, then $d = D\sqrt{m}$, so equation (3) is merely a different form of equation (2).

Square law effect

The previously stated flow formula is: $W = (0.0125)\, CZeEd^2 \sqrt{(h\rho)}$

So $W \propto \sqrt{h}$

Let W_1 = full flow and W_2 = half flow

$$\text{Then } \frac{W_1}{W_2} = \sqrt{\frac{h_1}{h_2}}$$

$$\text{So } h_2 = \left(\frac{W_2}{W_1}\right)^2 \times h_1 = \left(\frac{0.5}{1.0}\right) h_1 = 0.25\, h_1$$

In other words, the head is a quarter when the flow is halved. *Figures 7.21(a)* and *(b)* illustrate the square law relationship.

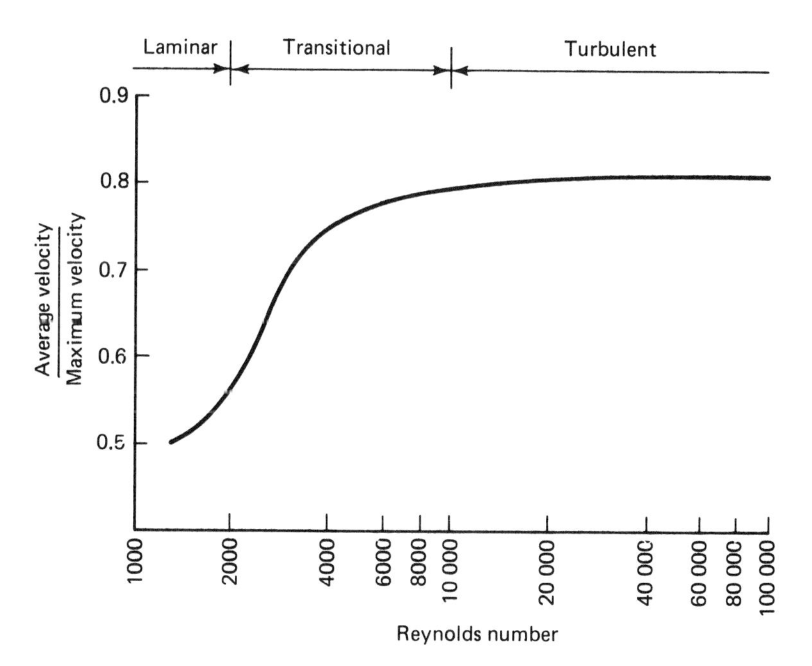

Figure 7.20 Ratio of average to maximum speed *vs* Reynolds Number for water

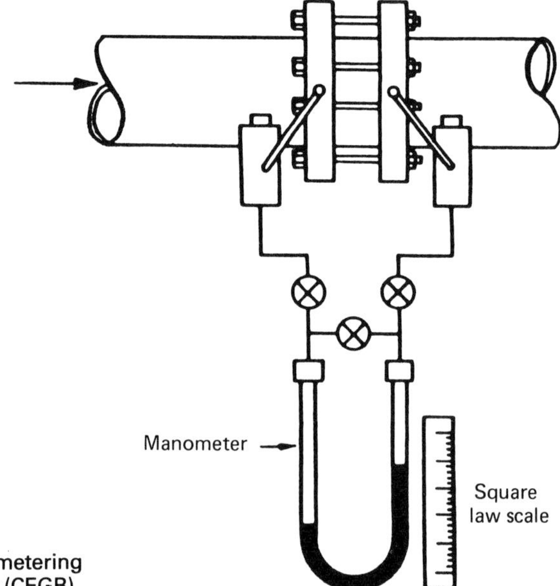

Figure 7.21(a) Simple flow metering system using a manometer (CEGB)

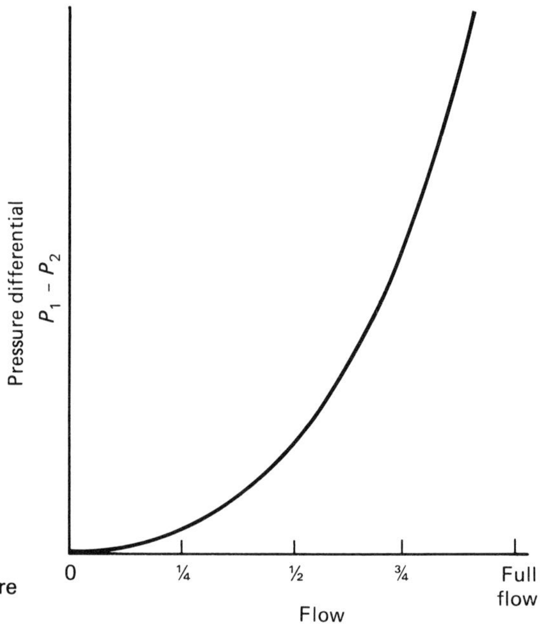

Figure 7.21(b) Graph of pressure differential *vs* flow

Figure 7.21 Relationship between pressure differential and flow (CEGB)

Precautions when using mercury

Many test instruments contain mercury, so it is important to appreciate the precautions necessary when it is handled. The essential point to note is that mercury is poisonous and so is the vapour it gives off. The amount of vapour released depends upon the ambient temperature and the area of mercury exposed. Thus, the basic requirements are to keep mercury as cool as possible; to expose only the minimum surface area; and to ensure that the room is well ventilated. If there is a lot to be handled a fume cupboard should be installed.

Stored mercury should be in suitable containers which are airtight or water sealed. The containers should stand on suitable smooth trays. The work bench should be smooth, impervious to mercury, and have a water trough to collect spillage.

Do not wear a watch, rings, etc. (particularly gold), and always wear protective clothing. Wash any part of the skin that is contaminated with the substance.

Spillage

If spillage should occur clean up as much of it as possible straight away. However, almost inevitably, there will be some left. In that case the area of floor affected should be coated with a mixture made up from equal parts of slaked lime and flowers of sulphur mixed with water. The Station Chemist will be able to provide this. Allow the paste to dry. After 24 hours wash the paste off with clean water.

Differential pressure transducers (flow transducers)

Flow transducers are now widely used for test purposes. They are more convenient to use than a manometer or flowmeter and, as they give an electrical output signal, can be used in conjunction with automatic data acquisition equipment. *Figure 7.22* shows the connections for a typical flow transducer for test work. The electrical supply to the instrument is at 28 volts.

The pressure connections from the orifice plate or other differential device are the same as for manometers. The differential pressure at the transducer causes a milliampere signal to flow, typical values at full load being 20 and 50 mA. This is translated into a voltage signal by measuring the potential across a suitable high quality resistor. *Figure 7.22* shows the connections for a 0–50 mA output transducer. To obtain a 100 mV signal at full load on the instrument it is thus necessary to use a 2 ohm resistor.

Figure 7.23 shows a typical transducer and 28 V supply source. The

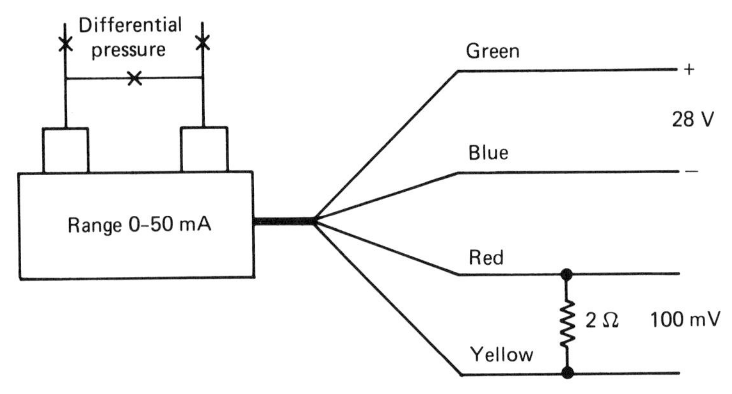

Figure 7.22 Connections to a flow transducer

Figure 7.23 KDG flow transducer and Weir supply source (CEGB)

instrument illustrated has a pressure differential range of 0–20 000 mm w.g. This is too high for many applications and so variable-range instruments are available, with which the range can be varied down to about 0–2500 mm w.g. There are 3-wire and 2-wire arrangements and these are illustrated in *Figure 7.24*. Usually they are operated between 4 and 20 mA output.

Before using a flow transducer for testing purposes it is desirable to carry out a calibration. This is done by applying a suitable head of water to the high-pressure connection with the transducer and a mercury manometer connected in parallel as shown in *Figure 7.25*. With the drain valve D shut and the equalizing valve E open, the differential pressure applied to both the

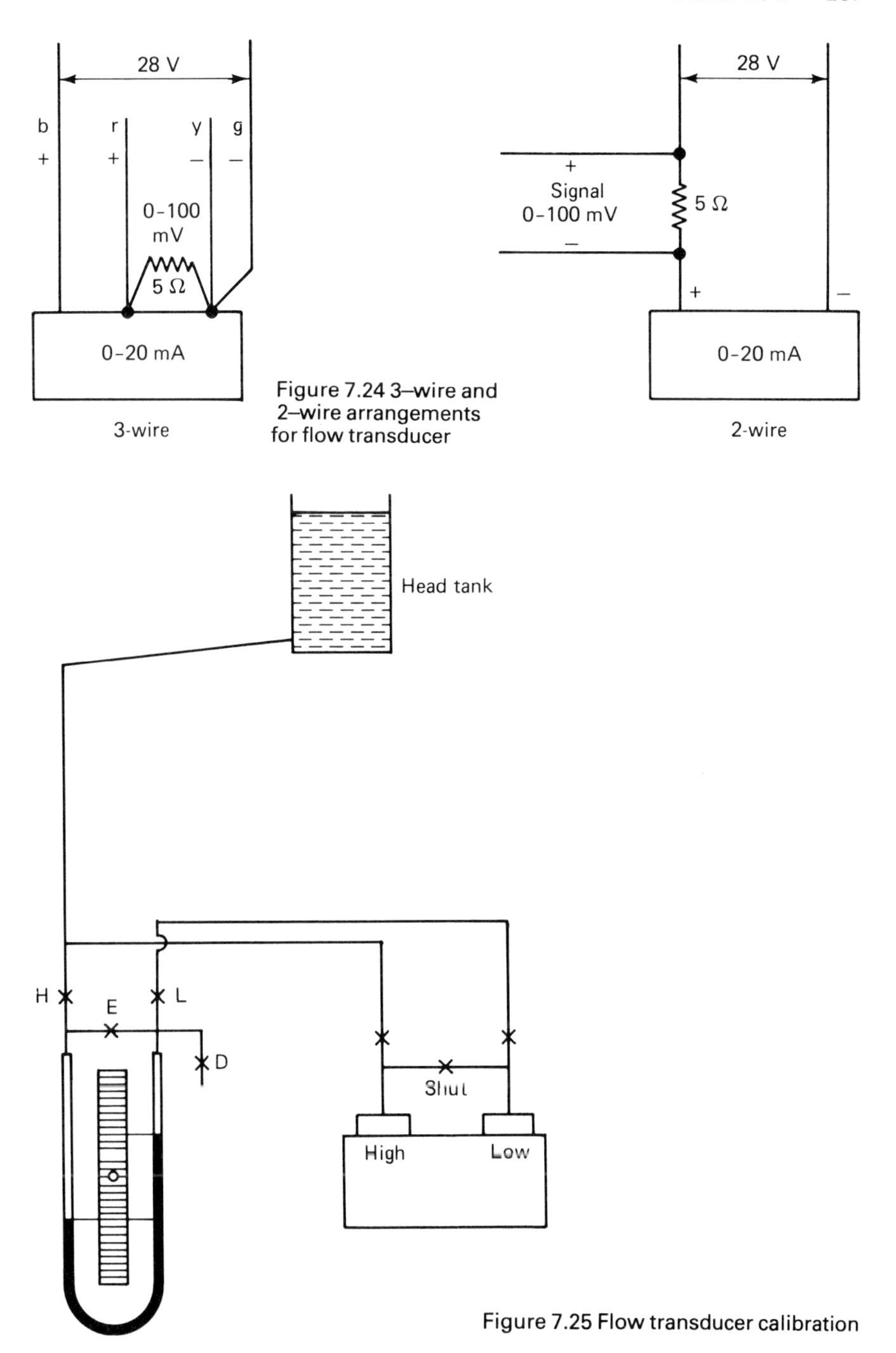

Figure 7.24 3–wire and 2–wire arrangements for flow transducer

Figure 7.25 Flow transducer calibration

transducer and the manometer will be zero. Then, with valve E shut, the differential can be increased to a maximum by operation of the drain valve

D. To reduce the differential to zero again in a controlled manner, close valve D and gradually open valve E. Readings of the manometer and transducer millivolt output are taken while increasing and decreasing the differential, and so the calibration can be determined.

A typical example is shown below for a variable-range instrument. It was desired to obtain about 100 mV output when the differential was 24 cm of mercury under water. The instrument range setting to achieve this was 6.54 in this case.

Differential Pressure Transducer
(Range setting 6.5400. Temp. 19.4°C)

Mano. Head as read (cm *H_2O/Hg*)	Head *(mbar)*	Transducer Output as read *(mV)*
0.000	0.000	0.227
3.020	94.407	12.390
6.250	195.380	25.250
9.200	287.599	37.120
11.760	367.626	47.270
15.020	469.536	60.420
13.100	565.819	72.860
21.020	657.100	84.500
23.940	748.382	96.210
24.100	753.383	96.790
21.070	658.663	84.660
18.090	565.507	72.320
15.070	471.099	50.530
11.970	374.191	48.160
9.050	282.910	36.380
6.070	189.753	24.470
2.930	91.594	11.960
0.000	0.000	0.236

The calibration of the device is determined by regression analysis as in the case of pressure transducers and is:

mbar = 7.7972 (mV − 0.20)

For example, what is the differential when the millivolt reading is 60.0?

Differential = 7.7972 (60 − 0.2) = 466.27 mbar

Flow measurements in open channels

Large flows

For very high volume flow measurements, such as the CW flow to a cooling tower, special facilities are required which normally are not available at a power station. For example, it may be that a battery of current meters is needed, located in a suitable length of straight culvert. For such measurements it is best to call on the services of specialists.

Small flows

Small flows may be measured by passing the water over a weir. The depth of water flowing over a weir is a function of the rate of flow, and so by measuring the depth it is possible to apply suitable formulae and thus determine the flow rate. However, certain precautions are necessary, such as:

(a) The depth should be measured well upstream, at least four times the depth.
(b) The depth should be between 0.05 and 0.3 metres.
(c) The width of the tank should be several times that of the weir.

Various types of weir can be used and reference should be made to standard textbooks for details.

If a V-notch is used, the notch must be sharp and straight. The channel area must be at least nine times that of the notch area at maximum head. The flow for a V-notch is given by:

$$Q = \frac{8}{15} C \tan\frac{\phi}{2} \sqrt{(2gH^5)}$$

Where Q = flow in m^3/s
C = coefficient of discharge, usually between 0.57 and 0.64
ϕ = notch angle, usually between 35° and 120°
H = head over the weir in metres

$$\text{So } Q = 2.3624\, C \tan\frac{\phi}{2} \sqrt{H^5}\ \text{m}^3/\text{s}$$

If the head over the weir is measured as h cm (see *Figure 7.26*), then

$$H = \frac{h}{100}$$

$$\text{and } Q = 85.046\, C \tan\frac{\psi}{2} h^{2.5}\ \text{litre/h}$$

Two commonly used notches have angles of 90° and 45°, and the corresponding formulae often used are:

90° notch, $Q = 52.7536\ h^{2.48}$ litre/h
45° notch, $Q = 26.376\ h^{2.48}$ litre/h

For example, what is the rate of flow over a 90° V-notch when h = 10 cm?

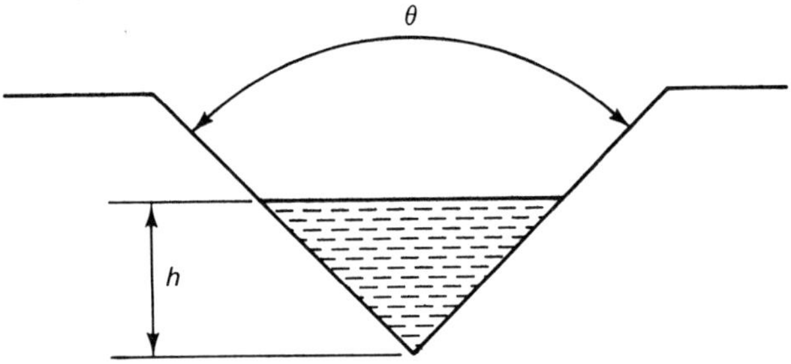

Figure 7.26 V–notch details

$$Q = 52.7536 \times 10^{2.48} \text{ litre/h}$$
$$\log Q = \log 52.7536 - 2.48 \log 10 = 1.7223 \quad 2.48$$
$$= 4.202$$
$$\therefore Q = \text{antilog } 4.202 = \quad 15\,930 \text{ litre/h}$$

To save the trouble of calculating the flows, it is usual to prepare a graph from which the answer may be read directly such as in *Figure 7.27*. For each notch angle calculate two widely separated flows and join them on a large sheet of log–log graph paper with a straight line.

Appendix 1

Determination of an expression for rate of flow

Bernouilli's theorem for incompressible fluids with streamline flow states that the sum of the pressure, kinetic and potential energies at any point is constant.

$$\text{So } P + \frac{\rho v^2}{2} + g \rho H = K$$

where P = pressure in N/m^2
v = velocity in m/s
ρ = density in kg/m^3
g = gravitational acceleration in m/s^2
H = height above an arbitrary datum in m
K = a constant

Consider a pipe with a constricted bore, as shown in *Figure 7.28*. The density of the fluid is the same at A_2 as at A_1

$$\text{So } P_1 + \frac{\rho v_1^2}{2} + g\rho H_1 = P_2 + \frac{\rho v_2^2}{2} + g\rho H_2 \qquad (1)$$

If the pipe is horizontal, $H_1 = H_2$, and in such a case:

$$P_1 + \frac{\rho v_1^2}{2} = P_2 + \frac{\rho v_2^2}{2}$$

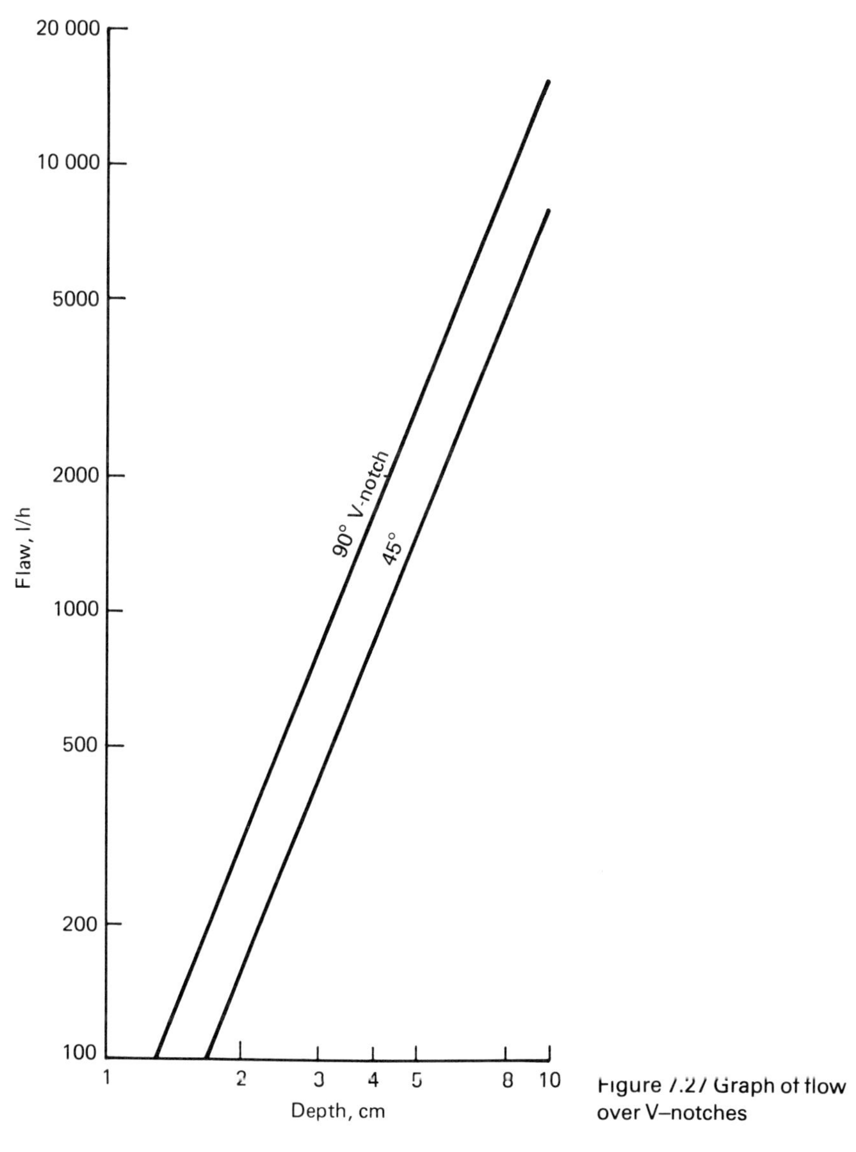

Figure 7.27 Graph of flow over V–notches

$$v_2^2 - v_1^2 = \frac{2}{\rho}(P_1 - P_2) \qquad (2)$$

The flow Q past $A_1 = A_1 v_1$, and past $A_2 = A_2 v_2$

$\therefore A_1 v_1 = A_2 v_2 = Q$

Let $m = \frac{A_2}{A_1}$, the area ratio.

Then $v_1 = \frac{A_2}{A_1} v_2 = m v_2$

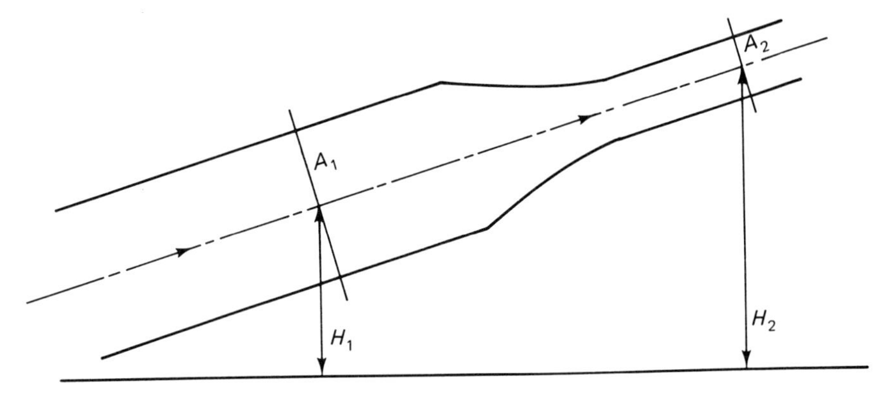

Figure 7.28 Pipe configuration

So (2) becomes:

$$v_2^2(1 - m^2) = \frac{2}{\rho}(P_1 - P_2) \tag{3}$$

$$v_2 = \frac{1}{\sqrt{\rho 1 - m^2}} \sqrt{\frac{2 \ P_1 - P_2}{\rho}} \tag{4}$$

Now $Q = A_2 v_2$

$$\therefore Q = \frac{A_2}{\sqrt{(1 - m^2)}} \sqrt{\frac{2(P_1 - P_2)}{\rho}} \tag{5}$$

The expression $\dfrac{1}{\sqrt{(1 - m^2)}}$ is called the 'velocity of approach' factor and is denoted by E.

$$\text{So } Q = EA_2 \sqrt{\frac{2(P_1 - P_2}{\rho}} \ \text{m}^3/\text{s} \tag{6}$$

But $P_1 - P_2 = gH\rho_W$

where H is the height of the equivalent water column in metres at 4°C, and ${}_{W}$ is the density of the water at 4°C = 1000 kg/m³

$$\therefore \text{From (6), } Q = EA_2 \sqrt{\frac{2gH\rho_W}{\rho}} \ \text{m}^3/\text{s}$$

$$= EA \sqrt{\frac{2 \times 1000 \times gh}{\rho}} \tag{7}$$

But H is in metres, whereas the head usually is measured in millimetres.

Let h be height in mm, then $H = \dfrac{h}{1000}$

$$\text{So from (7), } Q = EA_2 \sqrt{\frac{2gh}{\rho}} \ \text{m}^3/\text{s}$$

Also, $W = Q\rho = EA\sqrt{2gh\rho}$ kg/s

where W = mass rate of flow

E = velocity of approach factor, already defined

A_2 = area of constriction in m², $= \dfrac{\pi d^2}{4 \times 10^6}$ with d in mm

g = gravitational constant = 9.81 m/s²

ρ = density of fluid in kg/m³

h = height of manometer column in mm

$$\text{So } W = \frac{E d^2 \pi}{4 \times 10^6} \sqrt{(2 \times 9.81 \rho h)} \text{ kg/s}$$

$$= \frac{E d^2 \pi}{4 \times 10^6} \times 4.42945 \times 3600 \sqrt{(\rho h)} \text{ kg/h}$$

$$\therefore W = 0.01252\, E d^2 \sqrt{(\rho h)} \text{ kg/h}$$

However, this equation assumes ideal and streamline flow. In practice the flow is neither ideal nor streamline, and so correction factors are necessary in the form of the equation used in practice, i.e.

$$W = (0.01252)\, CZeEd^2 \sqrt{(\rho h)} \text{ kg/h}$$

where C = discharge coefficient

e = expansibility factor

Z = factor for Reynolds number and pipe size.

Appendix 2

Head correction for manometers containing mercury under water

With reference to *Figure 7.29*,

$$P_1 - H_1 \rho_1 g = P_2 - H_2 \rho_1 g - hm \rho_2 g$$

but $hm = H_1 - H_2$

$$\therefore \frac{P_1 - P_2}{g} = H_2\rho_1 - H_1\rho_1 - hm\,\rho_2$$

$$= \rho_1 (H_2 - H_1) - \rho_2 hm$$

$$= -\rho_1 hm - \rho_2 hm$$

$$\text{So } \frac{P_1 - P_2}{g} = hm(\rho_2 - \rho_1)$$

$$\therefore hm = \frac{P_1 - P_2}{g(\rho_2 - \rho_1)}$$

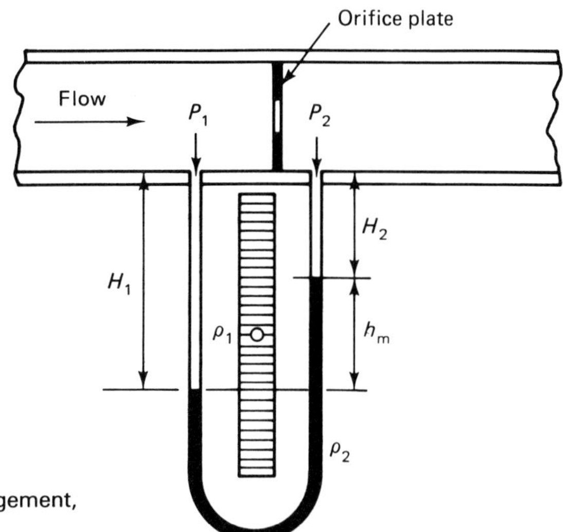

Figure 7.29 Manometer arrangement, water over mercury

but $P_1 - P_2 = h\rho g$
where h = equivalent head of fluid of density ρ

$$\text{So } hm = \frac{h\rho g}{(\rho_2 - \rho_1)}$$

$$\therefore h = hm\,\frac{(\rho_2 - \rho_1)}{\rho}$$

Appendix 3

Derivation of *Figure 7.12: m* v *CmE*

m	$E = \frac{1}{\sqrt{(1 - m^2)}}$	mE	C (*Figure 7.14*)	CmE
0.1	1.00504	0.10051	0.5980	0.06011
0.2	1.02062	0.20413	0.6042	0.12334
0.3	1.04829	0.31449	0.6082	0.19128
0.4	1.09109	0.43644	0.6070	0.26492
0.5	1.15470	0.57735	0.6060	0.34988
0.6	1.2500	0.7500	0.6073	0.45548
0.7	1.40027	0.98019	0.6185	0.60625

Appendix

Derivation of curve d/D **v.** *mE*

The velocity of approach factor $E = \dfrac{1}{\sqrt{(1 - m^2)}}$

Therefore $mE = \dfrac{m}{\sqrt{(1 - m^2)}}$

Thus, by selecting values of m the corresponding value of

$\dfrac{m}{\sqrt{(1 - m^2)}}$ can be determined, i.e. mE

m = the area ratio, so $\sqrt{m} = \dfrac{d}{D}$

Thus a table can be constructed as follows:

m	m^2	E	mE	$\sqrt{m} = d/D$
0.1	0.01	1.005	0.1005	0.3162
0.2	0.04	1.0206	0.2041	0.4472
0.3	0.09	1.048	0.3145	0.5477
0.4	0.16	1.0911	0.4364	0.6325
0.5	0.25	1.1547	0.5774	0.7071
0.6	0.36	1.2500	0.7500	0.7746
0.7	0.49	1.4003	0.9802	0.8367
0.8	0.64	1.6667	1.3333	0.8944
0.9	0.81	2.2942	2.0648	0.9487

In this manner the value of E and of d/D can be found for any value of m.

Questions

1 What are the main types of pressure difference devices used for test purposes?
2 What is the advantage of each?
3 Name some of the tappings used in conjunction with orifice plates.
4 State the general rules for design and installation of orifice plates with D and $D/2$ tappings.
5 What effect will pulsating flow have on the readings?
6 State the basic flow formula for use with orifice plates.
7 Where would the orifice plate drain hole be situated in a water pipe?
8 What is the purpose of determining Reynolds number?
9 What is the 'Discharge Coefficient?'?
10 State the formula for the equivalent head of water of a mercury-under-water reading.
11 State the main precautions to be taken when handling mercury.
12 State the main criteria for a flow-box layout for measuring flow by means of a V-notch.

Exercise 1

Determine the L.P. gland seal water supply to the turbine-driven boiler feed pump on a supercritical unit. The data is:

Pipe diameter D_a	= 76.2 mm I.D.
Orifice diameter d_a	= 51.79 mm
Differential head	= 71 mm Hg under H_20
Ambient temperature	= 25°C
Water temperature	= 36°C
Water pressure	= 15 bar abs.
Orifice plate type	= Sharp-edged with D and $D/2$ tappings

Exercise 2

Given the flow equation $W = (0.01252)\ CZeEd^2 \sqrt{(h\rho)}$ kg/h show that

$$C = \frac{90032q}{d^2 E \sqrt{(\Delta P \times \rho^1)}} \text{ for water flow in clean pipe at } R_e\ 10^6$$

where q = flow in kg/s
ΔP = differential pressure in millibars
$Z = 1$

Exercise 1 (Answer)

$$D_w = 76.2 \times 1.0002 = 76.215 \text{ mm}$$

$$\text{Head } h = 71.0 \times 12.5365 = 890.1 \text{ mm w.g.}$$

$$d^2/D^2 = \left(\frac{51.79}{76.2}\right)^2 = 0.462 = m;\ d_w = 51.8 \text{ mm}$$

$$C = 0.6061$$

$$E = \frac{1}{\sqrt{(1 - m^{22})}} = 1.1276$$

$$Z = 1.0$$

$$\rho = 994.3 \text{ kg/m}^3$$

$$\therefore W = 0.01252 \times 0.6061 \times 1.1276 \times 51.8^2 \times \sqrt{(994.3 \times 890.1)}$$

$$= 21\ 600 \text{ kg/h}$$

Exercise 2 (Answer)

For the conditions stated $e = 1$ and $Z = 1$

So $W = 0.01252\ CEd^2 \sqrt{(h\rho)}$ kg/h

$$\text{But } h = \frac{\text{mbar}}{0.0981} = 10.2 \text{ mbar}$$

$\therefore W = 0.01252 \times 3.1937\, CEd^2 \sqrt{(\triangle P \times \rho)}$ kg/h

$$\text{so } C = \frac{25.009W}{Ed^2 \sqrt{\triangle P \times \rho)}}$$

But $W = 3600q$

$$\text{so } C = \frac{90032q}{Ed^2 \sqrt{(\triangle P \times \rho)}}$$

Project 1

(1) Determine the value of the constant K in the equation $W = K\sqrt{h}$ for a square edged orifice plate, given the following information:

Duty: Supercritical unit boiler feed pump H.P. gland seal water supply.

Tappings	D and $D/2$
Pipe material	Mild steel
Pipe I.D.	65.5 mm
Water temperature	96°C
Water pressure	12 bar abs.
Ambient temperature	16°C
Orifice plate material	Staïnless steel
Differential head	1600 mm Hg under H_2O
Flow	18 kg/s

(2) (i) Would the plate have a bevel?
(ii) Would the plate have a drain hole?
(iii) What would be the flow if the mercury under water differential was 1250 mm at 10°C?

Project 1 (Answer)

$W = 18.0 \times 3600 = 64\ 800$ kg/h

$D_W = D_a \times 1.0009 = 65.5 \times 1.0009 = 65.559$ mm

$\rho = 961$ kg/m^3; $h = 1600 \times 12.5595 = 20\ 095$ mm w.g.

$$N = \frac{64\ 800}{0.01252 \times 65.559^2 \sqrt{(961 \times 20\ 095)}} = 0.274$$

$CmE = 0.274 \therefore m = 0.41; \sqrt{m} = 0.640 = \dfrac{d}{D}$

$E = 1.096$

$$Re = \frac{3.54 \times 64.800}{0.0031 \times 65.559 \times 0.64} = 1.76 \times 10^6$$

$C = 0.607$

$d/D = 0.640$, so $d_W = 41.96$ mm

$$d_a = \frac{41.96}{1.0014} = 41.90 \text{ mm}$$

Check: $W = 0.01252 \times 0.607 \times 1.0 \times 1.096 \times 41.96^2 \times 31 \times 141.76$
$= 64\ 440$ kg/h
Head $h = 20\ 095$ mm w.g. at 4°C
$64\ 440 = K\sqrt{20\ 095}$
$\therefore K = 454.6$
So $W = 454.6\sqrt{h}$ where h is in mm w.g.

(2) (i) Plate thickness = 2 mm. The maximum permissible thickness without a bevel is 4.2 mm, so none is required.
(ii) A drain hole is not considered to be necessary if the pipe diameter is less than 100 mm, as in this case.
(iii) $h = 1250 \times 12.5708 = 15\ 713.5$ mm w.g.
So $W = 454.6\sqrt{(15\ 713.5)} = 57\ 000$ kg/h

Additional Reading

1 JONES, E.B., *Instrument Technology Vol. 1,* (Butterworth)
2 *Fuels and Fuel Technology Vol. II,* W. FRANCIS, (Pegamon Press).
3 'Flowmeter types and their usage', G.A. WATSON, *Chartered Mechanical Engineer*, p. 27, February 1978.
4 *Power Hydraulics*, A.B. GOODWIN. (Cleaver-Hume Press)
5 *Elementary Practical Hydraulics of Flow in Pipes*, C.T. DONKIN. (Oxford University Press)
6 *The Efficient Use of Fuel* (HMSO)

Part III

Main Plant

8 Boiler efficiency and optimisation of air supplies

9 Pollution Control

10 Turbine performance and monitoring

11 Condensers and back pressure

12 Feed heating

8 Boiler efficiency and optimisation of air supplies

Boiler efficiency determination

There are two basic ways of determining the efficiency of a boiler:

(a) The Direct Method; (b) The Losses Method.

The direct method

This was standard for a long time, but is little used now. It is straightforward and consists of measuring the heat supplied to the boiler in a given time and the heat added to the steam in the boiler. Thus, the efficiency of a non-reheat boiler is given by:

$$\text{Efficiency} = \frac{(\text{enthalpy of steam} - \text{enthalpy of feed}) \times \text{steam flow}}{\text{quantity of coal} \times \text{calorific value}} \text{ per unit time.}$$

The trouble is that several of the quantities are difficult to measure accurately such as the coal weight. Accordingly the result may have an overall tolerance of about ± 1.5%.

The losses method

The efficiency of a boiler equals 100% minus the losses. Thus, if the losses are known the efficiency can be derived easily. This method has several advantages, one of which is that errors are not so significant; for example, if the losses total 10% then an error of 1.0% will affect the result by only 0.1%.

The losses method is now the usual one for boiler efficiency determination. In fact there is no provision on many modern boilers for fitting coal weighing equipment, in which case the direct method cannot be used. A typical pulverized fuel boiler heat balance is:

Gross CV Basis		*Net CV Basis*	
Loss due to:			
Dry flue gas	3.98%	Dry flue gas	4.3%
Wet flue gas	5.27%	Sensible heat in water vapour	0.75%
C in A	0.24%	C in A	0.25%
Radiation and unaccounted	0.44%	Radiation and unaccounted	0.45%
		Total loss	5.75%
Total loss	9.93%		
Boiler efficiency =	90.07%	Boiler efficiency =	94.25%

Another point to bear in mind is that if a boiler is tested and found to have an efficiency of, say, 94%, it would be quite wrong to imagine that it is operated normally at that efficiency. During testing, particular care is taken to keep the steam pressure, temperature and so on, as steady as possible and there is neither blowdown nor sootblowing. Also the boiler is probably tested immediately after a sootblow. So there are many factors common to normal operation that are absent when testing. Thus the test efficiency is probably the best that can be attained and for normal operation the value will be less.

Calorific value of fuels

There are four different bases for the determination of calorific value:

(a) Gross CV at constant volume (GCV_v). For example, this is determined by burning a sample of coal in a bomb calorimeter.
(b) Net CV at constant volume (NCV_v).
(c) Gross CV at constant pressure (GCV_p);
(d) Net CV at constant pressure (NCV_p).

Net calorific value at constant pressure (NCV_p) is commonly used.

Of course, fuels still have their calorific value determined on a GCV_v basis, and so it is necessary to convert the results to a NCV_p basis thus:

$$NCV_p = GCV_v - [212.1\,H + 24.4\,(M + 0.1\,A) + 0.7\,O]\ \text{kJ/kg}$$

where H = hydrogen %
M = moisture % (including the combined water of the mineral matter)
O = oxygen %
A = ash %

However, in the UK it has been decided to use a constant for the oxygen component equal to 6 kJ/kg for coal and coke, and zero for oil and natural gas.

So for coal and coke, $NCV_p = GCV_v - [212.1\,H - 24.4\,(M + 0.1\,A) - 6]$ kJ/kg
For oil and natural gas, $NCV_p = GCV_v - (212.1\,H + 24.4\,M)$ kJ/kg

Example
A certain coal has a Gross Calorific Value at constant volume, of 25 353 kJ/kg, $H = 4.0\%$, $M = 14.0\%$, $A = 16.0\%$.

$$\therefore NCV_p = 25\,353 - [(212.1 \times 4.0) - 24.4\,(14 + 1.6) + 6)]\ \text{kJ/kg}$$
$$= 25\,353 - (848.4 - 380.6 - 6) = 24\,118\ \text{kJ/kg}$$

The efficiency obtained when using the NCV_p is significantly higher than when using the GCV_v, so it is important that the calorific value used is clearly specified.

In addition to the gross and net calorific values there is also gross and net boiler heat. The gross boiler heat is that accepted by the boiler including the heat equivalent of the boiler auxiliaries. Thus, a 'gross on gross' thermal efficiency is one in which the gross boiler heat is considered and also the gross calorific value. If the heat of the boiler auxiliaries is deducted from the boiler heat it would be 'net on gross'. In a similar manner it is possible to have 'gross on net' (if the gross boiler heat and net CV. is used), or 'net on net' (if net boiler heat and net CV. are used).

The calorific value of a few substances is given in *Table 8.1* average values being given for coal, oil and gas.

Table 8.1 Calorific values of various substances (at atmospheric pressure and cooled to 25°C)

Substance	*Symbol*	*GCVv (kJ/kg)*	*NCVp(kJ/kg)*
Hydrogen	H_2	143 050	121 840
Carbon (to CO)	C	10 200	—
Carbon (to CO_2)	C	33 820	—
Carbon monoxide (to CO_2)	CO	10 165	—
Methane	CH_4	55 700	50 400
Sulphur (to SO_2)	S	9 304	—
Midlands coal	—	22 000	20 800
Fuel oil	—	44 000	41 500
Coal gas	—	36 800	32 800
Natural gas	—	54 000	48 800

Notice that the combustion of hydrogen releases considerably more heat than any of the other elements. For example, combustion of 1 kg hydrogen releases about four times as much heat as burning 1 kg carbon to carbon dioxide and about thirteen times as much as 1 kg of sulphur to sulphur dioxide. In fact, in any fuel the calorific value is determined primarily by the ratio of hydrogen to carbon present, as shown in *Table 8.2*.

Table 8.2 Approximate hydrogen: carbon ratio of different fuels

Fuel	*H %*	*C%*	*H: C ratio*	*GCVv*	*NCVp*
Coal	4.4	65.0	1:15	22 000	20 800
Fuel oil	12.0	83.0	1:7	44 000	41 500
Natural gas	24.0	74.0	1:3	54 000	48 800

Determination of approximate calorific value using Dulong's formula

As the only combustible substances present in fuels are hydrogen, carbon or sulphur, it follows that the approximate calorific value can be determined from a knowledge of the proportions of each substance present, as shown in Dulong's formula:

$$\text{Thus } GCV = 33\ 820C + 143\ 050\left(H - \frac{O}{8}\right) + 9304S \text{ kJ/kg fuel}$$

$$NCV = 33\ 820C + 121\ 840\left(H - \frac{O}{8}\right) + 9304S \text{ kJ/kg fuel}$$

where O, C, H and S are the kg/kg of fuel of each.

The term $(H - O/8)$ is assumed to contain a correction for the hydrogen which combines with the oxygen in the fuel, i.e. the oxygen combines with one-eighth of its mass of hydrogen, and so the hydrogen remaining equals $(H - O/8)$.

Example

A coal has the following ultimate analysis:

Moisture	15.96%
Ash	14.73%
Carbon	54.22%
Hydrogen	3.70%
Nitrogen	1.11%
Sulphur	1.43%
Oxygen	8.85%
GCV_V	21 995 kJ/kg (by bomb calorimeter)

From Dulong's formula:

$GCV_V =$

$$(33\ 820 \times 0.5422) + 143\ 050\left((0.037 - \frac{0.0885}{8}\right) + (9304 \times 0.0143) \text{ kJ/kg}$$

$$= 18\ 337 + 3711 + 133$$
$$= 22\ 181 \text{ kJ/kg}$$

The discrepancy between the two results is about 0.8%.

Air required for combustion and products of combustion

The theoretical quantity of air required for the combustion of a fuel can be determined from the following formula:

$$\text{Theoretical air required} = 4.31\left[\frac{8}{3}C + 8\left(H - \frac{O}{8}\right) + S\right] \text{kg/100 kg fuel}$$

where C = % carbon per kg fuel
H = % hydrogen per kg fuel
O = % oxygen per kg fuel
S = % sulphur per kg fuel

The values inside the square brackets indicate the quantity of oxygen required for each combustible constituent of the fuel. The multiplier 4.31 determines the air required to supply the necessary oxygen. This is derived from the fact that 100 kg of air contains 23.2 kg oxygen, so 1 kg of oxygen is contained in

$$\frac{100}{23.2} \text{ kg of air, i.e. } 4.31 \text{ kg}$$

Example

A certain coal has the following ultimate analysis:

	Symbol	%
Carbon	C	56.8
Hydrogen	H	3.7
Nitrogen	N	1.3
Sulphur	S	2.0
Oxygen	O	7.0
Ash	—	16.7
Moisture	—	12.5
		100.0

Theoretical air required

$$= 4.31\left[\left(\frac{8}{3} \times 56.8\right) + 8\left(3.7 - \frac{7}{8}\right) + 2\right] \text{kg/100 kg fuel}$$

$$= 4.31\,(151.5 + 22.6 + 2) \text{ kg/100 kg fuel}$$

(Thus, 56.8 kg carbon requires 151.5 kg oxygen, the hydrogen requires 22.6 kg and the sulphur 2 kg.)

$$= 4.31\,(176.1) = 759 \text{ kg/100 kg fuel}$$

So the total oxygen required = 176.1 kg and the air required = 759.0 kg
∴ The nitrogen = 759 − 176.1 = 582.9 kg

Of course excess air must also be supplied in practice. The quantity of excess air present in a boiler may be determined from a knowledge of the CO_2% present and the theoretical maximum CO_2% for the fuel:

$$\text{Excess air} = \frac{\text{Theoretical } CO_2\%}{\text{Actual } CO_2\%} - 1$$

The theoretical CO_2% for various fuels is given in *Table 8.3*.

Table 8.3 Theoretical CO_2% for various fuels

Fuel	*CO_2% by volume*
Natural gas	11.7
Fuel oil	15.3
Bituminous coal	18.6

So if the fuel specified in the previous example were burned with 15% CO_2 the excess air would be:

$$\text{Excess air} = \frac{18.6}{15.0} - 1 = 0.24\text{, or } 24\%$$

and the air for combustion would be 1.24 × 7.59 kg air/kg coal = 9.4 kg. In general, Actual air × actual CO_2% = Theoretical air × theoretical CO_2%.

Products of combustion

With only the theoretical quantity of air supplied but with complete combustion (an impossible situation in a real boiler) the products of combustion will be as shown in *Table 8.4*.

Should the fuel be burned with excess air there will be, in addition to the products listed in *Table 8.4*, the products shown in *Table 8.5*.

The table is derived from the previously determined values for the theoretical air, oxygen and nitrogen required, i.e.

Air = 759.0 kg/100 kg fuel
Oxygen = 176.1 kg/100 kg fuel
Nitrogen = 582.9 kg/100 kg fuel

For example, 10% excess air is equal to 10% of 759.0 = 75.9 kg, and so on for the other values.

Pulverized-fuel boilers are often operated with about 20% excess air. Thus, in addition to the flue gas products established in *Table 8.4*, there will be about 151.8 kg air/100 kg fuel, and this will comprise 35.2 kg oxygen and 116.6 kg nitrogen. So the products of combustion with 20% excess air will be as shown in *Table 8.6*.

Table 8.4 Products of combustion (theoretical air) (for fuel used in last example)

		CO_2	$H20$	SO_2	$N2$	*Total*
1	kg of gas/100 kg fuel (e.g. $CO_2 = C + 0_2 =$ $56.8 + 151.1 = 208.3$; $H_20 = 9H_2 = 9 \times 3.7$ $= 33.3$, etc.)	208.3	33.3	4.0	582.9	
2	Moisture kg/100 kg fuel		12.5			
3	Specific vol. at stp in $m^3/kg = 22.4 \div$ mol. mass of each gas	0.51	1.24	0.35	0.8	
4	Volume/100 kg fuel (wet) $= [(1) + (2)] \times (3) m^3$	106.23	56.8	1.4	466.3	630.75
5	% by volume (wet) = (CO_2, H_20 etc. $\div$ 630.75)100	16.8	9.0	0.22	73.9	
6	Vol./100 kg fuel (dry) (from (4)	106.23	—	1.4	466.3	572.53
7	% by vol. (dry) = ($C0_2$, H_20, etc. $\div$ 572.23)100	18.5	—	0.24	81.3	

Table 8.5 Extra products when excess air present

Excess air %	*0*	*10*	*20*	*30*	*40*	*50*
kg Air/100 kg fuel	0	75.9	151.8	227.7	303.6	379.5
kg 0_2/100 kg fuel	0	17.6	35.2	52.8	70.4	88.0
kg N_2/100 kg fuel	0	58.3	116.6	174.9	233.2	291.5

Table 8.6 Products of combustion (20% excess air)

		CO_2	H_2O	SO_2	N_2	O_2	*Total*
1	kg gas/100 kg fuel (Refer to Tables *8.4* and *8.5*)	208.3	45.8	4.0	582.9 + 116.6 = 699.5	35.2	992.8
2	Specific volume at stp	0.51	1.24	0.35	0.80	0.70	
	Wet products						
3	Volume m^3/100 kg fuel (=(1) × (2))	106.2	56.8	1.4	559.6	24.6	748.6
4	% by volume (wet)	14.2	7.6	0.2	74.7	3.3	100.0
	Dry products						
5	Volume m^3/100 kg fuel	106.2	—	1.4	559.6	24.6	691.8
6	% by volume (dry)	15.3	—	0.2	80.9	3.6	100.0

Note: The flue gas analysis obtained from an Orsat apparatus is on a 'dry' basis: the oxygen determined by a Zirconia analyser is on a 'wet' basis.

Boiler losses

The individual boiler losses include:

1 Dry flue gas.
2 Wet flue gas (this includes the loss due to combustion of the hydrogen in the fuel plus that due to moisture in the fuel).
3 Sensible heat in water vapour.
4 Moisture in combustion air.
5 Unburnt gas.
6 Combustible in ash.
7 Radiation and unaccounted.

1 Dry flue gas loss

The only components of a fuel which burn to form dry products of combustion are the carbon and sulphur. Of the two carbon has the greater significance, so for the present ignore the sulphur. The carbon can burn to either carbon dioxide or carbon monoxide thus:

(a) Carbon to carbon dioxide $C + O_2 = CO_2$
So masses $= 12 + 32 = 44$
$\therefore$ 44 kg of CO_2 contains 12 kg carbon.

So 1 kg of CO_2 contains $\frac{12}{44}$ kg of carbon, i.e. $\frac{3}{11}$ kg carbon.

(b) Carbon to carbon monixide $2C + 0_2 = 2CO$
So masses $= 24 + 32 = 56$
$\therefore$ 56 kg of CO contains 24 kg carbon.

So 1 kg of CO contains $\frac{24}{56}$ kg of carbon, i.e. $\frac{3}{7}$ kg carbon.

Total dry flue gas = kg carbon × (dry flue gas/kg carbon burned)

$$\text{So dry flue gas/kg carbon burned} = \frac{\text{Total dry flue gas burned}}{\text{kg carbon in flue gas}}$$

The total dry flue gas consists of the sum of all the dry constituents, i.e. $CO_2\% + O_2\% + N_2\% + CO\%$, and they will add up to 100 kg mol. For example, suppose the percentage by volume of the various constituents is:

CO_2 15.0%; O_2 4.4%; N_2 80.5%; CO 0.1%

Then the Relative Mass of each is:

	Vol %		*Molecular mass*		*Relative mass*
CO_2	15.0	×	44	=	660.0
0_2	4.4	×	32	=	140.8
N_2	80.5	×	28	=	2254.0
CO	0.1	×	28	=	2.8
	100.0				3057.6

Therefore 3057.6 kg of gas = 100 kg mol.

Thus, to revert to the dry flue gas loss, the total dry flue gas equals the sum of the percentage by volume of the CO_2, O_2, N_2 and CO and is equal to 100 kg mols.

$$\text{Hence dry flue gas/kg carbon burned} = \frac{100}{\text{kg carbon in flue gases}} \text{ kg mol}$$

It was shown earlier that the amount of carbon in the flue gas is $\frac{3}{11}$ kg for each kg of CO_2, and $\frac{3}{7}$ kg for each kg of CO.

$$\text{So dry flue gas/kg carbon burned} = \frac{100}{\frac{3\,CO_2\%}{11} + \frac{3\,CO\%}{7}} \text{ kg mol.}$$

But the $CO_2\%$ and CO% in the expression are in terms of mass of gas, whereas the flue gas analysis is usually in terms of volume of dry gas. Therefore the $CO_2\%$ by volume must be multiplied by 44 to give the corresponding relative mass. Similarly the CO% by volume must be multiplied by 28.

So dry flue gas/kg carbon burned =

$$\frac{100}{\left(44 \times CO_2\% \times \frac{3}{11}\right) + \left(28 \times CO\% \times \frac{3}{7}\right)} \text{ kg/mol}$$

where $CO_2\%$ and CO% are in terms of *volume*.

$$\therefore \text{ Dry flue gas/kg carbon burned} = \frac{100}{12\,(CO_2 + CO)} \text{ kg mol.}$$

$$\text{The carbon burned} = \frac{C}{100} - C \text{ in } A$$

Where C = % carbon in the fuel.
C in A = carbon in rough ash and dust, in kg/kg fuel.

$$\text{Hence dry flue gas} = \left[\frac{100}{12\,(CO_2 + CO)}\left(\frac{C}{100} - C \text{ in } A\right)\right] \text{kg mol./kg fuel}$$

There is a further complication. Sulphur in the fuel is almost all burned to SO_2 and this is absorbed along with the CO_2. Normally this effect can be ignored unless the sulphur content is very high, but if it is desired to allow for it the expression becomes:

$$\text{Dry flue gas} = \left[\frac{100}{12\,(CO_2 + CO)}\left(\frac{C}{100} + \frac{S}{267} - C \text{ in } A\right)\right] \text{kg mol./kg fuel}$$

Where S = % sulphur in fuel.

Note: The ratio of the atomic weights of carbon to sulphur $= \frac{12}{32} = \frac{1}{2.67}$

The sensible heat loss per unit mass of fuel = dry flue gas × kg mol. C_p $(T - t)$ kJ/kg.
Where kg mol C_p = kilogram molecular specific heat
= 30.6 kJ/kg mol.
T = A/H gas outlet temperature in °C.
t = Temperature at F.D. duct inlet in °C.

So dry flue gas loss =

$$\left[\frac{100}{12(CO_2 + CO)}\left(\frac{C}{100} + \frac{S}{267} - C \text{ in } A\right)\right] 30.6\,(T-t) \text{ kJ/ kg fuel}$$

The Seigert formula

A handy formula which gives a good idea of the dry flue gas loss on a gross CV basis is that due to Seigert:

$$\% \text{ loss} = \frac{K\,(T - t)}{\% \, CO_2}$$

where K = 0.68 for anthracite, 0.63 for bituminous coal, 0.70 for coke, and 0.56 for fuel oil.

2 Wet flue gas loss

The wet products of combustion are derived from the moisture and the hydrogen in the fuel. The combustion of hydrogen is represented by:

$$2H_2 + O_2 = 2H_2O$$

expressed as masses 4 + 32 = 36
So the combustion of 1 kg of hydrogen produces 9 kg of moisture.
The wet flue gas loss =

$$\frac{M + 9H}{100}\,[1.88\,(T - 25) + 2442 + 4.2\,(25 - t)] \text{ kJ/kg fuel.}$$

where M = % moisture per kg fuel
H = % hydrogen per kg fuel
T = Air heater gas outlet temperature (°C)
t = Air temperature at F.D. intake (°C)
Note: In the case of gaseous fuels the loss becomes:

$$\frac{9H}{100}[1.88\,(T - 25) + 2442 + 4.2\,(25 - t)] + \frac{M}{100}[1.88\,(T - t)] \text{ kJ/kg fuel}$$

The modified formula is necessary because the moisture in gaseous fuels is already in the vapour form.

3 Sensible heat of water vapour

This loss = [wet flue gas loss − (gross CV − net CV) kJ/kg fuel]
where the gross and net CV are in kJ/kg of fuel.

4 Moisture in combustion air loss

This is usually quite small and is not normally calculated.

Moisture in combustion air loss = $M_a \times h \times 1.88\,(T - t)$ kJ/kg fuel
Where M_a = Dry air for combustion kg/kg fuel.
h = kg moisture per kg dry air (from psychrometric tables or chart, see *Figure 8.1*)
A reasonably accurate value of M_a for solid and liquid fuels is given by

$$M_a = \frac{3.034\,N_2}{CO_2 + CO}\left(\frac{C}{100} + \frac{S}{267} - C \text{ in } A\right) \text{ kg/kg fuel}$$

where N_2, CO_2, CO = percent volume in dry gas, and
C, S = percent in fuel.

5 Unburnt gas loss

The mass of carbon monoxide in gas is given by the expression:

$$\frac{7CO}{3(CO_2 + CO)}$$

where CO_2 and CO represent the percentage of the constituents by volume in dry gas.

The mass of carbon in the carbon monoxide is derived from consideration of atomic weights, i.e. 28 kg of CO contains 12 kg of carbon. Therefore the

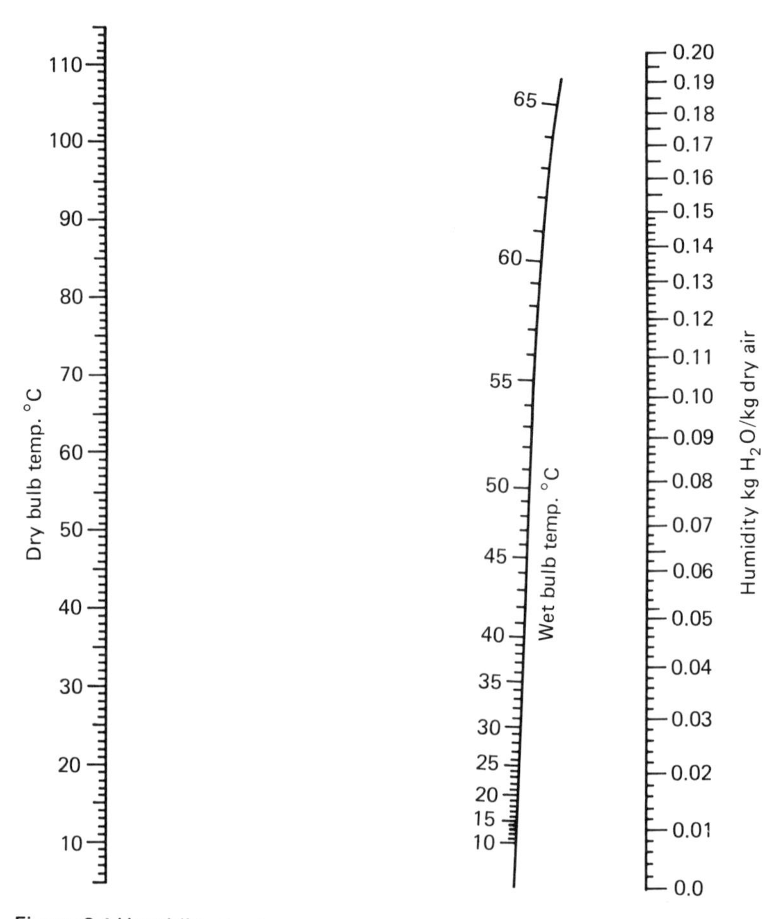

Figure 8.1 Humidity chart

carbon content is represented by:

$$\frac{12}{28} \times \frac{7CO}{3(CO_2 + CO)} = \frac{CO}{CO_2 + CO}$$

$$\text{Hence the loss} = \frac{CO}{CO_2 + CO} \times \text{the carbon burned} \times \text{CV of carbon in CO to } CO_2$$

$$= \frac{CO}{CO_2 + CO} \times \left(\frac{C}{100} + \frac{S}{267} - \text{C in A} \right) \times 23\ 717\ \text{kJ/kg fuel}$$

where 23 717 = CV of burning 1 kg of carbon in CO to CO_2, in kJ/kg.

6 Combustible in ash loss

$$\text{Loss} = \frac{cA}{100} \times 33\,820 \text{ kJ/kg fuel}$$

where c = % carbon in dry ash
A = Mass of ash kg/kg fuel
33 820 = calorific value of carbon burnt to CO_2 in kJ/kg

7 Radiation and unaccounted loss %

Figure 8.2 shows the value of this loss for various loads for boilers normally enclosed within a building. For outdoor boilers the values should be multiplied by 1.5. The values so obtained are for boilers in good condition.

Radiation loss is given by = $\log_{10}B = 0.8167 - 0.4238 \log_{10}C$,
where B = radiation and unaccounted loss,
where C = specific boiler capacity in kg/s.

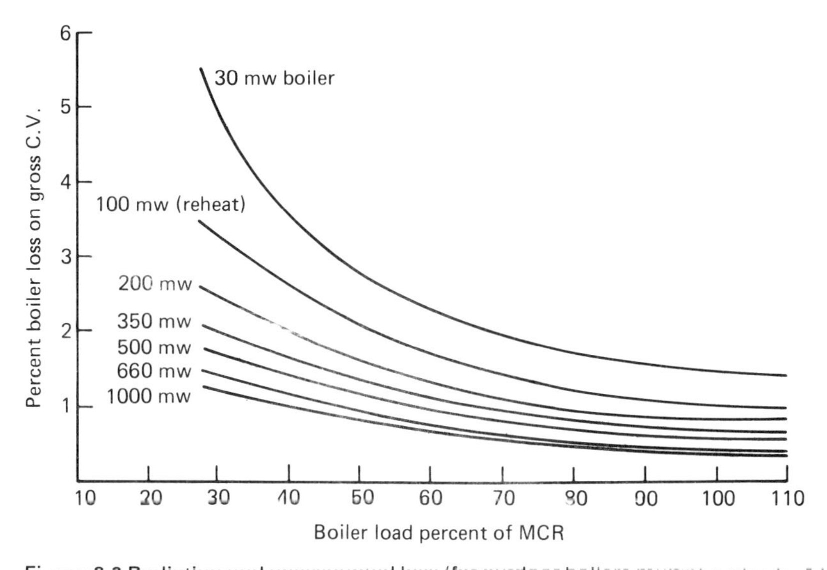

Figure 8.2 Radiation and unaccounted loss (for outdoor boilers multiply value by 1.5)

Summary of boiler losses

Symbols:

CO_2, CO, N_2 — % by volume in dry flue gas

C — % carbon per kg fuel

S	% sulphur per kg fuel
T	Air heater gas outlet temperature, °C
t	Air inlet temperature to F.D. intake duct, °C
M	% moisture per kg fuel
H	% hydrogen per kg fuel
GCV_v	Gross calorific value on constant volume basis, kJ/kg
NCV_p	Net calorific value on constant pressure basis, kJ/kg
Ma	Dry air for combustion, kg/kg fuel
h	kg moisture per kg dry air
c	% carbon in dry ash
A	Ash content, kg/kg fuel

1 *Dry flue gas*

$$= \left[\frac{100}{12(CO_2 + CO)}\left(\frac{C}{100} + \frac{S}{267} - C \text{ in } A\right)\right] \times 30.6(T - t)\text{kJ/kg fuel}$$

Alternatively:

$$\text{Dry flue gas loss \%} = \frac{K(T - t)}{CO_2\%} \quad (\text{on a } GCV_v \text{ basis})$$

Where $K = 0.68$ for anthracite, 0.63 for bituminous coal, 0.70 for coke, and 0.56 for fuel oil.

$$2.\ \textit{Wet flue gas} = \frac{M + 9H}{100}[1.88(T - 25) + 2442 + 4.2(25 - t)]\ \text{kJ/kg fuel}$$

for solid and liquid fuels.
For gaseous fuels the loss is
Wet flue gas =

$$\frac{9H}{100}[1.88(T - 25) + 2442 + 4.2(25 - t)] + \frac{M}{100}[1.88(T - t)]\ \text{kJ/kg fuel}$$

3. *Sensible heat in water vapour* = Wet flue gas loss − (gross CV − net CV) kJ/kg fuel

4. *Moisture in combustion air* = $M_a \times h \times 1.88(T - t)$ kJ/kg fuel

$$\text{For solid and liquid fuels } Ma = \frac{3.034\,N_2}{CO_2 + CO}\left(\frac{C}{100} + \frac{S}{267} - C \text{ in } A\right)$$

5. *Unburnt gas*

$$= \frac{CO}{CO_2 + CO}\left(\frac{C}{100} + \frac{S}{267} - C \text{ in } A\right) \times 23\,717\ \text{kJ/kg fuel}$$

$$6.\ \textit{Combustible in ash} = \frac{cA}{100} \times 33\,820\ \text{kJ/kg fuel}$$

7. *Radiation and unaccounted:* Refer to *Figure 8.2* for loss as percentage on GCV_v basis.

$$\text{The \% loss on } NCV_p \text{ basis} = \frac{GCV_v}{NCV_p} \times \% \text{ on } GCV_v \text{ basis.}$$

A convenient portable oxygen analyser for testing purposes is manufactured by Servomex. *Figure 8.3* shows a suitable model. Models are also available which have a digital read-out.

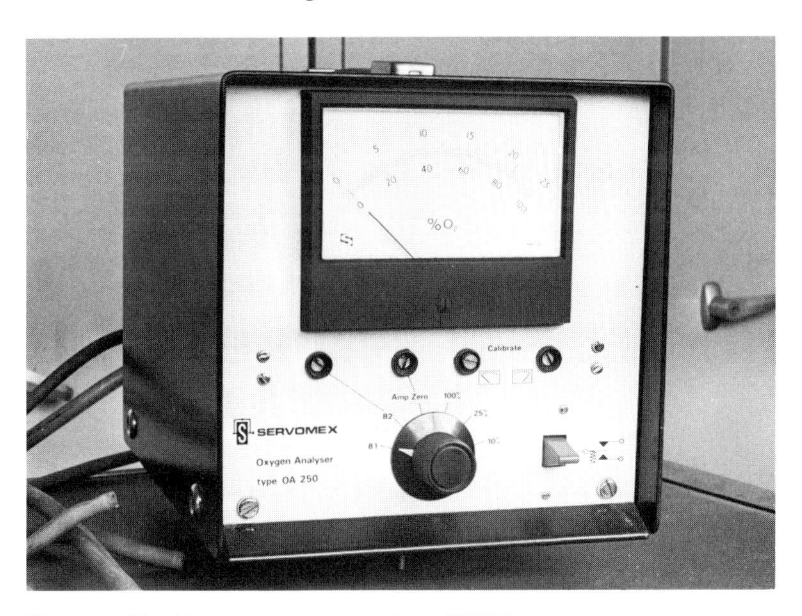

Figure 8.3 The Servomex oxygen analyser (CEGB)

A boiler efficiency calculation is given below. To convert a loss expressed in terms of kilojoules per kilogram of fuel to one expressed in terms of percentage loss, it is necessary merely to use the formula:

$$\% \text{ loss} = \frac{\text{loss in kJ/kg} \times 100}{GCV_v \text{ or } NCV_p}$$

Boiler efficiency calculation

Example

A boiler efficiency test produced the following full-load results:

Coal analysis

Moisture	17.2%
Ash	17.9%
Volatile matter	31.7%
Fixed carbon	33.2%
Hydrogen	3.83%
Sulphur	1.82%
Free carbon	50.1%
GCV_v	20 910 kJ/kg
NCV_p	19 628 kJ/kg

CO_2% at airheater outlet = 13.72 on L.H.S., 13.75 on R.H.S. — 13.73% average

O_2% (from CO_2/O_2 conversion chart) = 5.4%
N_2% (from $100 - CO_2 - O_2$) = 80.87%

Combustible in precipitator dust = 0.63, 0.51, 1.18, 0.91 — 0.81% average

Combustible in rough ash = 0.54%

A/H gas outlet temperature L.H.S. = 152°C, R.H.S. = 146°C — 149°C average = T

Air temperature at F.D. duct inlet L.H.S. = 21.2°C, R.H.S. = 20.0°C — 20.6°C average = t

Wet bulb temperature = 15°C
CO in flue gas = 200 ppm = 0.02%

Losses calculations

Assume 20% of the total ash is rough ash.
Then rough ash = 0.2 × 17.9 = 3.58% of coal
fine ash = 0.8 × 17.9 = 14.32% of coal
Carbon in rough ash = 0.0358 × 0.0054 = 0.00019 kg/kg coal
Carbon in fine ash = 0.1432 × 0.0081 = 0.00116 kg/kg coal

$$\text{So weight of carbon consumed} = \frac{C}{100} + \frac{S}{267} - 0.0002 - 0.00116 \text{ kg/kg coal}$$

$$= 0.501 + 0.0068 - 0.0014$$
$$= 0.5064 \text{ kg/kg coal}$$

Dry flue gas loss

$$\text{Loss} = \left[\frac{100}{12 \quad CO_2 + CO} \times \text{weight of carbon consumed}\right] \times 30.6\,(T - t) \text{ kJ/kg}$$

$$= \frac{100}{12\,(13.73)} \times 0.5064 \times 30.6\,(149 - 20.6)\ \text{kJ/kg coal}$$

$$= 1208\ \text{kJ/kg coal}$$

$$= \frac{1208 \times 100}{20\,910} = 5.8\%\ \text{on}\ GCV_v$$

$$= \frac{1208 \times 100}{19\,628} = 6.16\%\ \text{on}\ NCV_p$$

Wet flue gas

$$\text{Loss} = \frac{M + 9H}{100}[4.2(25 - t) + 2442 + 1.88\,(T - 25)]\ \text{kJ/kg fuel}$$

$$= \frac{17.2 + 9(3.83)}{100}\,[4.2(25 - 20.6) + 2442 + 1.88\,(149 - 25)]$$

$$= 0.5167\,[18.5 + 2442 + 233] = 0.5167\,[2693.5]$$

$$= 1391.7\ \text{kJ/kg fuel}$$

$$= \frac{1391.7 \times 100}{20910} = 6.6\%\ \text{on}\ GCV_v$$

Sensible heat in water vapour

$$\text{Loss} = 1391.7 - (20\,910 - 19\,628) = 109.7\ \text{kJ/kg fuel}$$

$$= \frac{109.7 \times 100}{19\,628} = 0.56\%\ \text{on}\ NCV_p$$

Moisture in combustion air

$$\text{Loss} = Ma \times h \times 1.88\,(T - t)$$

$$\text{Where}\ Ma = \frac{3.034 \times 80.87}{13.73 + 0.02} \times 0.5064 = 9.04\ \text{kg/kg coal}$$

$$h = 0.008\ \text{kg}\ H_2O\ \text{per kg dry air}$$

$$\therefore \text{Loss} = 9.04 \times 0.008 \times 1.88\,(1.49 - 20.6) = 17.5\ \text{kJ/kg}$$

$$= \frac{17.5 \times 100}{20\,910} = 0.08\%\ \text{on}\ GCV_v$$

$$= \frac{17.5 \times 100}{19\,628} = 0.09\%\ \text{on}\ NCV_p$$

Alternatively:

$$\text{kg mols of dry flue gas/kg fuel} = 0.5064 \times \frac{100}{12 \times 13.73} = 0.3074$$

$$\text{Mols of oxygen required for combustion of hydrogen} = \frac{3.83}{4 \times 100} = 0.0096$$

Mols of air for combustion = 0.3074 + 0.0096 = 0.3170
Air per kg fuel = 0.3170 × 28.92 = 9.17
kg moisture/kg dry air (from chart) = 0.008
kg moisture per kg fuel = 0.008 × 9.17 = 0.0734
∴ kJ heat lost per kg fuel = 0.0734 × 1.88 (149 − 20.6) = 17.7

$$\text{So loss} = \frac{17.7 \times 100}{20\,910} = 0.08\% \text{ on } GCV_v$$

$$= \frac{17.7 \times 100}{19\,628} = 0.09\% \text{ on } NCV_p$$

Unburnt gas

$$\text{Loss} = \frac{0.02}{13.73 \cdot 0.02} \times 0.5064 \times 23\,717 = 17.3 \text{ kJ/kg}$$

$$= \frac{17.3 \times 100}{20\,910} = 0.08\% \text{ on } GCV_v$$

$$= \frac{17.3 \times 100}{19\,628} = 0.09\% \text{ on } NCV\,p$$

Combustible in ash

(a) Rough ash loss = 0.0002 × 33 820 = 6.8 kJ/kg coal
(b) Fine ash loss = 0.00116 × 33 820 = 39.2 kJ/kg coal

$$\text{Total loss} = 6.8 + 39.2 = 46 \text{ kJ/kg coal}$$

$$= \frac{46 \times 100}{20\,910} = 0.22\% \text{ on } GCV_v$$

$$= \frac{46 \times 100}{19\,628} = 0.23\% \text{ on } NCV_p$$

Radiation and unaccounted

$$\text{Loss} = 0.92\% \text{ (from } \textit{Figure 8.2}) = \frac{20\,910 \times 0.92}{19\,628} = 0.98\% \text{ on } NCV_p$$

Heat account

Loss due to:	% GCV_v	%(NCV_p)
Dry flue gas	5.8	6.16
Wet flue gas	6.6	—
Sensible heat in water vapour	—	0.56
Moisture in combustion air	0.08	0.09
Unburnt gas	0.08	0.09
Combustible in ash	0.22	0.23
Radiation and unaccounted	0.92	0.98
Total loss	13.70	8.11
Boiler efficiency	86.3%	91.9%

Note: The CO on a well-run boiler will normally be less than 100 ppm and the moisture in combustion air is normally included with the unaccounted loss. The items are included here for completeness.

Correction to standard fuel

Often it is necessary to compare the results of a test with those obtained on previous occasions. For example, it is common to compare current test results with those obtained when the acceptance tests were carried out. Such comparisons cannot be made directly because it is almost certain that the composition of the fuel will have changed meanwhile. Therefore, corrections must be made to obtain the results that would have resulted had a standard fuel been burnt.

The method is best shown by an example, where subscripts $_s$ and $_c$ refer to standard and current results respectively. Consider the results just obtained for the losses on a boiler. The standard fuel (in this case the fuel used during the boiler acceptance test) and the current fuel analyses are given in *Table 8.7*

Table 8.7

	Current	*Standard*
Moisture %	17.2	13.51
Ash %	17.9	16.42
Volatile matter %	31.7	29.57
Hydrogen %	3.83	3.78
GCVv kJ/kg	20 910	22 732

Correction for moisture and hydrogen

$$WFG_S = WFG_C + i\left[\frac{M_S + 9H_S}{Q_S} - \frac{M_C + 9H_C}{Q_C}\right]$$

Where WFG = wet flue gas loss %
i = heat loss by moisture in flue gas in kJ/kg
M = moisture % in fuel
H = hydrogen % in fuel
Q = calorific value GCV_V

$$WFG_S = 6.6 + 2693.5\left[\frac{13.51 + (9 \times 3.78)}{22\,732} - \frac{17.2 + (9 \times 3.83)}{20\,910}\right]$$

$= 6.6 + 2693.5\,(0.0021 - 0.0025) = 6.6 + 2693.5\,(-0.0004)$
$\therefore WFG_S = 5.52\%$

Correction for ash and dust

$$C \text{ in } A_S = C \text{ in } A_C \frac{A_S \times Q_C}{A_C \;\; Q_S} + V$$

Where C in A = combustible in ash loss %
A = ash content % of fuel
V = zero, unless volatile matter of either fuel is less than 17%

$$C \text{ in } A_S = 0.22\left[\frac{16.42}{17.90} \times \frac{20\,910}{22\,732}\right] + 0 = 0.22\,(0.917 \times 0.92)$$

$\therefore C$ in $A_S = 0.19\%$

Note: If the volatile matter content of either fuel is less than 17% then:

$$V = 0.013\left[\frac{A_S}{A_C} \times \frac{Q_C}{Q_S}\right] \times k$$

Where $k = \exp.\left(0.225\dfrac{C_S}{H_S}\right) - \exp\left(0.225\dfrac{C_C}{H_C}\right)$

C = carbon content % of fuel
H = hydrogen content % of fuel

The heat balances (on GCV_V basis) are given in *Table 8.8*.

Accuracy of results

The various measurements required to obtain the boiler losses are each

Table 8.8

Loss %	*Current fuel*	*Standard fuel*
Dry flue gas	5.8	5.8
Wet flue gas	6.6	5.52
Combustible in ash	0.22	0.19
* Radiation and unaccounted	1.08	1.08
Total	13.70	12.59
Boiler efficiency %	86.30	87.41

* Includes loss due to unburnt gas and moisture in combustion air.

subject to a range of errors. The probable accuracy of each is as follows. from which the accuracy of the boiler efficiency result can be calculated.

1. *Dry flue gas*

	Approximate accuracy
O_2 determination	± 5.0%
Carbon (sampling and analysis)	± 5.1%
Specific heat	± 1.0%
$(T - t)$	± 6.0%
Calorific value	± 1.0%

So net accrued error $= \pm \sqrt{(5^2 + 5.1^2 + 1.0^2 + 6.0^2 + 1.0^2)}$
$= \pm \sqrt{89} = \pm 9.4\%$
Say ± **10.0%**

2. *Wet flue gas*

Moisture (sampling and analysis)	± 5.1%
Hydrogen	± 5.0%
$(T - t)$	± 6.0%
Calorific value	± 1.0%

So net accrued error $= \pm \sqrt{(5.1^2 + 5.0^2 + 6.0^2 + 1.0^2)}$
$= \pm \sqrt{88.01} = \pm 9.4$
Say ± **10%**

3. *Sensible heat in water vapour*

Wet flue gas	± 7.1%
Calorific value (sampling)	± 5.0%
calorific value (analysis)	± 1.0%

Net accrued error $= \pm \sqrt{(7.1^2 + 5.0^2 + 1.0^2)}$
∴ N.A.E. = ± 8.7%

4. *Moisture in combustion air* is normally included with the unaccounted loss.

15. *Unburnt gas* is normally a very small loss.

6. *Combustible in ash loss*

Combustible in ash (sampling ± 10.0%
(analysis) ± 20.0%

Net accrued error = $\pm \sqrt{(10^2 + 20^2)}$
∴ N.A.E. = ± **22.5%**

7. *Radiation and unaccounted loss*

This is based upon agreed data. Normally the value used will have an error of up to ± 50.0%.

All the net accrued errors are next combined into the 'Total Tolerance Error' (T.T.E.), as follows:

$$\text{T.T.E.} = \pm \frac{\sqrt{\Sigma\ (\text{losses} \times \text{N.A.E.})^2}}{\text{losses}}$$

	Loss %	*NAE %*
Dry flue gas	5.8	± 10.0
Wet flue gas	6.6	± 10.0
Moisture in combustion air	0.08	0
Unburnt gas	0.08	0
Combustible in ash	0.22	± 22.5
Radiation and unaccounted	0.92	0
Total loss	13.70	

So boiler efficiency = 86.3%

Total tolerance error (T.T.E.) is:

$$\text{T.T.E.} = \pm \frac{\sqrt{[(5.8 \times 10)^2 + (6.6 \times 10)^2 + (0.22 \times 22.5)^2]}}{13.7}$$

$$= \pm \frac{\sqrt{(58^2 + 66^2 + 5^2)}}{13.7}$$

$$= \pm \frac{88}{13.7} = \pm \mathbf{6.4}$$

The cumulative total measurement error (C.T.M.E.) is:

$$\text{C.T.M.E.} = \pm \frac{100 - 86.3}{86.3} \times 6.4 = \pm 1.02\%$$

$$\text{The effect of compounding the errors} = \pm \frac{86.3 \times 1.02}{100} = \pm 0.88\%$$

So the efficiency is probably within the range 86.3 ± 0.88%

Optimizing total air supplies

An important item of information for the efficient operation of any boiler is the optimum CO_2% or O_2% for any load. In other words the total air supplies should be optimized. Traditionally this involved the elimination, as far as possible, of sources of air ingress and then carrying out a series of tests to determine the optimum value at various loads.

Thus, at say, full load, a series of four or five tests are carried out at CO_2 or O_2% which span the optimum value. For example, at full load one would expect the CO_2 to be at optimum at about 15.5% at boiler outlet when burning bituminous coal. Therefore tests would be carried out at about 14.0, 15.0, 15.5, 16.0 per cent CO_2, the boiler being kept at a steady output. The information recorded should permit the calculation of:

1 Combustible in ash loss
2 Dry flue gas loss
3 Unburned gas loss
4 Auxiliary power loss

as each of these is affected by variations of air. The optimum value is determined by plotting the total loss and so finding the CO_2 or O_2 which corresponds to minimum loss such as shown in *Figure 8.4*.

In the case considered it is 15.2% CO_2 at, say, 100% M.C.R. A further set of tests is then carried out in a similar manner but at a different load, say 80% M.C.R., followed by 60% and 40% M.C.R. loads. The optimum for each loading is, say,

Load(% M.C.R.)	100	80	60	40
% CO_2	15.2	14.6	14.15	13.8

from which *Figure 8.5* is drawn for use by the operations staff. It will be appreciated that the time and effort involved is quite considerable. Consequently if a station has identical boilers it is often sufficient to test only one and apply the results to them all.

Optimization tests were carried out on a 120 MW boiler and some results are tabulated later. The calculations are given for Test 1 and it is left as an

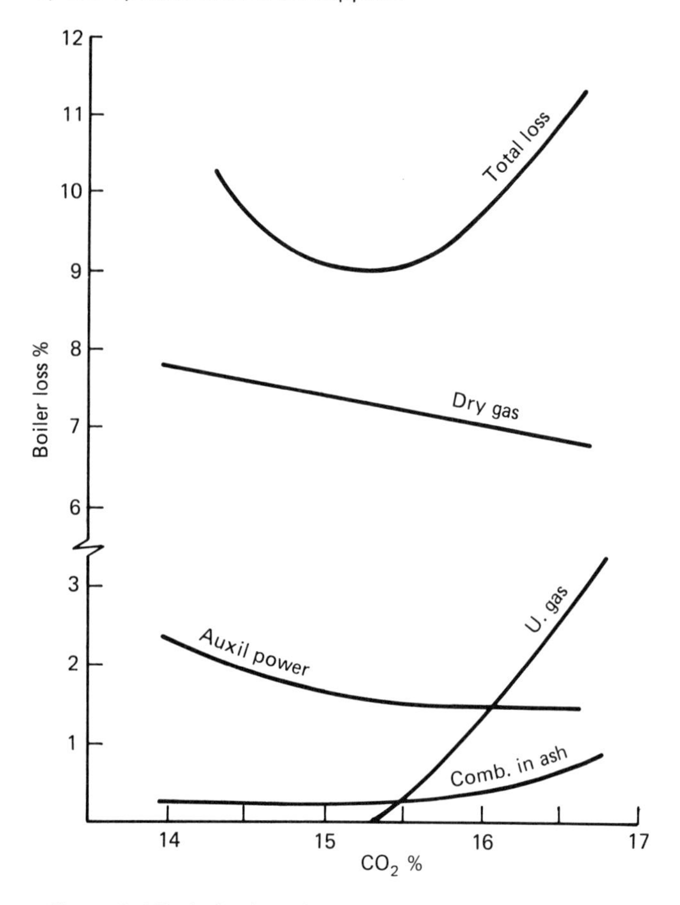

Figure 8.4 Optimisation of total air supply

exercise for the reader to calculate the losses for Tests 2 and 3 (see Exercise 1).

Notice from *Figure 8.4* that the optimum CO_2 is just a little lower than that at which unburned gas is produced. So if one could measure the unburned gas it would be easy to determine the optimum air requirement. The main unburned gas in boiler work is carbon monoxide. Various devices are now available which measure CO in flue gas down to minute quantities. Because of stratification of the flue gas it is normally considered desirable to mount the equipment after the ID fan.

The flue gas in a pulverized fuel boiler will normally have a residual quantity of carbon monoxide amounting to something less than 100 ppm, the actual amount depending upon the conditions at the time, such as load, mills in service and so on. For oil-fired boilers the value is about 400 ppm. As the excess air is reduced there is a slight increase in the CO content and, at a particular value of excess air, there is a dramatic increase, see *Figure 8.6(a)*.

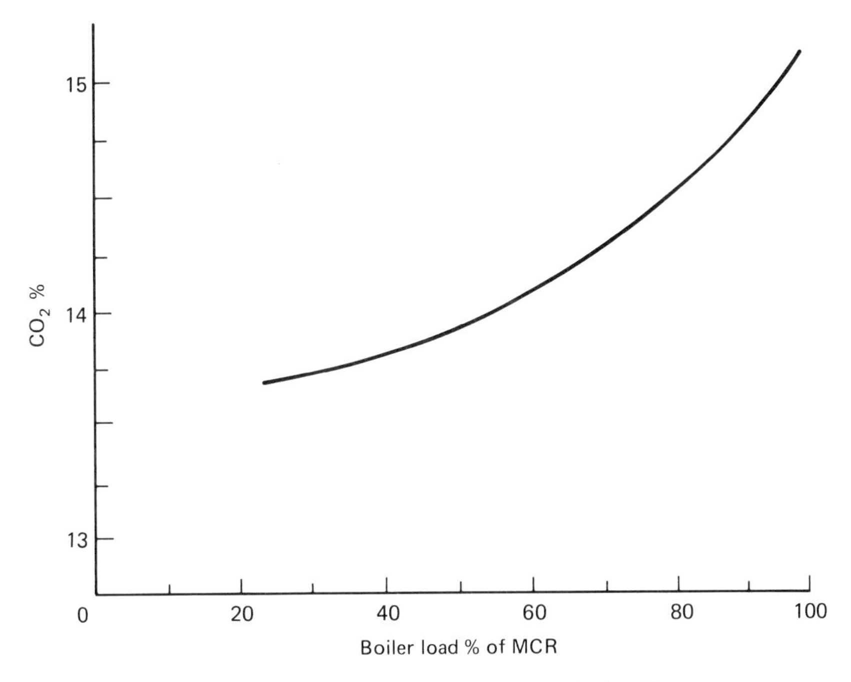

Figure 8.5 Optimum CO_2% at boiler outlet for various boiler loadings

Figure 8.6(b) shows various conditions on a 500 MW unit. Notice that the break-point occurs at different values of O_2% as the conditions change. *Figure 8.7* shows a section of chart upon which the O_2% and the CO in ppm are recorded. Notice that for any O_2 less than 4% the CO increases dramatically, often exceeding 4000 ppm. The reason why the O_2 is rather high is because of air ingress. Therefore, although the O_2% was high at the boiler outlet where the zirconia oxygen probes were located, there was barely sufficient air at the burners.

Consequently the carbon monoxide indicator provides a valuable guide to the optimization of total air supplies. Quite apart from its benefit to the operation of the boiler the elimination of unnecessary excess air has the added advantage that the precipitator performance is improved because of the reduced gas flow.

Types of analyser

Various analysers are now available which permit the measurement of carbon monoxide in flue gas down to very low levels of the order of 50 ppm or less. In one type the gas sample is withdrawn from the main flue gas stream and passed through the instrument. *Figure 8.8(a)* shows a typical permanent installation. The main problem with this type of installation is getting the sample to the analyser, as the probes may become blocked and

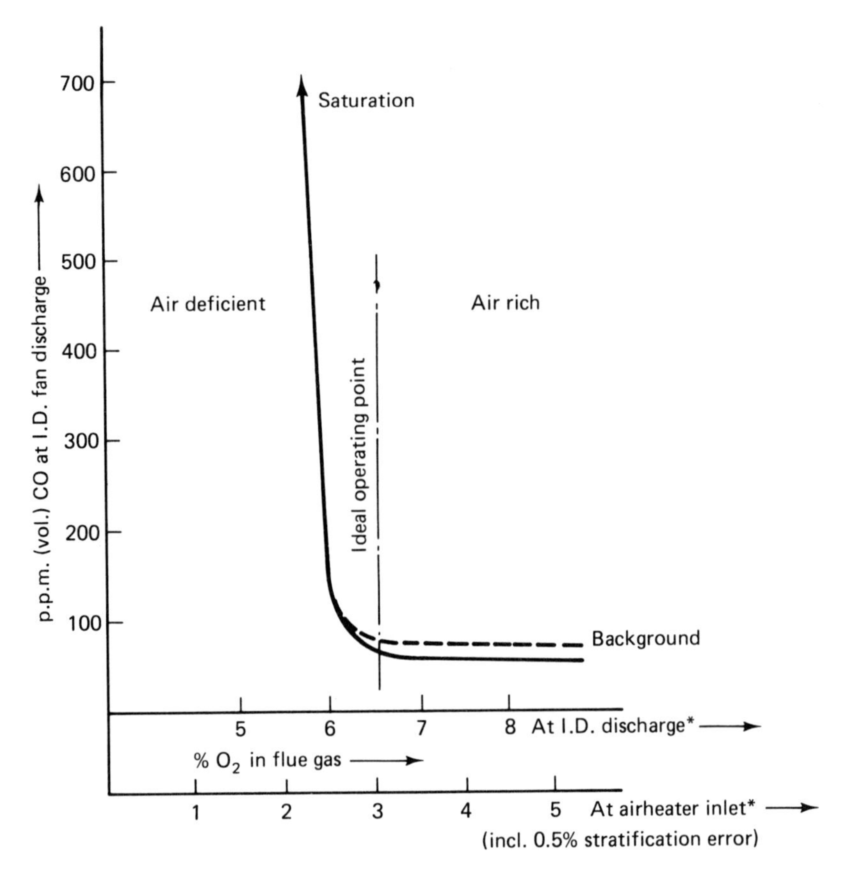

Figure 8.6(a) Variation of CO with O_2 in flue gas (CEGB)

there may be deposition of wet products in the piping. On the other hand the equipment can be made portable and so it is useful for test department use. *Figure 8(b)* shows a portable assembly supplied by a different manufacturer.

An alternative equipment measures carbon monoxide and various other gases down to a few parts per million and does not depend upon a gas sample being withdrawn. Absorption spectroscopic analysis in the ultra-violet, infra-red or visible light ranges is used, depending upon which gas is being analysed (e.g. CO, CO_2, SO_2, H_2O, NO, plus opacity can be measured).

Effects of air inleakage

The effect of air ingress to the gas circuit is to cause dilution of the com-

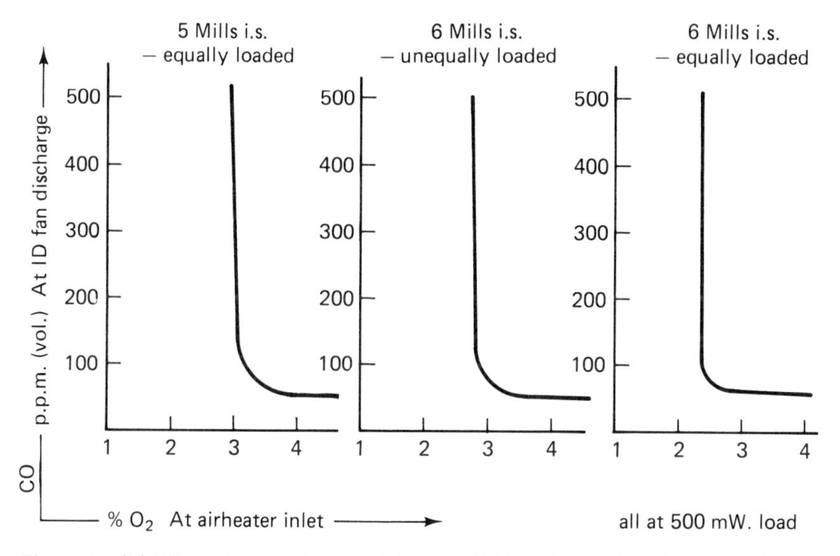

Figure 8.6(b) Effect of operating conditions on CO breakpoint (500 MW boiler) CEGB)

ponent flue gases. The effects of 1% and 5% dilution by air is given by the following:

Air contains 21% oxygen and 79% nitrogen by volume
So 1% dilution = 0.01 (21% O_2 + 79% N_2) = 0.21% O_2 + 0.79% N_2
5% dilution = 0.05 (21% O_2 + 79% N_2) = 1.05% O_2 + 3.95% N_2

Consider the effect of dilution on the flue gas formed by burning a coal with the following ultimate analysis and 20% excess air.

Carbon	56.8%
Hydrogen	3.7
Nitrogen	1.3
Sulphur	2.0
Oxygen	7.0
Moisture	16.7
Ash	12.5
	100.0

The undiluted products of combustion expressed as percentage by volume (wet) are, say

CO_2	H_2O	SO_2	O_2	N_2
14.2	7.6	0.2	3.3	74.7

In addition assume there is a very small quantity of carbon monoxide, say 50 parts per million.

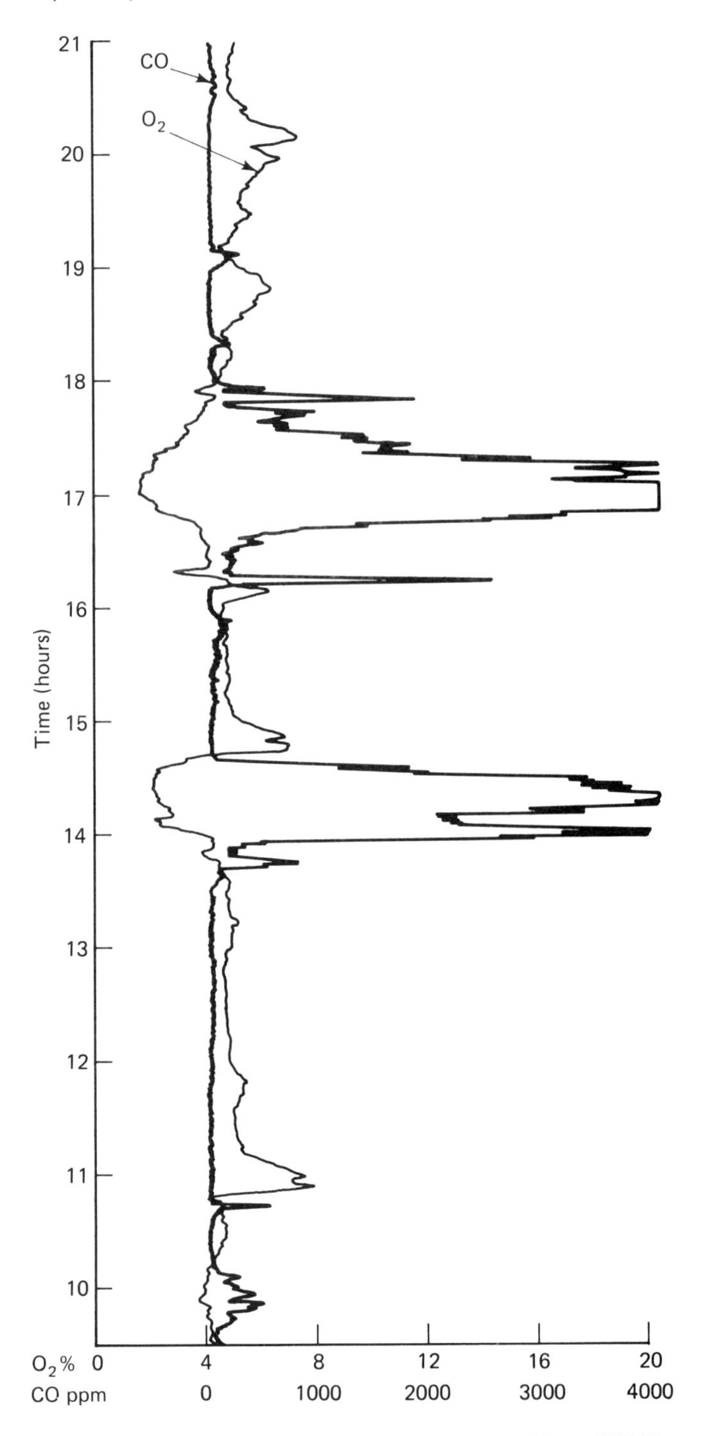

Figure 8.7 Chart of CO and O_2% for various operating conditions (CEGB)

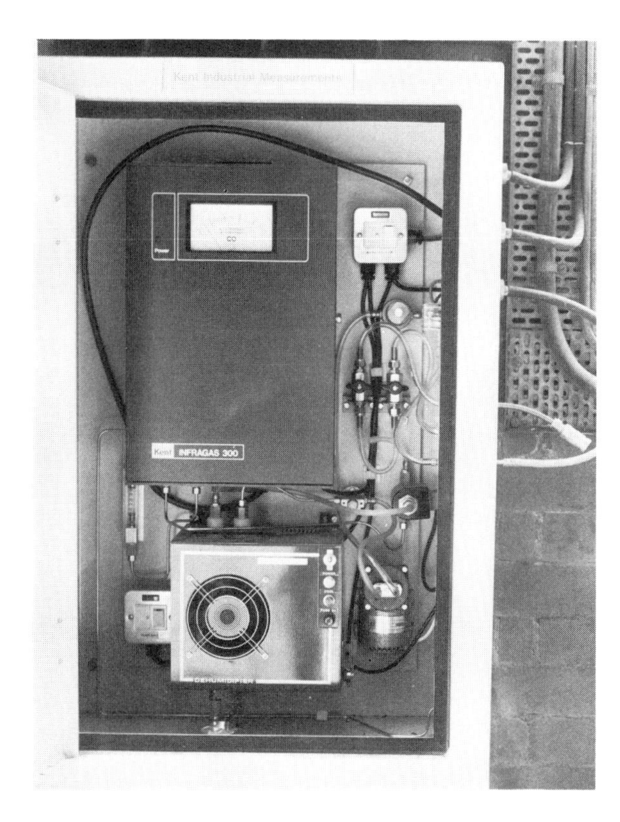

Figure 8.8(a) Permanent CO monitoring installation (CEGB)

Figure 8.8(b) Portable CO monitoring installation (CEGB)

Next consider how these values will change when diluted.

	Gas	*1% dilution*		*5% dilution*	
CO_2	14.2%	14.2/1.01	= 14.1%	14.2/1.05	= 13.5
H_2O	7.6%	7.6/1.01	= 7.5%	7.6/1.05	= 7.2
SO_2	0.2%	0.2/1.01	= 0.2%	0.2/1.05	= 0.2
O_2	3.3%	(3.3 + 0.21) /1.01	= 3.5	(3.3 + 1.05) /1.05	= 4.1
N_2	74.7 %	(74.7 + 0.79) /1.01	= 74.7	(74.7 + 3.95) /1.05	= 74.9
CO	50 ppm	50/1.01	= 49.5	50/1.05	= 47.6

Hence, the errors caused by dilution are:

	1% dilution	*5% dilution*
CO_2	(−) 0.7%	(−) 5.2%
H_2O	(−) 1.3%	(−) 5.6%
SO_2	0	0
O_2	(+) 5.7%	(+) 19.5
N_2	0	(+) 0.3%
CO	(−) 1.0	(−) 5.0%

Notice that the effect of the dilution is almost directly proportional for the CO_2, H_2O and CO values. However, the effect on the oxygen value is quite considerable, and this should be borne in mind if O_2 indicators are installed. *Figure 8.9* shows the *trend* of some combustion gases as air supplies are varied above and below the theoretical (i.e. the *stoichiometric* quantity. Note that the CO_2% decreases with variations of air both above and below the theoretical quantity. Also it only changes slightly for variations of fuel compositions within the same fuel category and is not greatly diluted by air ingress. On the other hand, O_2 in flue gas is independent of the composition of the fuel but alters significantly when diluted.

Determination of excess air

The excess air is determined from the formula:

$$\text{Excess air} = \frac{O_2\% \times 100}{21 - O_2\%}$$

Substituting values of O_2% gives these results:

O_2%	0	2	4	6	8	10	10.5
Excess air %	0	11	24	40	62	91	100

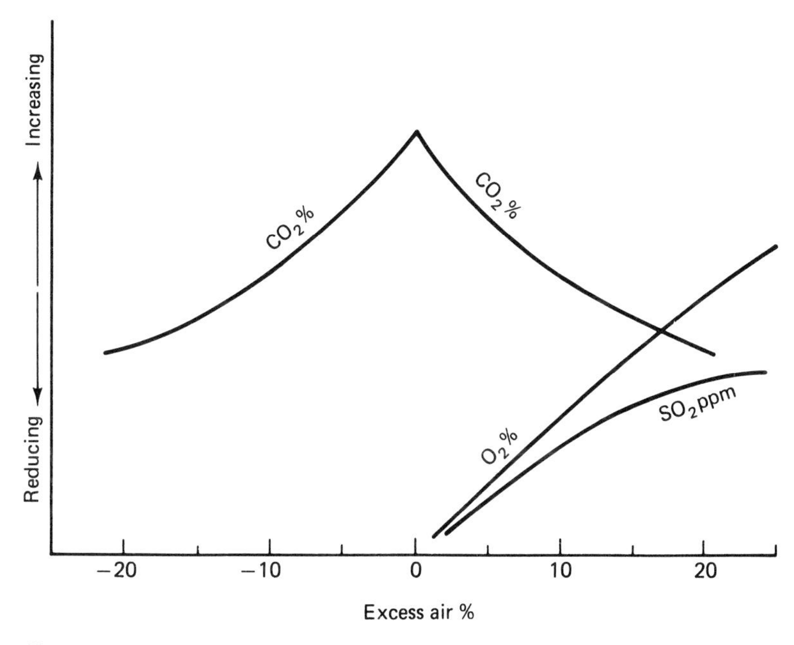

Figure 8.9 Trend of boiler gases with variations of excess air

Alternatively the excess air can be determined from the CO_2%, although in this case it is necessary to establish the theoretical maximum CO_2 for the fuel being burned. In the case of bituminous coal the maximum is 18.6%. So for this fuel the excess air is given by:

$$\text{Excess air} = \frac{CO_2\%\ (\max) \times 100}{CO_2\%} - 100 = \frac{1860}{CO_2\%} - 100$$

from which this set of values is derived:

CO_2%	18.6	16.0	14.0	12.0	10.0	8.0	6.0
Excess air %	0	16.3	33	55	86	133	210

For fuel oil the theoretical maximum CO_2 is about 15.3%. Therefore the relationship between fuel oil CO_2% and excess air is given by

$$\frac{15.3 \times 100}{CO_2\%} - 100$$ from which the table was calculated.

CO_2%	15.3	14	12	10	8	6
Excess air %	0	9.3	27.5	53.0	91.3	155

Figure 8.10 shows curves of oxygen and carbon dioxide versus excess air for

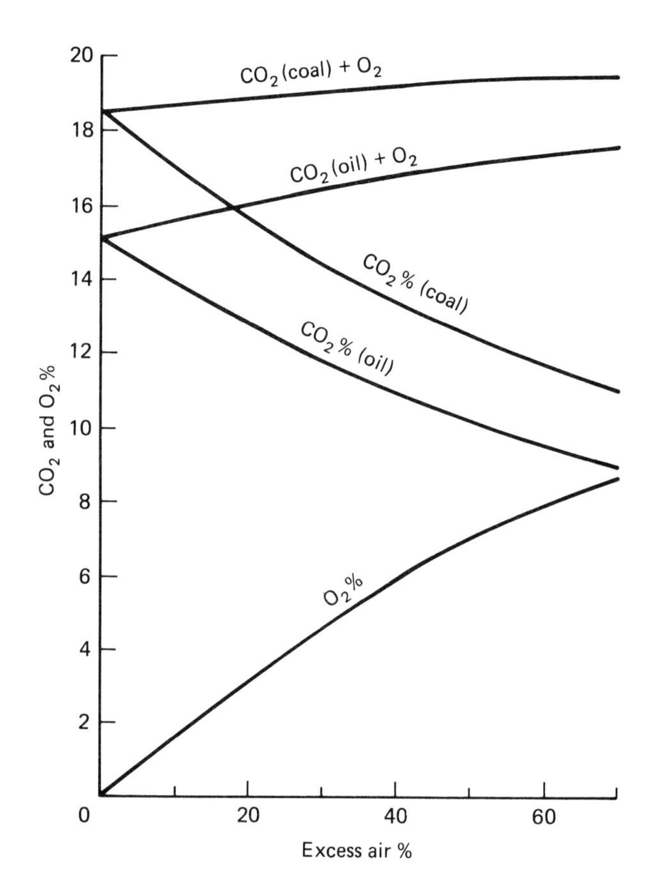

Figure 8.10 Graph of CO_2% and O_2% *vs* excess air %

pulverized bituminous coal and for fuel oil. Also shown in the figure is the sum of the oxygen and carbon dioxide values for both fuels. Notice that the sum of CO_2 and O_2 varies with excess air in both cases. In normal operation of the plant, though, the range of excess air encountered is limited. Thus, it is usual to operate a p.f. boiler with about 20–25% excess air. Over this small range it is reasonable to assume that the sum of the CO_2 (coal) and O_2 is constant at 19.0%. It follows that if a boiler is operated at, say, 3.5% O_2 then the equivalent CO_2 is given by 19 − 3.5 = 15.5%.

In the case of oil-fired boilers the usual excess air is very small, being of the order of 2 – 3%. Within this band the sum of the CO_2 (oil) and O_2 is constant at 15.5%. Thus, for a CO_2 of 15.0% the equivalent O_2 is 15.5 − 15.0 = 0.5%.

Calculation of air in-leakage

Often it is necessary to determine the percentage inleakage into a boiler or to some specific item. For example, on a 375 MW boiler,tests were carried out to determine the leakage at the primary air airheaters. These heaters are supplied with air at a pressure of about 110 mbar and so the seal leakage is quite high (about 17.0%) even when the seals are in good condition. The results obtained were:

'A' A/H average O_2% at gas inlet = 3.42%
'A' A/H average O_2% at gas outlet = 7.50%
'B' A/H average O_2% at gas inlet = 6.43%
'B' A/H average O_2% at gas outlet = 9.74%

$$\text{So 'A' A/H leakage} = \frac{7.5 - 3.42}{21 - 7.5} \times 100 = 30.22\%$$

$$\text{'B' A/H leakage} = \frac{9.74 - 6.43}{21 - 9.74} \times 100 = 29.4\%$$

$$\text{In general, \% leakage} = \frac{\text{downstream } O_2\% - \text{upstream } O_2\%}{21 - \text{downstream } O_2\%} \times 100$$

Gas tracer method

It should be remembered that the results obtained by using the oxygen difference method are subject to error. The main source of uncertainty is the difference 'downstream O_2% − upstream O_2%. Analysis indicates that for a downstream oxygen value of 5% the accuracy would be about ± 3.0%, and for 8% oxygen it would be about ± 4.0%, assuming 36 samples were obtained.

Therefore, the gas tracer technique is often used as an alternative. A measured rate of flow of suitable tracer gas is injected into the system under test at a location which will allow adequate mixing of the tracer with the gas being measured.

For example, suppose A cubic metres per second of tracer at temperature T_t and pressure P_t is injected into an air stream and well mixed. The conditions after mixing are T_m and P_m.

$$\therefore \text{Volume flow of the tracer after mixing} = A \times \frac{P_t}{P_m} \times \frac{T_m}{T_t}$$

$$= B \text{ cubic metres per second}$$

Measured concentration of tracer after mixing = C ppm

$$\text{So rate of flow} = \frac{10^6 B}{C} \text{ m}^3/\text{s}$$

Carbon monoxide is a suitable tracer for air flows.

Determination of air heater performance and tramp air to boiler

Boilers are sometimes operated with considerable quantities of air inleakage (often called tramp air), particularly so for coal-fired boilers with suction mills. The various undesirable results from this include:

(a) The tramp air is possibly not contributing to combustion.
(b) The tramp air is often cold.
(c) The demand for forced draught is possibly reduced. If it is considerably reduced the heat abstracted from the flue gas at the air heater will also be reduced and the air heater gas outlet temperature will be high. This, in its turn, will increase the gas velocity through the electrostatic precipitators and so worsen the emission on high loads.

Notice that air which bypasses the air heater, such as attemperating air, is regarded as tramp air.

It is not at all uncommon for over 50% of the total demand for air at a boiler to be supplied as tramp air, and typical sources of inleakage include:

(a) suction milling plant;
(b) ash hopper seals;
(c) ash hopper doors left ajar;
(d) grit hoppers, etc. valves or slides left open;
(e) defective expansion joints;
(f) duct openings uncovered (e.g. test and sampling holes);
(g) boiler roof seals defective;
(h) attemperating air dampers passing;
(i) air heater air bypass dampers passing;
(j) burner secondary air not shut off when burner out of service;
(k) worn shaft seals on exhausters.

Therefore, the tramp air quantity should be determined to indicate whether or not work is necessary to stop excessive ingress. Also, it is desirable to determine periodically the log mean temperature difference (L.M.T.D.) between the gas and air sides of the air heaters as this is a measure of the effectiveness of their heat transfer. As with all routine calculations such as these, it is desirable to use a standard calculation sheet to ease the work. There are two types of investigation normally undertaken.

Investigation Type 1

This utilizes only information obtained readily from the unit instrumentation, plus some assumptions (such as fuel composition) which should be reasonably accurate. Therefore this method is suitable for routine purposes.

Investigation Type 2

When boiler tests are carried out there is a wealth of detailed and accurate information available. This can be utilized to enable a more rigorous determination of tramp air.

Pro-formas for both types of investigation are given with examples. If a series of tramp air investigations is undertaken on a boiler at comparable loadings it is desirable to keep the gas flow constant (i.e. constant $O_2\%$) and vary the combustion chamber suction.

The results, when plotted, will approximate to a straight line law. Use 'air-heater gas outlet temperature' as the *X*-axis and 'percentage tramp air from air heater air outlet to air heater gas inlet' as the *Y*-axis. From this it will be possible to determine the order of reduction of gas temperature for a given reduction of air ingress, thus enabling potential savings to be calculated.

A/H L.M.T.D. and tramp air determination

Boiler No. 6 Test No. 2 Load 120 MW Date 9/2/1984

Combustion chamber draught (−) 0.9 mbar

1 Average current fuel analysis:

$H_2 = 3.8\%$, $M = 14\%$, $A = 16\%$, GCV = 22 750 kJ/kg

2 Conditions at air heaters:

(a) Air inlet temperature = 32°C
(b) Air outlet temperature = 270°C
(c) Gas inlet temperature = 307°C
(d) Gas outlet temperature = 121°C
(e) Gas inlet O_2 = 3.6%
(f) Gas outlet O_2 = 4.6%

3 Theoretical air required $= \dfrac{3.27 \times \text{GCV}}{10\ 000}$

$$\frac{3.27 \times 22\ 750}{10\ 000} = 7.44 \text{ kg/kg fuel}$$

4 L.M.T.D. at A/H $= \dfrac{\theta_1 - \theta'_2}{2.3 \log_{10}\left(\dfrac{\theta_1}{\theta_2}\right)}$

$\theta_1 = (2c) - (2b) = 37°\text{C}$
$\theta_2 = (2d) - (2a) = 89°\text{C}$

$$\text{L.M.T.D.} = \frac{37 - 89}{2.3 \log \frac{37}{89}} = \mathbf{59.3°C}$$

5 A/H leakage % $= 100 \times \dfrac{[(2f - (2e)]}{21 - (2f)} = \dfrac{100\,(4.6 - 3.6)}{21 - 4.6} = 6.1\%$

6 Excess air at A/H gas inlet $= \dfrac{(2e)}{21 - (2e)} = \dfrac{3.6}{21 - 3.6} = 0.207$

7 Air required for gas inlet condition $= [1 + (6)] \times (3)$
$= 1.207 \times 7.44 = 8.98$ kg/kg fuel

8 Excess air at A/H gas outlet $= \dfrac{(2f)}{21 - (2f)} = \dfrac{4.6}{21 - 4.6} = 0.28$

9 Air required for gas outlet condition $= [1 + (8)] \times (3)$
$= 1.28 \times 7.44 = 9.52$ kg/kg fuel

10 Leakage air $= (9) - (7) = 0.54$ kg/kg fuel

11 Weight of flue gas at A/H inlet = (7) + weight of coal in combustion products $= (7) + \left(1 - \dfrac{A\%}{100}\right)$
$= 8.98 + (1 - 0.16) = 9.82$ kg/kg fuel

12 Heat given to leakage air $= [(2d) - (2a)] \times (10) \times 1.01$
$= (121 - 32) \times 0.54 \times 1.01 = 48.54$ kJ/kg fuel

13 Wet flue gas $= \dfrac{M\% + 9H\%}{100} = \dfrac{14 + (9 \times 3.8)}{100} = 0.48$ kg/kg fuel

14 Heat given up by wet flue gas $= [(2c) - (2d)] \times 2.03 \times (13)$
$= (307 - 121) \times 2.03 \times 0.48 = 181.2$ kJ/kg fuel

15 Heat given up by dry flue gas $= [(2c) - (2d)] \times [(11) - (13)]$
$= (307 - 121) \times (9.82 - 0.48) = 1737.2$ kJ/kg fuel

16 Total heat given up by flue gas $= (14) + (15) = 1918.4$ kJ/kg fuel

17 Heat given to combustion air $= (16 - (12) = 1918.4 - 48.54 = 1869.9$ kJ/kg fuel

18 Heat gained by combustion air $= [(2b) - (2a)] \times 1.01$
$= 238 \times 1.01 = 248.4$ kJ/kg air

19 Combustion air (i.e. air at A/H air outlet) $= (17 \div (18)$
$= \dfrac{1869.9}{248.4} = 7.53$ kg/kg fuel

20 Air at A/H air inlet $= (19) + (10) = 7.53 + 0.54 = 8.07$ kg/kg fuel.

21 Tramp air from A/H air outlet to A/H gas inlet $= (7) - (19) = 8.98 - 7.53 = 1.45$ kg/kg fuel

22 Tramp air (inc. A/H leakage) $= (21) + (10) = 1.45 + 0.54 = 1.99$ kg/kg fuel

23 Item (21) as % of theoretical air $= \dfrac{(21)100}{(3)} = \dfrac{145}{7.44} = 19.5\%$

24 Item (22) as % of total air $= \dfrac{(22)\,100}{(20)} = \dfrac{199}{8.07} = 24.7\%$

25 Heat to air/°C L.M.T.D. $\dfrac{(16)-(12)}{(4)}$ = **31.5 kJ/kg fuel/°C**

Investigation Type 2 A/H L.M.T.D. and tramp air determination

Boiler No. 6 Test No. 2 Load 120 MW Date 9/2/1984

Combustion chamber draught (−) 0.9 mbar

1 Test fuel analysis:
$C = 55.5\%$, $H_2 = 3.8\%$, $O_2 = 7.4\%$, $S = 1.6\%$, $M = 14\%$, $A = 16\%$, $N_2 = 1.75\%$

2 Conditions at air heaters:
(a) Air inlet temperature = 32°C
(b) Air outlet temperature = 270°C
(c) Gas inlet temperature = 307°C
(d) Gas outlet temperature = 121°C
(e) Gas inlet O_2 = 3.6%, equiv. CO_2 = 15.4%, N_2 = 81.0%
(f) Gas outlet O_2 = 4.6%, equiv. CO_2 = 14.4%, N_2 = 81.0%

3 Theoretical air required $= \dfrac{4.31}{100}\left[\dfrac{8}{3}C + 8\left(H - \dfrac{O}{8}\right) + S\right]$ kg/kg fuel

$$= \frac{4.31}{100}\left[\left(\frac{8}{3} \times 55.5\right) + 8\left(3.8 - \frac{7.4}{8}\right) + 1.6\right]$$

$= 7.44$ kg/kg fuel

4 Carbon burnt $= \dfrac{C}{100}$ − combustible in ash

$= 0.555 - 0.014 = 0.54$ kg/hg fuel

5 Wet products of combustion $= \dfrac{M + 9H}{100}$

$$= \frac{14 + (9 \times 3.8)}{100} = 0.48 \text{ kg/kg fuel.}$$

6 Dry products of combustion at A/H inlet

$$= \frac{11\,CO_2 + 8O_2 + 7N_2}{3\,CO_2}\left[(4) + \frac{S\%}{183}\right]$$

$$= \frac{(11 \times 15.4) + (8 \times 3.6) + (7 \times 81)}{3 \times 15.4}\left[0.54 + \frac{1.6}{183}\right]$$

$$= \frac{169.4 + 28.8 + 567}{46.2}(0.549) = 9.09 \text{ kg/kg fuel}$$

7 Products of combustion at A/H outlet

$$= \frac{11\,CO_2 + 8O_2 + 7N_2}{3CO_2}\left((4) + \frac{S\%}{183}\right)$$

$$= \frac{(11 \times 14.4) + (8 \times 4.6) + (7 \times 81)}{3 \times 14.4}\left(0.54 + \frac{1.6}{183}\right)$$

$$= \frac{158.4 + 36.8 + 567}{43.2}(0.549) = 9.69 \text{ kg/kg fuel}$$

8 Leakage air at A/H = (7) − (6) = 9.69 − 9.09 = 0.6 kg/kg fuel
9 Heat given to leakage air = (8) [(2d) − (2a)] × 1.01
= 0.6 × 89 × 1.01 = 53.9 kJ/kg fuel
10 Heat given up by dry products = (6) [(2c) − (2)]
= 9.09 × (307 − 121) = 1690.7 kJ/kg fuel
11 Heat given up by wet products = 2.03 × (5) [(2c) − (2*d*)]
= 2.03 × 0.48 × 186 = 181.2 kJ/kg fuel
12 Total heat given up = (10 + (11) = 1690.7 + 181.2 = 1871.9 kJ/kg fuel
13 Heat received by combustion air (i.e. air at A/H air outlet = [(2b) − (2a)] × 1.01 = 238 × 1.01 = 240.4 kJ/kg air

14 Air at A/H outlet $= \frac{(12) - (9)}{(13)} = \frac{1871.9 - 53.9}{240.4} = 7.56$ kg/kg fuel

15 Excess air at A/H outlet = (14) − (3) = 7.56 − 7.44 = 0.12 kg/kg fuel

16 Excess air % of theoretical air $= \frac{(15) \times 100}{(3)} \quad \frac{0.12 \times 100}{7.44} = 1.6\%$

17 Total equivalent air at A/H gas inlet condition $= \quad 1 + \frac{(2e)}{21 - (2e)} \times (3)$

= (1 + 0.207) × 7.44 = 8.98 kg/kg fuel
18 Air at A/H air inlet = (14) + (8) = 7.56 + 0.6 = 8.16 kg/kg fuel
19 Tramp air from A/H air outlet to A/H gas inlet = (17) − (14)
= 8.98 − 7.56 = 1.42 kg/kg fuel

20 Tramp air as % of theoretical air $= \frac{(19) \times 100}{(3)} = \frac{1.42 \times 100}{7.44} =$ **19.1%**

21 A/H L.M.T.D. $= \dfrac{\theta_1 - \theta_2}{2.3 \log_{10} \dfrac{\theta^1}{\theta_2}}$

$\theta_1 = (2c) - (2b) = 37°C$
$\theta_2 = (2d) - (2a) = 89°C$

$$\text{L.M.T.D.} = \frac{37 - 89}{2.3 \log_{10} \frac{37}{89}} = \mathbf{59.3°C}$$

22 Heat to air/°C L.M.T.D. $= \left[\dfrac{(12) - (9)}{(21)}\right] = \mathbf{30.7\ kJ/kg\ fuel/°C}$

23 % Leakage at air heater $= \dfrac{100\,[(2f) - (2e)]}{21 - (2f)} = 6.1\%$

If necessary the investigation can be extended to determine the air and gas flows.

24 Fuel throughput = 13.9 kg/s
25 Air at A/H inlet = (18)(24) = 113 kg/s

26 Specific volume of air to A/H $= 0.7736 \left[\dfrac{(2a) + 273}{273}\right] = 0.86\ m^3/kg$

27 Volume of air to A/H = (26)(25) = 97.2 m^3/s
28 Flue gas at A/H outlet = (5) + (7) = 10.17 kg/kg fuel
29 Flue gas at A/H outlet = (28)(24) = 141.4 kg/s

30 Specific volume of flue gas $= 0.76 \left[\dfrac{(2d) + 273}{273}\right] = 1.1\ m^3/kg$

31 Volume of flue gas leaving A/H = (29)(30) = 155.5 m^3/s

Combustible material in ash

The combustible material in ash often accounts for about 0.5% boiler loss under acceptance test conditions and, of course, is often more than this in normal operation. The amount of unburned material is a measure of the effectiveness of the combustion process in general and the milling plant in particular. The combustible material is normally regarded as being all carbon. Now 1 kg carbon, if burned completely, would release 33 820 kJ. Hence each kilogram of carbon in the ash represents a significant loss of heat from the boiler. For example, if a certain coal had 15% ash and the combustible material in ash (C in A) was 2.2% then the heat loss would be:

$$\frac{2.2 \times 0.15}{100} \times 33\,820 = 111.6\ \text{kJ/kg fuel}$$

So if the calorific value of the coal were 20 934 kJ/kg then the percentage boiler loss would be:

$$\frac{111.6 \times 100}{20\,934} = \mathbf{0.54\%}$$

Incidentally, the heat contained in the ash when it is removed from the boiler represents a further heat loss, although it is not normally calculated.

Causes of low carbon in ash

It is uneconomic to eliminate all the combustible matter from getting into the rough ash and dust – a small amount (say 1.5%) will usually be regarded as normal. If the amount is much below this it is probable that the coal is being too finely ground. In such a case the C in A loss is reduced, but at the expense of increased milling power consumption and, possibly, some load restriction if it is necessary for the mills to give maximum throughput to achieve the required boiler loading.

Causes of overgrinding on a medium speed suction mill of the Lopulco type include:

(a) separator speed too high;
(b) exhauster speed too low;
(c) mill in need of adjustment, e.g. rolls too low, spring tension too great;
(d) mill table dam ring too high;
(e) rich fuel/air mixture.

Similar reasoning applies to other mill types. Generally speaking overgrinding can be said to be taking place if the PF fineness is more than 80% through a 75 μm (200 mesh) sieve for bituminous coal or 85% for low volatile coal.

Causes of coarse grinding

If the PF is too coarse the combustion will be poor and there will be high carbon in ash. Grinding which results in 10% or more being retained on a 150 μm (100 mesh) sieve or less than 70% passing a 75 μm (200 mesh) sieve is bad. Causes of coarse grinding include:

(a) mill in need of adjustment, e.g. rolls too far off table; spring tension insufficient, etc.;
(b) separator speed too low – possibly belt slipping;
(c) exhauster speed too high relative to coal feed;
(d) weak fuel/air mixture;
(e) excessive air inleakage to mill.

Other causes of high combustible in ash

Apart from the milling plant itself the actual combustion process can lead to high carbon in ash. Of course, particles that are grossly oversized will promptly fall as 'sparklers' after leaving the burner mouth. The time required to burn a particle of coal is roughly proportional to the square of its diameter. Thus, a particle whose diameter is twice the size of another will require about four times as long to burn. Hence, the length of the flame is proportional to the size of the particles.

During combustion a particle of coal is surrounded by an atmosphere of combustion products through which the oxygen has to diffuse to react with the coal. Experiments have shown that the time taken for the combustion of a 75 μm (200 mesh) particle of coal containing 30–40% volatile matter is a fraction of a second. If the air supplies are badly adjusted and, as a consequence, the flame touches the wall of the chamber while combustion is incomplete, then excess carbon in ash will be produced even though the PF grading is quite acceptable leaving the mill.

For the best control of the flame all the mills should ideally produce the same size product, and also all the mills should be equally loaded as this spreads the fire evenly across the furnace. Unequal loads and/or unequal grading produce flames which have different characteristics and so are relatively insensitive to secondary air adjustments. The air temperature is also important because it influences the rate of ignition and the flame length. The primary air temperature is the easiest to control and the air/fuel temperature leaving the mill should be kept within the range 90°C – 65°C. Higher temperatures will cake the coal and lower ones will possibly cause condensation.

The Cegrit automatic dust sampler

The purpose of the Cegrit sampler is to obtain a representative dust sample from the flue that can be used to determine the combustible material in dust. The sampler was developed in the South Eastern Division of the CEGB and is marketed by Airflow Developments Ltd. The equipment is illustrated in *Figure 8.11*. The sampler is mounted on a suitable section of flue ducting and, when correctly set to work, will sample the dust continuously and isokinetically for any boiler loading.

An advantage of the apparatus is that it has no moving parts. The action of the gas flow past the ejector creates a suction at the ejector mouth and this is utilized to draw a sample of dust from the nozzle to the small cyclone. The dust is detrained and deposited in a glass container. The cyclone is heated to prevent dampness which could cause obstruction.

Pulverised fuel sampling

For good combustion, not only should the fuel leaving individual burners be of comparable standard of acceptable grading (e.g. within the range 70% to 80% through a 75 μm (200 mesh) sieve for bituminous coal), but also the

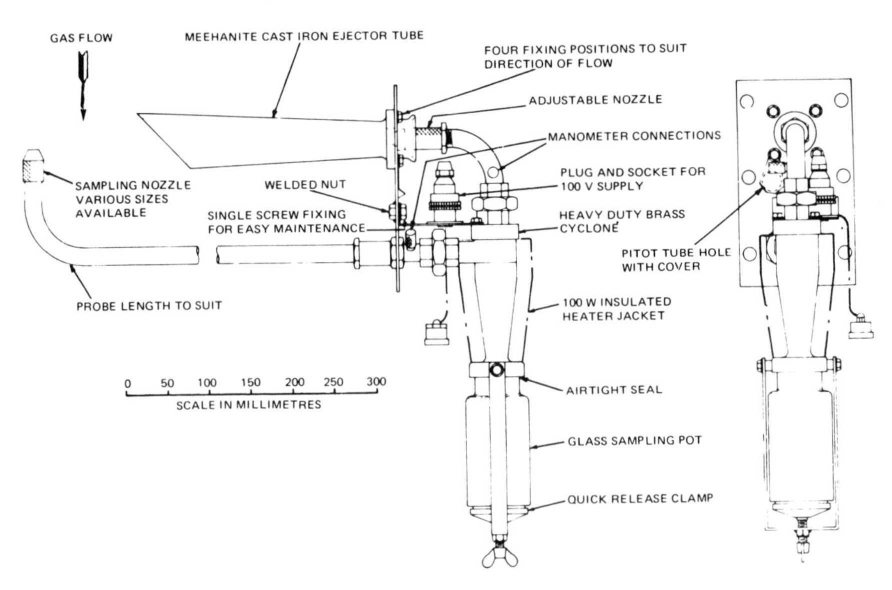

Figure 8.11 Detail of Cegrit dust sampler (CEGB)

fires should be comparable. In other words there should be a similar air/fuel flow from each burner.

On modern boilers it is often very difficult to see the flames produced from individual burners. Therefore it is necessary to sample the contents of the individual PF pipes. This enables the air-to-fuel ratio, the grading of the fuel and the fuel flow to be determined. Thus, for example, the effectiveness of a PF pipe trifurcation device was determined, as shown in *Figure 8.12.*

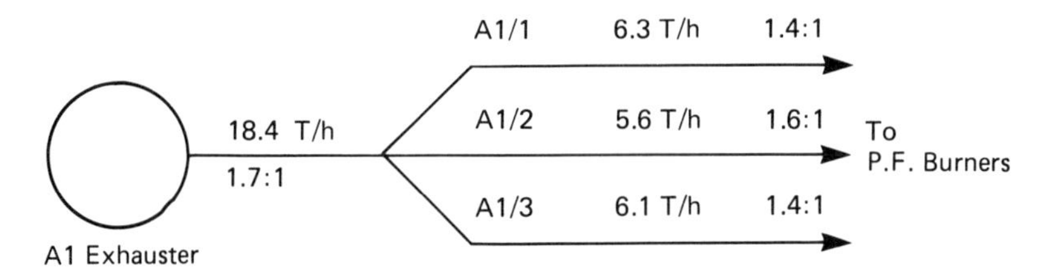

Figure 8.12 PF pipework from exhauster

The coal throughput and the air/fuel ratio are in good agreement with each other.

In the past, the standard PF sampler (*Figure 8.13*) was cumbersome to transport, and could not be accommodated on narrow walkways. More compact and effective samplers are now available. They retain the advantages of the older version such as sampling isokinetically, but in addition they are easier to operate, are more accurate and much more portable.

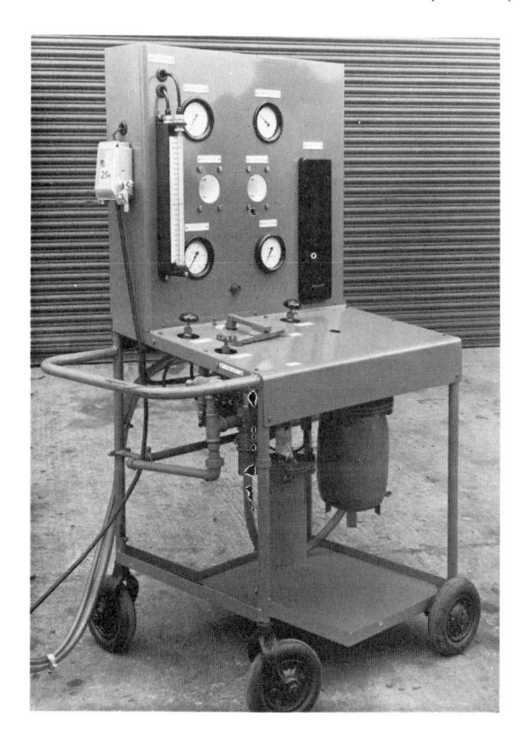

Figure 8.13 Old type PF sampler (CEGB)

One such equipment is shown in *Figure 8.14.* The design of the probe is novel as it enables semi-automatic sampling to be undertaken without the

Figure 8.14 Modern PF sampler and probes (CEGB)

PE Sampler calculation sheet

Date / 198

Unit No. 10 Mill A Pipe A1/1 Test No. 1

1 No. of Points Sampled 9 2 Sampling time per point 30 secs

3 Barometer 77.3 cm Hg 4 Area of pipe 0.1257 m^2 5 Area of Nozzle 0.000031 m

6 PF collected in (1) × (2) seconds = 1217 grams

7 Area ratio of pipe to nozzle $= \dfrac{(4)}{(5)}$ = 4055

8 Coal flow in pipe $\dfrac{(6) \times (7)}{1000 \times (1) \times (2)}$ = 1.8278 kg/s

9 Volume of air measured at Rotameter in (1) × (2) secs = 0.207 m^3
10 Temperature of air measured at Rotameter = $(t_a + 273)$ = 292 K
11 Pressure maintained at ejector = (−) 25.4 cm. *Hg*.
12 Pressure of air measured at Rotameter = (3) + (11) = 51.9 cm. *Hg*.
13 Temperature of contents of fuel pipe = $(t_f + 273)$ = 326 K
14 Static pressure in fuel pipe = 0.426 cm Hg
15 Absolute pressure in fuel pipe = (3) + (14) = 77.726 cm Hg

16 Actual volume sampled $= \dfrac{(9) \times (13) \times (12)}{(10 \times (15)}$ in (1) × (2) secs = 0.1544 m^3

17 Volume flow of air in pipe $= \dfrac{(7) \times (16)}{(1) \times (2)}$ = 2.32 m^3/s

18 Density of air in pipe $= \dfrac{355 \times (15)}{(3) \times (13)}$ = 1.095 kg/m^3

19 Mass flow of air in pipe = (17) × (18) = 2.54 kg/s

20 Density of PF sample $= \dfrac{(6)}{(16) \times 1000}$ = 0.788 kg/m^3

21 Volume of flow of PF $= \dfrac{(8)}{(20)}$ = 2.319 m^3/s

22 Volume flow of air plus coal = (17) + (21) = 4.639 m^3/s

(23) Velocity of air and coal mixture $= \dfrac{(22)}{(4)}$ = 36.9 m/s

(24) Air: Coal ratio by mass $= \dfrac{(19)}{(8)}$ = 1.39:1

Figure 8.15 PF sampler calculation sheet

use of an additional Pitot tube to measure velocity. The three-tube design enables a comparison to be made of the PF/air velocity both external and internal to the probe. A specimen calculation is shown in *Figure 8.15*. In the example quoted the probe was positioned in nine different locations for 30 s each. To ensure that the probe is correctly located it is essential that a suitable positioning plate is constructed and fastened to the pipe.

Of course, the time and effort required to carry out a pulverized fuel survey is considerable, and so it is not the sort of task that would normally be undertaken on a regular basis. For routine purposes it is normally only required to obtain samples of pulverized fuel for grading, say once per week. For this purpose it is sufficiently accurate to use a small cyclone sampler and obtain the sample from one location. Obviously the results will not be particularly accurate, but the intention is only to determine whether the gradings are near the acceptable range or far removed from it.

Milling plant constraints

Milling plant limitations often result in reduced load capability on pulverized fuel plant. As there are so many interacting variables it is desirable to consider the problem in a little detail. Basically any milling plant is required to fulfil the following conditions:

(a) It must be able to handle the design quantity of coal and produce an acceptable product, even with worn components.
(b) To be acceptable the product must be within the desired grading range at all stable loads. Grinding which is unnecessarily fine wastes milling power and could result in load limitations. If it is too coarse the combustible-in-ash loss will be high.
(c) Wet coal, up to the design wetness, must be adequately dried while full output is maintained, the coal/air mixture being at an acceptable temperature, usually in the region of 70°C.
(d) At no time must it be necessary to operate the milling plant in an unsafe condition. For example, the turn-down ratio must be adequate without instability.

Even though a mill can satisfy these conditions there will still be various operational constraints imposed, the most important of which are:

(a) *Drying capacity*

This is determined by two factors, namely (i) the mass flow of air through the mill; (ii) the temperature of the air to the mill. Obviously, the higher the air temperature the lower the necessary mass flow for a given amount of drying. An approximate drying formula is:

$$W_f = \frac{A_o}{1 + \beta} \times \frac{T_i - T_o}{M_c} \times 4.043 \times 10^4$$

where W_f = coal throughput
A_o = air flow at mill outlet
A_i = air flow at mill inlet

$$\beta = \text{leakage factor} = \frac{A_o - A_i}{A_i}$$

T_i = air temperature at mill inlet
T_o = coal/air temperature at mill outlet
M_c = total moisture fraction of coal

It should be noted that the pulverized coal leaving a mill is not normally dry – in fact it is common to have about 5% moisture present.

(b) *Grinding limit*

This is determined by the design of the plant. There are acceptable grading ranges for different types of coal and, even at full load, the product should not be outside the appropriate range. For example, bituminous coal should normally be within the range 70 – 80% below 75 μm (i.e. through 200 BS mesh sieve).

Should the grinding requirement be relaxed it is usually possible to obtain more than MCR output from a mill. Conversely, as the mill components wear, it becomes more difficult to keep within the grading range and the permissible limit of wear is reached when the product must be at the bottom of the grading range if full load is to be achieved.

(c) *Pulverized fuel fall-out*

Should the transport velocity be too low in the PF pipes and fittings some pulverized fuel will fall out of suspension. This could result in fires inside the pipes and so it is a condition to be avoided. Therefore, the minimum safe throughput of carrying air should be ascertained and the air flow always maintained above that value. Normally the minimum velocity of the coal/air mixture is about 18–20 m/s.

(d) *Erosion limit*

The rate of erosion determines the frequency with which the PF pipes and fittings need to be replaced. It can be shown that erosion varies approximately as the air/coal velocity raised to a power, i.e.

$$\text{erosion} \propto (\text{air/coal velocity})^{5/2}$$

Thus, if the velocity is doubled the rate of erosion will increase by about six times. Therefore, there is a limit to the rate of erosion beyond which the cost of replacement of pipes and fittings becomes uneconomic. Often the erosion limit is of the order of 1.5 times the fall-out limit air flow.

(e) *Flammability*

Should the air/fuel ratio become too high an explosive mixture may result. A ratio of 5:1 is regarded as the safe limit. In fact it is felt in some quarters that it should be 3:1.

(f) *Attemperation*

As mill coal flow is reduced it is also necessary to reduce the air flow until the fall-out limit is reached, which inhibits any further reduction. Further reduction of coal throughput would result in excessive coal/air mixture temperature, so it is necessary to start admitting attemperating air. When the flow of attemperating air is a maximum the temperature of the hot air to mill will be at a minimum. Of course, for a fixed maximum flow of attemperating air the mixed temperature attained will depend upon the quantity of hot air. For our purposes we can assume that the minimum air temperature which can be achieved is constant.

(g) *Fan power*

The primary air fans or exhausters provide the power to transport the pulverized coal. It follows that when the fans are operated at maximum it is a milling constraint. Investigations show that fan performance can be represented by a simple formula with sufficient accuracy for our purpose, i.e.

$W_f + W_a =$ a constant

where W_f and W_a are the fuel and air flows. This provides a means of determining the constraints for various fan speeds and various air/fuel ratios.

(h) *Flame stability*

Unless supported by an oil fire it is generally accepted that a bituminous coal fire could become unstable at throughputs less than 50% of maximum.

The Mill operating window

Studies of milling plant performance are being carried out within the CEGB. One concept that has been developed is that of the 'operational window'. This entails quantifying each of the constraints for a particular mill and, from this, determining the safe and practical limits of operation in terms of coal and air flow.

Consider the following example of the method. It relates to a vertical-spindle pressure mill.

Basic data:

Coal type	Bituminous
Total moisture	24% (max); 14% (nominal)
Coal flow	12 kg/s (max); 10.3 kg/s (nominal)
Grading	94% < 150 μm
Hot air to mill temperature	295°C (max); 200°C (min)
Air flow to mill	30.2 kg/s
Seal air flow to mill	0.5 kg/s at 15°C
Rated primary air fan power	406 kW at 42.7 kg/s flow
Minimum air flow	21 kg/s
Erosion limit	33 kg/s air flow
Air/fuel mixture temperature	70°C

From the basic data it is possible to list a number of limiting values, i.e.:

$$\text{Air temperature} = \frac{(30.2 \times 295) + (0.5 \times 15)}{30.7} = 290°\text{C}$$

Coal throughout = 12 kg/s at 94% <150 μm
Stability = 0.5 × 12 = 6 kg/s coal flow
Drying limit is at 290°C air temperature and 24% moisture
Explosion limit is at an air/fuel ratio of 5:1
Fan power = $W_f + W_a$ = 42.7 kg/s
Fall out = 21 kg/s air flow
Erosion = 33 kg/s air flow

These can now be used to construct a diagram such as that shown in *Figure 8.16*. The lines of constant air/fuel ratio are easily plotted.

The required air/fuel ratio to dry the coal is determined from the formula given earlier, i.e.:

$$W_f = \frac{A_o}{1 + \beta} \times \frac{T_i - T_o}{M_c} \times 4.043 \times 10^4$$

$$\beta = \frac{30.7 - 30.2}{30.2} = 0.017$$

Substituting values:

$$W_f = \frac{A_o}{1.017} \times \frac{(290 - 70)}{0.24} \times 4.043 \times 10^{-4} = 0.36 A_o$$

So $A_o = 2.7\ W_f$
Therefore the air/fuel ratio is 2.7:1

In a similar manner the air/fuel ratio corresponding to the attemperating

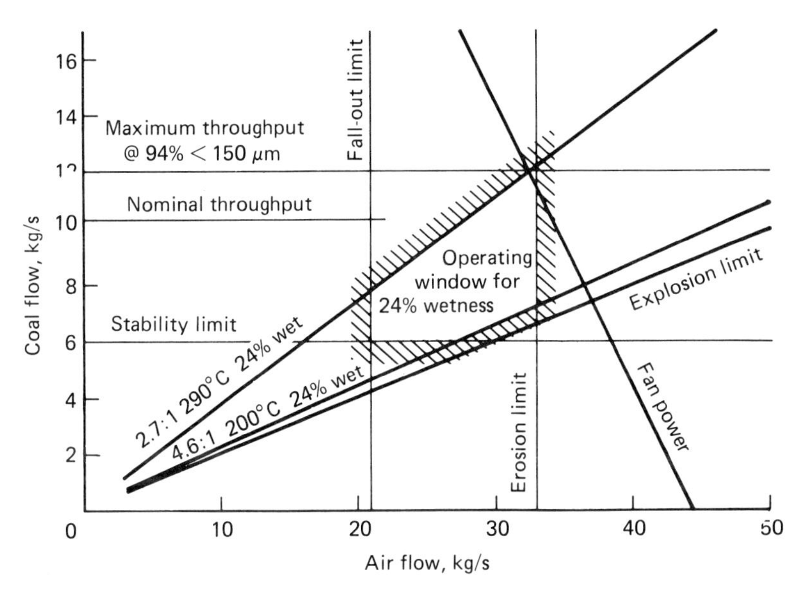

Figure 8.16 Operating window for vertical spindle mill

limit can be determined. The air to mill temperature in this case is 200°C and the moisture content remains 24%.

$$W_f = \frac{A_o}{1.017} \times \frac{(200 - 70)}{0.24} \times 4.043 \times 10^{-4}$$

so $W_f = 0.22A_o$, and $A_o = 4.6\,W_f$
Therefore, the air/fuel ratio is 4.6:1

It is seen from the figure that when all of the constraints are considered there is only a 'window' left within which the operating point should be located at all times if the fuel has a moisture content of 24%. Thus, for example:

1 For maximum fuel throughput, 32.5 kg/s of air is required at 290°C inlet temperature, i.e. the air/fuel ratio is 2.7:1.
2 With an inlet temperature of 290°C the minimum coal throughput is about 8 kg/s. Should a lower coal throughput be required it will be necessary to admit attemperating air, as the minimum permissible hot air flow has been reached and so its temperature must be reduced.
3 At no point does the 'window' reach the explosion limit so it is not a constraint in this case.
4 The minimum coal flow is 6 kg/s.

Of course, the condition of maximum fuel throughput and 24% moisture is the most onerous for which the mill was designed – in normal operation the conditions would be less onerous. For example, the nominal design conditions are:

Moisture 14%, and coal throughput 10.3 kg/s

The minimum air/fuel ratio for these conditions is represented by a line from the origin which passes through the intersection of the fall-out line and 10.3 kg/s coal flow. The ratio is found from inspection to be 2:1 (*Figure 8.17*).

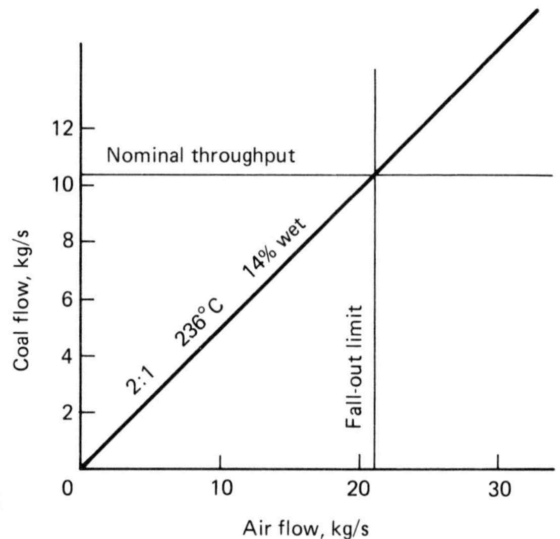

Figure 8.17 Minimum air/fuel ratio for nominal throughput

The required air temperature is found from the drying formula:

$$W_f = \frac{A_o}{1 + \beta} \times \frac{T_i - T_o}{M_c} \times 4.043 \times 10^{-4}$$

$$1 = \frac{2}{1.017} \times \frac{T_i - T_o}{0.14} \times 4.043 \times 10^{-4}$$

$$\therefore T_i = 236°\text{C}$$

Practical application of the opreating window

The plant operator does not have any direct knowledge of either the coal flow or the air flow. However, there are related parameters from which the flows may be inferred, and thus the following correlations may be useful:

1 Mill differential pressure (inc. classifier)	Coal flow plus air flow (recirculating)
2 Primary air differential	Air flow
3 Coal feeder speed	Coal flow
4 Fan power or speed	Coal flow plus air flow
5 Mill power	Coal flow (v.s. mills only)
6 Pressure drop in PF pipe	Coal flow plus air flow

Once suitable inferential parameters have been selected for the air and coal flows (or, if necessary, coal/air flow and air flow) the signals from the measuring points can be displayed on a modified vectormeter. These instruments normally display megawatts and megavars as shown in *Figure 8.18*.

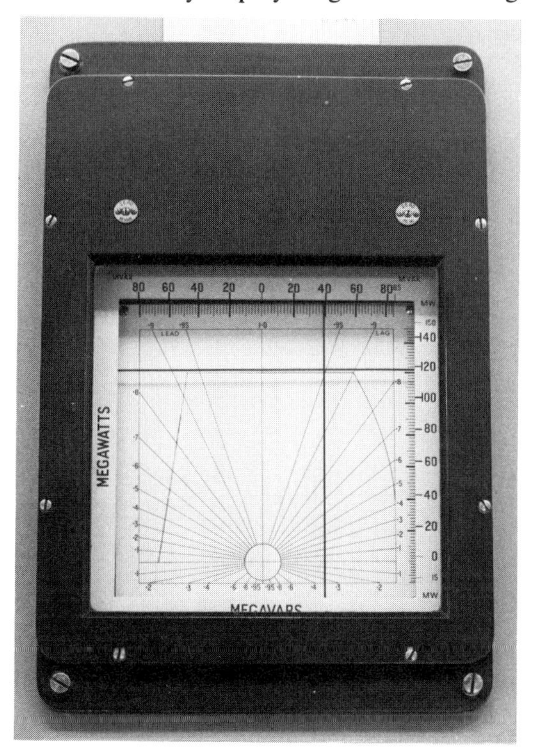

Figure 8.18 Vectormeter, suitable for use for 'operating window' display (CEGB)

However, the axes could be re-scaled to indicate air flow and coal flow and the operating window drawn. The intersection of the vertical and horizontal pointers would then indicate the operating point of the mill to the operator. Alternatively the information could be displayed on a VDU (visual display unit) if required.

Questions

1 What is the normal method of boiler testing?
2 Why was the Direct Method of efficiency determination superseded?
3 What is 'gross on gross' efficiency?
4 Name the boiler losses and state typical values for a modern PF boiler?
5 What precautions are necessary when comparing boiler efficiency results obtained over a number of years?
6 What is the test procedure for determining a curve of optimum O_2% against load?
7 State the expression for excess air per cent using an O_2 meter.
8 State the expression for excess air per cent using a CO_2 meter.
9 State the expression for air inleakage per cent.
10 State an advantage of using CO_2 meters for combustion control rather than O_2 meters.
11 State an advantage of using O_2 meters.
12 Why is it important to monitor CO in flue gas?
13 Describe two types of CO monitoring equipment and give the advantage of each.
14 Name some causes of low carbon in ash.
15 Name some causes of high carbon in ash.
16 What is the desirable temperature range of the fuel/air mixture leaving a mill when burning bituminous coal?
17 Describe the action of a device for collecting dust samples from a flue gas duct.

Exercise 1

Optimization of total air

Boiler: Drakelow No. 3 Date:

Item	*Data*	*Test 1*	*Test 2*	*Test 3*
1	Boiler load kg/s	66.8	66.5	68.0
2	T/A load MW	61.75	61.5	62.0
3	CO_2% at boiler outlet	14.62	16.45	15.33
4	CO_2% at A/H outlet	11.48	13.20	12.21
5	O_2% at A/H outlet (from conversion graph)	8.10		
6	N_2% at A/H outlet (100− (5) − (4))	80.42		
7	CO% at A/H outlet	0	0.3	0.00
8	Flue gas temp. at A/H outlet °C (LHS/RHS)	166/176	171/181	170/179
9	Air temp. at F.D. intake °C (LHS/RHS)	30.0/31.6	31.4/32.3	35.0/36.0
10	Carbon per kg coal *C* %	51.3	51.5	51.9

11	Sulphur per kg coal *S* %	1.5	1.5	1.5
12	Ash per kg coal *A* %	17.5	16.6	16.3
13	Hydrogen per kg coal *H* %	3.42	3.41	3.43
14	Gross calorific value kJ/kg	20 536	20 541	20 722
15	Combustible in coarse ash % *Cr*	0.01	0.01	0.01
16	Combustible in fine ash % *Cf* (LHS/RHS)	1.41/1.27	1.29/1.64	0.92/1.2
17	I.D. fan motor power consumption kW	591	476	526
18	F.D. fan motor kW	192	128	165
19	Milling plant power consumption kW	276	270	258

Combustible in rough ash loss

20	Wt of rough ash/100 kg coal= 20% × (12)kg	3.5
21	Carbon loss per 100 kg coal $= \dfrac{(20) \times (15)}{100}$ kg	0.00035
22	C.V. of carbon = 33 820 kJ/kg	
23	Heat loss/100kg coal = (21) × (22) kJ	11.8
24	% heat loss $= \dfrac{(23)}{(14)}$	0.0006
25	Wt. of dust per 100 kg coal = 80% ×(12) kg	14.0
26	Carbon loss per 100 kg coal $= \dfrac{(25) \times (16)}{100}$ kg	0.188
27	Heat loss/100 kg coal = (26) × (22) kJ	6 358
28	% heat loss $= \dfrac{(27)}{(14)}$	0.31

Dry flue gas loss

29	$\dfrac{100}{12 \times [(4) + (7)]}$	
30	$\dfrac{(10)}{100} + \dfrac{(11)}{267} - \dfrac{(21)}{100} - \dfrac{(26)}{100}$	0.517
31	30.6 [(8) − (9)]	4290

32	DFG loss = (29) × (30) × (31) kJ/kgcoal	1 610
33	% loss = $\frac{(32) \times 100}{(14)}$	7.8
34	DFG loss (by Seigert) = $\frac{0.63\ ((8) - (9)\ )}{(4)}$	7.75
Unburned gas loss		
35	$\frac{7 \times (7)}{3\ [(4) + (7)]}$	0
36	Unburned gas loss = (35) × (30) × 23 620 kJ/kg coal	0
37	% loss = $\frac{(36) \times 100}{(14)}$	0
Auxiliary power loss		
38	Total auxiliary power = (17) + (18) + (19) kW	1049
39	Boiler power = (2) × 1000kW	61 750
40	% auxiliary power = $\frac{(38) \times 100)}{(39)}$	1.7
Total losses		
41	Total losses = (24) + (28) +(33) + (37) +(4) %	9.81

Exercise 1 (Answer Optimization of Total air

Boiler: Drakelow No. 3 Date:

Item	*Data*	*Test 1*	*Test 2*	*Test 3*
1	Boiler load kg/s	66.8	66.5	68.0
2	T/A load MW	61.75	61.5	62.0
3	CO_2% at boiler outlet	14.62	16.45	15.33
4	CO_2% at A/H outlet	11.48	13.20	12.21
5	O_2% at A/H outlet (from graph)	8.10	6.8	7.6
6	N_2% at A/H outlet (100 −(5) − (4))	80.42	80.0	80.2

7	CO% at A/H outlet	0	0.3	0.0
8	Flue gas temp. at A/H outlet°C(LHS/RHS)	166/ 176	171/181	170/179
9	Air temp. at F.D. intake °C (LHS/RHS)	30.0/31.6	31.4/32.3	35.0/36.0
10	Carbon per kg coal *C* %	51.3	51.5	51.9
11	Sulphur perkg coal *S* %	1.5	1.5	1.5
12	Ash per kg coal *A* %	17.5	16.6	16.3
13	Hydrogen per kg coal *H* %	3.42	3.41	3.43
14	Gross calorific value kJ/kg	20 536	20 541	20 722
15	Combustible in coarse ash % Cr	0.01	0.01	0.01
16	Combustible in fine ash % Cr (LHS/RHS)	1.41/1.27	1.29/1.64	0.92/1.2
17	I.D. fan motor power consumptionkW	591	476	526
18	F.D. fan motor power consumption kW	192	128	165
19	Milling plant power consumption kW	276	270	258
Combustible in rough ash loss				
20	Wt of rough ash/100 kg coal= 20% × (12)kg	3.5	3.32	3.26
21	Carbon loss per 100 kg coal $= \frac{(20) \times (15)}{100}$ kg	0.00035	0.00033	0.00033
22	C.V. of carbon = 33 820 kJ/kg	—	—	—
23	Heat loss/100kg coal − (21) × (22) kJ	11.8	11.16	11.16
24	% heat loss $= \frac{(23)}{(14)}$	0.0006	0.0005	0.0005
25	Wt of dust per 100 kg coal = 80% × (12) kg	14.0	13.3	13.0
26	Carbon loss per 100 kg coal $= \frac{(25) \times (16)}{100}$ kg	0.188	0.195	0.138
27	Heat loss/100 kg coal = (26) × (22) kJ	6 358	6 595	4 667
28	% heat loss $= \frac{(27)}{(14)}$	0.31	0.32	0.23

	Dry flue gas loss			
29	$\frac{100}{12 \times [(4) + (7)]}$	0.7259	0.6173	0.682
30	$\frac{(10)}{100} + \frac{(11)}{267} - \frac{(21)}{100} - \frac{(26)}{100}$	0.517	0.519	0.523
31	30.5 [(8) − (9)]	4290	4413	4238
32	DFG loss = (29) × (30) × (31) kJ/kg coal	1 610	1 414	1 512
33	% loss = $\frac{(32) \times 100}{(14)}$	7.8	6.9	7.3
34	DFG loss (by Seigert) = $\frac{0.63 ((8) - (9))}{(4)}$	7.75	6.9	7.7
	Unburned gas loss			
35	$\frac{7 \times (7)}{3 [(4) + (7)]}$	0	0.05	0
36	Unburned gas loss = (35) ×(30) × 23 620kJ/kg coal	0	613	0
37	% loss = $\frac{(36) \times 100}{(14)}$	0	3.0	0
	Auxiliary power loss			
38	Total auxiliary power = (17) + (18) +(19) kW	1049	874	949
39	Boiler power = (2) × 1000 kW	61 750	61 500	62 000
40	% auxiliary power = $\frac{(38) \times 100}{(39)}$	1.7	1.4	1.5
	Total losses			
41	Total losses = (24) + (28) +(33) + (37) +(40)%	9.81	11.62	9.03

Exercise 2

Calculate the air:fuel ratio

PF Sampler calculation sheet

Date 6/1/1984

Unit No. 9 **Mill** A **Pipe A1/3** **Test No.** 2

1 No. of points sampled 9

2 Sampling time per point 30 secs

3 Barometer 76.202 cm Hg

4 Area of pipe 0.1257m²

5 Area of nozzle 0.000031 m²

6 PF collected in (1) × (2) seconds = 183.5 gram

7 Area ratio of pipe to nozzle $= \frac{(4)}{(5)}$ =

8 Coal flow in pipe $\frac{(6) \times (7)}{1000 \times (1) \times (2)}$ = kg/s

9 Volume of air measured at Rotameter in (1) × (2) secs = 0.262 m³

10 Temperature of air measured at Rotameter = $(t_a + 273)$ = 299 K

11 Pressure maintained at ejector = (−) 25.4 cm Hg

12 Pressure of air measured at Rotameter = (3) + (11) = cm Hg

13 Temperature of contents of fuel pipe = $(t_f + 273)$ = 339 K

14 Static pressure in fuel pipe = (+) 0.762 cm Hg

15 Absolute pressure in fuel pipe = (3) + (14) = cm Hg

16 Actual volume sampled $= \frac{(9) \times (13) \times (12)}{(10) \times (15)}$ in (1) × (2) secs

= m³

17 Volume flow of air in pipe $= \frac{(7) \times (16)}{(1) \times (2)}$ = m³/s

18 Density of air in pipe $= \frac{355 \times (15)}{(3) \times (13)}$ = kg/m³

19 Mass flow of air in pipe = (17) × (18) = kg/s

20 Density of PF sample $= \frac{(16)}{(16) \times 1000}$ = kg/m³

21 Volume flow of PF $= \frac{(8)}{(20)}$ = m³/s

22 Volume flow of air plus coal = (17) + (21) = m³/s

23 Velocity of air and coal mixture $= \dfrac{(22)}{(4)}$ = m/s

24 Air : coal ratio by mass $= \dfrac{(19)}{(8)}$ = :1

Exercise 2 (Answer)

PF Sampler calculation sheet

Date / **198**

Unit No. 9 Mill A Pipe A1/3 Test No. 2

1 No. of points sampled 9 2 Sampling time per point 30 secs

3 Barometer 76.202 cm Hg 4 Area of pipe 0.1257 m^2

5 Area of nozzle 0.0000031 m^2

6 PF collected in (1) × (2) seconds = 183.5 gram

7 Area ratio of pipe to nozzle $= \dfrac{(4)}{(5)}$ = 4055

8 Coal flow in pipe $\dfrac{(6) \times (7)}{1000 \times (1) \times (2)}$ = 2.76 kg/s

9 Volume of air measured at Rotameter in (1) × (2) sec = 0.262 m^3

10 Temperature of air measured at Rotameter = $(t_a + 273)$ = 299 K

11 Pressure maintained at ejector = (−) 25.4 cm Hg

12 Pressure of air measured at Rotameter = (3) + (11) = 50.8 cm Hg

13 Temperature of contents of fuel pipe = $(t_f + 273)$ = 339 K

14 Static pressure in fuel pipe = (+) 0.762 cm Hg

15 Absolute pressure in fuel pipe = (3) + (14) = 76.964 cm Hg

16 Actual volume sampled

$= \dfrac{(9) \times (13) \times (12)}{(10 \times \quad (15)}$ in (1) × (2) sec = 0.196m^3

17 Volume flow of air in pipe $= \dfrac{(7) \times (16)}{(1) \times (2)}$ = 2.945m^3/s

18 Density of air in pipe $= \dfrac{355 \times (15)}{(3) \times (13)}$ = 1.0577 kg/m^3

19 Mass flow of air in pipe = (17) × (18) = 3.115 kg/s

20 Density of PF sample = $\dfrac{(6)}{(16) \times 1000}$ = 0.9363 kg/m^3

21 Volume flow of PF $= \frac{(8)}{(20)}$ $= 2.9478\ m^3/s$

22 Volume flow of air plus coal = (17) + (21) $= 5.8928\ m^3/s$

23 Velocity of air and coal mixture $= \frac{(22)}{(4)}$ = 46.88 m/s

24 Air : coal ratio by mass $= \frac{(19)}{(8)}$ = 1.13 : 1

Project 1

Two 2-hour tests were carried out on a 350 MW boiler. The results are given in *Table 8.9.*

Table 8.9

Test item	*Unit*	*Test 1*	*Test 2*
Fuel analysis: (coal)			
Moisture	%	15.7	17.7
Ash	%	20.4	13.6
Volatile matter	%	26.2	28.2
Fixed carbon	%	50.66	53.89
Hydrogen	%	3.46	3.66
Sulphur	%	1.53	2.03
GCV	kJ/kg	20 600	22 080
Combustible in PFA	%	0.79	0.85
Combustible in rough ash	%	0.6	0.6
CO_2 at A/H gas inlet	%	13.0	12.5
CO_2 at A/H gas outlet	%	11.2	10.9
Gas temperature at A/H outlet	°C	115.5	115.5
Air inlet temperature at FD duct	°C	31.2	33.7
CO in flue gas	ppm	Negligible	Negligible

(a) Determine the heat balance for each test.
(b) What is the probable order of error of the results for Test 1?
(c) What is the percentage air inleakage at the A/Hs?
(d) What would be the heat balance for Test 2 if standard fuel had been used having this composition:

Moisture %	14.0
Ash %	16.0
Volatile matter %	29.0
Fixed carbon %	41.0
Hydrogen %	3.6
Sulphur %	1.6
GCV kJ/kg	22 725

Project 1 (Answer)

(a) The calculation for Test 1 heat balance is shown on page 363.

Heat balance (gross on gross)

	Test 1	*Test 2*
Dry flue gas loss %	4.76	4.71
Wet flue gas loss %	5.92	6.20
Combustible in ash loss %	0.21	0.17
Radiation and unaccounted loss %	0.81	0.78
	11.70	11.86
Boiler efficiency %	88.3	88.14

(b) The order of error is found from:

$$\text{T.T.E.} = \pm \frac{\sqrt{[(4.76 \times 10)^2 + (5.92 \times 10)^2 + (0.21 \times 22.5)^2]}}{11.7}$$

$$= \frac{\pm \sqrt{[47.6^2 + 59.2^2 + 4.7^2]}}{11.7} = \pm \frac{\sqrt{(2266 + 3505 + 22)}}{11.7}$$

$$= \pm \frac{76.1}{11.7} = \pm\ 6.5\%$$

$$\text{C.T.M.E.} = \pm \frac{100 - 88.3}{88.3} \times 6.5 = \pm\ 0.86$$

$$\delta\ \eta = \pm \frac{88.3 \times 0.86}{100} = \pm 0.76, \text{ say } 0.8$$

So probable efficiency is within 88.3% ± 0.8%

(c) From *Figure 8.10*, O_2 at A/H inlet = 6.1%; O_2 at A/H outlet = 8.5%

$$\therefore \text{Inleakage} = \frac{8.5 - 6.1}{21 - 8.5} \times 100 = 19.2\%$$

(Note: The very high O_2% at the A/H inlet is indicative of either considerable air ingress to the boiler or far too much forced draught. Also the inleakage at the air heaters is very much greater than optimum, indicating badly worn or incorrectly set seals).

(d) *Correction for standard fuel*

Wet flue gas =

$$6.2 + (2707 - 143)\left[\frac{14.0 + (9 \times 3.6)}{22\ 725} - \frac{17.7 + (9 + (9 \times 3.66)}{22\ 080}\right]$$

$$= 6.2 + 2564\ (0.00205 - 0.00230) = 5.56\%$$

$$\text{Combustible in ash} = 0.17\left[\frac{16.0}{13.6} \times \frac{22\,080}{22\,725}\right] + 0 = 0.21\%$$

So heat balance corrected to standard fuel for Test 2 is:

Dry flue gas loss %	4.71
Wet flue gas loss %	5.56
Combustible in ash loss %	0.21
Radiation and unaccounted loss %	0.78
	11.26

∴ Boiler efficiency = 88.74%

Test 1
Heat balance calculation

Carbon in rough ash = 0.006 × 0.204 × 0.2 = 0.0002 kg/kg fuel
Carbon in dust = 0.0079 × 0.204 × 0.8 = 0.0013 kg/kg fuel
So total carbon in ash and dust = 0.0015 kg/kg fuel

Dry flue gas

$$\text{Loss} = \left[\frac{100}{12\,(CO_2 + CO)}\left(\frac{C}{100} + \frac{S}{267} - 0.0015\right)\right] \times 30.6 \times (T - t)$$

$$= \left[\frac{100}{12 \times 11.2}\left(0.5066 + \frac{1.53}{267} - 0.0015\right)\right] \times 30.6\,(115.5 - 31.2)$$

$$= 0.744 \times 0.51083 \times 30.6 \times 84.3$$

$$= 980.4 \text{ kJ/kg fuel or } \frac{980.4 \times 100}{20\,600} = 4.76\%$$

Wet flue gas

$$\text{Loss} = \frac{M + 9H}{100}[(25 - t) + 2442 + 1.88\,(T - 25)]$$

$$= \frac{15.7 + (9 \times 3.46)}{100}[(25 - 31.2) + 2442 + 1.88\,(115.5 - 25)]$$

$$= 0.468\,[-6.2 + 2442 + 170.1]$$

$$= 1219.6 \text{ kJ/kg fuel or } \frac{1219.6 \times 100}{20\,600} = 5.92\%$$

Combustible in ash

$$\text{Loss to dust} = \frac{33\,820\,cA}{100} = 338.20 \times 0.79 \times 0.8 \times 0.204$$

$$= 43.6 \text{ kJ/kg fuel or } \frac{43.6 \times 100}{20\,600} = 0.21\%$$

$$\text{Loss to rough ash} = 338.20 \times 0.006 \times 0.2 \times 0.204 = 0.08 \text{ kJ/kg}$$

$$= \frac{0.08 \times 100}{20\,600} = 0.0004\%$$

So total loss due to C in A = 0.2104%, say 0.21%
Radiation and unaccounted = 0.81%

Project 2

The attached table lists the results of a series of tests to determine the optimum CO_2% at 80% MCR boiler loading.

(a) What is the optimum CO_2%?
(b) If the boiler is rated at 315.0 kg/s what is the extra cost of operating at:
(i) 14.65% CO_2; (ii) 16.65% CO_2 at 80% MCR load?

Table 8.10 Tests to establish optimum excess air (CO_2)

Controllable losses calculated from test results, % boiler efficiency	*Test air settings (% CO_2 at A/H inlet)*				
	13.0	14.25	15.5	16.25	17.0
Dry gas	7.4	6.8	6.2	5.8	5.4
Combustible in ash and dust	0.1	0.2	0.42	0.9	2.5
Combustible gas (CO)	0	0	0	0.1	1.2
Aux power (fans)	2.2	1.9	1.76	1.65	1.6
Total loss	9.7	8.9	8.38	8.45	10.7

The heat received by the steam/water is 2500 GJ/h.
The fuel cost is £24.0 per tonne; average heat = 23.0 GJ/tonne.
So cost of heat = £1.044/GJ.

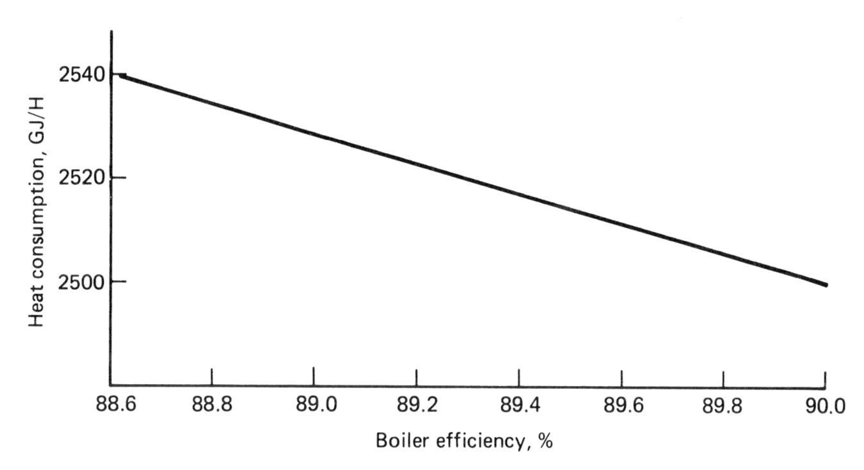

Figure 8.19(a) Boiler heat consumption *vs* efficiency. Project No 2

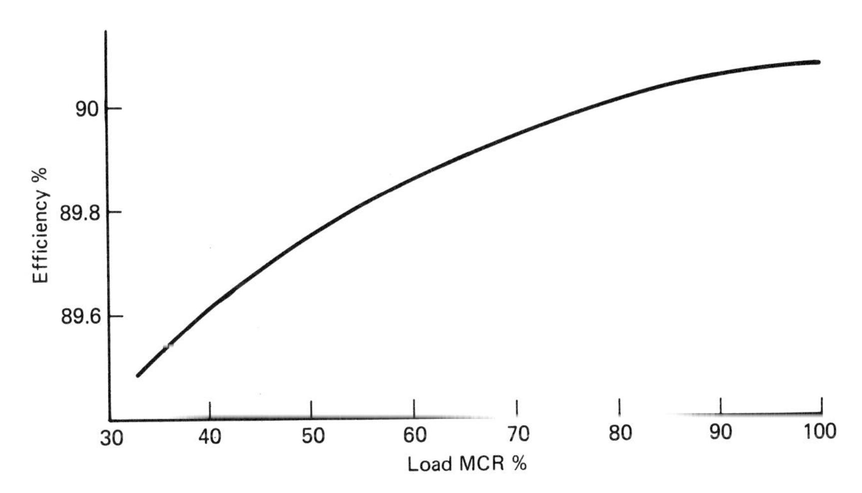

Figure 8.19(b) Boiler efficiency *vs* load. Project No 2

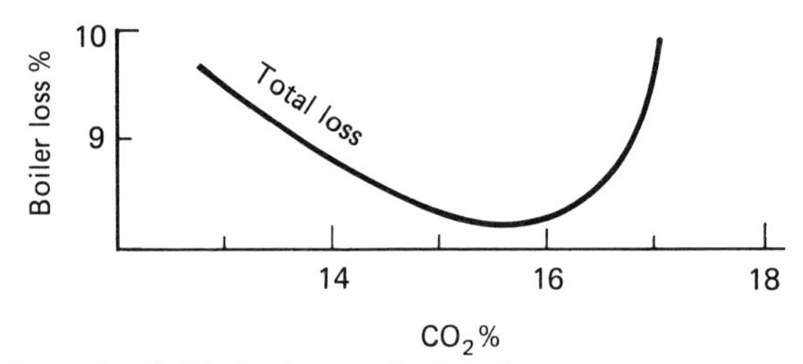

Figure 8.19(c) Boiler losses. Project No 2

Project 2 (Answer)

(a) 15.8% CO_2, (see *Figure 8.19(c)*.

(b) Optimum efficiency at 80% MCR is 90%, from *Figure 8.19(b)*. At 14.65 CO_2 losses increase by 0.4, so efficiency is 89.6% (See *Figure 8.19(c)*)

Heat input at 89.6%	= 2511 GJ/h	
Heat input at 90.0%	= 2500 GJ/h	
Extra heat	= 11 GJ/h	
Cost at £1.044/GJ	= £11.48/h	
	= £275.6/day	Assuming continuous
	= £1 929/week	operation at 14.65/CO_2
	= £100 324/year	and 80% load

(c) At 16.65% CO_2 losses increase by 0.9, so efficiency is 89.1%

Heat input at 89.1%	= 2525 GJ/h	
Heat input at 90%	= 2500 GJ/h	
Extra heat	= 25 GJ/h	
Cost at £1.044/GJ	= £26.1/h	
	= £626.4/day	Assuming continuous
	= £4385/week	operation at 16.65% CO_2
	= £228 000/year	and 80% load

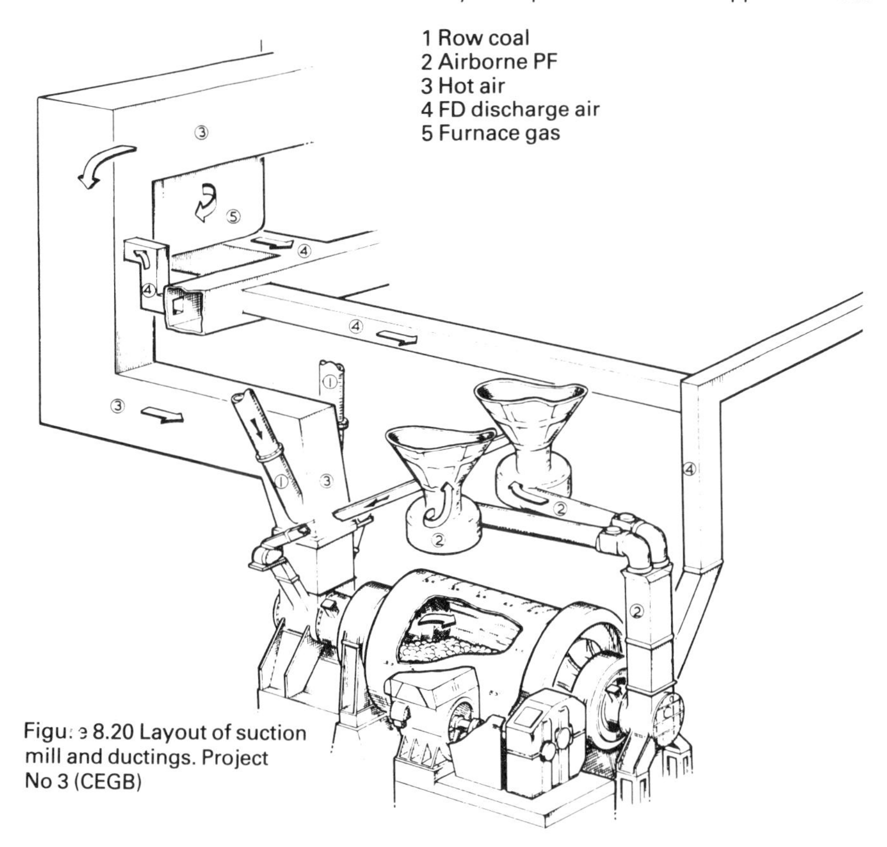

Figure 8.20 Layout of suction mill and ductings. Project No 3 (CEGB)

Project 3

Figure 8.20 shows the layout of a suction mill. The required coal throughput with acceptable grading is 12.0 kg/s and outlet air flow limit is 21 kg/s. Leakage factor β is 0.5 and the hot air temperature is 300°C. The temperature of the air/PF mixture is 70°C and the moisture in the coal is 14%.

(a) What is the maximum coal throughput that can be attained?
(b) What must the leakage be reduced to if full coal throughput is to be attained, assuming the hot air temperature can be raised to 330°C?
(c) In the future the coal wetness is expected to reach 18%. Assuming the leakage can be reduced to $\beta = 0.1$ what is the necessary hot air temperature to attain 12 kg/s coal flow?

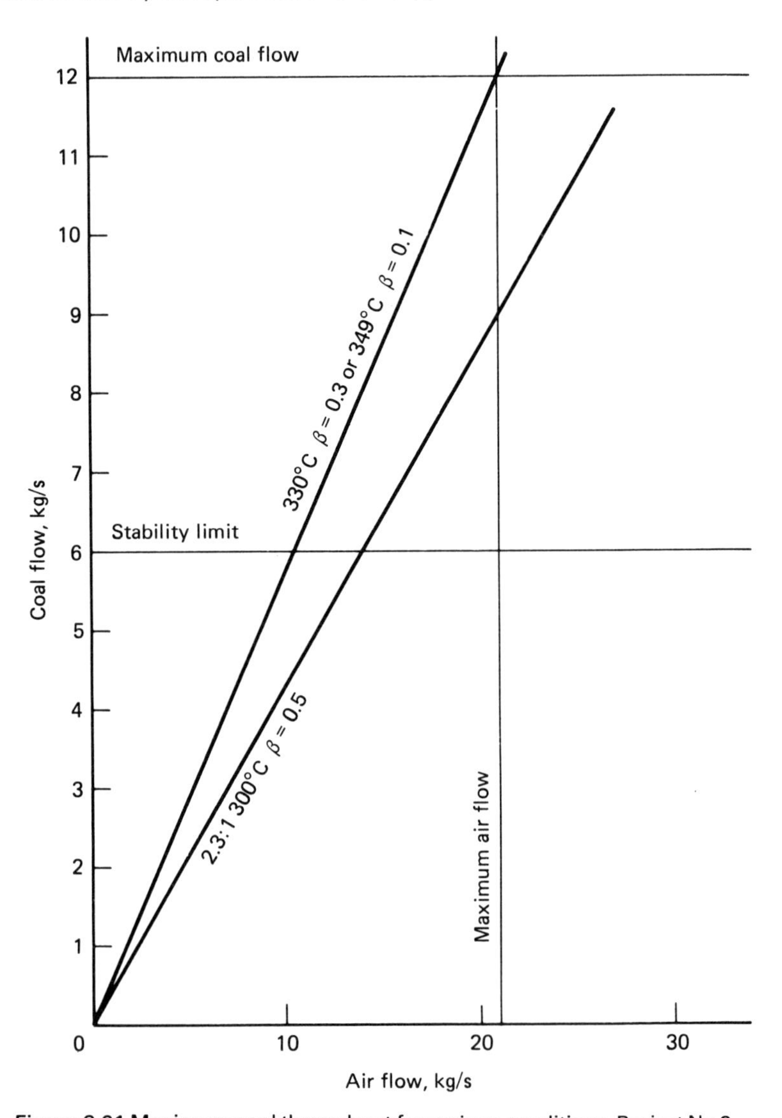

Figure 8.21 Maximum coal throughput for various conditions. Project No 3

Project 3 (Answer)

(a) $W_f = \dfrac{A_o}{1 + \beta} \times \dfrac{T_i - T_o}{Mc} \times 4.043 \times 10^{-4}$

So $W_f = \dfrac{A_o}{1.5} \times \dfrac{230}{0.14} \times 4.043 \times 10^{-4}$

so air/fuel ratio = 2.3:1

Reference to *Figure 8.21* shows that this air/fuel ratio line intersects the air flow limit line at 9 kg/s coal flow, i.e., air/fuel ratio = 1.7:1

(b) $$12 = \frac{21}{1+\beta} \times \frac{260}{0.14} \times 4.043 \times 10^{-4}$$

$$12(1 + \beta) = 15.8 \text{ from which } \beta = 0.3$$

(c) $$12 = \frac{21}{1.1} \times \frac{T_i - 70}{0.18} \times 4.043 \times 10^{-4}$$

$$12 = 0.043\,(T_i - 70)$$

$\therefore$ **Ti = 349°C**

Additional Reading

1 BS, 2885 *Code for Acceptance Tests on Stationary Steam Generators of the Power Station Type* (1974).

2 FENTON, K., *Thermal Efficiency and Power Production*, Pitman (1966).

3 THURLOW, C.C., 'The combustion of coal in fluidised beds', *Proc. I. Mech. E.,* **192**, No. 15 (1978)

4 COOKE, G. 'Design and operation of a once-through supercritical steam pressure boiler installation', *Proc. I. Mech. E.,* **176**, No. 24 (1962)

5 DAVIS, R.F., 'The development of the large assisted circulation boiler in England', *Proc. I. Mech. E.,* **177**, No. 20 (1963)

6 FRANCIS, W., *Fuels and Fuel Technology* (2 vols), Pergamon.

7 '375 MW supercritical 'Monotube' boiler for Drakelow "C" ', *The Engineer* (6 July 1962)

8 BAGLEY, R., 'Progress in modern high pressure boilers', Société Royale Belge des Électriciens, Brussels (20 May 1964)

9 HART, A.B. and LAWN, C.J., 'Combustion of coal and oil in power station boilers, *CEGB Research*, No. 5 (August 1977)

9 Pollution control

Power stations can cause environmental pollution in several ways, such as:

(a) Chimney emission;
(b) Heat rejection;
(c) Noise;
(d) Accidental discharges;
(e) Miscellaneous causes.

The first two categories will be dealt with here. The others, while of importance, are not of direct relevance in a book such as this. Suffice to say that the main source of noise is due to such things as lifting of safety valves and the operation of steam release valves when pressure raising. Accidental discharges include such things as the discharge of, say, boiler acid cleaning fluid into a river without adequate neutralization. At one station the river was contaminated by fuel oil because the storage tanks were over-filled. The excess oil should have been contained within the oil tank bunds but unfortunately the bund drains had been left open so the oil flowed into the storm water drains and from there was pumped to the river.

Included in the category of 'miscellaneous causes' are such things as dust blowing off dust piles; disturbance to the community by lorries delivering coal or removing dust; smoke from rubbish fires; and so on.

Chimney emission

Clean air legislation is now in force in many countries and often imposes severe restrictions on the permitted emission from chimneys. Typically, such emission includes the discharge of dust and grit, but increasingly, it often also includes the discharge of undesirable substances such as sulphur products.

Dust arrestment is effected usually be means of electrostatic precipitators. The basic formula for the efficiency of such plant is that due to Deutsch,

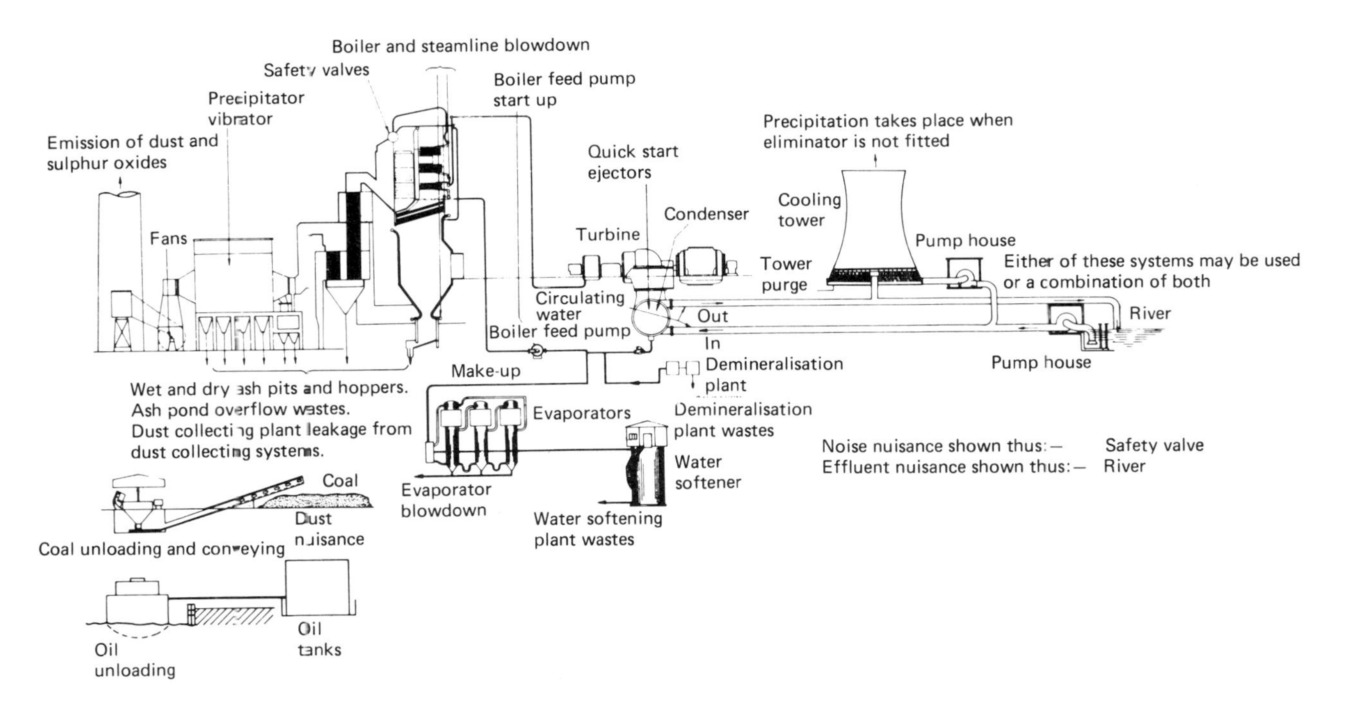

Figure 9.1 Possible sources of pollution and nuisance from a power station (CEGB)

i.e. $y = 100\ (1 - e^{-k})$
where y = collecting efficiency percent
k = a factor

Figure 9.2 shows the graph of $y = 100\ (1 - 1^{-k})$ and it can be used to determine the size ratio of precipitators. For example, how much larger must a precipitator be for an efficiency of 99% compared to one for 98%?

k for 98% = 3.75
k for 99% = 4.60

So increase in size $= \dfrac{4.60}{3.75} = 1.23$

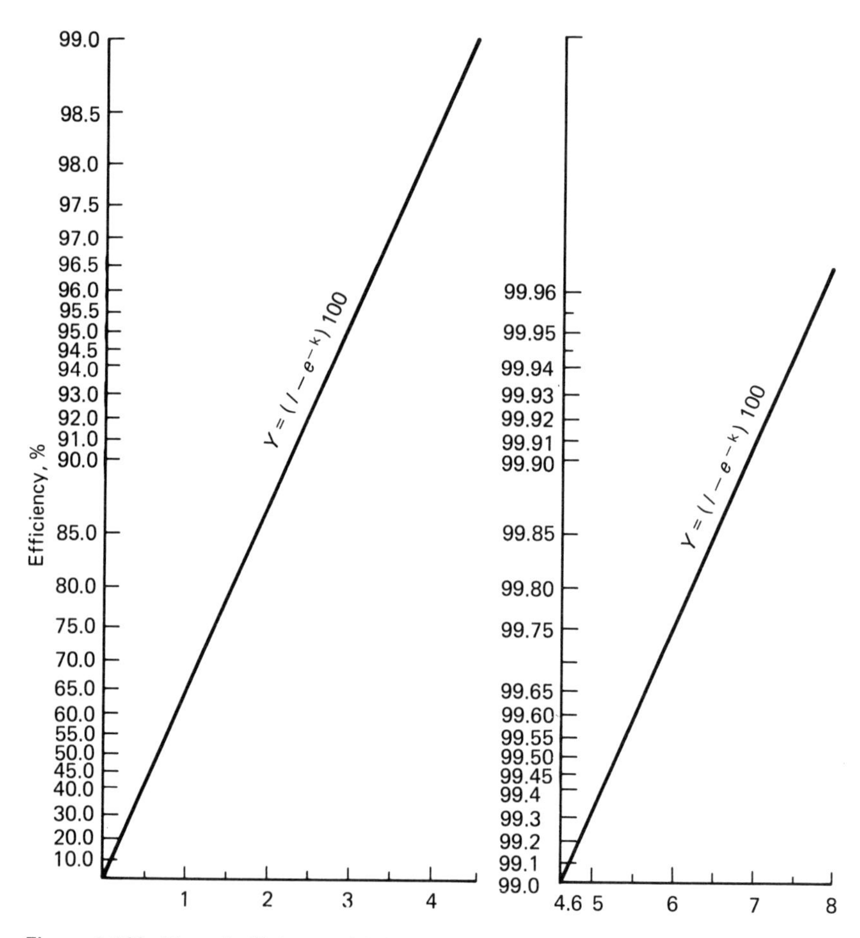

Figure 9.2 Varition of efficiency with factor 'K' (CEGB)

In other words, it will be 23% larger.

A useful formula which utilizes the factor k is $100k = WF$

where W = effective migration velocity (e.m.v.) in cm s

F = specific collecting surface

$$= \frac{\text{total collecting area in m}^2}{\text{total gas volume in m}^3\text{/s}}$$

Example

Consider a plant which has an electrostatic precipitator with a design efficiency of 99%. In addition there is a mechanical pre-collector whose efficiency is 32%. The total gas flow is 457.8 m³/s and the total collector plate area is 23 836 m². What is the overall efficiency of the plant and the effective migration velocity of the charged particles?

Answer

The outlet dust burden = (1 − 0.32) (1 − 0.99) = 0.0068 gram/gram, i.e. for every gram of dust entering the arresting plant 0.0068 gram will be discharged to the chimney.

$$\text{So the overall efficiency of collection} = \frac{1 - 0.0068}{1.0} = 0.9932$$

or 99.32%

Consider now the electrostatic precipitator only:

If the efficiency is 99.0% then $k = 4.6$ (*Figure 9.2*)

$$F = \frac{\text{Total collector plate area}}{\text{Total gas volume flow}} = \frac{23\,836\text{ m}^2}{457.8\text{ m}^3\text{/s}}$$

$$= 52.07\text{ m}^2\text{/m}^3\text{/s}$$

$$\text{So } W = \frac{100k}{F} = \frac{460}{52.07} = 8.8\text{ cm/s}$$

The value of the effective migration velocity is a measure of ease or difficulty of collection. Easy conditions would have e.m.v. values of about 15 cm/s, while difficult ones would be about 7.5 cm/s, see *Figure 9.3*.

The permitted emission varies from country to country, but the clean air legislation in the UK is probably typical. The essential wording of the legislation does not specify a particular value of emission – instead it states that the 'best practical means' will be used to limit such discharge. However, an agreement reached between the appropriate government agency and the generating industry states that the presumptive standard of emission will be 0.115 g/m³ of flue gas for plants whose arresting plant is designed for 99.3%

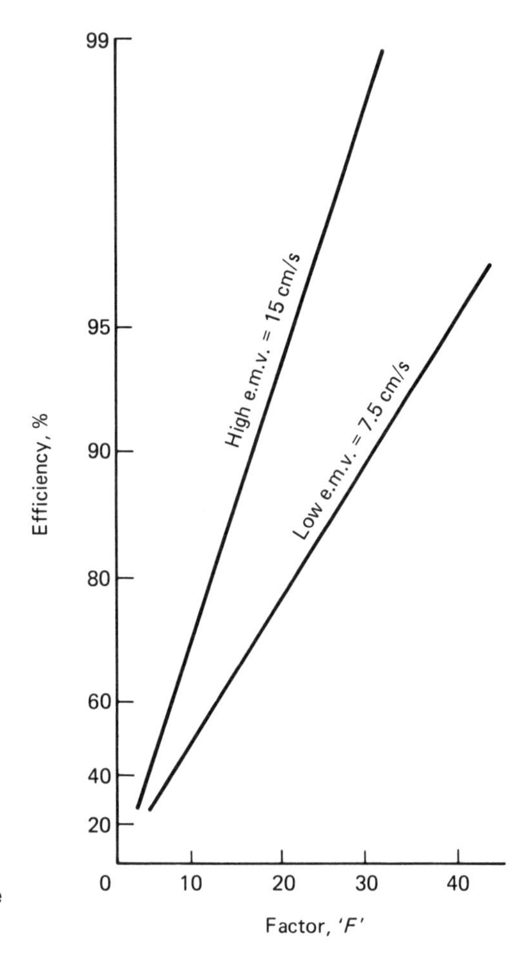

Figure 9.3 High and low effective migration velocities

efficiency, the gas conditions being reduced to 1.013 bar, 15°C, 12% CO_2 (wet).

Standards such as this are quite stringent and so there may be difficulty in meeting the requirements. Some of the more common and troublesome aspects of poor precipitator performance include:

(a) *Discharge electrode breakage*

Often the discharge electrodes consist of thin wires such as are shown in *Figure 9.4(a)* and the wires are mounted on frames which are located within the precipitator. *Figure 9.4(b)* shows a completed frame being hoisted into position. The wires may be flat, circular or square section, barbed or plain, twisted or straight, rigidly or loosely fastened. In addition there are many possible wire materials.

It is most important that whatever electrodes are used their availability

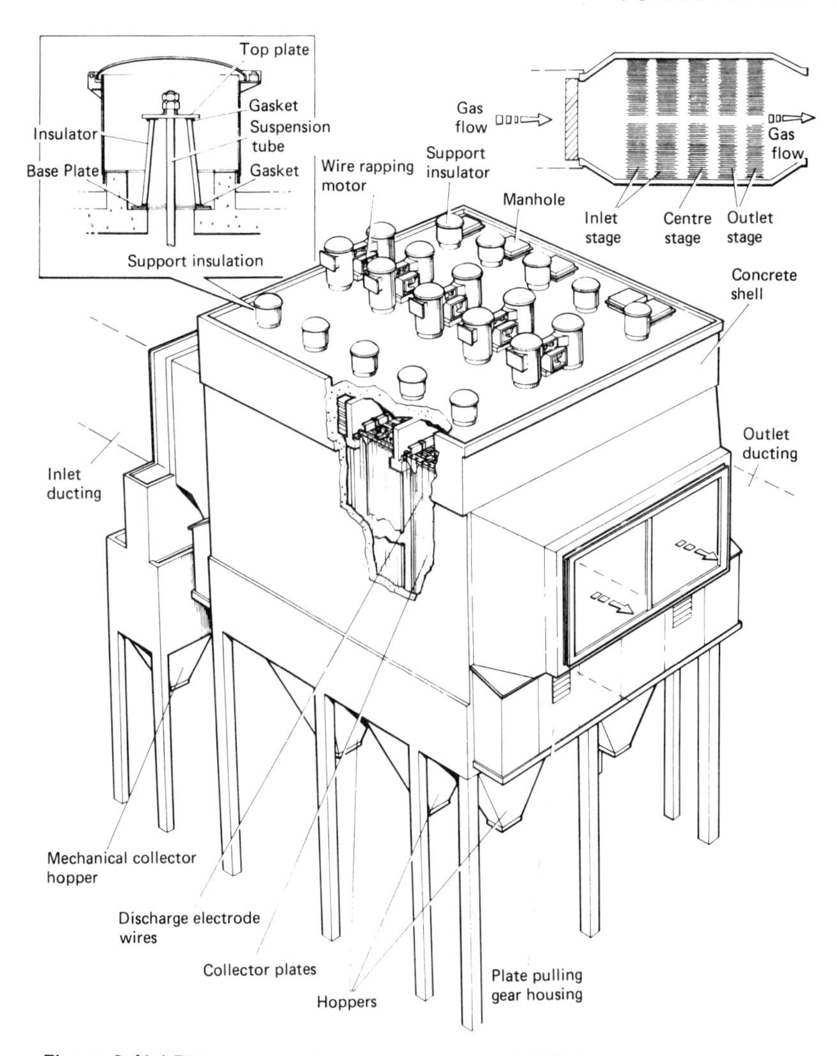

Figure 9.4(a) Plate type electrostatic precipitator (CEGB)

should be high. Should only one wire break out of the huge number in a particular zone it could cause electrical instability that would effectively put the whole zone out of service. One partial solution is to divide each zone electrically into several sub-zones so that a wire failure will only affect the one associated sub-zone. A common cause of wire failure is spark erosion, particularly near the top fixing. Mechanical failure is also common, particularly if the wires have been 'nicked', say by undue vice pressure when forming the fixing loop, or kinks have been left in the wire during erection.

Figure 9.4(b) Precipitator discharge electrodes being assembled (CEGB)

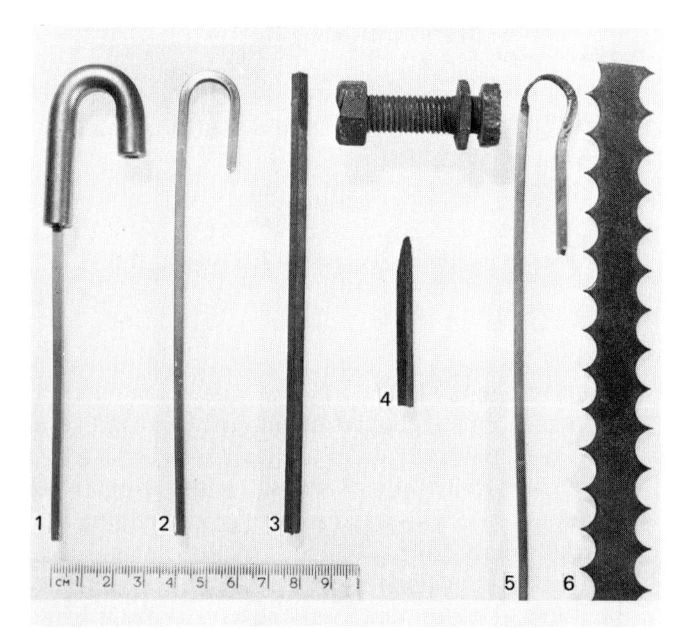

Figure 9.5 New and worn discharge electrodes (CEGB)

Various electrodes and fixings are shown in *Figure 9.5*. They are:

1 New 3 mm square section wire with sheathed supporting loop.
2 New 3 mm square section wire with supporting loop.
3 Used star section wire.
4 Supporting fixture.
5 Used star section wire showing spark eroded end which led to breakage.
6 3 mm square section wire showing considerable spark erosion at supporting loop.
7 'Unbreakable' wire 2 mm thick and 23 mm across 'spikes'.

The 'unbreakable type of electrode is becoming increasingly popular.

(b) *Collector plates*

The plates are mechanically strong, but even so they can suffer from metal fatigue brought about by excessive rapping, and also from corrosion due to low temperatures permitting acid deposition.

(c) *Tracking and air inleakage*

Precipitators operate at very high voltages of the order of 40–50 kV. It follows that there is always the problem of preventing tracking across insulators, steadying bars and so on. Dust deposits on such items often provide a 'tracking path', which is aggravated considerably if there is any dampness present. Such a situation could arise if there is considerable air ingress nearby. Defective seals on rapping rods, access doors, ducts, expansion joints and so on, can allow cold and damp air to blow across discrete areas of the precipitator, and this may lead to tracking. Tests have shown that it is quite common to have a drop of CO_2 in flue gas of over 1% from inlet to outlet of a precipitator, i.e. about 10% inleakage, so it can be seen that this is often a severe problem. Apart from causing possible trouble due to tracking, air inleakage also results in reduced gas temperature and increased mass flow.

It has been found that sometimes a considerable improvement in performance is obtained if a 'roof-house' is fitted over outdoor precipitator casings to keep the roof and insulators both warm and dry.

(d) *Rapping*

Older plants had rapping acceleration values of about 30*g*. but modern plants may be as high as 70*g*. In some installations two-tier rapping is fitted, the first tier at about one-third and the second at two-thirds the height of the collector plates. The timing of the rapping should be such that the dust layer does not become sufficient to cause the plant performance to suffer unduly. On the other hand each time rapping takes place some of the dislodged dust is re-entrained with the flue gas thus reducing the performance. Hence, there is an optimum rapping time and efforts should be made to determine what it is. Typical times on a three-pass, three-zones-per-pass precipitator are 10, 20 and 120 minutes for each rapping cycle for the inlet, centre and outlet zones respectively and 15 minutes for the discharge electrodes.

When the collector plates are inspected, the dust layer should be less than 1 mm for high resistance dust and 3 mm for 'easy' dust, i.e. that from fuel with a sulphur content of 2% or more. Urgent attention should be given to the rapping gear timing, acceleration values and mechanical condition if excessive dust thickness is left on the plates. The discharge electrodes should have only a very light dust deposit.

Figure 9.6 shows how the thickness of the dust layer is affected by the *g*

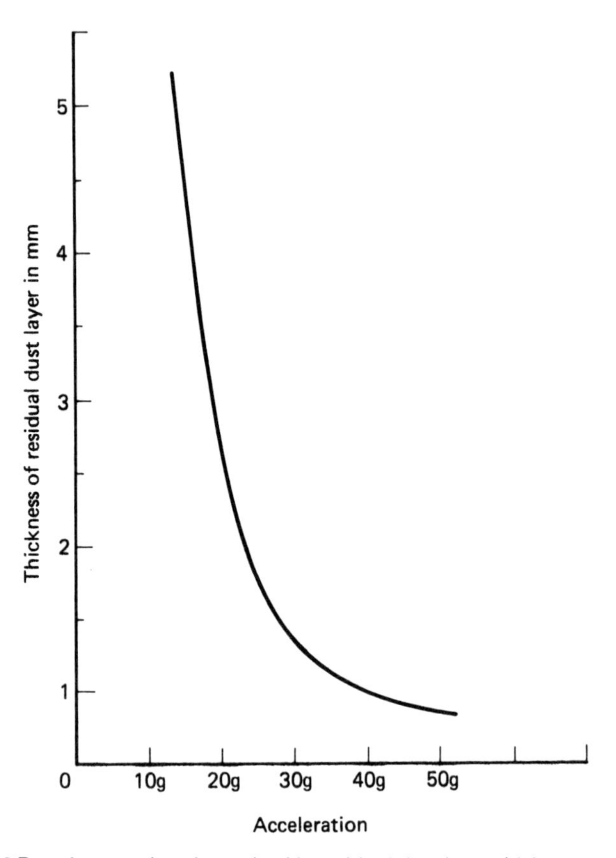

Figure 9.6 Rapping acceleration value Vs residual dust layer thickness

values of the rapping system. It has been established that the necessary *g* value for effective rapping is halved if the h.t. electrical supply is switched off. Hence, rapping which is relatively ineffective in normal operation may be quite satisfactory when the unit is off-load and so an inspection may show nothing amiss.

(e) *Gas volume*

If the gas volume is high the velocity of the gas through the precipitator will increase, thus reducing the treatment time. Hence the efficiency suffers. High gas volume can be due to high mass flow of gas or high gas temperature, or a combination of both. *Figure 9.7* shows the effect of gas

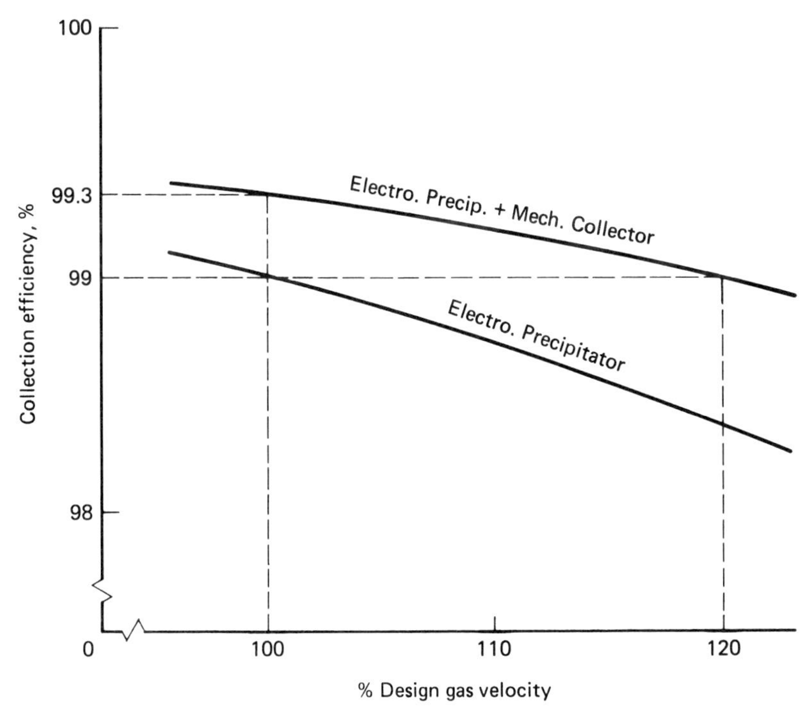

Figure 9.7 Effect of gas velocity on efficiency of typical precipitator (CEGB)

velocity on the efficiency of a typical plant. Usually the gas velocity efficiency should be less than 2 m/s. Excess velocity can be due to such things as too much excess air, air inleakage, faulty rotary air heater seals and so on. It should be remembered that for a given sized opening the amount of air inleakage increases as the suction of the gas stream increases and so it is at a maximum at the I.D. fan inlet.

If the air ingress into the precipitator itself is considerable there will be a significant reduction of gas temperature, and also of CO_2%. For example, suppose the CO_2 at precipitator inlet is 13.0% and the gas temperature is 130°C and at outlet is 120°C, the ambient temperature being 30°C. The CO_2% at outlet can be calculated from:

$$\text{Oulet } CO_2\% = 13.0\% \times \frac{(120 - 30)}{(130 - 30)} = 11.7\%$$

High gas temperature can be due to many things such as:

1 Defective sootblowers.
2 Defective gas baffles in the boiler.
3 Boiler fouling.
4 Air heater gas bypass dampers passing.
5 Excessive air heater air recirculation.
6 Excessive attemperating air.
7 Excessive tramp air, particularly before the combustion zone.

It is because of variations of gas flow and temperature that it is necessary to reduce the results obtained to standard conditions for purposes of comparison.

(f) *Gas distribution*

Even though the total gas flow is acceptable it is still quite possible to have considerable variations of velocity across the gas flow. Thus, those paths where the velocity is low could have very good precipitation, while those with high velocity may be very poor, and the poor precipitation outweighs the good. Therefore the first requirement is to ensure that each pass, if there is more than one, receives the same total gas flow. If this is satisfactory it is then necessary to establish that the flow distribution across each pass is acceptable.

Below are the results of cold air tests carried out at the inlet of the pre-collectors on a three-pass precipitator. The numbers are velocities in metres per second.

'A' duct

AV	*1.0*	*2.4*	*3.1*	*4.4*	*14.0*	*1.4*
6.1	0.8	4.0	4.0	7.0	19.0	1.8
5.6	1.0	2.0	5.0	7.0	16.0	2.3
2.3	1.0	1.4	2.5	2.0	11.0	1.0
2.7	1.2	2.1	1.0	1.4	10.0	0.6

'A' duct average = 4.4 m/s

'B' duct

5.0	*6.3*	*3.4*	*2.2*	*1.5*	*0.9*	*Av*
4.5	9.0	6.0	2.4	1.4	1.3	*4.1*
6.0	9.0	4.0	2.0	1.5	0.9	*3.9*
7.0	4.5	3.0	3.0	2.0	0.6	*3.4*
2.5	2.5	0.6	1.3	1.0	0.6	*1.4*

'B' duct average = 3.2 m/s

'C' duct

2.3	*3.8*	*2.5*	*2.7*	*4.9*	*3.5*	*Av*
4.0	6.0	4.5	4.0	8.0	6.0	5.4
3.0	4.5	2.5	4.0	8.0	5.0	4.5
0.8	3.2	3.0	1.4	2.3	2.5	2.2
1.3	1.5	0.1	1.2	1.3	0.4	1.0

'C' duct average = 3.3 m/s

Notice that the velocity increases in each case towards the top of the ducts, being of the order of 100% greater at the top than the bottom. Also notice the considerable lateral variation.

Of course, variations from point to point during a traverse will normally occur, and such variations can be ignored if the velocity is within 25% of the average velocity for the duct. Thus, for example, the following is the acceptable velocity range for any point in the case just considered:

'A' duct 3.3 to 5.5 m/s

'B' duct 2.4 to 4.0 m/s

'C' duct 2.5 to 4.1 m/s

Notice how few of the points meet this requirement. Consequently, it is hardly surprising that these results were obtained on a precipitator whose emission was unsatisfactory.

(g) *Particle size and dust burden*

A typical particle size spectrum for the dust from a large pulverized fuel boiler would be:

Size (μm)	0–10	10–20	20–40	>40
Percentage	32	21	25	22

(1 μm = 0.001 mm).

Up to about 20 μm diameter, the effective migration velocity usually increases as the particle size increases. Particles over 20 μm are, therefore, likely to be captured and so the emission from the chimney will normally contain a preponderance of fine particles, see *Figure 9.8*.

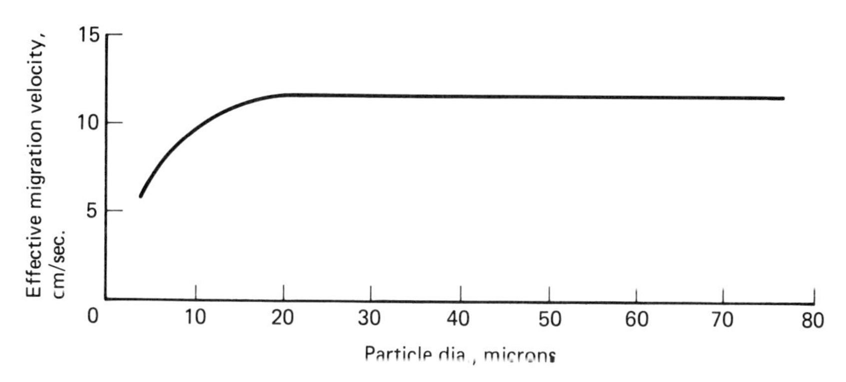

Figure 9.8 Typical relationship between effective migration velocity and particle size (CEGB)

(h) *Ash resistivity*

If the combustion is poor it may be that the dust will contain an abnormal amount of carbon. The effect of this is to make the dust electrically conductive. Such particles surrender their charge readily to the collector plate and are then easily re-entrained. Alternatively, it is common to have dust particles whose resistivity is high. This effect is usually associated with low sulphur fuels. When such particles migrate to the collector plates they form an insulating layer which interferes with the deposition of further particles as they cannot easily surrender their electrical charge. Thus, the effectiveness of the field is reduced and it could result in it being necessary to reduce the power input to the precipitator to prevent flashover from the highly charged dust layer. High resistivity is regarded as more than 1×10^9 ohm cm.

Deposition of high-resistance dust on the discharge electrodes has the effect of reducing the corona discharge and so is particularly undesirable. The sulphur content of the fuel plays a key role in determining whether the resistivity of the dust will be high or low. The sulphur burns to sulphur dioxide (SO_2), but a tiny proportion becomes sulphur trioxide (SO_3) as it passes through the furnace. The sulphur trioxide combines with water vapour to form sulphuric acid which is absorbed by the surface layer of the dust particles. Hence the dust is 'conditioned' and its low resistivity assists precipitation.

On the other hand, if the fuel contains little sulphur the chances are that the conditioning will be poor and so collection will be more difficult. *Figure 9.9* shows a typical sulphur/efficiency correction curve.

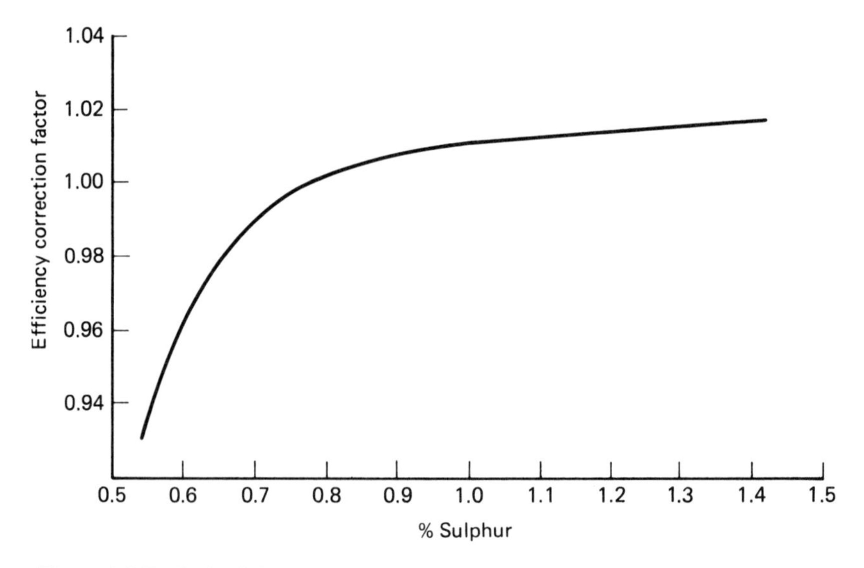

Figure 9.9 Typical sulphur curve

The problem of high-resistivity dust can be resolved in various ways, including:

(a) Change to high sulphur fuel; (b) Use a conditioning agent;
(c) Install pulse-energization equipment; (d) Extend the precipitator.

Changing to a high-sulphur fuel involves the least trouble assuming such supplies are available and economic. Failing that, a conditioning agent can be used to provide a surface conducting layer on the ash particles. Typical agents are sulphur trioxide, sulphuric acid, sulphamic acid, ammonium bisulphate, ammonium sulphate, and ammonia.

The third alternative is to install pulse-energization equipment so that high-frequency pulses are added to the rectified waveform. The resulting high-ion-density corona acts along the length of the discharge electrode, instead of just at discrete locations as is the case without the equipment. Consequently the dust particles are more easily precipitated and the improved performance of the plant is called the 'Enhancement Factor', designated by H.

$$H = \frac{\text{Pulsed migration velocity}}{\text{Unpulsed migration velocity}}$$

H values up to 2.0 or even higher can be attained. Thus, the improvement of the plant performance is significant, as can be seen from *Figure 9.10*.

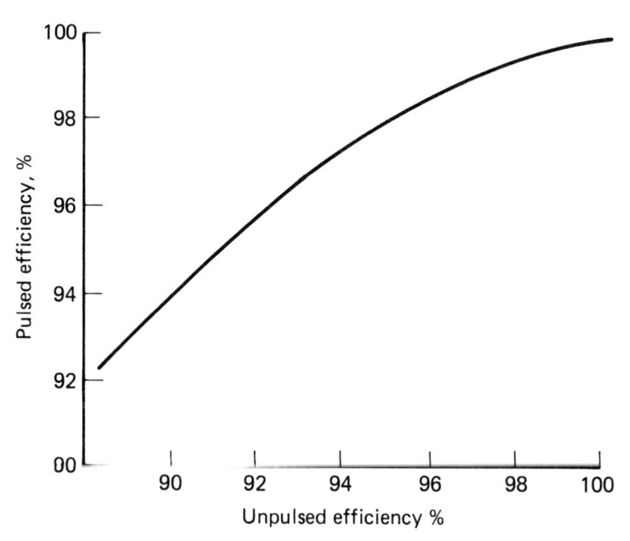

Figure 9.10 Improvement in collecting efficiency with pulsed energisation (H = 1.5)

The last of the alternatives, i.e. extend the precipitator, is very expensive and is really a last resort.

(i) *Ash hoppers full*

If the precipitator hoppers are allowed to become too full the dust will rise to the level of the internal metalwork such as electrodes and collectors, sometimes causing damage. Also, dust can be blown off the top of the dust pile and out of the precipitator. Note that about 80–85% of all the ash will be collected at the precipitators, the greatest proportion going into the first stage hoppers. Therefore they require special attention when being emptied.

Other hoppers on the boiler, while not so important in their effects on precipitation, should also be considered. For example, if the economizer grit hoppers are full, some particles which would normally have been deposited in the hopper will be carried forward to the precipitator, thus unnecessarily increasing the inlet dust burden.

(j) *Electrical conditions*

The power input to the precipitator is obviously of fundamental importance as can be seen from *Figure 9.11*. The higher the power the better the

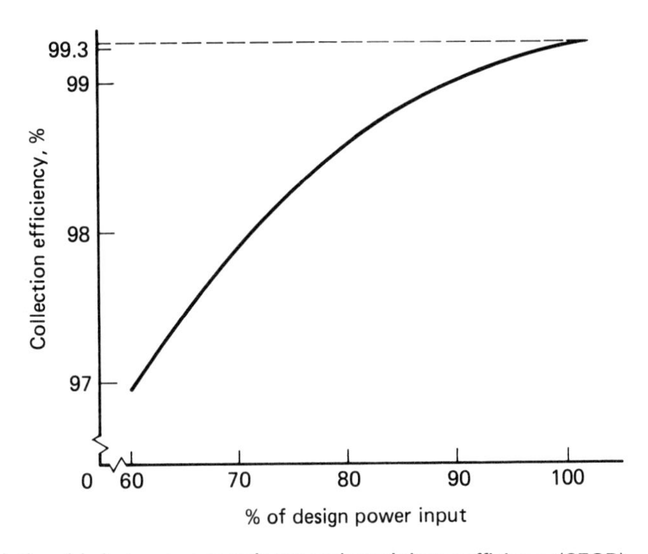

Figure 9.11 Typical relationship between power input and precipitator efficiency (CEGB)

performance, provided it does not produce unstable electrical conditions due to tracking or flash-over. In this connection tests were carried out on a precipitator whose electrical supplies were obtained from four rectifiers. For each rectifier a note was made of the current as the voltage was varied over a substantial range. The results are shown in *Figure 9.12*.

Notice that the general shape of the curve produced is similar for each rectifier, although no two of them are identical. Consider the results for A1 rectifier. Commencing with low voltage and current the power output was steadily increased until the voltage was 36 kV. Attempts to increase the voltage beyond this value resulted in electrical instability, causing the current to increase but the voltage to be reduced. The power output from

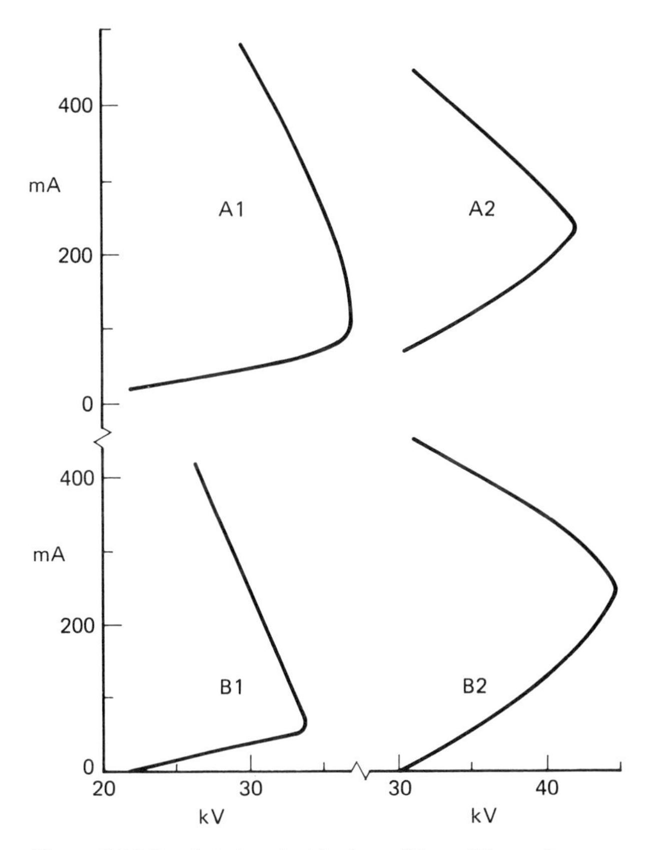

Figure 9.12 Precipitator electrical conditions kV *vs* mA

the rectifier in the unstable zone is greater than in the stable zone, but, of course, it is being expended largely in tracking and arcing, so is serving no useful purpose.

The point of demarcation between stable and unstable operation is the 'knee' of the curve. Ideally, the precipitators should always be operated at the highest stable power input to the precipitator, and this is what the automatic voltage control attempts to achieve. However, not only does each rectifier have a different curve to its fellows, but each one also varies with time. Therefore, before testing a precipitator it is worthwhile to establish the optimum power for each rectifier. This will indicate whether or not the precipitator is in electrically good condition. For example, the specified electrical power input to the precipitator supplied by the rectifiers in *Figure 9.12* is 80 kW. The actual optimum power from *Figure 9.12* is:

Rectifier A1 = 36 kV × 110 mA = 3.96 kW
Rectifier A2 = 42 kV × 220 mA = 9.24 kW

Rectifier B1 = 34 kV × 60 mA = 2.04 kW
Rectifier B2 = 44.5 kV × 230 mA = 10.23 kW

Total = 25.47 kW

So it is immediately apparent that electrical instability was a serious cause of performance limitation at the time, and that A1 and B1 zones were particularly poor.

Where instability or flash-over does occur it is usually because of one or more of the following:

(a) Over-full dust hoppers causing bridging of the discharge electrodes and the collector plates.
(b) Misaligned electrodes, possibly due to over-full dust hoppers at some time.
(c) Rapping gear ineffective, possibly because the timing is wrong or because of mechanical defects.
(d) Tracking across insulators because of dust build-up and/or local draughts from inleakage through casing door seals, etc.
(e) Arcing and poor contact at electrical connections such as sub-zone selectors for electrical isolation.

The design power input varies from one plant to another, but typical values (from a 350 MW unit) are:

	kV	*mA*	*kW*
Inlet zone	50	750	37.5
Centre zone	50	750	37.5
Outlet zone	60	350	21.0

So the total power per pass is 96 kW, and as there are three parallel passes, the total power to the precipitator will be 288 kW.

Mechanical dust arresters

Often there are mechanical arresters before the electrostatic precipitators and they are very effective for the removal of larger particles. For example, a mechanical collector will remove over 90% of dust of 30 μm diameter or more. A typical pre-collector consists of a number of cells at the entrance to the dust removal plant. An individual cell is shown in *Figure 9.13*. The inlet guide vanes impart an intense swirl to the flue gas so that the dust is concentrated toward the sides of the cell. Hence a considerable portion of the heavier dust particles are discharged, along with some flue gas, through the annular slot at the back of the cells. The main volume of relatively clean gas passes through the central outlet tube to the electrostatic precipitator.

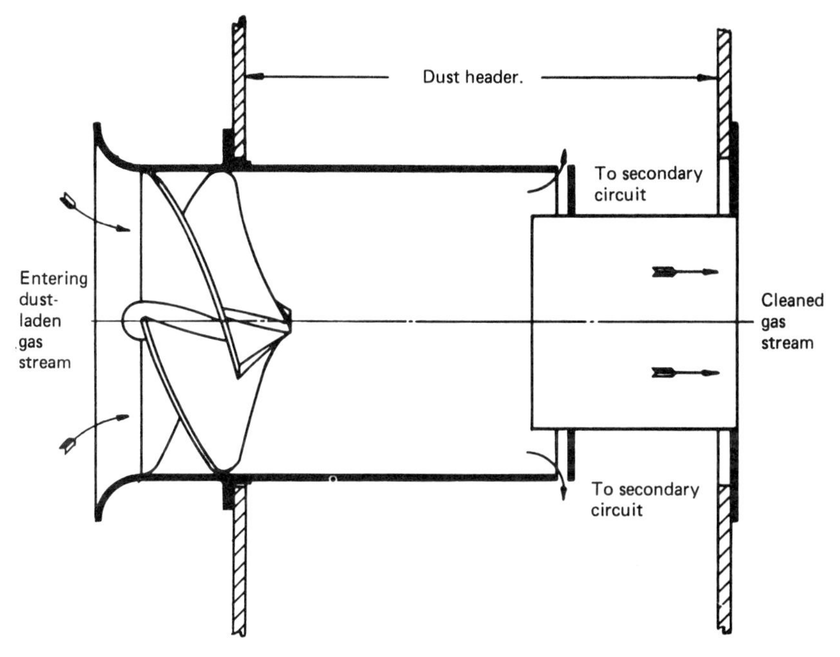

Figure 9.13 Arrangement of Sirocco patent cellular dust collector (Davidson and Co. Ltd.)

In addition to the primary mechanical collection there may be a secondary collection circuit. In this the gas which carries the dust through the annular gap in the primary collectors is exhausted by booster fans via a set of secondary collectors in the form of mechanical cyclones shown in *Figure 9.14*. The cleaned gas is then passed back to the main gas stream.

With mechanical collectors it is of the utmost importance that any holed and worn parts are repaired immediately, otherwise the performance of the plant will be adversely affected.

Dust monitors

Attempts have been made to develop suitable equipment which will provide a continuous indication of the dust burden of the flue gas going to the chimney so that the plant is always operated within the limits agreed with the Clean Air Inspectorate.

The two main monitors in use at present in the UK are the CERL and the SEROP and each type responds best to a different particulate size spectrum.

In the case of the CERL (Central Electricity Research Laboratories) instrument the larger particles are preferentially sampled, see *Figure 9.15*. The dust sample is deposited on the glass plates and the resultant obscuration is integrated over a quarter of an hour, after which the glasses

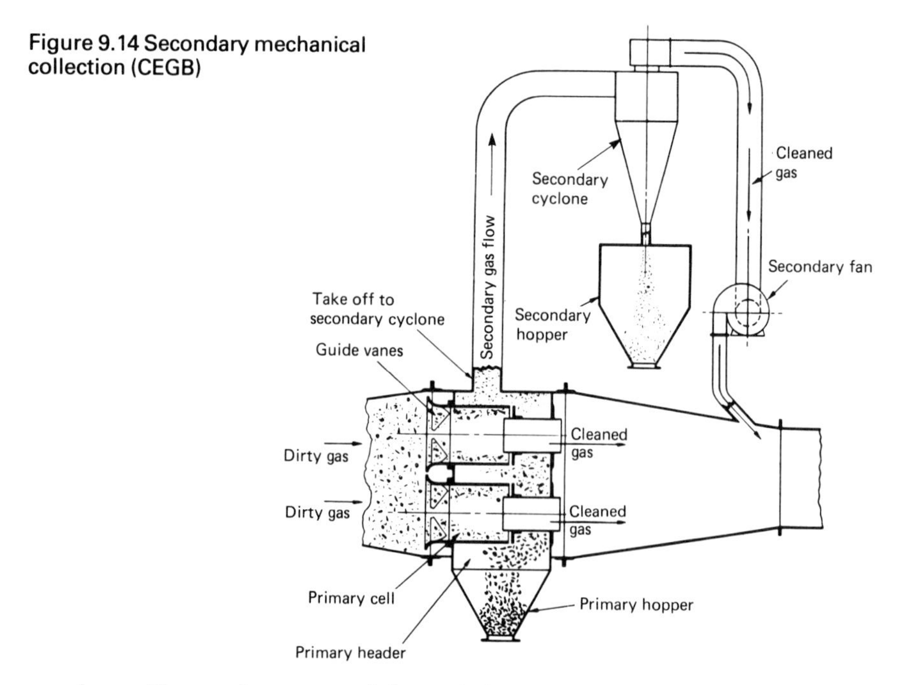

Figure 9.14 Secondary mechanical collection (CEGB)

are cleaned by an air purge and the cycle is repeated.

The SEROP (South East Region Optical Probe) responds preferentially to smoke and very small particles, see *Figure 9.16*. The probe is 1.5 metres

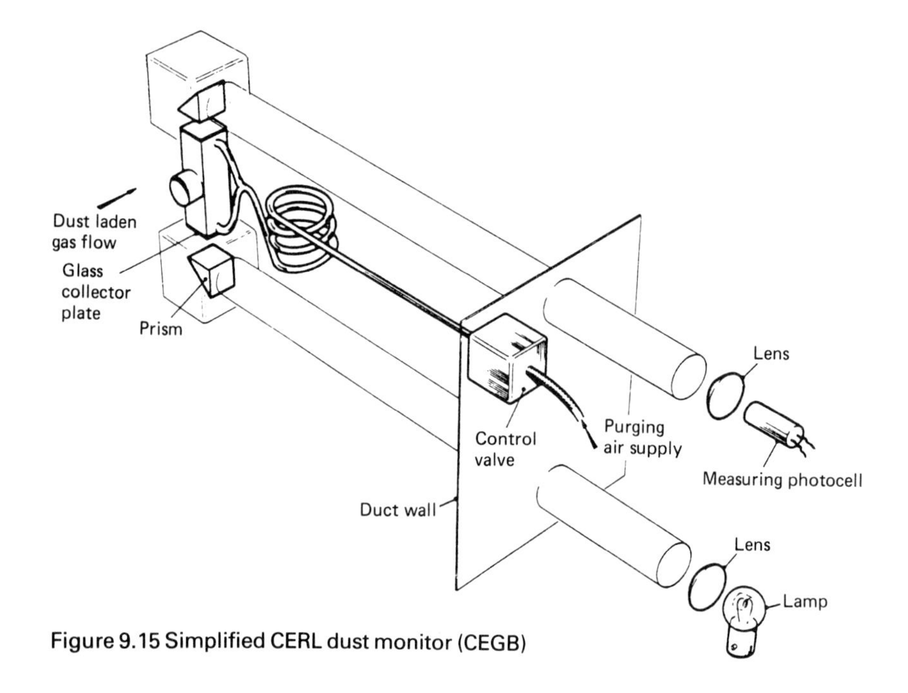

Figure 9.15 Simplified CERL dust monitor (CEGB)

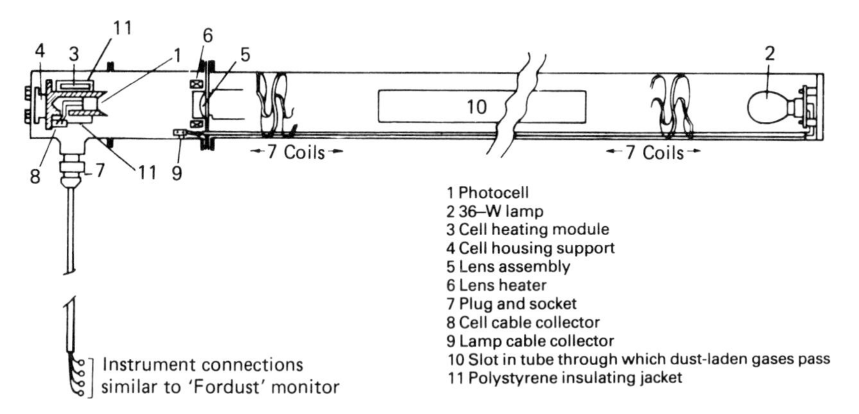

Figure 9.16 SEROP dust monitor (CEGB)

long and the light from a lamp at the remote end of the probe is detected by a photo-electric cell mounted outside the duct. Thus, the passage of dust causes partial obscuration of the light received by the detector.

The typical response of the two types to various particulate sizes is shown in *Figure 9.17.* A combination of both types would seem to be the most effective form of monitoring currently available. It is worth pointing out that a highly desirable feature of both types is that the instruments are self-contained. Some instruments depend upon sending a signal from one side of a duct to a receiver mounted on the other side. On the huge ducts associated with modern power stations and the attendant problems of vibration and distortion it is very difficult to maintain satisfactory alignment of the receiver with the transmitter.

Messrs. Erwin Sick manufacture a monitor that has a transmitter and receiver on opposite sides of the duct, but special provision is made to obviate misalignment.

Figure 9.18 shows a section of recorder chart from a CERL monitor. Notice the gradual increase of reading for 15 minutes followed by a rapid reduction to zero. The units used for this instrument are 'per cent obscuration per minute' (p.o.p.m.).

Precipitator testing

Testing should be carried out at least once per year. The location of the test points on a typical plant is shown in *Figure 9.19*, and so various tests can be carried out. For example, if only the total emission is to be measured then the test points near the chimney will be used. Alternatively the emission from each pass or the efficiency of each pass can be measured. The basic method of testing is to insert a probe into the duct and withdraw a sample of the gas. The rate of flow of the gas through the probe is measured and all the

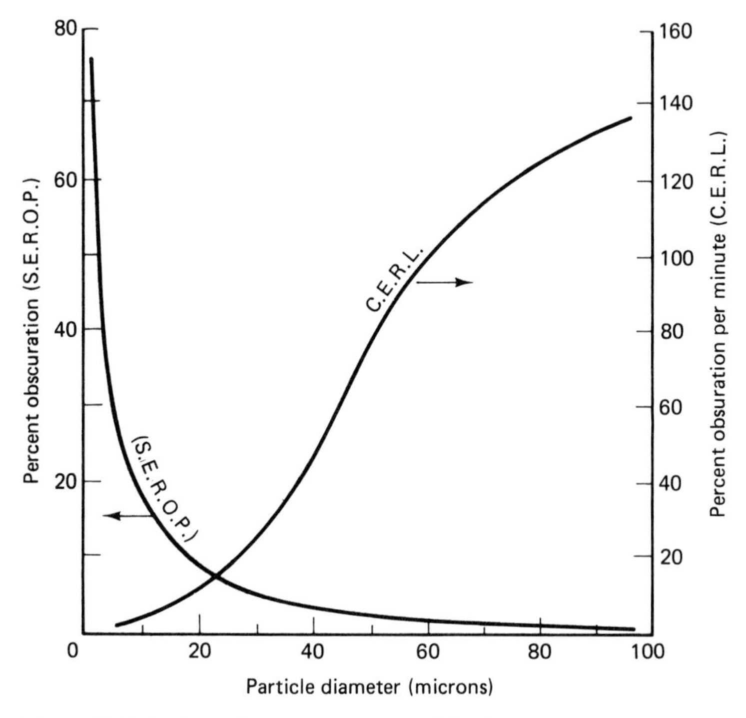

Figure 9.17 Dust monitor response to particle size

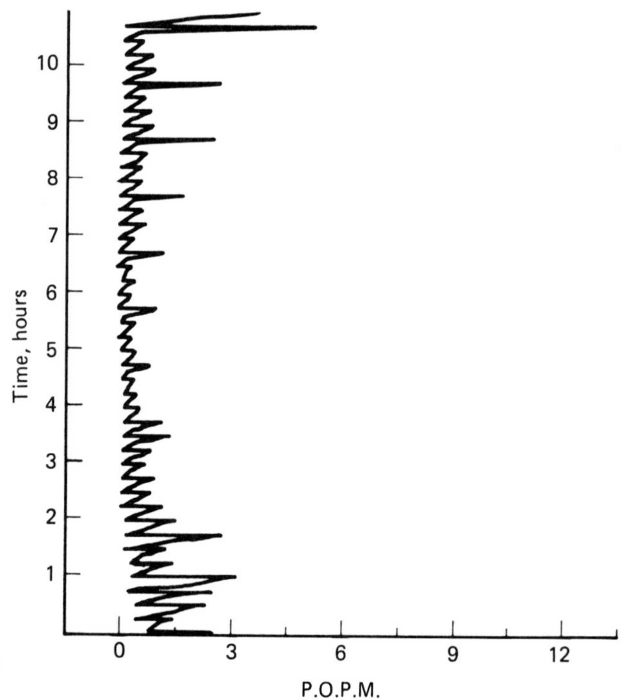

Figure 9.18 CERL dust monitor chart (CEGB)

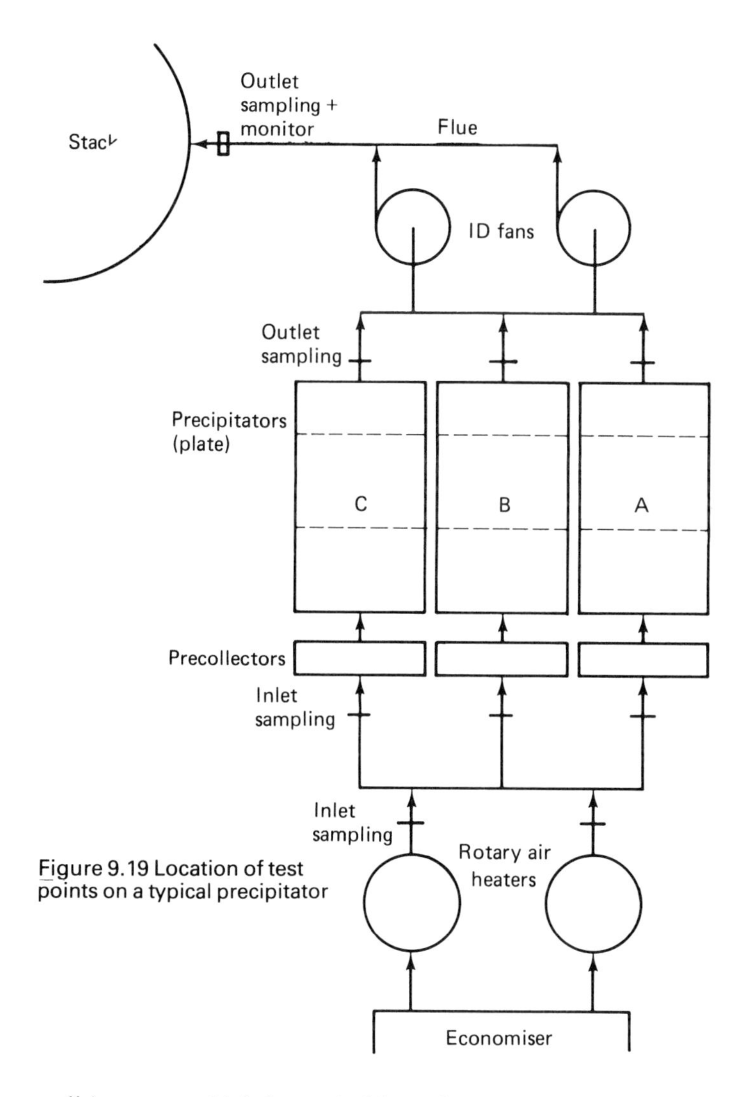

Figure 9.19 Location of test points on a typical precipitator

solid matter which is carried into the probe is collected. It is then an easy matter to determine that so many grams of dust are contained in so many cubic metres per second of gas flow. The quantity of dust in the duct may then be found by multiplying the sample collected per unit time by the ratio of the duct and sampler nozzle areas, see *Figure 9.20*.

With such a simple arrangement, though, there are two basic snags:

1 The sampled dust may not be representative of the dust at the sampling point, i.e. the sampler may receive too much or too little. Therefore it is necessary to ensure that the sampling rate is 'isokinetic', i.e. the gas velocity into the nozzle is the same as that in the duct at the measuring point, see *Figure 9.21*. Typical dust sampling equipment is shown in *Figure 9.22*.

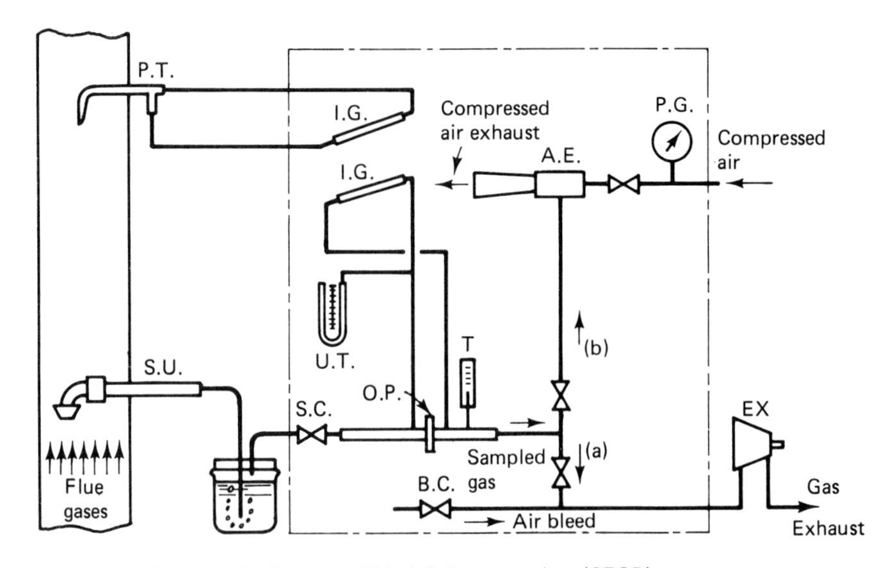

Figure 9.20 Schematic diagram of Mark II dust samplers (CEGB)

S.V. Sampler unit
W.B. Wash bottle
O.P. Orifice plate
EX. Exhauster
A.E. Air ejector
P.T. Pitot tube
I.G. Inclined gauge
U.T. U-tube
T. Temperature indicator
P.G. Pressure gauge
S.C. Suction control
B.C. Bleed control

(a) and (b) are alternative paths for sampled gas depending on method of extraction.

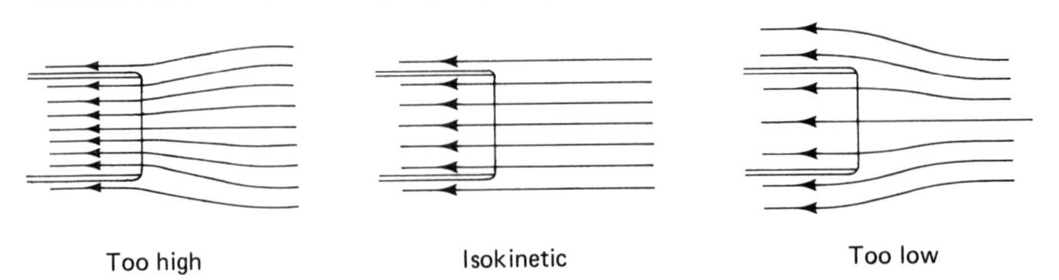

Figure 9.21 Effect of various sampling rates (CEGB)

2 Because of variations of flow of gas and dust over the cross-section of the duct it is necessary to obtain samples from a number of positions, i.e. the duct must be traversed, see *Figure 9.23*. Inexperienced testers are advised to obtain a separate sample for each point, but once confidence has been gained it is usual to obtain a gross sample by moving the nozzle to each test point in turn.

It is important that adequate sampling time is allowed at each point. Failure to allow sufficient time per point (5–10 min) will seriously reduce the accuracy of the result. A total testing time of 10 min will give an accuracy of about ± 50% if taken from one point. On the other hand if 24 points are used and one sample is taken from each over a period of four hours (i.e. 10 min each) the accuracy would be about ± 5%. The usual sampling time is

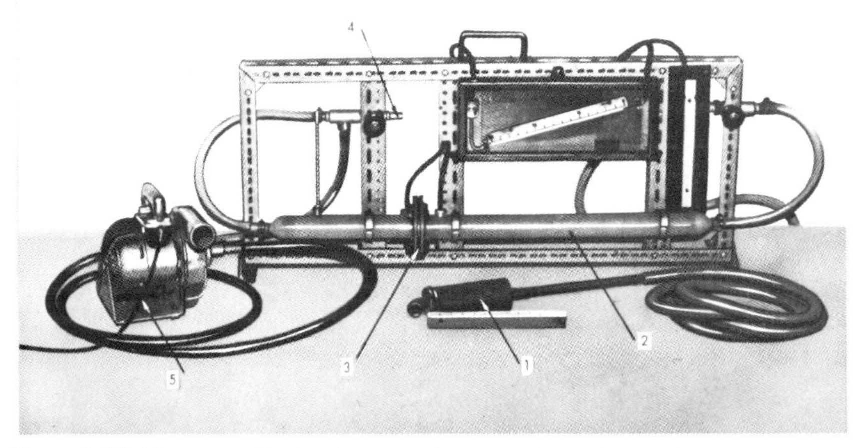

Figure 9.22(a) Dust sampling equipment — incorporating poly-propylene orifice carrier assembly (CEGB)

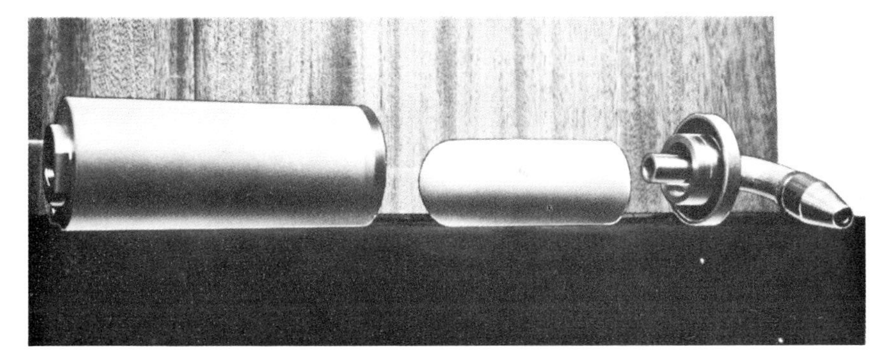

Figure 9.22(b) Sampling unit with paper thimble

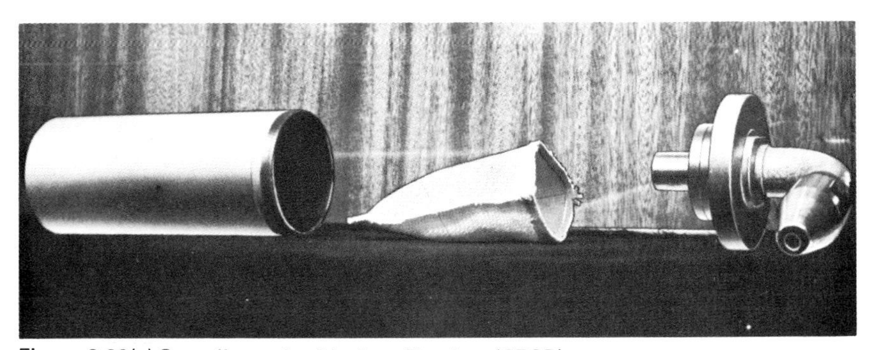

Figure 9.22(c) Sampling unit with glass fibre bag (CEGB)

about 5 min per point and the resulting error may be estimated from:

$$\text{Percentage error} = \frac{\pm 20}{\sqrt{(\text{number of points})}}$$

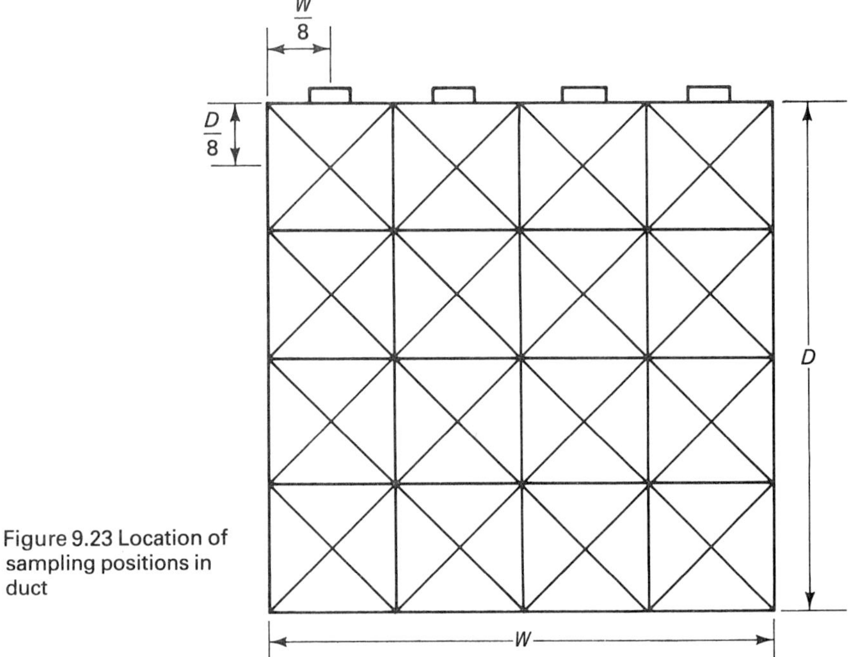

Figure 9.23 Location of sampling positions in duct

As stated earlier the results are referred to standard conditions before being reported.

The method of calculation is best shown by an example. A test log sheet is shown on page 395 for the emission from a 350 MW unit. The test points are indicated on the diagram, i.e. six points at each of four locations. The moisture in the flue gas is about 7%. The bag in which the dust is collected is carefully weighed before and after the test to determine the amount of dust collected. The sampled volume of the gas is determined as follows:

(a) The gas is sampled isokinetically and so the velocity entering the sampling nozzle is the same as that of the gas in the duct.

(b) The product of the gas velocity, nozzle area and time will therefore give the volume gas flow through the nozzle at duct conditions.

At the standard conditions of 15°C, 1013 mbar, 12% CO_2, the volume will be:

$$\text{Volume at duct conditions} \times \frac{288}{T} \times \frac{10\,363 + h_s}{10\,363} \times \frac{12.0}{CO_2\%}$$

where T = absolute temperature of gas in duct (K); h_s = static pressure of gas in duct (mm w.g.); $CO_2\%$ of gas in duct by volume.

Dust arrester test — log sheet

A B C D

6
5
4
3
2
1

6.046 m

4.877 m

Bag + dust	29.2544 grams
Bag	23.8272 grams
Dust	5.4272 grams

Gas Velocity in duct ______ m/s

Gas flow in duct ______ m^3/s

Gas flow at 15°C 1013 mbar ______ $m/^3s$

Sampled volume at 15°C 12% CO_2; 1013 mbar ______ m^3

Dust burden at 15°C; 1013 mbar; 12% CO_2 (wet) ______ g/m^3

Dust burden (actual) ______ g/m^3

Moisture in flue gas 7%

Point	h_V (mm w.g.)	$\sqrt{hv}$	Temp (°C)	Pressure (mm w.g)	Time start	CO_2%
A1	21.5	4.64			0955	
2	21.0	4.58			1000	
3	16.5	4.06	136	−4.0	05	11.3
4	16.0	4.00			10	
5	12.5	3.54			15	
6	9.5	3.08			20	
B1	15.5	3.94			25	
2	15.0	3.87			30	
3	13.5	3.67	138	−4.0	35	11.5
4	14.0	3.74			40	
5	13.0	3.61			45	
6	9.5	3.08			50	
C1	14.5	3.81			55	
2	13.3	3.65			11 00	
3	13.5	3.67	138	−4.0	05	11.5
4	15.5	3.94			10	
5	19.0	4.36			15	
6	19.5	4.42			20	
D1	14.5	3.81			25	
2	14.0	3.74			30	
3	13.5	3.67	139	−4.0	35	
4	15.0	3.87			40	
5	17.5	4.18			45	
6	15.5	3.94			50	
TOTAL AVERAGE		92.87 3.867	138	−4.0		11.5

Load
294 MW

Barometer
= 1010 mbar

Test set No.

Nozzle area
$\frac{1}{2190}$ m^2

Sampling time per point
5 mins

Average power to precipitator zones (kW)

A1	14.6
2	10.2
3	10.2
B1	5.7
2	12.1
3	13.3
C1	9.6
2	20.1
3	12.3

Dust Arrester Test – Calculation Sheet

Averages: $CO_2\%$ = 11.5; $\sqrt{h_V}$ = 3.867; Temperature = 138°C (411 K).
Barometer = 1010 mbar; Moisture = 7.0%; h_S = (−) 4.0 mm w.g.

	Dry			*Wet*			*Rel. wt.*
$CO_2\%$	11.5	× 0.93	=	10.7	× 44	=	470
$O_2\%$	7.5	× 0.93	=	7.0	× 32	=	223
$N_2\%$	81.0	× 0.93	=	75.3	× 28	=	2108
$H_2O\%$	—			7.0	× 18	=	126
	100.0			100.0			2927

Density of flue gas $\rho = \dfrac{29.27}{22.4} = 1.307\ \text{kg/m}^3$ at s.t.p.

At duct conditions $\rho = \dfrac{273}{411} \times \dfrac{10\,359}{10\,363} \times \dfrac{1010}{1\,013} \times 1.307$

$= 0.865\ \text{kg/m}^3\ \therefore \sqrt{\rho} = 0.9302$

Velocity in duct $= 4.43 \times \dfrac{3.867}{0.9302} = 18.4\ \text{m/s}$

Volume flow in duct $= 18.4\ \text{m/s} \times 29.7\ \text{m}^2 = 546.5\ \text{m}^3\text{/s}$

Volume flow at 15°C $= 546.5\ \text{m}^3\text{/s} \times \dfrac{(15 + 273)}{(138 + 273)} = 383\ \text{m}^3\text{/s}$

Sampled volume at duct $= 18.4\ \text{m/s} \times \dfrac{1}{2190}\ \text{m}^2 \times 7200\ \text{sec}$

$= 60.49\ \text{m}^3$

Dust burden at duct $= \dfrac{5.4272\ \text{g}}{60.49\ \text{m}^3} = 0.089\ \text{g/m}^3$

Sampled volume at n.t.p., 12% CO_2

$$= 60.49\ \text{m}^3 \times \frac{288}{411} \times \frac{10\,359}{10\,363} \times \frac{1010}{1013} \times \frac{12.0}{11.5}$$

$= 44.1\ \text{m}^3$

Dust burden at n.t.p., 12% CO_2 $= \dfrac{5.4272\ \text{g}}{44.1\ \text{m}^3} = 0.123\ \text{g/m}^3$

(n.t.p. = 15°C; 1013 mbar)

Fault-finding chart

Symptoms

Possible causes	Low voltage, excessive sparking	Unstable, low voltage, high current	Regular and sustained instability	Variation of voltage and current from one pass to another	Excessive wire breakage	Instability, low current	Voltage OK but medium current. Dust conductivity OK.	Low voltage, high current, slight instability	Pronounced and uncontrolled instability	Excessive dust deposit on discharge electrodes	High voltage, low current	Electrical readings steady but poor performance	Excessive spark rate (normal 50–100 sparks/min)
Poor rapping										X	X	X	
Faulty A.V.C.							X						X
Inleakage of air into hoppers							X		X	X	X	X	
Electrodes misaligned	X			X	X								X
Local air ingress	X				X								X
Re-entrained dust	X											X	
Broken wires		X	X						X				X
Over-full dust hoppers		X					X					X	
Cracked insulators or tracking		X							X				
H.T. frame swinging			X										X
Large temperature diffs. between flows				X									
High-resistance ash				X		X		X					
Non-uniform gas flow							X						
Local arcing			X		X								X
Low-resistance ash												X	
Excess gas flow												X	
Condensation on insulators		X											X
Insufficient electrode tension					X								X

Questions

1 What are the presumptive standards?
2 To what standard conditions are precipitator emissions referred?
3 State the Deutsch formula and state a use to which it may be put.
4 What is a typical e.m.v. for modern plant?
5 State some common causes of trouble with precipitator performance.
6 Why is air inleakage troublesome?
7 By how much can the gas velocity at any point over the cross-section of a duct differ from the mean velocity and still be satisfactory?
8 Does an electro-precipitator capture larger (>20 μm) or smaller particles more easily?
9 State the operating principles of two dust monitors.
10 How frequently should electro-precipitators be tested in the CEGB?
11 What is meant by 'isokinetic' sampling and why is it necessary?
12 Gas flow varies across a duct. How is this effect allowed for when testing?

Exercise 1

In a certain power station there are two units, one of which has a dust arresting plant as specified in the example on page 373. The other has the same pre-collector and electrostatic precipitator efficiency, but its gas flow is 472 m^3/s. Calculate the total collector plate area if the effective migration velocity is 8.5 cm/s.

Exercise 2

Comment upon the following results:

	Unit	*Specified*	*Test*
Oulet gas flow	m^3/s	207.5	228
Outlet gas temperature	°C	170	146
Outlet CO_2	%	14.5	13.3
D/B at 15°C, 12% (wet)	g/m^3	0.46	0.66
H.T. power	kW	77	64
Precollector efficiency	%	50	
Electro-precip efficiency	%	95.2	

What is the inlet dust burden at 15°C, 12% CO_2 (wet)?
What would be the outlet dust burden on test if the gas flow and arrestor plant efficiency had been as specified?

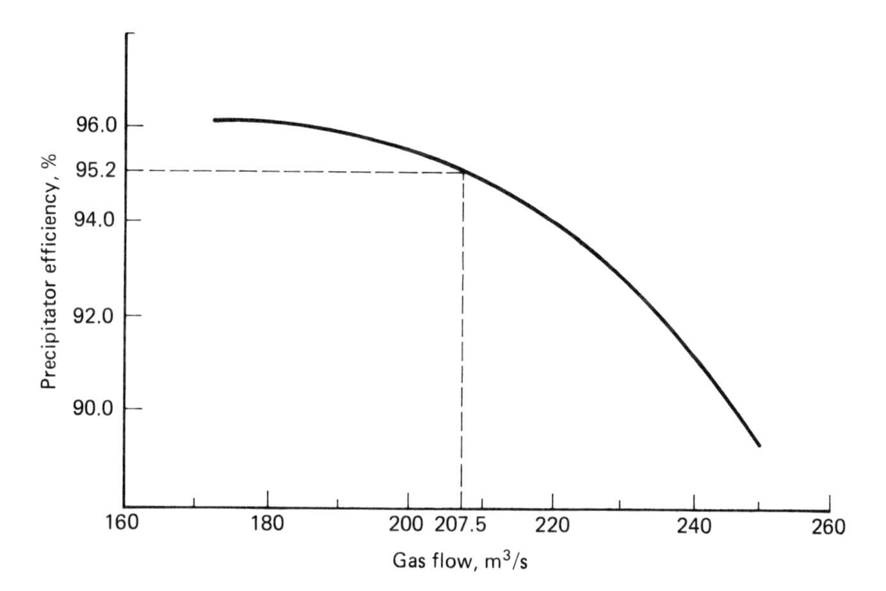

Figure 9.24 Variation of efficiency with gas flow. Exercise 2

Exercise 1 (Answer)

$$F = \frac{100\,k}{W}$$

$$\text{So } \frac{\text{Area}}{472} = \frac{100 \times 4.6}{8.5}$$

$$\therefore \text{Area} = \frac{472 \times 100 \times 4.6}{8.5}$$

$$= \mathbf{25\ 543\ m^2}$$

Exercise 2 (Answer)

Reference to the curve in *Figure 9.24* shows that the electro-precipitator efficiency at the test flow is 93%. Assuming the pre-collector efficiency is acceptable (say 50%) then the overall efficiency will be found from:

Oulet dust = (1 − 0.5) (1 − 0.93)
= 0.035 g/m³ for each g/m³ at inlet

The actual emission is 0.66 so there must be

$$\frac{0.66}{0.035} = 18.8 \text{ g/m}^3 \text{ at inlet.}$$

If the pre-collector efficiency had been 50% and the electro-precipitator efficiency been 95.2% then for an inlet dust burden of 18.8 g/m³ the outlet burden would be:

Outlet dust burden at 15°C, 12% CO_2 (wet) = 18.8 (1 − 0.5) (1 − 0.952)
= **0.45 g/m³**

Project 1

At a particular power station considerable emission is taking place from the chimney. The input electrical conditions to the precipitator are 40 kV, 30 mA (design 45 kV, 40 mA) and the CO_2% of the flue gas is 10.5 (design 12.5% CO_2). There are indications of electrical instability and flash-over.

(a) What are the probable causes of the poor performance?
(b) The design efficiency is 99.3% and it is suggested that this should be increased to 99.5%. What percentage extra building volume would be required?

Project 1 (Answer)

(a) The electrical input power is 1200 kW and the design is 1800 kW, hence the power input is now:

$$\frac{1200}{1800} = 66.6\% \text{ of design}$$

From *Figure 9.11*, this in itself will reduce the efficiency from 99.3% to 97.6% approx.
The low CO_2 indicates that the excess gas flow is:

$$\frac{12.5}{10.5} = 1.2, \text{ i.e. } 120\% \text{ of design.}$$

From *Figure 9.7* this in itself will reduce the efficiency from 99.3% to about 99.0%.
The electrical instability indicates:
broken wires;
over-full dust hoppers;
incorrect or defective rapping;
dirty or contaminated and cracked E.T. insulators;
misaligned electrodes.

(b) k for 99.3% = 5.0 k for 99.5% = 5.3 (see *Figure 9.2*)

So for 99.5% efficiency, size must be increased by:

$$\frac{(5.3 - 5.0)}{5.0} = 6.0\%$$

Project 2

Dust arrester test – Calculation sheet

Averages: $CO_2\%$ = $\sqrt{hv}$ = Temp. = °C(K);
Barometer = mb; Moisture = %; h_S = mm w.g.

	Dry			Wet		Rel. Wt.
$CO_2\%$		×	=		× 44 =	
$O_2\%$		×	=		× 32 =	
$N_2\%$		×	=		× 28 =	
$H_2O\%$					× 18 =	
	100.0			100.0		

Density of flue gas $\rho = \frac{100.0}{22.4} =$ kg/m³ at s.t.p.

At duct conditions $\rho = \frac{273}{\quad} \times \frac{\quad}{10363} \times \frac{\quad}{1013} \times$

= kg/m³ ∴ $\sqrt{\rho}$ =

Velocity in duct = $4.43 \times \frac{\quad}{\quad} =$ m/s

Volume flow in duct = m/s × m² = m³/s

Volume flow at 15°C = m³/s × $\frac{(15 + 273)}{(\quad + 273)}$ = m³/s

Sampled volume at duct = m/s × m² × secs = m³

Dust burden at duct = $\frac{\text{grams}}{\text{m}^3}$ = g/m³

Sampled volume at n.t.p. 12%

CO_2 = $\frac{288}{K} \times \frac{\quad}{10363} \times \frac{\quad}{1013} \times \frac{12.0}{\quad}$ m³ ×

= m³

Dust burden at n.t.p. 12% CO_2 = $\frac{\text{grams}}{\text{m}^3}$ = g/m³

(n.t.p. = 15°C 1013 mb)

Project 2 Dust arrestor test–Calculate emission

A B C D

6 5 4 3 2 1

6.046 m

4.877 m

Bag + dust	33.629 grams
Bag	23.1626 grams
Dust	10.4670 grams

Gas velocity in duct		m/s
Gas flow in duct	m_4/s	m^3/s
Gas flow at 15°C 1013 m bar		m^3/s
Sampled volume at 15°C 1013 mbar		m^3
Dust burden at 15°C, 1013 mbar, 12% CO_2 (wet)		g/m^3
Dust burden (actual)		g/m^3

Moisture in flue gas 7.5%

Point	h_V *(mm w.g.)*	$\sqrt{h_V}$	*Duct* *Temp (°C)*	*Duct* *Pressure (mm w.g.)*	*Duct* *Time Start*	CO_2%
A1	24.5	4.95			1515	
2	21.0	4.58			20	
3	16.5	4.06	136	–6.0	25	11.0
4	14.0	3.74			30	
5	12.5	3.54			35	
6	9.5	3.08			40	
B1	19.2	4.38			45	
2	15.0	3.87			50	
3	14.0	3.74	138	–6.0	55	11.0
4	13.5	3.67			1600	
5	14.0	3.74			05	
6	10.5	3.24			10	
C1	15.0	3.87			15	
2	14.0	3.74			20	
3	14.5	3.81	140	–6.0	25	11.0
4	15.5	3.94			30	
5	18.0	4.24			35	
6	19.5	4.42			40	
D1	9.5	3.08			45	
2	12.0	3.46			50	
3	15.5	3.94	138	–6.0	55	
4	15.5	3.94			1700	11.0
5	17.5	4.18			05	
6	17.5	4.18			10	
TOTAL AVERAGE		93.43 / 3.893	138	–6.0	OPERATOR	

Load

325 MW

Barometer
= 1015 mbar

Test set no.

Nozzle area
$\frac{1}{2190}$ m^2

Sampling time per point
5 mins

Average power to precipitator zones (kW)

A1	*9.6*
2	*7.4*
3	*10.7*
B1	*5.6*
2	*9.9*
3	*13.3*
C1	*9.9*
2	*27.3*
3	*10.4*

Project 2 (Answer)

Dust arrester Test – Calculation Sheet

Averages: $CO_2\%$ = 11.0; $\sqrt{h_V}$ = 3.893; Temperature = 138°C (411 K).
Barometer = 1015 mbar; Moisture = 7.5%; hs = (−) 6.0 mm w.g.

	Dry		*Wet*		*Rel. Wt.*
$CO_2\%$	11.0	× 0.925 =	10.17	× 44 =	447.5
$O_2\%$	8.0	× 9.25 =	7.4	× 32 =	236.8
$N_2\%$	81.0	× 0.925 =	74.93	× 28 =	2098.0
$H_2O\%$	—		7.5	× 18 =	135.0
	100.0		100.0		2917.3

Density of flue gas $\rho = \dfrac{29.17}{22.4} = 1.302$ kg/m³ at s.t.p.

At duct conditions $\rho = \dfrac{273}{411} \times \dfrac{10\ 357}{10\ 363} \times \dfrac{1015}{1013} \times 1.302$

$= 0.866$ kg/m³ ∴ $\sqrt{\rho} = 0.931$

Velocity in duct $= 4.43 \times \dfrac{3.893}{0.931} = 18.5$ m/s

Volume flow in duct $= 18.5$ m/s × 29.7 m² = 549.5 m³/s

Sampled volume at duct $= 18.5$ m/s $\times \dfrac{1}{2190}$ m² × 7200 sec

$= 60.82$ m³

Dust burden at duct $= \dfrac{10.467\ \text{g}}{60.82\ \text{m}^3} = 0.172$ g/m³

Sampled volume at n.t.p., 12% CO_2

$= 60.82\ \text{m}^3 \times \dfrac{288}{411\ \text{K}} \times \dfrac{10\ 359}{10\ 363} \times \dfrac{1015}{1013}$

$\times \dfrac{12.0}{11.0} = 46.56$ m³

Dust burden at n.t.p., 12% CO_2 $= \dfrac{10.467\ \text{g}}{46.56\ \text{m}^3} = 0.225$ g/m³

(n.t.p. = 15°C; 1013 mbar)

Water pollution

The regulations governing water pollution control vary from country to country. However, there is a trend towards international standards. For example, in the United Kingdom there is comprehensive national legislation intended to improve the wholesomeness of the rivers, and this will be brought into line with EEC (European Economic Community) legislation in the future. When the EEC nations have implemented the regulations almost all of Europe will have identical standards.

The parameters of the 'consent to discharge' effluent into a watercourse depend upon the river and the use to which the river water is put. A typical example is the River Trent in England. This is large by English standards and it has many power stations and other industrial complexes along its banks. It has many tributaries, some of which are badly polluted.

Typical values of the EEC consent parameters for rivers such as the Trent are as follows, bearing in mind that they refer to the river and not to the discharge.

(a) *Temperatures*

Maximum temperature 28°C; Temperature differential 3°C

The discharge of heat from a power station to a river has to be controlled carefully to meet the quite stringent requirements of the EEC. At present UK legislation is in force, and it is not quite so demanding. For example, with cooling towers the maximum temperature at the purge outfall is 30°C. For mixed river/cooling tower stations the maximum temperature one hundred metres downstream of the outfall is 30°C. The maximum temperature differential from intake to outfall is 8.5°C. The reason for restricting the temperature of the river water is that the higher the temperature the lower the solubility of oxygen and this is detrimental to life.

On the other hand, if the water which is returned has passed through a cooling tower (such as in a mixed cooled station) the water will have been aerated significantly. (Incidentally, if it contained ammonia when taken from the river it will have a considerably reduced ammonia level when returned to the river). For example, tests were conducted at Drakelow A and B Power Stations which have mixed cooling. Typical river flows are 1 700 000 m^3/day in summer and 2 600 000 m^3/day in winter. It was found that the warm effluent added about 3.9 Mg of oxygen to the river during a summer day and 2.0 Mg on a winter day. Furthermore, the oxygenating effect was measurable at least 1.6 km downstream from the outfall.

The biological oxygen demand (BOD) is a measure of the oxygen requirement of the water. If the oxygen demand exceeds the supply, anaerobic bacteria take over, objectionable odours are produced and the water becomes more corrosive to metals. At present, UK legislation is that the maximum is 20 ppm but EEC regulations stipulate 6 ppm maximum.

(b) *Suspended solids*

After heat rejection this is probably the next most important parameter. A typical situation occurs where dust is conveyed to an ash lagoon in the form of water-borne slurry. Once deposited in the lagoon the water is drained off and returned to the river. If it were returned directly to the river the dust concentration in the water would be much too high. Therefore, it is passed through two or more decanting ponds. In these the water travels slowly across the pond to give time for the heavier particles of ash to fall to the bottom and the lighter ones to float on the surface. At the outlet from the pond there are damboards from the bottom to a few centimetres below the surface. Also there is a scumboard across the exit which goes from above the surface to a few centimetres below. Therefore, most of the suspended ash particles are trapped by one or the other sets of boards. After passing through two or three such ponds the water should be within the consent parameter limits. The present UK limit is 50 ppm but this will become 25 ppm when the EEC regulations come into force.

(c) *Chlorine*

One way to ensure that a condenser is being given enough chlorination is to measure the free chlorine at the condenser outlet. Provided there is any free chlorine at all the dosage is satisfactory. Should it be excessive it may be returned to the river and so cause problems for fish and other living matter in the water. Therefore, the maximum permissible free chlorine in the discharge is 0.5 ppm. When the EEC regulations come into force the maximum permitted in the river will be 0.005 ppm of HOC1 (hypochlorite). This will mean that very strict control of the chlorination of the CW will be necessary.

(d) *Acidity/alkalinity*

The pH value of water is a function of its acidity or alkalinity. The numerical value is determined from the reciprocal of the logarithm of the hydrogen ion concentration. A pH of 0 – 7 indicates acidity, zero being strongly acid and seven neutral water. Values from 7–14 indicate increasing alkalinity. Water which has been in prolonged contact with ash, such as the water drained from ash lagoons, will usually be alkaline with a pH of about 9. On the other hand, regeneration of demineralized water treatment plants could produce effluent that is either acid or alkaline.

Both the UK and EEC permissible pH range is from 6 to 9.

(e) *Oil*

Oil storage tanks should have bunds to contain any oil spillage or overflow. However, with outside tanks rainwater collects in the bunds and so it is necessary periodically to open the bund drain to let the rainwater out. Care must be taken to ensure that the drains are normally kept tightly closed. Otherwise if there is oil spillage, leakage or overflow from the tank, the oil would flow to the storm water system via the grids in roadside gutters. From there it may eventually be pumped into the river. Similarly, oil leakage or spillage from bearings, etc. inside the station may get into the drain channels and then into the river. Of course the storm water and station drains should be discharged via an oil intercepter pit and so this also must be checked regularly to ensure that no oil has collected.

Stations should be prepared to cope with any contamination that does occur. The oil will float on the river so portable dams should be kept on hand to isolate quickly any area of oil on the water. The UK prescribed limit is 5 ppm, but in practice no visible trace of oil on the water is permitted, and this also applies to the EEC regulations.

(f) *Toxic metals*

When chemical cleaning of boilers, feed heaters, condensers, etc. is undertaken the effluent often contains metals such as copper and zinc. If the concentration is higher than the regulations allow then special measures must be taken to ensure compliance. It may be that the effluent must be passed to a lagoon where dilution can be carried out or it may be economic to put it into tankers and dispose of it at an approved site.

In the UK the permitted limit for any toxic metal is 1.0 ppm. The EEC regulations allow:

Total zinc 1.0 ppm; total dissolved copper 0.4 ppm.

(g) *Sewage*

This does not normally constitute a problem. Perhaps this is why the EEC have not stipulated any limits for such discharge. In the UK the limits are:

20 ppm biological oxygen demand; 30 ppm suspended solids.

With increased awareness of the effects of contamination of rivers (and lakes and coastal waters) upon the environment it is reasonable to expect that the consent parameters will become more and more strict as time goes by.

Incidentally, power stations are often blamed for one source of contamination which is, in reality, nothing to do with them. That is the collection of detergent suds at the CW outfall. The detergent is already mixed with the river water before it gets to the power station. Inside the station the water is churned up and often stable foam is produced. There is nothing whatever in the power station process to add any detergent to the water to that already there.

Questions

1 Why is it necessary to restrict the water temperature of rivers?
2 What is the most important form of contamination from power stations?
3 How much oil is permitted to escape to a river?
4 How is dust and silt prevented from getting into a river?
5 How would you dispose of effluent from a boiler chemical clean?
6 Is the aeration of river water altered by passing it through a mixed cooling station?

Additional Reading

1 HAWKSLEY, BADZIOCH and BLACKETT, *Measurement of Solids in Flue Gases*, The British Coal Utilisation Research Association.
2 BARRIMORE, M. 'Energy and environment' (Sixty-fourth Thomas Hawksley Lecture), *Proc. I. Mech. E.*, **192**, No. 18, (1978)
3 LITTLEJOHN, R.F. and SMITH, B. 'Sampling gasborne solids: some factors affecting the characteristics of miniature cyclones', *Proc. I. Mech. E.*, **192**, No. 22, (1978)
4 BS 893 *Method for the Measurement of the Concentration of Particulate Materials in Ducts Carrying Gases.*
5 BS 3405: *Simplified Methods for Measurement of Grit and Dust Emission.*
6 HAWKINS, A., *Electricity Supply and the Environment*, (CEGB 1973)
7 WATKINS, E.R. and DARBY,K., 'Electrostatic precipitation for large boilers', *Proc. I. Mech. E.*, (1966/67)
8 RICHARDS, D.J.W., JONES, W.S. and LAXTON, J.W., 'Monitoring and control of flue gases, *CEGB Research* (August 1977)
9 LUTYNSKI, J., 'The physical principles of electrostatic precipitator performance', *Przeglad Elektrotech*, **36**, No. 7 (
10 HEINRICK, D.E., 'The science and art of electro-precipitation', *Engineering and Boiler House Review* (June 1953)
11 BRUCE, J., 'Electrostatic precipitation of dust from boiler – plant flue gases, *J. I.E.E.*, **92**, Part II, No. 26 (1945)
12 SCRIVOM, R.A. and HOWELLS, G., 'Stack emissions and the environment', *CEGB Researvh*, No. 5 (August 1977).
13 GALLEAR, C.A., 'Electrostatic precipitator manual', CPRI. CS–.809, *Electric Power Research Institute*, 1983 (Palo Alto)

10 Turbine performance and monitoring

Reference should be made to standard textbooks for detailed information about the different turbine types. Here we are concerned only with aspects of the machines which have a basic effect upon the performance.

Turbine performance

Steam turbines are of two basic types:
1 Impulse.
2 Impulse–reaction

An impulse stage has no pressure drop across the moving blades, whereas an impulse–reaction stage has a pressure drop across both the fixed and moving blades. The former can be sub-divided into the following classes:

(a) Simple impulse;
(b) Velocity compounded;
(c) Prssure compounded;
(d) Pressure–velocity compounded.

In actual turbines it is common for the best feature of various types to be incorporated in one machine. For example, a turbine may have a velocity compounded first stage followed by pressure compounded impulse stages and, at the low pressure end of the machine, reaction blading.

Nozzles

All turbines have nozzles in which the pressure of the steam is reduced and the velocity increased. In impulse machines the nozzles are stationary whereas in impulse–reaction machines both the moving and the fixed blades are nozzles.

Within limits the greater the pressure drop of the steam from inlet to outlet of a nozzle the greater the velocity of the steam. Consider the converging nozzle shown in *Figure 10.1.* The inlet steam pressure P_i *is*

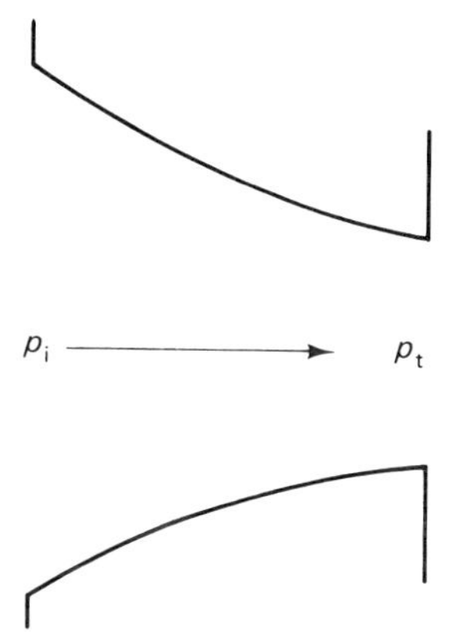

Figure 10.1 Converging nozzle

assumed to be fixed and that at the throat P_t variable. When $P_t = P_i$ there will be no flow. Reducing P_t causes the flow to increase until, at a particular value of P_t, the flow is a maximum. Reducing P_t further does not increase the flow, see *Figure 10.2.* The pressure ratio P_t/P_i at which maximu flow occurs for superheated steam is 0.547. For lower values of P_t a converging–diverging nozzle is used.

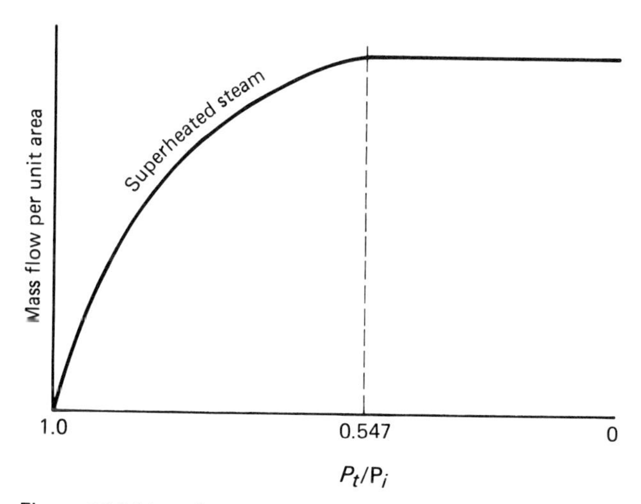

Figure 10.2 Mass flow of steam per unit area vs P_t/P_i ratio

Let 'a' represent the conditions at the inlet of the nozzle (*Figure 10.3*). If there were no friction the state point of the steam through the nozzle would be represented by 'ab' where 'b' is at the outlet pressure P_2. However, the

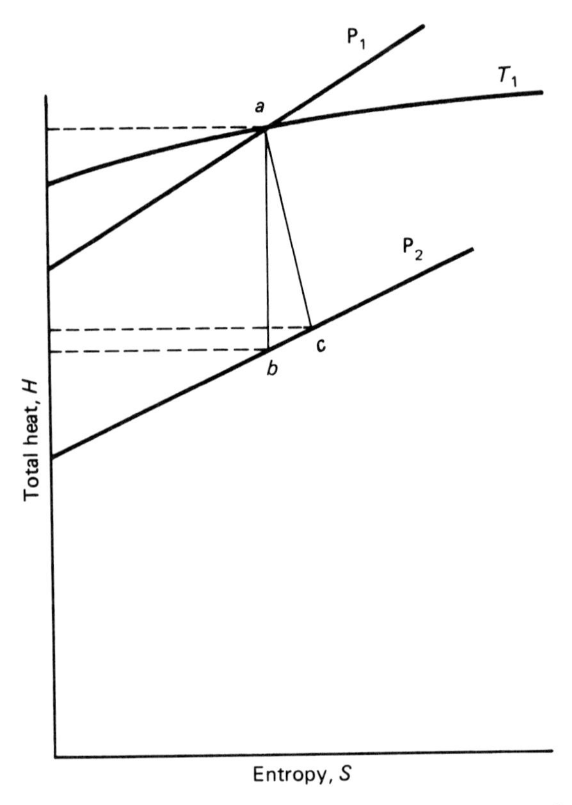

Figure 10.3 Section of H–S diagram showing isentropic expansion and the effect of friction (CEGB)

effect of friction is to cause some reheating of the steam such that although the discharge pressure is P_2 as before, the heat content of the steam at outlet is at 'c'. Thus, the actual state line of the steam through the nozzle is represented by 'ac'. In practice it is possible to achieve a heat drop of only about 0.9 to 0.95 of the theoretical value.

So $V = 44.72\sqrt{(KH)}$ metres per second
where V = velocity of steam at exit in m/s
H = the isentropic heat drop in kJ/kg
K = ratio of the heat drops $\frac{\text{ac}}{\text{ab}}$

Action of the steam on impulse blades

The steam flow from the fixed blades is directed on to the moving ones such that the steam glides on to the blade as shown in *Figure 10.4*. The motive

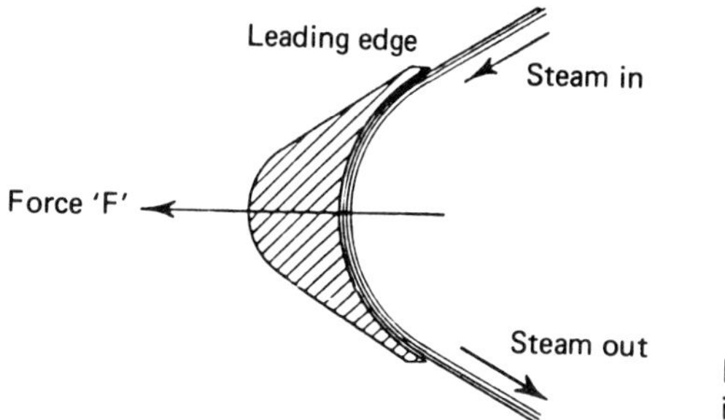

Figure 10.4 Action of steam on an impulse blade (CEGB)

power is derived from the momentum of the steam because its direction is continuously changed as it flows over the blade and because of the centrifugal force exerted. No work is done by impact of the steam on the blade and neither does the static pressure contribute to it.

Efficiency of an ideal simple impulse turbine

Consider an ideal simple impulse turbine consisting of a row of fixed nozzles and a row of moving blades. In this ideal case the steam leaves the nozzles in the direction of blade motion and leaves the moving blade in the opposite direction, as shown in *Figure 10.5*.

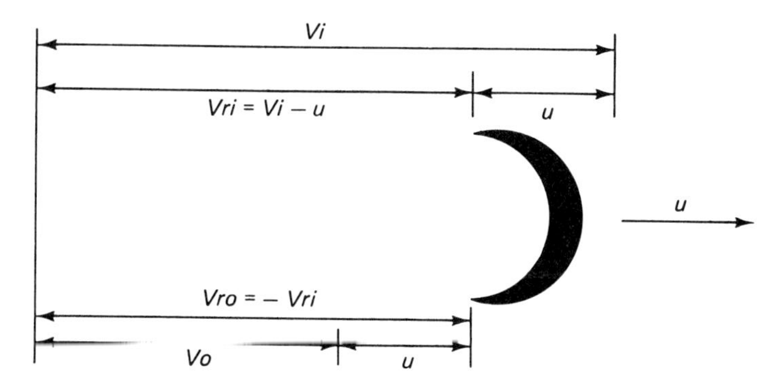

Figure 10.5 Ideal impulse blade velocity diagram

V_i = absolute steam velocity at blade inlet
u = blade speed
V_{ri} = steam velocity relative to blade = $V_i - u$
V_o = absolute steam velocity at blade outlet
V_{ro} = steam relative velocity at blade outlet

The change of velocity from inlet to outlet of the blade is $V_i - V_o$ but reference to *Figure 10.5* shows that

$V_o = -(V_i - 2u) = -V_i + 2u$

So change of velocity $V_i - V_o = V_i - (-Vi + 2u)$

$= 2\,Vi - 2u = 2(Vi - u)$

But change of velocity is equal to acceleration and the force F acting on the blades is given by the product of mass and acceleration,

i.e. Force = mass × acceleration

$\therefore F = m \times 2\,(V_i - u)$ newtons

The work done = Force × distance moved in newton-metres and the power developed P is equal to the work done per unit time.

$$\text{So Power} = \frac{\text{Force} \times \text{distance moved}}{\text{Unit time}} \text{Nm/s}$$

But the distance moved per unit time = blade speed u

$\therefore P = 2m\,(V_i - u) \times u$ Nm/s

$= 2mu\,(V_i - u)$ Nm/s

$$\text{Power available in the steam} = \frac{mV_i^2}{2} \text{Nm/s}$$

So the blade efficiency

$$\eta\,b = \frac{\text{Power developed}}{\text{Power available}}$$

$$= \frac{2mu\,(V_i - u)}{\frac{mV_i^2}{2}} = \frac{4u\,(V_i - u)}{V_i^2}$$

$$= 4\left[\frac{uV_i}{V_i^2\,V_i^2} - \frac{u^2}{V_i^2}\right]$$

$$\therefore \eta\,b = 4\left[\frac{u}{Vi} - \frac{u^2}{Vi^2}\right]$$

Thus, if the blade speed/steam speed (i.e. u/V_i) is, say, 0.5, the blade efficiency will be:

$$\eta\,b = 4\quad[0.5 - 0.5^2]$$
$$= 1.0$$

Proceeding in a similar manner, a series of values can be calculated as follows:

$\dfrac{\textit{Blade speed}}{\textit{Steam speed}} = \dfrac{u}{V_i}$	0	0.2	0.4	0.5	0.6	0.8	1
Blade efficiency $= \eta\,b$	0	0.64	0.96	1.0	0.96	0.64	0

With an ideal nozzle, the blade efficiency is equal to the stage efficiency.

When the values are plotted the curve is as shown in *Figure 10.6*. Notice

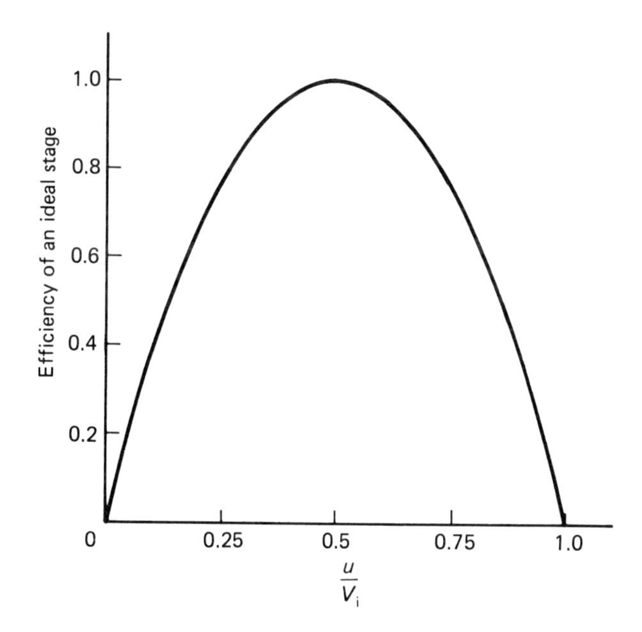

Figure 10.6 Efficiency of an ideal stage (CEGB)

that in this ideal case the maximum efficiency is 100%, and that it occurs at a blade speed/steam speed ratio of 0.5, or in other words, when the blade speed is a half of the steam speed. But it was shown earlier that the outlet steam velocity $V_o = V_i - 2u$ and so at the point of maximum efficiency the outlet absolute steam velocity will be zero. Observe how dramatically the efficiency changes with change of u/V_i ratio in *Figure 10.6*.

So much for the case of an *ideal* stage. Now consider a similar analysis for practical blades.

The simple impulse turbine

This consists of one set of nozzles followed by one row of moving blades (*Figure 10.7*). When considering practical blades some of the foregoing reasoning must be modified, commencing with the velocity diagram.

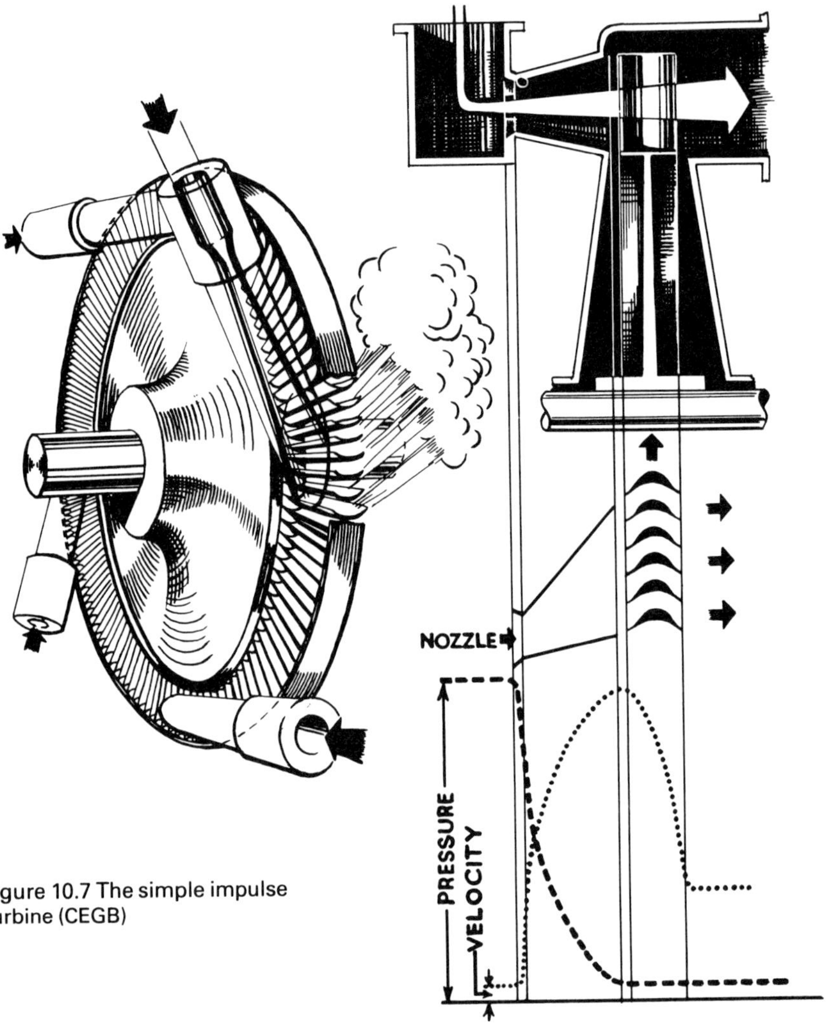

Figure 10.7 The simple impulse turbine (CEGB)

Velocity diagrams for blades

The following symbols will be used:

- u Linear velocity of the moving blade
- V_i Absolute velocity of steam at moving blade inlet
- V_o Absolute velocity of steam at moving blade outlet
- V_{wi} Velocity of whirl at moving blade inlet
- V_{wo} Velocity of whirl at moving blade outlet
- V_{fi} Velocity of flow at inlet to moving blade
- V_{ri} Relative velocity of steam at inlet to moving blade
- V_{ro} Relative velocity of steam at outlet from moving blade
- α Nozzle angle or exit angle of fixed blade
- β Inlet angle of fixed blade

θ Inlet angle of moving blade
ϕ Outlet angle of moving blade

Consider *Figure 10.8*. Vi represents the velocity of the steam from the nozzle

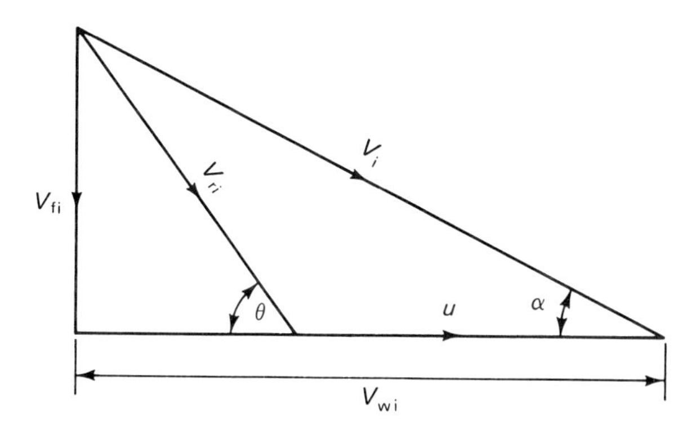

Figure 10.8 Simple velocity diagram

at a nozzle angle α. Because of the velocity of the moving blade, u, the velocity of the steam relative to the blades is given by V_{ri}. So for the steam to glide on to the moving blade the blade inlet angle must be θ.

Meanwhile the absolute steam velocity V_i can be resolved into two components V_{wi} and V_{fi}. V_{wi} is the *velocity of whirl*, and it is this component which does work on the blade as it is in the direction of blade motion. The component V_{fi} acts at right-angles to the direction of the blade movement, so it is this which causes the steam to flow through the turbine. *Figure 10.9* shows the arrangement applied to a moving blade whose inlet angle is θ and outlet angle ϕ. The velocity of whirl V_{wo} at outlet, is negative because it is opposite in direction to V_{wi} at the inlet. The outlet absolute steam velocity V_o is at angle β and so this must be the inlet angle of the next row of fixed blades.

For convenience it is usual to combine both the inlet and outlet vector diagrams such that the blade speed u is common to both of them, as shown in *Figure 10.10*. It is assumed that there is no blade friction, so $V_{ri} = V_{ro}$. The change of steam velocity in the direction of blade motion is given by:

$$V_i \cos\alpha - (-V_o \cos\beta) = V_i \cos\alpha + V_o \cos\beta$$
$$= V_{wi} + V_{wo} = V_w, \text{ the velocity of whirl}$$

The force F acting on the blading is given by
$F = mV_w$ newtons

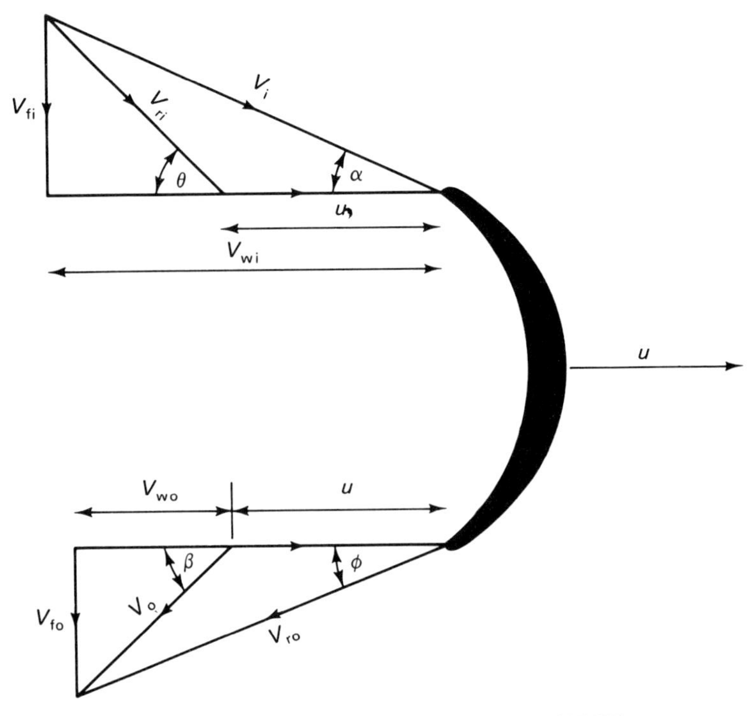

Figure 10.9 Blade velocity diagrams at inlet and outlet (CEGB)

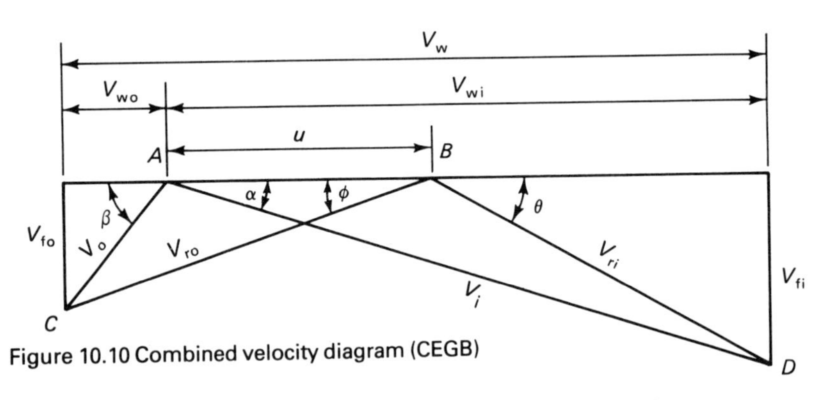

Figure 10.10 Combined velocity diagram (CEGB)

Consider the magnitude of the vectors only and let $\theta = \phi$ Also ignore friction loss as the steam passes over the blades, so $V_{ri} = V_{ro}$.

$$V_i \cos\alpha - u = V_{ro} \cos\phi$$
$$\text{but } V_{ro} \cos\phi = V_o \cos\beta + u$$
$$\text{So } V_i \cos\alpha - u = V_o \cos\beta + u$$
$$\therefore V_o \cos\beta = Vi \cos\alpha - 2u$$
$$\text{But } V_w = V_i \cos\alpha + V_o \cos\beta$$
$$\text{So } V_w = V_i \cos\alpha + (Vi \cos\alpha - 2u)$$

Therefore velocity of whirl $V_w = 2(V_i \cos\alpha - u)$ = change of velocity.
Power developed $P = umV_w$ Nm/s
Power available $= \dfrac{mV_i^2}{2}$ Nm/s

So blade efficiency $\eta_b = \dfrac{\text{Power developed}}{\text{Power available}} = \dfrac{umV_w}{\dfrac{mV_i^2}{2}}$

$$\therefore \eta_b = \frac{um2(V_i \cos\alpha - u)}{\dfrac{mV_i^2}{2}}$$

$$= \frac{4u(V_i \cos\alpha - u)}{V_i^2}$$

$$= 4\left[\frac{uV_i \cos\alpha}{V_i^2} - \frac{u^2}{V_i^2}\right]$$

So blade efficiency $\eta_b = 4\left[\dfrac{u\cos\alpha}{V_i} - \left(\dfrac{u}{V_i}\right)^2\right]$

Thus if the value of $u/V_i = 0.5$ and the nozzle angle $\alpha = 20°$, the blade efficiency will be:

$$\eta_b = 4(0.5\cos 20° - 0.5^2) = 4(0.5 \times 0.9397 - 0.5^2) = 0.8782$$

Table 10.1 was constructed by proceeding in a similar manner for a range of values of u/V_i and for various nozzle angles.

Table 10.1

	u/Vi	0	0.2	0.4	0.5	0.6	0.8
($\alpha = 10°$)	η_b	0	0.6276	0.9356	0.9696	0.9232	0.5912
($\alpha = 20°$)	η_b	0	0.5916	0.8632	0.8792	0.8152	0.4468
($\alpha = 30°$)	η_b	0	0.5328	0.7456	0.7320	0.6384	0.2112

The results are plotted in *Figure 10.11.*

The effect of increasing the nozzle angle is to reduce the efficiency, so in practice it is kept as small as possible consistent with practical requirements. The dotted line is the locus of maximum efficiency. However, the curves are drawn from information which assumed that there is no friction, whereas, in fact, not only is it present but there are also losses due to tip leakage and windage. So in an actual wheel the maximum efficiency will

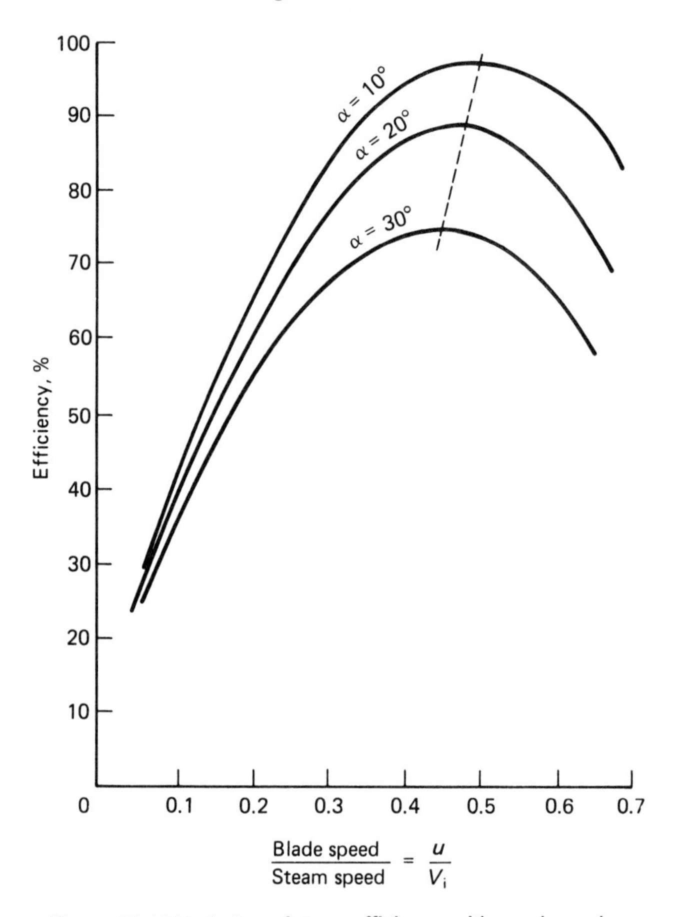

Figure 10.11 Variation of stage efficiency with nozzle angle

be about 84% when the nozzle angle is 20° as shown in *Figure 10.12*.

The blade speed/steam speed ratio for maximum efficiency remains the same in both cases and is equal to cos $\alpha/2$, so for a nozzle angle of 20° the value of u/V_i for maximum efficiency is 0.47. The main trouble with the simple impulse turbine is that the blade rotational speed is very high, often over 30 000 rev/min. This is because all the heat drop takes place in one set of nozzles, thus producing high velocity steam. As the blade speed for maximum efficiency is almost half the steam speed, it follows that it, too, will be high.

There are two main frequencies for electrical supply industries in the world, i.e. 50 and 60 Hz. Thus, directly-coupled turbines must run at 3000 or 3600 rev/min respectively. To achieve these comparatively low speeds it is necessary to resort to 'compounding' the turbines. This involves having several stages in the machine, each of which does only a fraction of the total work. Details of the various compounded turbine types can be found in

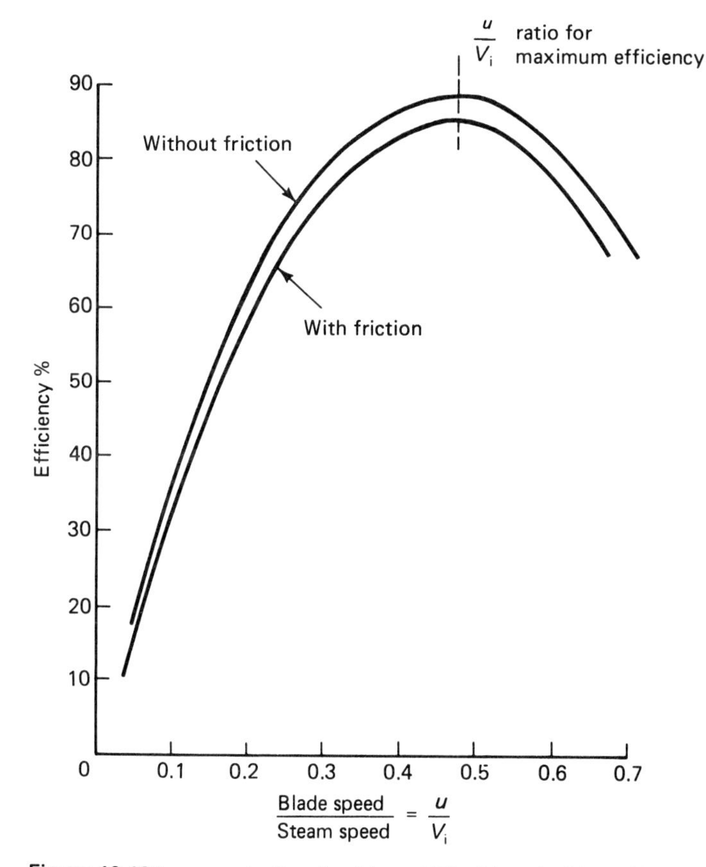

Figure 10.12 1–row velocity wheel (= 20°) with and without friction

standard textbooks, so here we will only study a few points of interest in some of them.

The velocity compounded turbine

This type is illustrated in *Figure 10.13*. The steam is admitted to a row of nozzles in which the steam pressure is reduced from inlet conditions to exhaust pressure. Thus, all the subsequent stages are subjected to the exhaust pressure. The high-velocity jet of steam which issues from the nozzles is utilized in the subsequent moving rows of blades which are interspersed with fixed blades whose function is to change the direction of the steam for admission to the next set of moving blades.

In *Figure 10.5* it was shown that with an ideal impulse blade the steam speed at exit is equal to the steam speed at entrance minus twice the blade speed, i.e. $V_o = V_i - 2u$. This is the speed of the steam entering the next row of moving blades, assuming that there is no loss in the intervening fixed row.

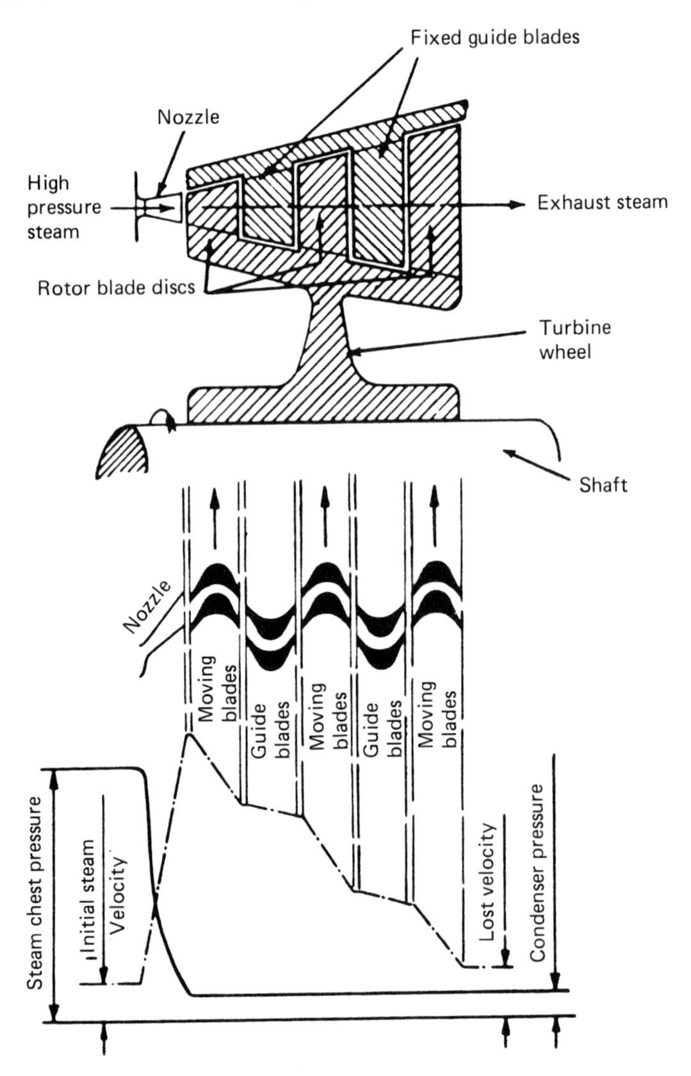

Figure 10.13 Compounding for velocity (CEGB)

The speed at outlet of the second row of moving blades will be $(V_i - 2u) - 2u$, i.e. $V_i - 4u$. By similar reasoning the speed at the outlet of the third moving row will be $V_i - 6u$ and so on. *Table 10.2* summarizes these statements.

It was determined when considering the ideal single-row turbine that the blade efficiency is given by:

$$\eta_b = 4\left[\frac{u}{V_i} - \left(\frac{u}{V_i}\right)^2\right]$$

Table 10.2

Moving row no.	*Inlet steam speed*	*Outlet steam speed*
1	V_i	$V_i - 2u$
2	$V_i - 2u$	$V_i - 4u$
3	$V_i - 4u$	$V_i - 6u$
4	$V_i - 6u$	$V_i - 8u$
5	$V_i - 8u$	$V_i - 10u$
etc.		

and that the efficiency is a maximum when the absolute outlet steam speed from the moving blades is zero. Thus, in the ideal two-row case maximum efficiency will occur when $V_i - 4u = 0$; in other words, when $u = V_i/4$.

$$\text{So } \eta_b(\text{max}) = 4\left[\frac{V_i/4}{V_i} - \left(\frac{V_i/4}{V_i}\right)^2\right] = 4(1/4 - 1/16)$$
$$= 0.75$$

Proceeding in a similar manner, the maximum efficiency for any number of rows may be calculated. *Table 10.3* immediately highlights the basic trouble

Table 10.3 Maximum efficiencies of ideal blades

No of rows	*Max. efficiency (%)*
2	75.0
3	55.56
4	43.76
5	36.00

with velocity compounded turbines – the efficiency is not very good, even with ideal blades. With practical blades the efficiencies are even lower and *Figure 10.14* shows the variation of efficiency with u/V_i for one- and two-row wheels; maximum efficiency occurs at 0.47 and 0.232 respectively.

This type of turbine was invented in 1896 by an American engineer, Charles Gordon Curtis. Although the rather poor efficiency precludes its use for large turbines, it does have one particular use in conjunction with other types, as the first stage of the high-pressure cylinder. Normally such a stage consists of a two-row wheel and it is interesting to see why a two-row rather than a one-row wheel is used. *Figure 10.15* shows a typical arrangement.

Table 10.4 compares the performance of one- and two-row Curtis wheels. Assume the nozzle angle $\alpha = 20°$; nozzle efficiency $\eta_n = 0.95$; blade speed 124 m/s. Thus, for the case considered, the two-row wheel absorbs more heat than four one-row wheels.

The advantages of having a Curtis stage are:

(a) The heat drop is very high.

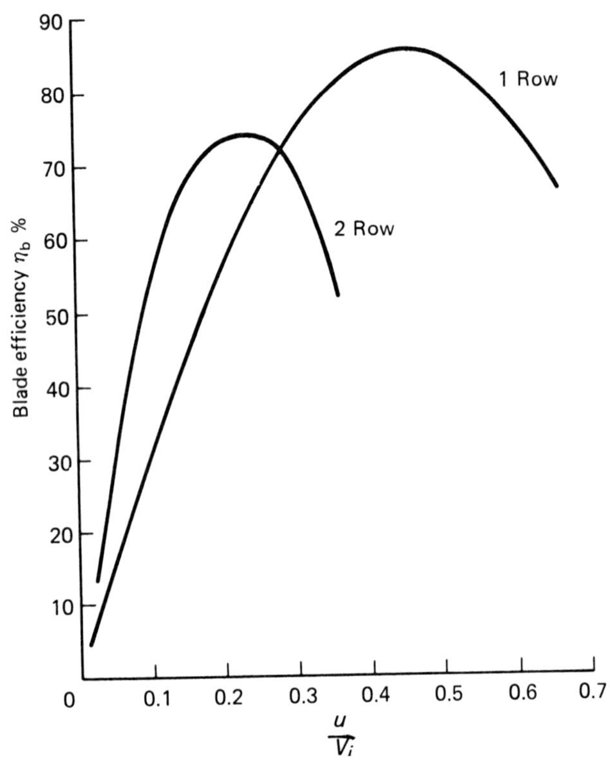

Figure 10.14 Variation of efficiency with u/V. For 1–row and 2–row wheels with friction ($\alpha = 20^{\circ}$, $K = 0.9$)

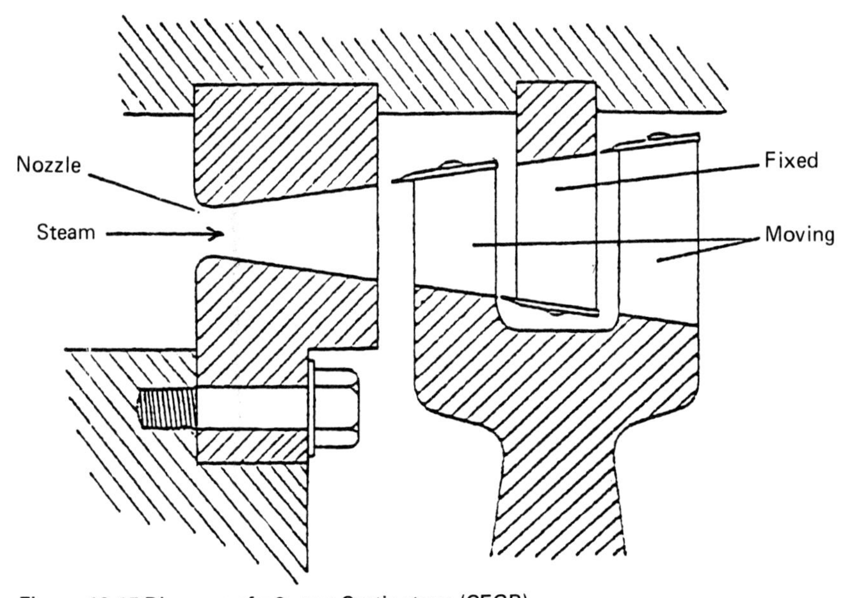

Figure 10.15 Diagram of a 2–row Curtis stage (CEGB)

Table 10.4 Comparison of 1-row and 2-row curtis wheel

	Item	*Derivation*	*No. of rows* 1	2
1	Optimum blade speed/ steam speed ratio	*Figure 10.14*	0.47	0.232
2	Steam velocity Vi if u = 124 m/s	$\frac{124}{(1)}$ m/s	264	534
3	Isentropic heat drop	$Vi = 44.72\sqrt{H}$ $\therefore H = \left(\frac{Vi}{44.72}\right)^2$ $= \frac{(2)^2}{44.72}$	34.85	142.59
4	Relative number of stages	$\frac{142.59}{(3)}$	4.1	1.0
5	Max. blade efficiency	*Figure 10.14*	0.84	0.73
6	Gross stage efficiency	$(5) \times \eta_n$	0.80	0.69

(b) Because of (a) the length of the high-pressure cylinder is reduced.
(c) Because of (b) the cost is reduced.
(d) The temperature and pressure of the steam to be handled after the nozzles is reduced and so the need for exotic materials is often avoided.
(e) The reduced pressure reduces the shaft gland loss.

Implications of blade-speed/steam-speed ratio

It is clear from what has already been said that the main factor governing the efficiency of a turbine is the blade-speed/steam-speed ratio u/V_i. In fact,

$$\text{Efficiency} \propto \frac{u}{V_i} \propto \sqrt{\frac{\text{speed}^2 \times \text{diameter}^2 \times \text{no. of stages}}{\text{sum of stage heat drops}}}$$

It follows that if a turbine is to have a certain efficiency then it must have the corresponding u/V_i ratio. If, in addition, the total heat drop is fixed then the value of speed² × diameter² × number of stages is also fixed.

Let H = heat drop; N = speed of rotation; D = diameter of rotor; S = number of stages.
Also, let suffix 1 refer to initial conditions and suffix 2 to final conditions.

$$\text{Then} \sqrt{\frac{N_1^2 D_1^2 S_1}{\Sigma H}} = \sqrt{\frac{N_2^2 D_2^2 S_2}{\Sigma H}}$$

If the total heat drop is the same in both cases the above expression reduces to:

$$N_1^2 D_1^2 S_1 = N_2^2 D_2^2 S_2$$

This is a very important expression as will now be shown.

Effect of change of diameter of rotor on number of stages

Suppose a turbine HP cylinder has a 76 cm diameter rotor and requires 10 stages. How many stages will be required if the diameter is increased to 142 cm, the speed, efficiency and the heat drop remaining the same?

$$N_1^2 D_1^2 S_1 = N_2^2 D_2^2 S_2$$

$$N_1 = N_2,$$

$$\text{so } S_2 = \left(\frac{D_2}{D_1}\right)^2 S_1 \qquad = \left(\frac{76}{142}\right)^2 \times 10$$

$$= 3 \text{ stages}$$

The advantages of increasing the rotor diameter and thus reducing the length of the turbine are obvious in terms of building volume, cost, etc. (*see Figure 10.16*). All the machines are drawn to a common scale. Notice that the 500 MW turbine is only a little over twice as long as the 60 MW, although the output is over eight times as great. The trend towards increased rotor diameters is clear in the diagrams. However, it should be pointed out that the main difficulty in increasing rotor diameters is to be found in the cylinder casing and *not* the rotor. The availability of suitable castings and the problems of bolting often determine the rotor diameter used for a particular cylinder. The most onerous conditions are found at the HP cylinder.

This may be a convenient point to digress slightly and mention double casings. These, of course, permit much greater flexibility of operation because more rapid temperature and loading changes are permissible than with single casings. However, there are other advantages. Consider a 200 MW turbine HP cylinder. If it had been designed with a single casing, 23 cm bolts would have been required and the casing thickness would have been about 20 cm, but by using a double casing, the bolt size is reduced to 11 cm and the casing thickness to 9 cm. There are also other advantages, namely:

1 The pressure difference across the inner casing is reduced and the bolting operates at a lower temperature.
2 The outer casing has a reduced steam pressure and its bolting works at a lower temperature.
3 The HP end shaft gland operates at a lower pressure, see *Figure 10.17(a)* and *(b)*.

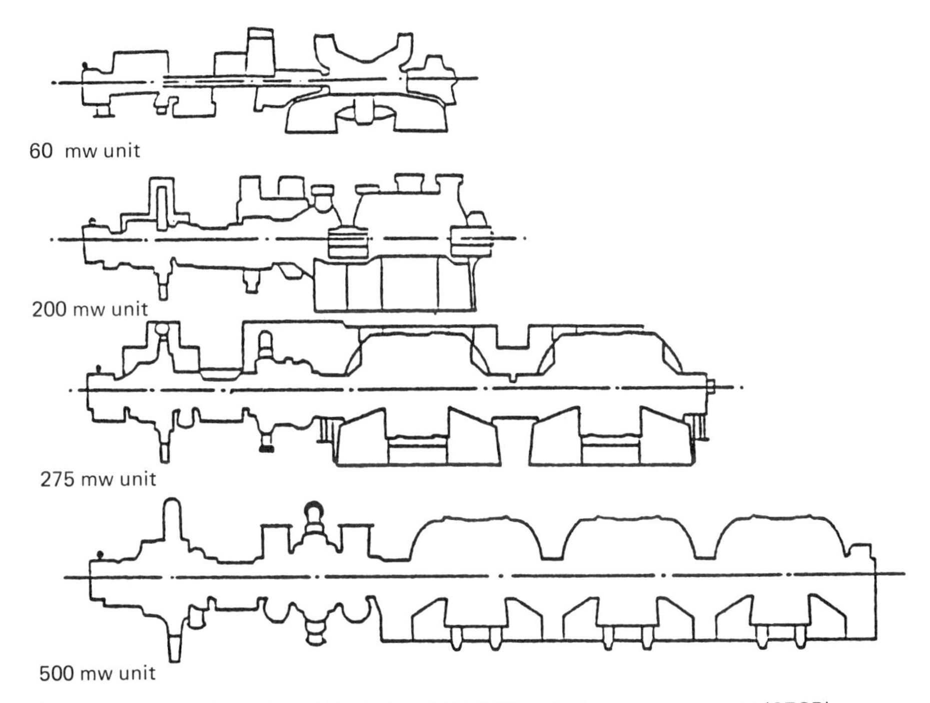

Figure 10.16 Sections of 60, 200, 275 and 500–MW units to a common scale (CEGB)

Effect of change of speed of rotation

It has been mentioned that the rotor diameter is determined primarily by considerations of the casing and bolting. Thus it is in order to have the same diameter rotor on, say, a 3600 as on a 3000 rev/min machine. So if the diameter remains constant but the speed is changed then the number of stages must change.

$$D_1 = D_2 \text{ so } N_1^2 S_1 = N_2^2 S_2$$

$$\text{so } S_2 = \left(\frac{N_1}{N_2}\right)^2 S_1 = \left(\frac{3000}{3600}\right)^2 S_1$$

$$= 0.7\, S_1$$

Therefore a 3600 rev/min machine requires only 70% of the number of stages required by one for 3000 rev/min for comparable output, efficiency and steam conditions. This is illustrated in *Figure 10.18*, which shows 50 Hz and 60 Hz machines drawn to a common scale.

The effect of speed of rotation is also important at the low-pressure end of the turbine. Consider a last row of moving blades rotating at 3000 rev/min. For the same blading running at 3600 rev/min the stresses will increase by:

$$\left(\frac{N_2}{N_1}\right)^2 = \left(\frac{3600}{3000}\right)^2 = 1.44 \text{ times}$$

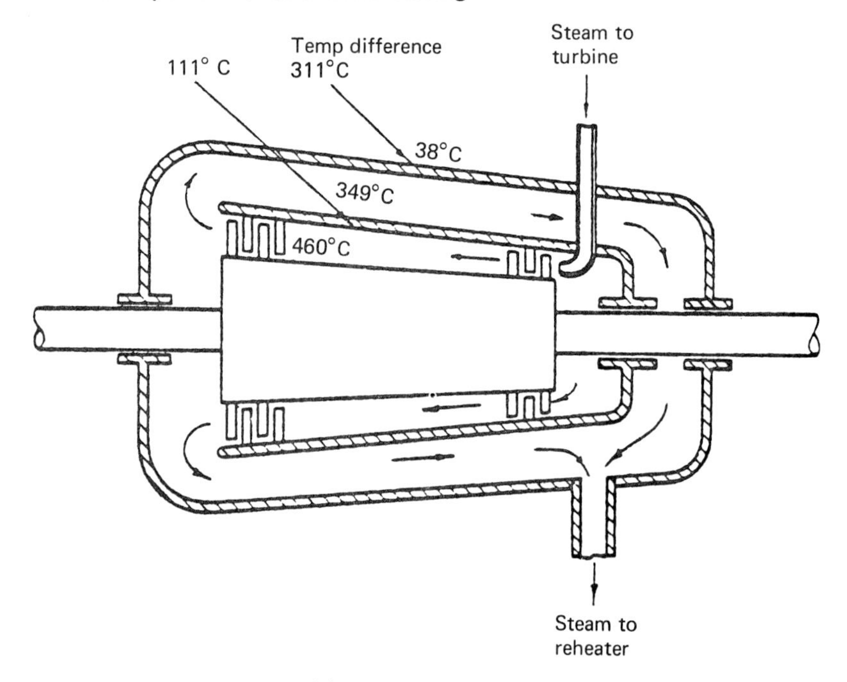

(a) Double wall cylinder

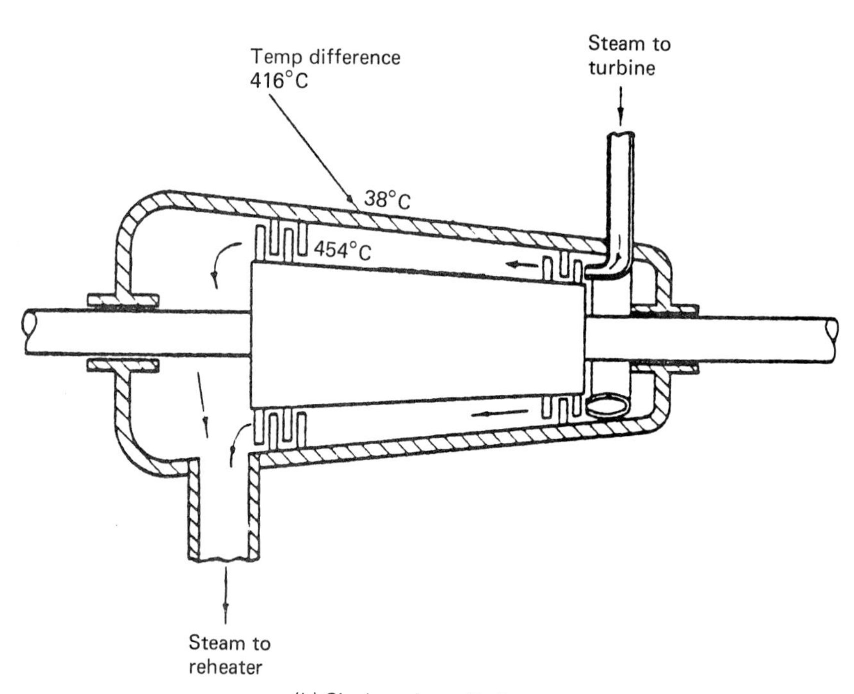

(b) Single casing cylinder

Figure 10.17 Showing how a double wall cylinder reduces temperature difference through metal casing (CEGB)

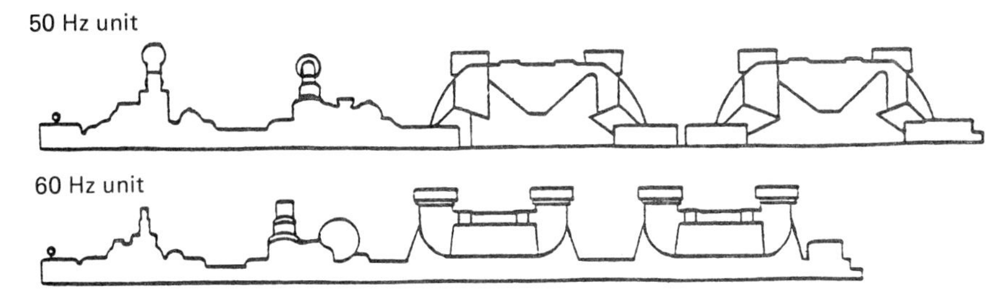

Figure 10.18 A comparison of the size of 275 MW units designed respectively for 50 Hz and 60 Hz (CEGB)

Hence, the maximum blade exhaust annular area at 3000 rev/min can be 44% greater than at 3600 rev/min. This is of very great importance as the magnitude of the leaving loss (i.e. the kinetic energy of the steam leaving the last row of moving blades) is a function of the last row annular area. The smaller area permissible at 3600 rev/min because of stress limitations, means that for comparable outputs the leaving loss will be high compared with a 3000 rev/min machine.

Figure 10.19 shows that the gain by going from 3600 to 1800 rev/min is

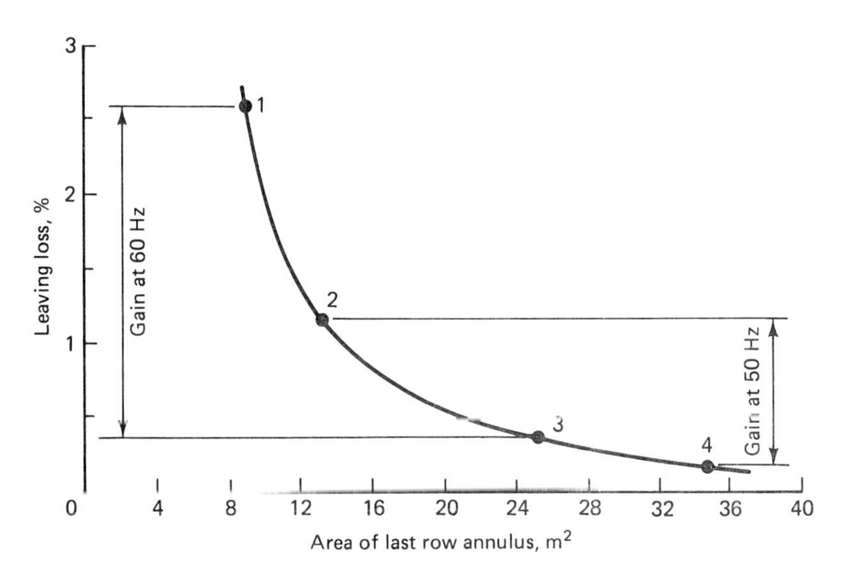

Figure 10.19 Comparison of leaving loss for 50 Hz and 60 Hz units

much greater than from 3000 to 1500 rev/min. The points in the figure are for 3600 rev/min (point 1), and 3000 rev/min (point 2) machines of 200 MW, output and identical steam conditions. Point 3 is for 1800 and point 4 for 1500 rev/min. Therefore, there is an inducement to change to cross-compounded machines earlier in the USA than in Europe.

Turbine losses

Next consider briefly some losses which occur in turbines. They can be divided conveniently into two groups; namely internal and external.

Internal losses:

(a) Nozzle friction (b) Blade friction; (c) Disc friction; (d) Diaphragm gland and blade tip leakage; (e) Partial admission; (f) Wetness; (g) Exhaust.

External losses:

(a) Shaft gland leakage; (b) Journal and thrust bearing; (c) Governor and oil pump.

Consider each internal loss:

(a) *Nozzle friction*

The effect of nozzle friction is to reduce the actual heat drop of the steam as it passes through the nozzle. This results in a lower steam velocity at outlet and consequently it will also be lower when entering the subsequent row of moving blades. Now the blade is designed to allow the steam to glide on to it, so if the velocity is reduced there will be some shock as the steam strikes the blade.

(b) *Blade friction*

This is a similar case to that of nozzle friction in that its effect is to reduce the steam speed passing over the blades. Without friction the relative velocity at outlet would be the same as that at inlet. In fact it is commonly reduced to 90%. *Figure 10.20* shows the conditions for two complete stages (i.e. two nozzles and moving blades), where *ab* represents the frictionless heat drop across the nozzle. Friction causes the steam to actually leave the nozzle with a heat content represented by *c*. In passing over the subsequent row of moving blades friction causes the state point of the steam to move from *c* to *d*.

$$\text{So Stage efficiency} = \frac{\text{Heat drop } ad}{\text{Heat drop } ab} \times 100 \text{ per cent}$$

Increasing blade friction will cause point d to be displaced along the pressure line P_2 to the right. The stage efficiency will suffer accordingly. The steam at d is admitted to the next stage nozzles and the previous pattern of events is repeated, *de* being the isentropic heat drop across the next stage and *df* the actual state line of the steam.

(c) *Disc friction*

The discs on impulse turbine shafts rotate in an atmosphere of steam. The

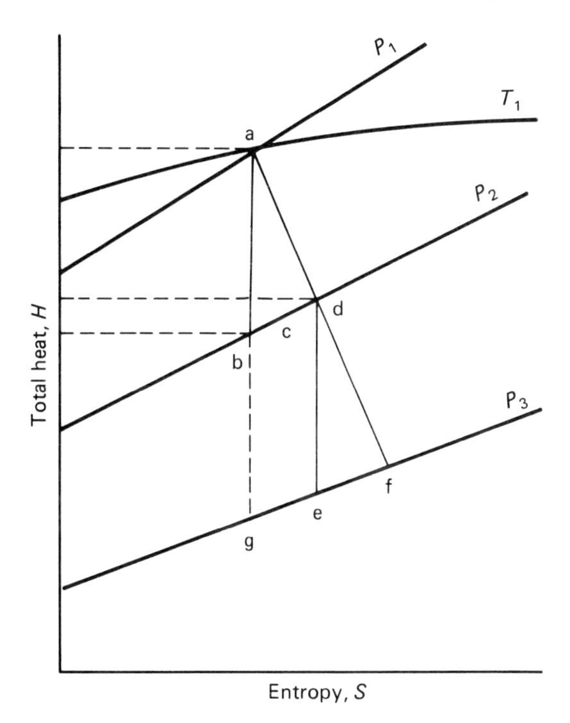

Figure 10.20 Section of Mollier diagram showing locus of state point (CEGB)

disc surface is in contact with a layer of steam which it drags with it, thus causing some steam circulation. This is done at the expense of some of the power developed at the blades and so the efficiency suffers. The effect is most pronounced where the steam is densest, but it is present to some degree in all stages.

(d) *Diaphragm gland and tip leakage*

With pressure compounded turbines there is a pressure drop across each fixed nozzle, i.e. across each diaphragm. Therefore, the gap between the diaphragm and the shaft is a source of steam leakage. Such leakage is minimized by fitting interstage glands between the shaft and diaphragm. The moving blades, on the other hand, have theoretically zero pressure drop across them, although in practice there will be a slight drop, so there is no need for sophisticated steam sealing. Tip clearances are generous. In fact it is normal to have several balance holes drilled in the discs to equalize the pressures on either side. *Figure 10.21* shows the HP rotor from a 350 MW turbine, the balance holes being clearly visible.

It is obvious that any wear of the diaphragm interstage glands will increase the steam leakage considerably. In addition the leakage steam will cause disturbance when it joins the steam issuing from the nozzles. It

Figure 10.21 HP rotor from 350–MW unit (CEGB)

is therefore important that shaft eccentricity is kept to a minimum particularly during start-up and loading of the machine.

On impulse-reaction machines there is a pressure drop across every blade, whether fixed or moving. Thus, there is a steam flow around the tips of all the fixed and moving blades. Consequently each blade has sealing arrangements such as shown in *Figure 10.22*. Leakage is greatest at the initial stages as the specific volume of the steam is low. This problem is sometimes overcome by fitting an impulse stage at the inlet of the machine.

On smaller turbines (up to 60 MW), 'end tightening' was often fitted by means of which the shaft could be moved axially. Thus, for start-up and loading the shaft would be moved to give good axial clearances, but when fully expanded the shaft could be moved to give fine clearances and so reduce tip leakage to a minimum. On large, modern machines interstage leakage accounts for about 0.5 to 1.0 per cent loss if the seals are in good condition.

If the efficiency is determined for a series of blade-speed/speed ratios a curve such as shown in *Figure 10.23* will be obtained. Notice that the curve is fairly flat over a large range of values of u/V_i. The degree of reaction is defined as the ratio of the heat drop in the moving blades to the sum of the heat drops in the fixed and moving blades, i.e.

$$\text{Reaction} = \frac{H_m}{H_m + H_f}$$

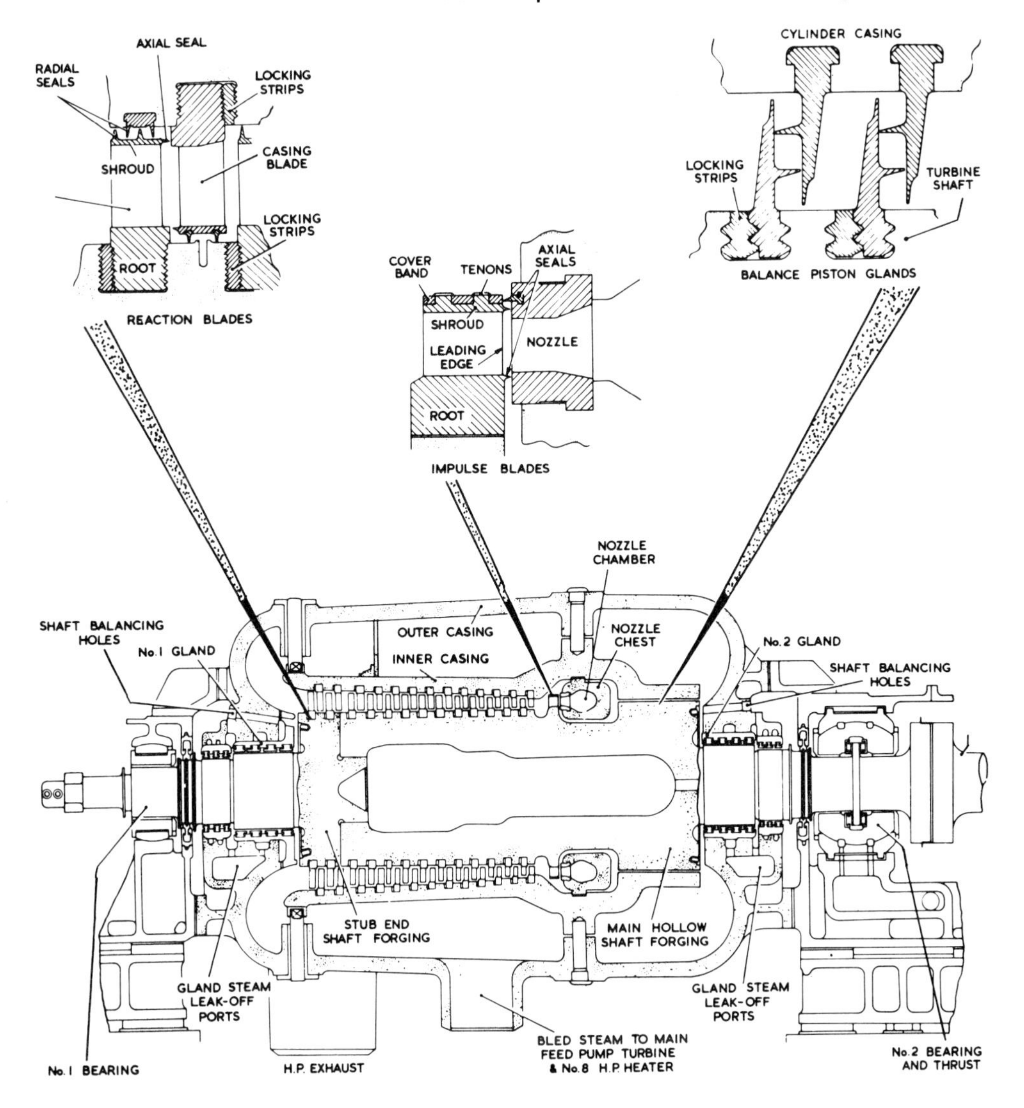

Figure 10.22 Reaction type blading (CEGB)

In Parsons turbines the reaction is typically 50%.

There is an axial thrust towards the LP end of the rotor caused by the differential steam pressure acting on the moving blades. Balance pistons (often called 'dummy pistons') are incorporated in the turbine to counteract the end thrust, as illustrated in *Figure 10.24*.

(e) *Partial admission*

In nozzle-governed turbines, the steam is admitted to one or more arcs of

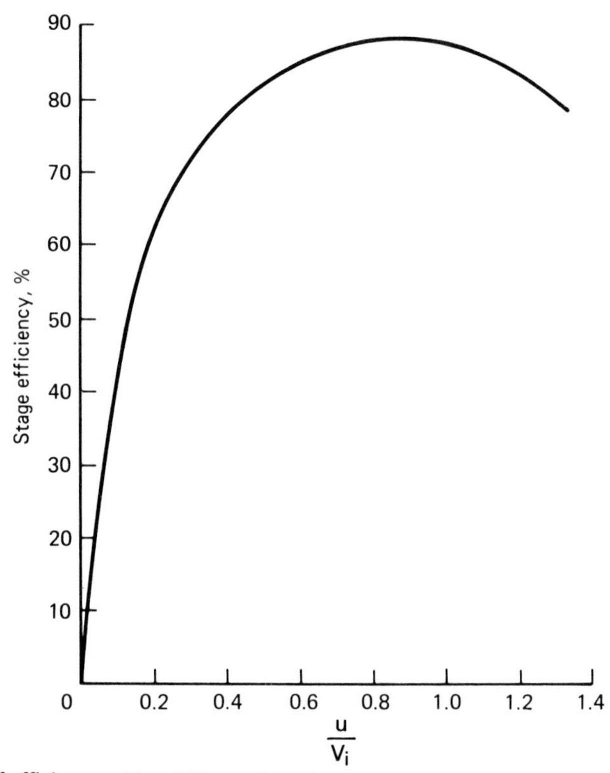

Figure 10.23 Variation of efficiency with u/Vi for an impulse reaction stage

the inlet nozzle ring. For example, *Figure 10.25* shows a half nozzle ring split into three arcs, each supplied by a control valve. The valves lift in sequence as the loading is increased until, at full load, all are open and full admission takes place to the nozzle ring. At part loads only certain arcs are in use. When the arc of the first row of moving blades is aligned with a 'running' nozzle arc they run 'full' of steam. When they pass a 'non-running' arc eddies are formed. Also the blades at the beginning and the end of the group under the influence of steam from a 'running' arc will not be filled properly and so the flow will be disturbed. This effect is referred to as 'blade windage'.

If, as must happen, some of the moving blades are full of smooth-flowing steam and others are not, it follows that where the transition occurs during each revolution the steam will be accelerated and, later decelerated. These effects all contribute to the losses. If possible the machine should be operated only at loads which permit all the nozzle arcs in use to have full-open control valves. This eliminates the additional loss that would be caused by throttling at one of the nozzle valves.

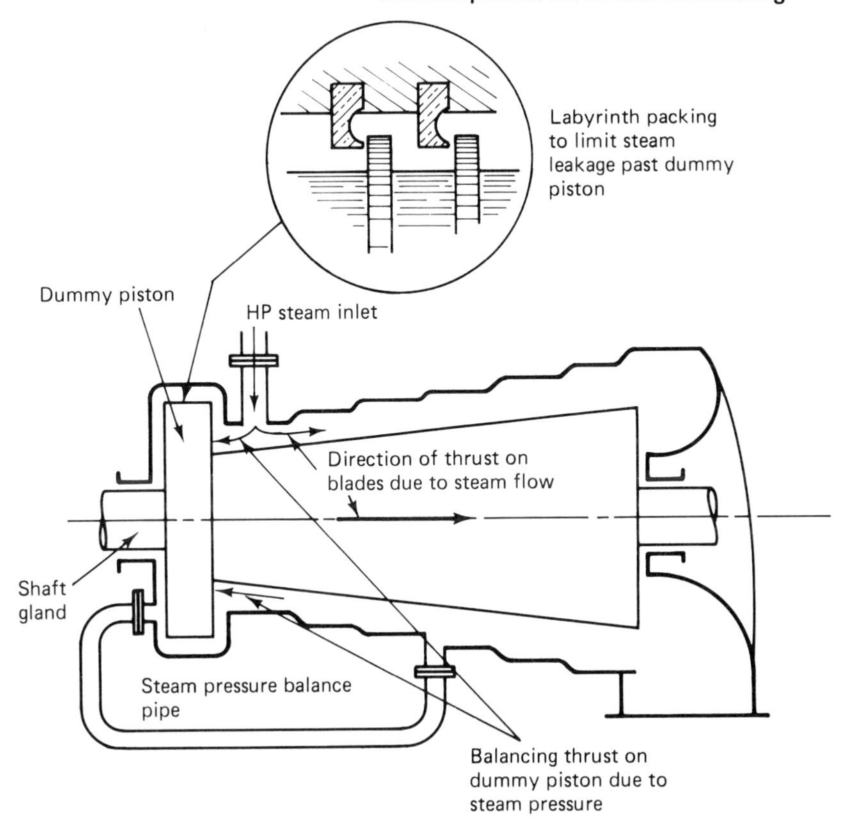

Figure 10.24 Dummy piston and balance pipe (CEGB)

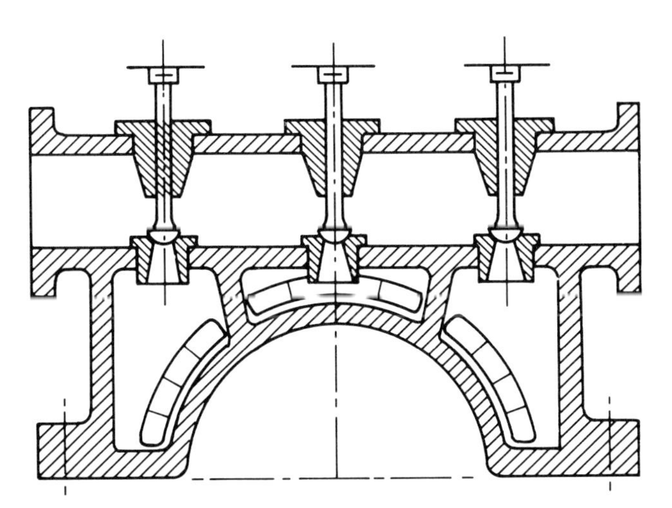

Figure 10.25 Nozzle governing (CEGB)

(f) *Wetness*

When the steam state point during the passage of steam through the turbine passes into the wet region some of the steam will condense into tiny droplets of water and the water quantity will increase as the steam continues its expansion. The maximum wetness normally tolerated is about 12%. The last few stages of the LP cylinder are the worst affected, see *Figure 10.26.* As the droplets increase in size they travel much more

Figure 10.26 Blade damage caused by moisture (CEGB)

slowly than the steam. Consequently, unlike the steam which glides on to the moving blades, the water droplets impinge on the inlet edge of them as shown in *Figure 10.27.*

Thus, the blade does mechanical work in knocking the droplets out of the way. The loss of efficiency from this cause is roughly one per cent for every one per cent of wetness at the particular stage. Physical damage to the blades is normally minimized by fitting Stellite shields to the inlet edges. Stellite is the proprietary name for a series of extremely hard alloys of cobalt, chromium, tungsten and carbon. *Figure 10.28* shows how the percentage wetness varies with variations of inlet steam pressure for typical UK steam temperatures.

Reheating reduces the wetness of the steam as explained in the section on Ideal Steam Cycles. Feed heating also eases the problem of wetness at the LP stages because steam bled to the heaters does not pass through the turbine exhaust and thus does not contribute to the moisture formation. However, even the effect of reheating and feed heating does not remove the very real problem of wetness in the steam. *Figure 10.29* shows a collecting annulus for water centrifuged from the moving blades.

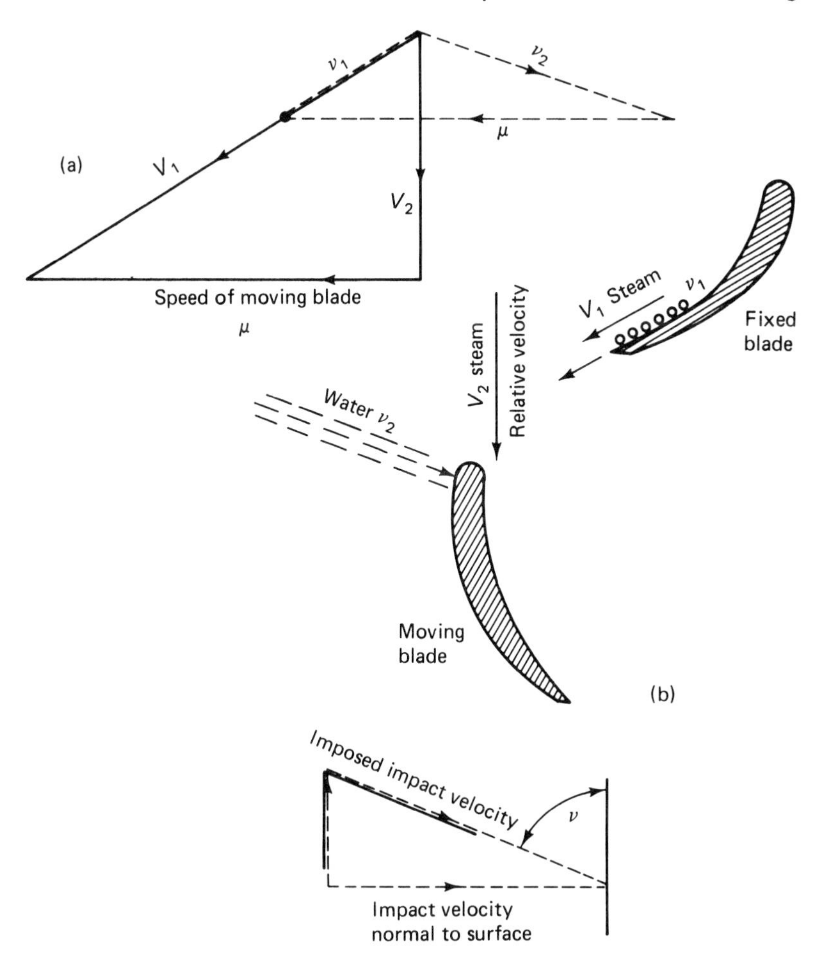

Figure 10.27 Effect of angle of impact on damage (CEGB)

(g) *Exhaust*

The considerable kinetic energy of the steam when it leaves the last row of moving blades does no further useful work. This loss of energy is known as the 'leaving loss' or the 'residual loss'.

$$\text{Thus the leaving loss} = \frac{mV_O^2}{2}$$

where m = mass steam flow
V_O = absolute velocity of the steam at the outlet of the last row of blades

Figure 10.30 shows the effect of the loss. For example, for a particular

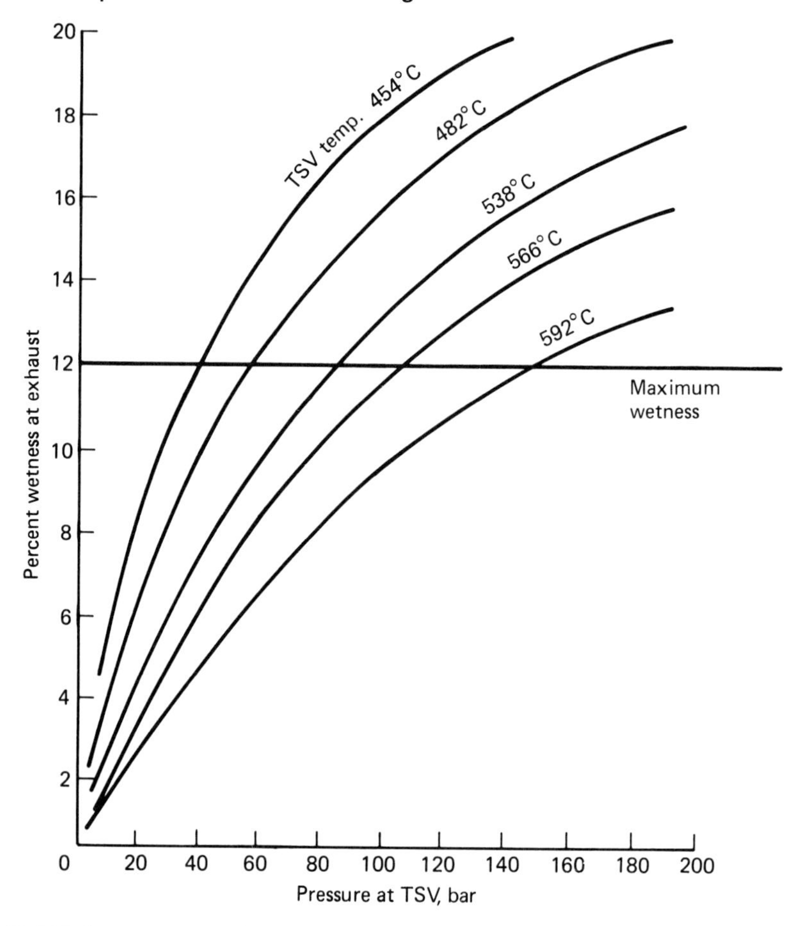

Figure 10.28 Exhaust wetness of non-reheat turbines for different TSV temperatures

turbine the absolute velocity of the steam leaving the last row of blades is 366 m/s.

$$\text{So leaving loss} = \frac{366^2}{2} = 66\ 978 \text{ J/kg of steam.}$$

The loss varies as the square of the velocity, and the velocity varies with the back pressure of the turbine. Thus, if the back pressure is improved from, say, 63 to 33 mbar the specific volume of the steam will double. Hence the steam must go twice as fast past the last row of blades. But doubling the velocity will increase the leaving loss by four times.

In a 500 MW turbine the volume of steam passing to the condenser at 44 mbar back pressure is of the order of 12 000 m^3/s. To keep the loss as small as possible the last row blades must be as long as possible and there are three double-flow LP cylinders, so that each LP last row blade

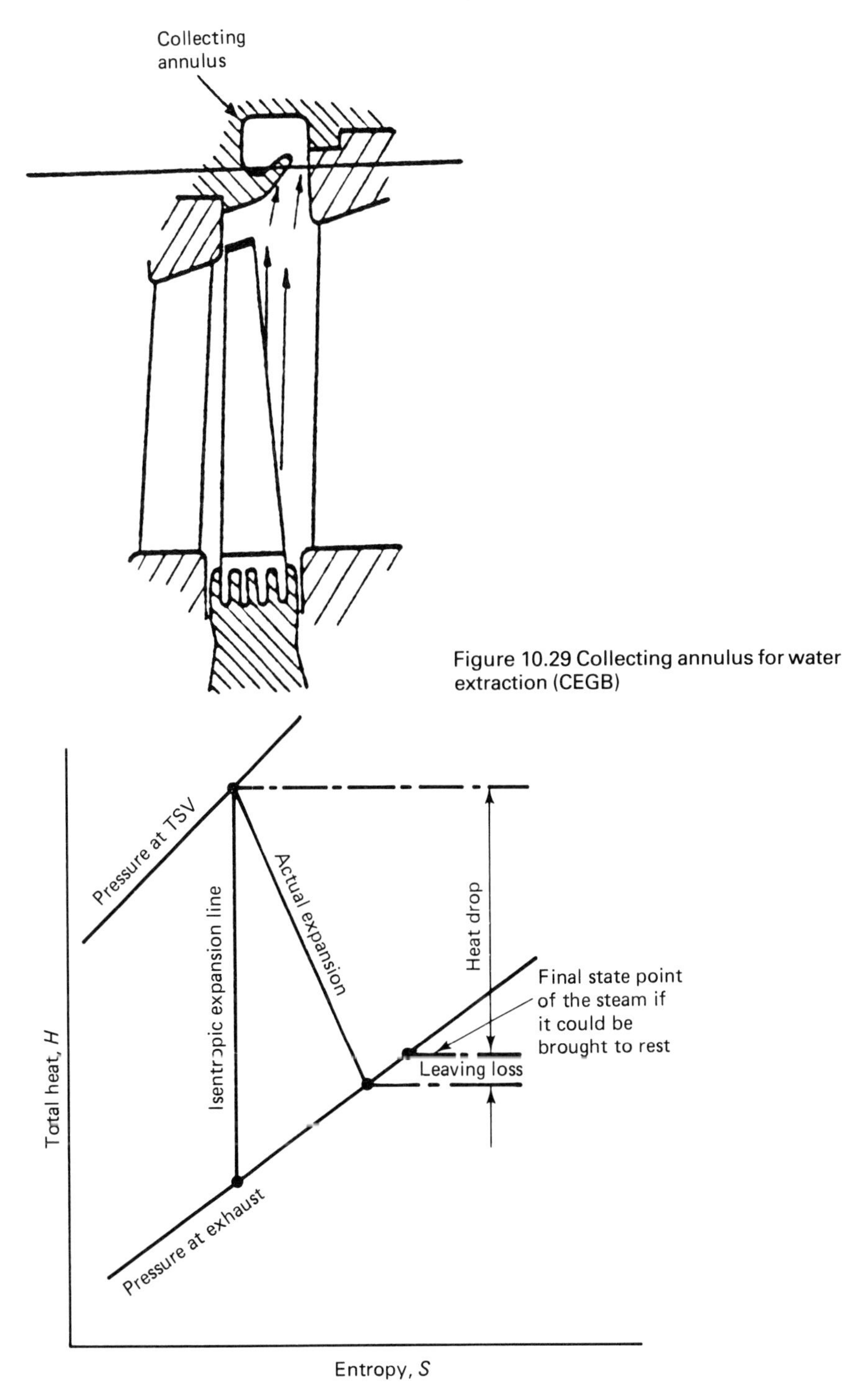

Figure 10.29 Collecting annulus for water extraction (CEGB)

Figure 10.30 Diagrammatic representation of leaving loss (CEGB)

annulus only has to handle one sixth of the total quantity of steam entering the condenser.

Example

A 350 MW unit has two double-flow LP cylinders. The last row exhaust area is 7.9 $m^2$and the specific volume of the steam at that point is 31.96 m^3/kg (44 mbar). The turbine stop valve steam flow is 302.9 kg/s and the total steam entering the condenser is 189.0 kg/s. Enthalpy change from TSV to exhaust is 1586.3 kJ/kg, and the steam at exhaust is 90% dry. Calculate the leaving loss.

Exhaust area of last row blades = 7.9m^2
Steam volume at 44 mbar, 10% wet = 28.76 m^3/kg
Steam flow to condensers at full load = 189.0 kg/s
Number of flows = 4

Steam flow per exhaust $= \frac{189.0}{4} = 47.25$ kg/s

Steam velocity at last stage $= \frac{47.25 \times 28.76}{7.9}$

$= 172.0$ m/s

Leaving loss $= \frac{mV^2}{2} J = \frac{1.0 \times 172^2}{2 \times 1000} = 14.79$ kJ/kg per flow

Leaving loss per kg of TSV steam flow $= 14.7 \times \frac{189.0}{302.9}$

$= 9.17$ kJ per flow

Work done per kg of TSV steam flow = 1586.3 kJ/kg

So leaving loss $= \frac{4 \times 9.17 \times 100}{1586.3}$ = **2.3%**

Having left the last row of blades the steam then has to be turned through 90° to enter the condenser. This has to be done with the minimum pressure loss and so a fairly gentle bend is provided. Even so there is an appreciable loss of the order of 3.5 mbar which constitutes a significant proportion of the total back pressure. This is known as the 'Hood Loss'. The 'Leaving Loss' plus the 'Hood Loss' gives the 'Exhaust Loss'.

It has already been mentioned that because of limitations of last-row blade length it is often necessary to use multiple exhausts. Such an arrangement reduces the exhaust loss. *Table 10.5* give some details of exhausts.

The relationship between the area of a multi-exhaust and a single one for comparable areas is given by:

$$D_m = \frac{D_i}{\sqrt{m}}$$

Table 10.5 Turbine last row details

Rating (MW)	*Number of exhausts*	*Exhaust area (m^2)*
120	3	9.8
120	2	9.1
200	4	18.2
500	6	43.8
550	8	43.8

where D_m = diameter of each exhaust in the multi-exhaust case
D_i = diameter of equivalent single exhaust
m = number of exhausts in the multi-exhaust case

Another means of increasing the exhaust area without undue lengthening of the last row blades is to use a Baumann exhaust. This method was used originally by the Metropolitan Vickers Company, which later became A.E.I. and is now part of the General Electric Company. *Figure 10.31* shows the last few stages of a turbine fitted with a Baumann exhaust. As the steam passes through the turbine to the exhaust the blading is conventional until it reaches the fixed blade A. This blade has a circular division ring B which splits the steam into two paths. The outer path of steam is expanded to back pressure and passed to the condenser via the moving blades C. Meanwhile the other stream is discharged from A at a pressure higher than the exhaust pressure. It passes through the penultimate moving row of blades, after which it passes to a further row of fixed blades D contained within a shroud E. Here the pressure is reduced to that of the exhaust before being discharged to the condenser via the last row of blades F.

It is interesting to compare the final LP stages of Nos. 11 and 12 turbines at Drakelow 'C'. Each unit is designed for 375 MW and has identical steam conditions, i.e. 241 bar/593°C/566°C. The No. 11 turbine is of English Electric manufacture and has a conventional four-flow exhaust, whereas the No. 12 turbine is of A.E.I. manufacture and has a four-flow exhaust incorporating the Baumann exhaust just described. *Table 10.6* shows the comparison of the two machines.

Table 10.6 Comparison of 375 MW Turbine exhausts

Unit No.	*Last blade Length (mm)*	*Mean Diameter (m)*	*Tip Diameter (m)*	*Tip Velocity (m/s)*
11	915	2.54	3.45	542
12	749	2.108	2.86	449

Notice that the blade length is considerably greater on No. 11 turbine as also is the tip velocity. It follows that the blading is subjected to more onerous conditions than on No. 12.

It may be of interest to note that the first reheat turbines in the world

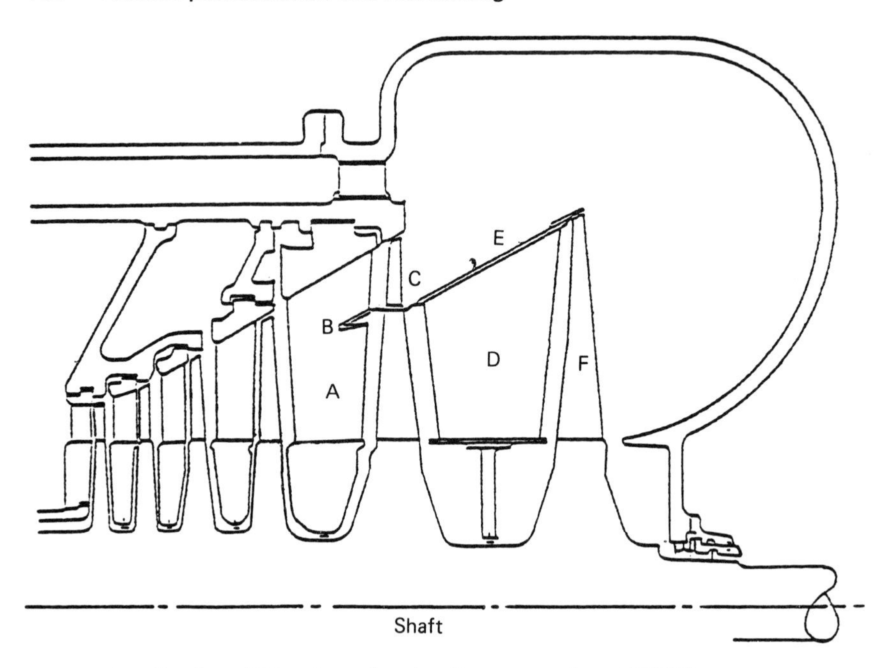

Figure 10.31 Section of LP turbine showing Baumann exhaust (CEGB)

for commercial operation were installed at North Tees Power Station in England. The turbines had Baumann triple-exhaust systems, ran at 2400 rev/min and were rated at 20 MW. The steam conditions were 31 bar/343°C/260°C, very advanced for the time.

Table 10.7 Baumann exhausts

No of additional exhaust blades	*increase in area (%)*
1	40
2	120
3	170

Bled steam turbines

In the past 20 years it has become common to use bled steam turbines to drive the main boiler feed pump on large units. Steam for the turbine is taken from, say, the cold reheat line and the discharge steam is passed to a suitable heater such as the deaerator or to a condenser. During its passage through the turbine the steam is tapped at suitable points to provide steam for some of the HP feed heaters. The bled steam turbine shown in *Figure 10.32* is for a 600 MW unit.

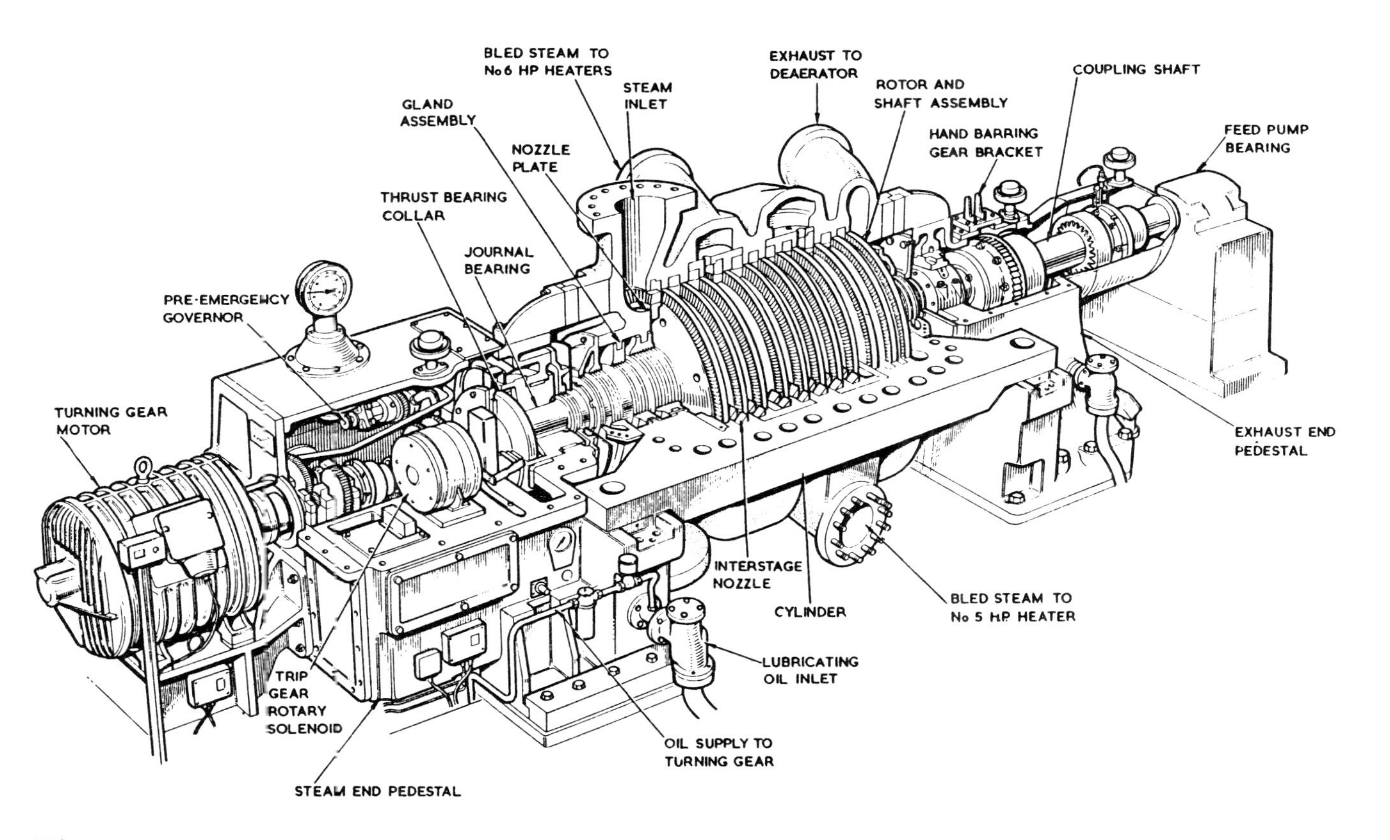

Figure 10.32 Boiler feed pump turbine (CEGB)

The advantages of bled steam turbine drives may be stated as:

1 If the bled steam is derived from the cold reheat the steam flow through the reheater is reduced. This permits a reduction of cost of reheat steam pipework because of the reduction of size made possible.
2 Thermodynamically it is advantageous to use the low-temperature steam at the bled steam turbine for feed heating, rather than the higher temperature steam which would be necessary if it was tapped from the IP cylinder of the main turbine. Hence, the cycle efficiency is improved.
3 Bleeding steam from the auxiliary turbine for feed heating has the added advantage that it results in a greater mass steam flow being admitted to the early stages of the machine. This, in its turn, means that the blades for such stages can be longer and so more efficient.
4 Normally there is no need for gearing between the turbine and the pump as the turbine speed can be adapted to suit the pump.
5 Because of the reduction of auxiliary power compared to electric motor drives more electricity is available to the consumers.

Other advantages could be listed, but the above serve to illustrate the main points.

There are various ways in which a boiler feed pump turbine can be incorporated into the heat cycle, such as:

(a) Bled steam turbine exhausting to the main turbine or to a heater, i.e. a back-pressure turbine.
(b) Bled steam turbine exhausting to a condenser.
(c) Auxiliary or waste heat boiler supplying the turbine with steam, i.e. a topping turbine.

The back-pressure turbine

Usually the bled steam is obtained from the cold reheat, i.e. the HP cylinder exhaust. After doing work in the BS turbine the exhaust steam is either fed back to the main turbine or fed into a feed heater. If the steam is returned to the main turbine it is most important that good mixing of the main and auxiliary turbine steam takes place. This can be accomplished by mixing the two in the main turbine cross-over pipe. Of course, protection is necessary to prevent steam flow between the machines in the event of a turbine trip.

Alternatively, the BS turbine exhaust can be piped to a feed heater such as the deaerator, but this type of layout makes the feed heating installation and the BS turbine inter-dependent. Other disadvantages are:

(a) If cold reheat steam is used, the pressure may be such that the bled steam turbine final expansion will be wet.
(b) Because the cold reheat pressure is quite high the volume of the steam at entry to the BS turbine will be low.

The condensing turbine

An alternative to using cold reheat steam to drive the BS turbine is to extract it from a point after the reheater. Such steam will, of course, be at a lower pressure. Because of the lower heat drop compared with the earlier case the steam flow will be greater and the specific volume larger because of the lower pressure. Consequently the early stage efficiencies are improved because the blades are longer. The exhaust wetness is comparable with that of the main turbine steam.

For a given last row exhaust area on the main turbine the steam bled to the auxiliary turbine will reduce the main steam volume and, hence, exhaust velocity. This will result in a reduced leaving loss. The auxiliary turbine exhausts into either its own condenser or into the main one. If an independent condenser is provided the cooling water supply is common for both that and the main condenser. The condensing turbine provides a reliable and operationally simple feed pump drive.

The topping turbine

The design of these machines is simple. A single stage wheel is used, usually overhung to avoid the leakage loss from a second high-pressure gland. The efficiency of the turbine stage is quite high because of the high steam flow. On the other hand the pressure drop at the regulating device compared to the low heat drop in the turbine results in a large loss. The regulating devices often cost a lot more than the turbine itself. The heat drop in the topping turbine must be regulated by controlling the steam pressure before the topping turbine and before the main turbine in accordance with the power requirements of the pump.

The back pressure and condensing turbines are the types used normally in large stations to drive the feed pump. Just in passing, it should be pointed out that other possibilities for feed pump drives include gas turbines and a drive from the main turbine shaft, plus, of course, electric motor drives. In any case electric drives must also normally be provided for starting and standby duties.

Description of cylinders of a 500 MW turbine

The following description of a 500 MW turbine may be of interest as it illustrates various considerations which may not readily be apparent.

High-pressure cylinder

The high-pressure cylinder (*Figure 10.33*) has eight impulse stages, the first five of which are contained within a double casing. The steam flow is in a

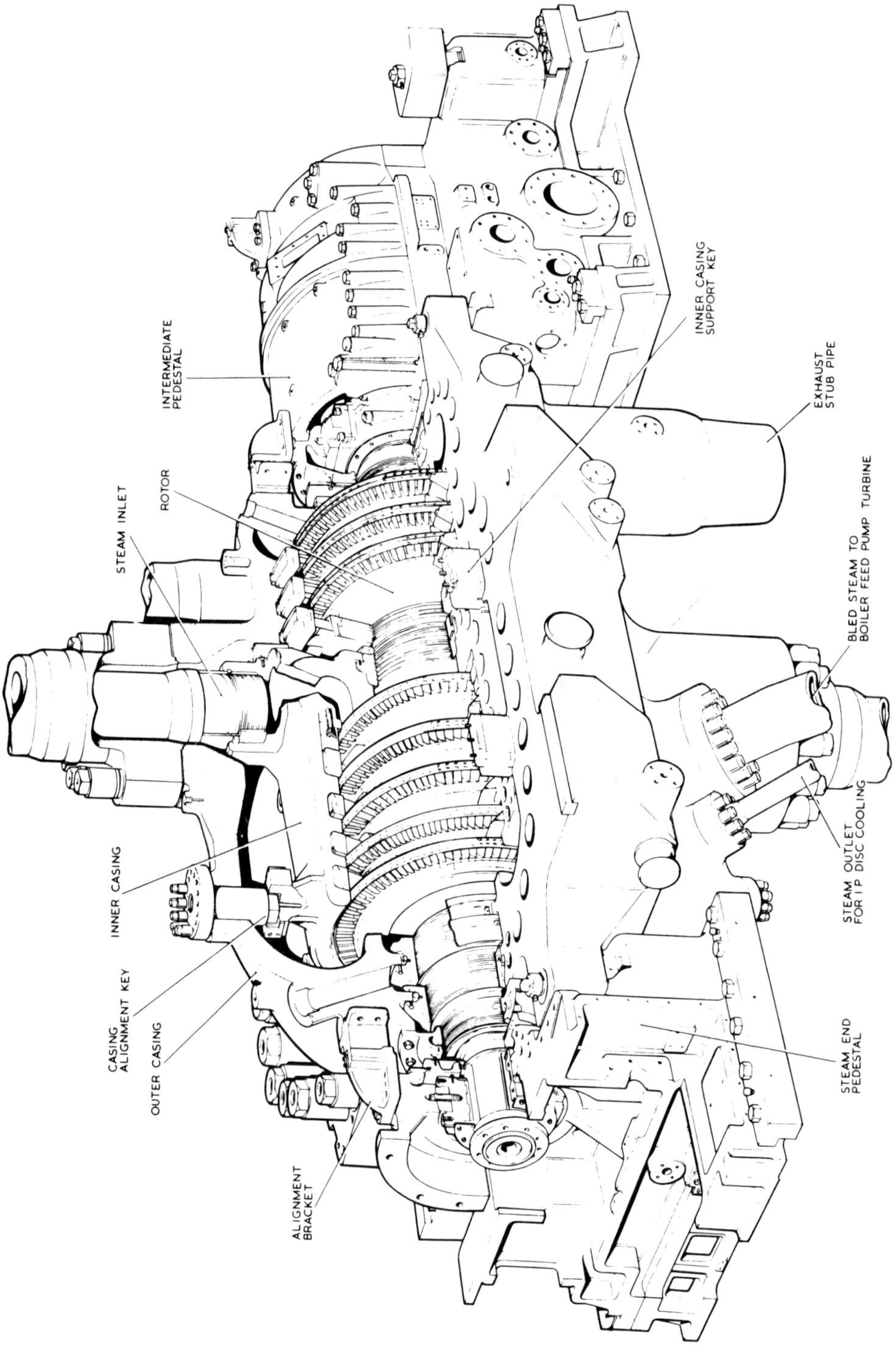

Figure 10.33 Reverse flow, double casing HP cylinder – 500–MW turbine (CEGB)

direction away from the IP cylinder. The flow is then reversed to pass between the inner and outer double casings to flow through the last three stages. This arrangement has several advantages compared to a single-flow, double-casing cylinder, such as:

(a) The steam flow between the inner and outer casings provides positive temperature control of them because of the steam washing effect.
(b) The condition of the steam at full load at the reversal point (i.e. after stage 5) is the optimum for the steam flowing between the cylinders with regard to bolting, flange and wall thickness considerations. The fairly high steam temperature gives reduced differential temperatures across the inner casing.
(c) The high-pressure shaft gland situated between rows 1 and 6 has advantages compared to being located at one end of the cylinder, such as:

    (i) The gland loss is reduced as any leakage steam passes to stages 6, 7 and 8 and so contributes to the work done.
    (ii) The temperature differentials across the gland and its housing are reduced.

(d) The shaft glands located at the ends of the cylinder are subjected to less severe steam conditions.

Intermediate-pressure cylinder

Each flow of the double-flow cylinder has seven stages (*Figure 10.34*). Stage one is supplied with steam cooling for the rotor discs to limit the temperature because of creep considerations. The cooling system is supplied from the HP cylinder reversal point, i.e. the primary exhaust. There is a partial double casing for the initial stages. Although not shown on the drawing, the interceptor valves are mounted directly on the cylinder. This is because the rotating element inertia is small compared to the turbine output. Therefore, it is important to keep the entrained steam to a minimum after the valves in the event of a high-load throw-off and so limit the transient overspeed.

Low-pressure cylinder

There are three double-flow, low-pressure cylinders (*Figure 10.35*). The last moving row blades are about 1 m long and the mean diameter is 250 cm. They are fitted with Stellite erosion shields brazed on to the inlet edge and extending from the mean diameter to the tip. The rate of erosion varies approximately as the cube of the blade velocity. The tip velocity is 542 m/s.

When the turbine is running at no-load or light load the churning action of the blades on the steam could be sufficient to cause excessive heating of the last row of blades and of the LP casing. This, in its turn, could cause distortion in relation to the cool condenser. Therefore, water sprays are located in the exhaust hoods which can direct water towards the last blade

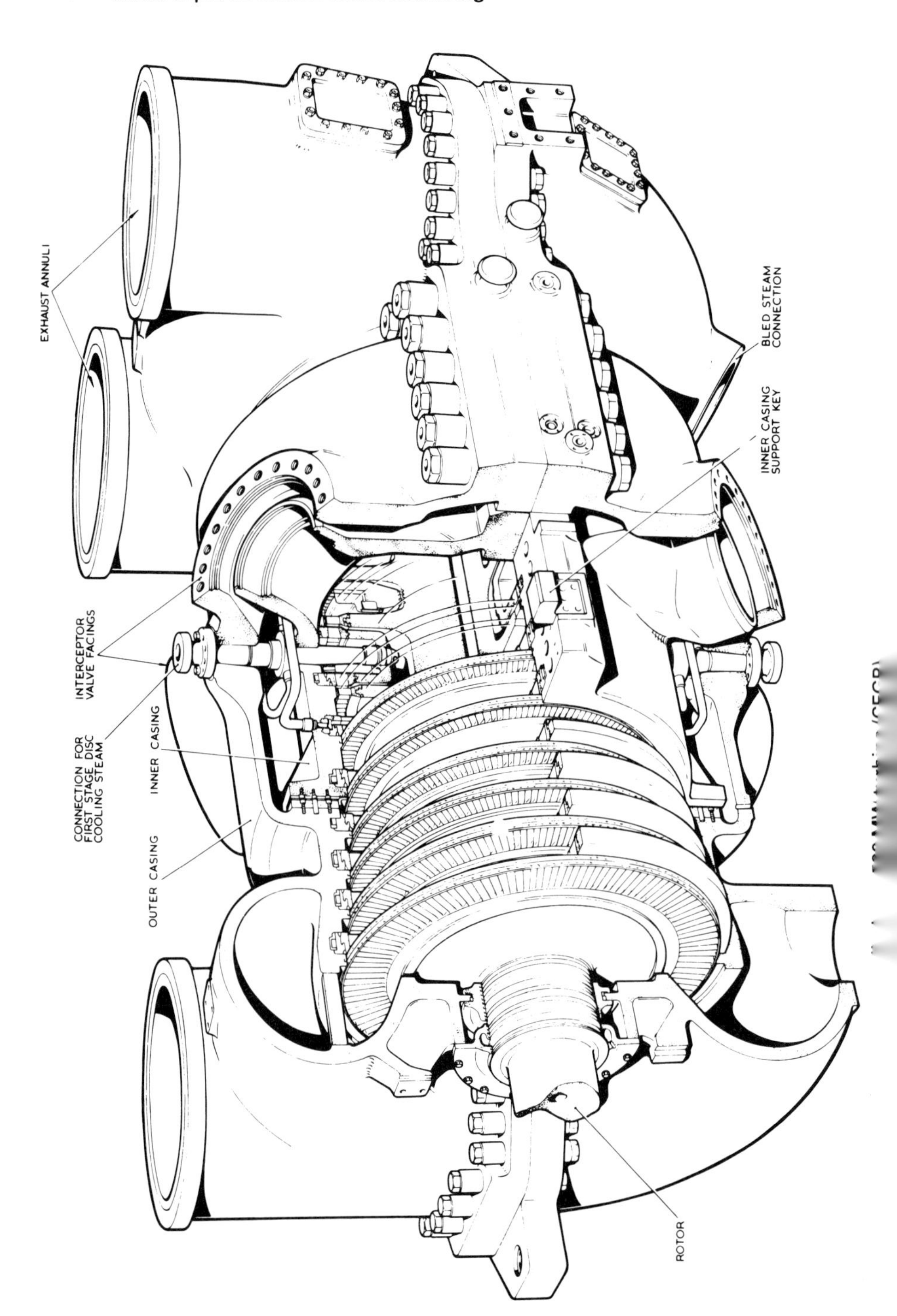
EXHAUST ANNULI
INTERCEPTOR VALVE FACINGS
CONNECTION FOR FIRST STAGE DISC COOLING STEAM
INNER CASING
OUTER CASING
BLED STEAM CONNECTION
INNER CASING SUPPORT KEY
ROTOR

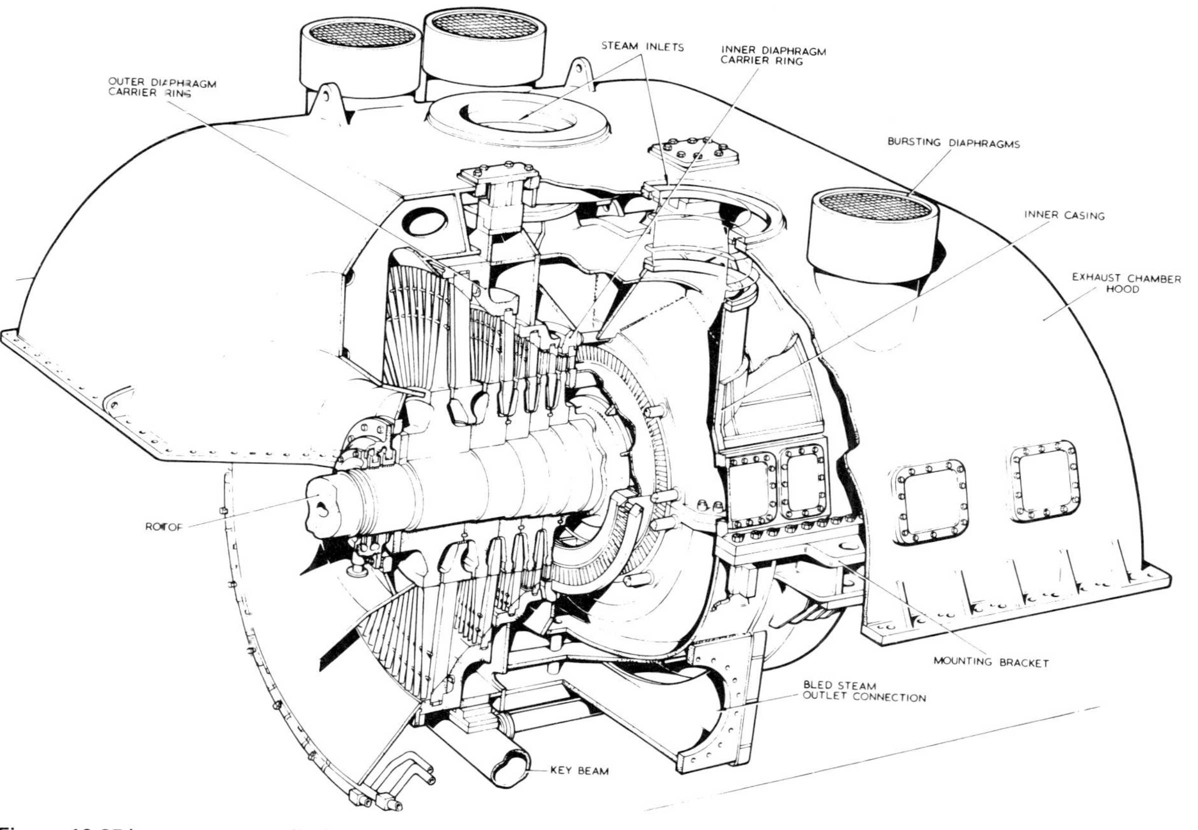

Figure 10.35 Low pressure cylinder — 500–MW turbine (CEGB)

row where it mixes with the steam and so maintains a uniform temperature of the LP casing and condenser.

It may be of interest to note that in the late 1960s, only a few years after the introduction of the 500 MW units, plants of 660 MW capacity were being installed at Drax Power Station in the UK. By world standards even these units are only of moderate size as, in 1973, cross-compounded plant of 1300 MW capacity was installed in Tennessee Valley Authority's Cumberland Power Station in the USA. However, such machines are exceptional so it is possibly more instructive to briefly consider the 660 MW machines and note how they differ from the 500 MW plant considered earlier.

The general arrangement is shown in *Figure 10.36*. The turbine is a five-cylinder tandem compound machine. The HP cylinder is single flow with a double casing. After the steam has passed through the stages of the HP cylinder it is passed to the cold reheat pipework via four vertical branches in the bottom half casing, two branches being at either end. Thus, about half of the exhaust steam flows between the inner and outer shells of the cylinder. The blading is of the reaction type and axial and radial seals are provided. No rotor cooling is employed but passages are provided through the innermost casing to ensure that the steam flowing through the dummy piston is at the temperature downstream of the first stage.

The IP cylinder is of the double-flow type. The nozzles of the first stage and the first three diaphragms are carried in an inner casing. The rotor is made from a one-piece forging and the discs are fitted with pressure balance holes. As the rotor is of the double-flow type there is no undue increase in axial thrust due to high root reaction. Steam is discharged from the two IP cylinder exhausts through cross-over pipework to the adjacent LP cylinder and via cross-under pipework to the other two. The balance connection from the feed pump turbine joins the main turbine at the IP–LP cross-unders.

The LP cylinder last-stage moving blades are fitted with erosion shields extending 254 mm from the blade tips and have a width of 9.5 mm. The double tube-plate condensers are mounted at the sides of the cylinder, the tubes being arranged longitudinally with single-pass flow. The shaft glands on the turbine are of the spring-backed labyrinth type. A condensate-cooled gland steam condenser is provided, the condensed gland steam being returned to the turbine drains tank or to waste.

Monitoring turbine performance

It is important that the condition of a turbine is monitored regularly. In addition to regular heat consumption testing (which is dealt with later), various other investigations should be carried out such as those considered next.

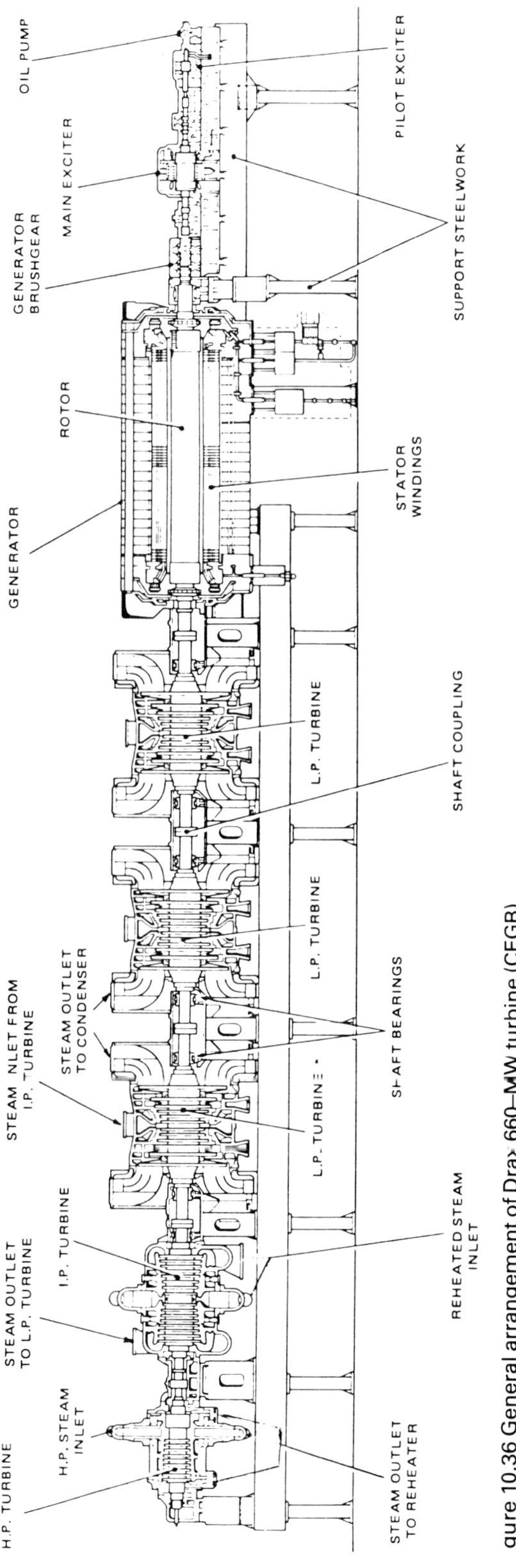

gure 10.36 General arrangement of Drax 660–MW turbine (CEGB)

Cylinder efficiency tests

By accurately measuring the steam temperature and pressure at the inlet and outlet of the HP and IP cylinders it is quite easy to determine the respective cylinder efficiencies. However, the value for the LP cannot be obtained by this means because the steam at the exhaust is wet and so its state point cannot be located. Referring to *Figure 10.37*, the HP cylinder inlet conditions are shown by the point marked 'After governor valves'. However, it is normal to have only a pressure indication at this point. This does not matter, though, because the enthalpy of the steam is the same as before the turbine stop valve whose temperature and pressure is known.

If there were no friction, turbulence, windage or other source of loss, the expansion of the steam would be isentropic, the heat drop being equal to B. But because of the losses the actual heat drop is as shown by the point marked 'HP cylinder exhaust to reheater'. The exhaust pressure is the same as for the isentropic case but the temperature is higher.

$$\text{Cylinder efficiency} = \frac{\text{heat drop A} \times 100 \text{ per cent}}{\text{heat drop B}}$$

The same applies to the IP cylinder efficiency. Of course, any two points can be used as well as the cylinder inlet and exhaust, provided the pressure and temperature can be measured and the steam is not wet. For example, the efficiency can be determined between two bled steam points.

The high pressure and intermediate pressure cylinder efficiencies should be determined on each running unit every six months if possible. The calculations are easier if a standard calculation sheet is used as shown below. Alternatively a desk-top computer can be programmed to carry out the calculations. It is important that reference data is provided so that comparisons can be made. The acceptance test data is usually used for reference. Alternatively, if none are available design information can be used.

The reference efficiencies for the 120 MW machine considered below and for a large modern machine are:

	120 MW	*Large*
HP cylinder	81.58%	89.00%
IP cylinder	90.07%	92.0%

As small errors in temperature measurement have a pronounced effect upon the resulting cylinder efficiency it is important that every care be taken to obtain temperatures that are accurate to within 0.5°C, and accuracy is also needed for the pressures. Because of these requirements determination of cylinder efficiency is really a job for the Efficiency Department, as the Operations Staff does not have the necessary test equipment at their disposal.

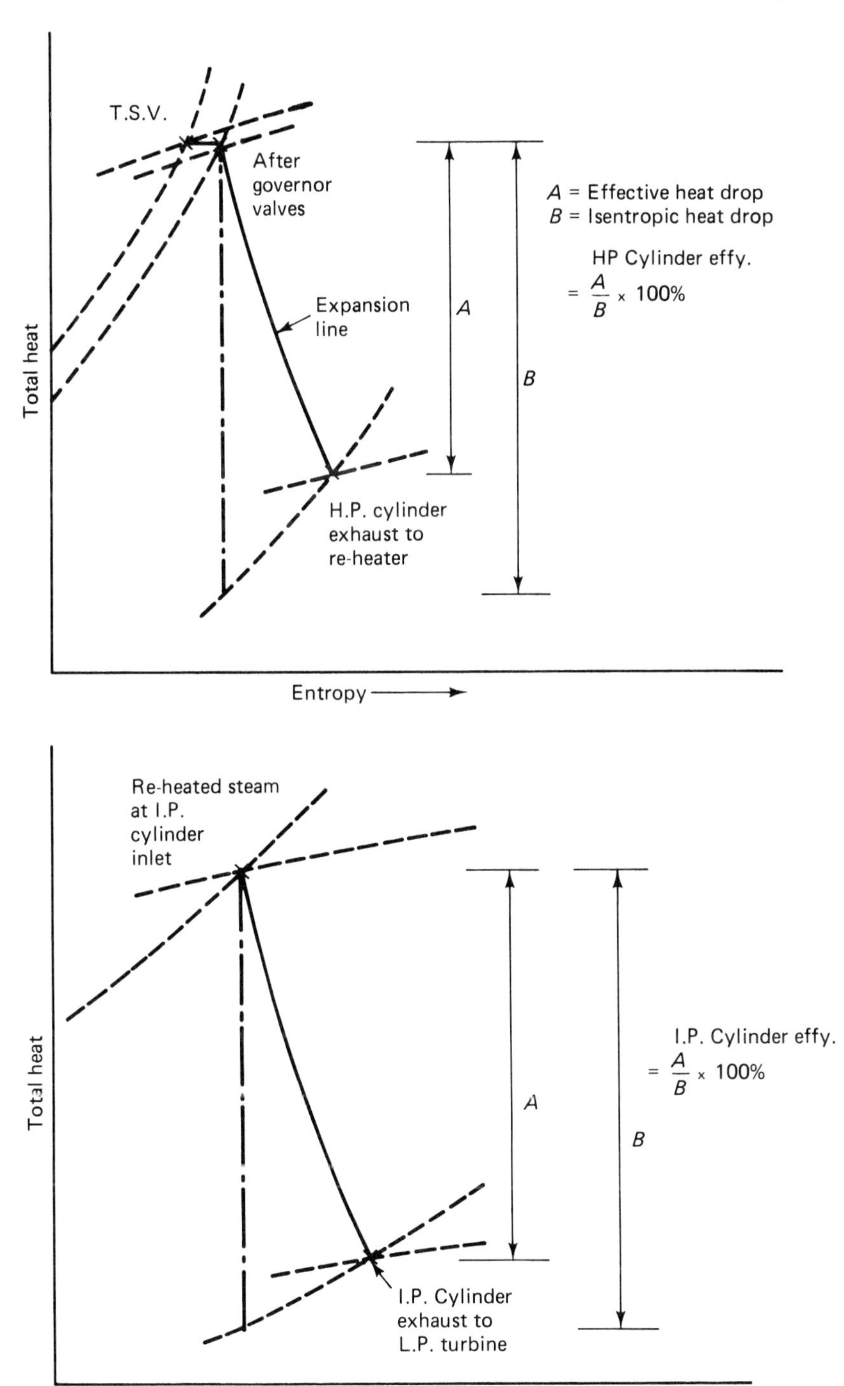

Figure 10.37 Part of H–S chart for turbine cylinder efficiency determination (CEGB)

Exercise

Calculate the routine test efficiencies:

T/A No. ______ Cylinder efficiency Date ______________

	Condition	Symbol	Unit	Design	Routine Test
	Load		MW	120	120.3
	Pressures				
1	Before turbine stop valve LHS		bar (abs)	104.5	105.0
2	Before turbine stop valve RHS		bar (abs.)	104.5	105.0
3	Impulse stage, top		bar (abs.)	98.6	95.5
4	Impulse stage, bottom		bar (abs.)	98.6	94.5
5	HP cylinder exhaust LHS		bar (abs.)	28.6	27.0
6	HP cylinder exhaust RHS		bar (abs.)	28.6	27.0
7	IP cylinder inlet LHS		bar (abs.)	26.0	22.5
8	IP cylinder inlet RHS		bar (abs.)	26.0	23.5
9	LP cylinder inlet		bar (abs.)	2.6	2.2
	Temperatures				
10	Before turbine stop valve LHS		°C	538	536
11	Before turbine stop valve RHS		°	538	532
12	HP cylinder exhaust LHS		°	366	368
13	HP cylinder exhaust RHS		°	366	364
14	IP cylinder inlet LHS		°	537.8	540.0
15	IP cylinder inlet RHS		°	537.8	530.0
16	LP cylinder inlet		°	238.5	234.0
	HP cylinder efficiency				
17	Mean TSV pressure	P	bar (abs.)	104.5	
18	Mean TSV temperature	T_1	°C	538	
19	Mean impulse stage pressure	P_1	bar (abs.)	98.6	
20	Mean HP exhaust pressure	P_2	bar (abs.)	28.6	
21	Mean HP exhaust temperature	T_2	°C	366	
22	Enthalpy at PT_1	H_1	kJ/kg	3465.3	
23	Entropy at P_1T_1	S_1	kJ/kgK	6.720	
24	Enthalpy at P_2T_2	H_2	kJ/kg	3157.6	
25	Enthalpy at P_2S_1		kJ/kg	3088.1	
26	HP cylinder efficiency = $\frac{(22)-(24)}{(22)-(25)} \times 100$		%	81.58	77.5
	IP cylinder efficiency				
27	Mean IP cylinder inlet pressure	P_3	Bar (abs.)	26.0	
28	Mean IP cylinder inlet temperature	T_3	°C	537.8	
29	Mean LP cylinder inlet pressure	P_4	Bar (abs.)	2.6	
30	Mean LP cylinder inlet temperature	T_4	°C	238.5	
31	Enthalpy at P_3T_3	H_3	kJ/kg	3544.5	
32	Entropy at P_3T_3	S_3	kJ/kgK	7.407	
33	Enthalpy at P_4T_4	H_4	kJ/kg	2945.9	
34	Enthalpy at P_4S_3	H_5	kJ/kg	2879.9	
35	IP cylinder efficiency $= \frac{(31)-(33)}{(31-(34)} \times 100$		%	90.07	88.8

Notice, from the efficiencies quoted, that the HP cylinder has a lower design efficiency than the IP cylinder. LP cylinders, incidentally, have a lower efficiency still. Typical values for modern machines, and the principal causes of the variations are:

HP cylinder 89% Short blades, particularly at the early stages, and consequent high tip losses.
IP cylinder 92% The blades are longer so tip losses are reduced, and the velocities are moderate.
LP cylinder 80% The blades are very long, velocities very high, wetness in the steam at the last stages and the steam flow path is highly flared.

Studies made on the 500 and 660 MW machines indicate that some condensing stages have lower efficiencies than expected.

Effect of loading upon cylinder efficiency

A series of efficiencies has been calculated for the HP cylinder of a 120 MW T/A at various loads, the mechanical condition of the turbine being the same for each of the tests.

	Load (MW)			
	120.3	*90.5*	*72.2*	*49.6*
HP cylinder efficiency	80.36	79.87	80.41	79.62

It is apparent that loading has little effect upon the efficiency of the cylinder. The same is true for the IP and the LP cylinders, although in the latter case it is assumed that the steam is dry. The reason why the efficiency remains substantially the same over a very wide range of loads is that the ratio of blade speed to steam speed (u/V_i) remains the same. It is obvious that the blade speed will not vary with load, but perhaps it is not quite so clear why the steam speed remains the same.

Consider *Tables 10.8* and *10.9*. They illustrate the temperature and pressure at an IP and an LP stage respectively at full, three quarters, half, and quarter loads. The corresponding absolute pressure will be full, three quarters, half and quarter of that at full load. The remainder of the information in the tables has been obtained from an H–S chart.

Table 10.8 IP steam volume at various loadings

1 Load	2 Steam *flow*	3 Pressure *(bar abs.)*	4 Temp. *(°C)*	5 Enthalpy *(kJ/kg)*	6 Volume *(litre/kg)*	7 (2) × *(6)*
Full	1.0	24	550	3574	156	156
¾	0.75	18	548	3574	208	156
½	0.5	12	545	3574	312	156
¼	0.25	6	541	3574	624	156

Table 10.9 LP steam volume at various loadings

Load	Steam flow	Pressure (bar abs.)	Temp. (°C)	Enthalpy (kJ/kg)	Volume (litre/kg)	(2) × (6)
1	2	3	4	5	6	7
Full	1.0	2.4	250	2970	998	998
¾	0.75	1.8	249	2970	1330	998
½	0.5	1.2	248	2970	1996	998
¼	0.25	0.6	245	2970	3992	998

Column 7 shows that the total volume of steam flowing at any stage remains the same over the range of loads considered and so the steam velocity will also remain the same. The only deviations from this general case are:

1 The first HP cylinder stage on a nozzle-governed turbine.
2 The final (wet) stages of the LP cylinder.
3 Very low machine loadings.

Therefore it is of little consequence what the turbine loading is when carrying out cylinder efficiency checks provided it is not extremely low.

To illustrate what has been said, consider the following results obtained from a series of tests on a 120 MW machine. The information refers to the final stage of the HP turbine.

Load	MW	125.3	90.5	72.2	49.6
Steam flow	kg/s	103.4	74.6	61.0	42.6
Steam pressure	bar (bs)	29.1	21.2	17.2	12.1
Steam temperature	°C	369.5	362.9	359.8	355.3
Steam volume	litre/kg	97.5	135.0	164.9	236.6
Enthalpy	kJ/kg	3166	3166	3166	3166

Hence, the volume flow at the stage in question is obtained from the product of steam flow and steam volume for each of the loadings:

Load	MW	125.3	90.5	72.2	49.6
Flow × volume	litre/s	10 081	10 071	10 059	10 079

It is seen that, within very narrow limits, the volume flow at the stage was constant over a considerable range of loads.

Effect of deterioration of cylinder efficiency on T/A performance

Having determined the cylinder efficiencies and compared them to the reference values it is next necessary to know what the deterioration means in terms of the T/A efficiency or heat rate. A method for doing this is given in *Methods for Measuring Steam Turbine Generator Performance* by Cotton and Westcott, and another appears in *Modern Power Station Practice*. In both of them it is necessary to know the steam flow in the turbine and so this data will be available if the turbine heat consumption and cylinder efficiencies are determined at the same time.

The formulae from the *Modern Power Station Practice* correspondence course, suitably modified for SI units are:

HP cylinders

$$\delta HR = \frac{0.43\,(H_1 - H_2)\delta\eta\%}{kW_a}\left[\frac{2.326\,Q_r}{HR_a} - \frac{2.158\,Q_h}{3600}\right]$$

where $\delta\ HR$ = % change in heat rate
H_1 = Enthalpy at TSV kJ/kg (reference data)
H_2 = Enthalpy at HP cylinder exhaust, kJ/kg (reference data)

$$\delta\ \eta\ \% = \%\ \text{change in HP cylinder efficiency} = \frac{\eta_a - \eta_c}{\eta_a} \times 100$$

kW_a = Reference alternator output, kW
Q_r = Present steam flow to reheater, kg/h
HR_a = Reference test heat rate, kJ/kWh
Q_h = Present steam flow to HP cylinder, kg/h

For example, heat consumption and cylinder efficiency tests were carried out on a 120 MW machine. The HP cylinder efficiency was 77.5% and the design value was 81.58%. The effect on the turbine heat rate is calculated as follows:

$H_1 - H_2$ = 307.75 kJ/kg
kW_a = 120 000 kW

$$\delta\ \eta\ \% = \frac{0.8158 - 0.7750}{0.8158} \times 100 = 5.00\%$$

Q_r = 331 220 kg/h (routine test)
HR_a = 8651 kJ/kWh (reference)
Q_h = 366 113 kg/h (routine test)

$$\text{So}\ \delta\ HR = \frac{0.43 \times 307.75 \times 5.0}{120\,000}\left[\frac{2.326 \times 331\,220}{8651} - \frac{2.158 \times 366\,113}{3600}\right]$$

$= 0.0056\ (89.06 - 219.46)$
$= (-)$ **0.7%**

IP cylinder

The effect of a change of IP cylinder efficiency is given by:

$$\delta\ HR\ \% = \delta\ \eta\ \%\left[\frac{0.928\,(H_1 - H_2)Q_r}{kW_a \times 3600} - 1\right]$$

and the symbols have already been defined.

So, if the routine test showed the IP cylinder efficiency to be 88.84% and the design 90.07% the effect on turbine heat rate would be:

$$\delta\, \eta\, \% = \frac{0.9007 - 0.8884}{0.9007} \times 100 = 1.37$$

$$\text{So}\, \delta\, HR\, \% = 1.37 \left[\frac{0.928 \times 307.75 \times 331\,220}{120\,000 \times 3600} - 1 \right]$$

$$= 1.37\,(0.2190 - 1) = 1.37 \times (-)\,0.781$$
$$= (-)\, \mathbf{1.07\%}$$

Therefore the cylinder efficiencies are contributing (−) 0.7 + (−) 1.07 = (−) 1.77% to the turbine heat rate deterioration.

Common causes of cylinder efficiency deterioration include:

(a) Damage to blades caused by debris getting past the steam strainers. The early HP or IP stages will be most affected.
(b) Damage to tip seals and interstage glands.
(c) Deposition on the blades. For example, if silica compounds are deposited they will normally start at the last few IP stages and carry on to the first few LP stages.
(d) Increased roughness of the blade surface.

Effect of surface roughness of blades on heat rate

Effect of blade friction

If there were no blade friction the relative speed of the steam at outlet of the blade would be the same as at inlet. However, even with highly polished blades friction may cause the outlet relative speed to be 5–15% lower then inlet.

So $V_{ro} = kV_{ri}$
where k is a co-efficient which takes the blade friction loss into account.

For example if $k = 0.9$ then *Figure 10.38(a)* would become *10.38(b)*. The output of the machine depends upon the magnitude of $V_{wi} + V_{wo}$ and so the blade friction would cause a loss of output. Sometimes the roughness is caused by deposition on the blading such as that shown in *Figure 10.38(c)*

Various investigations have been carried out to determine the effect of roughness on turbine heat rate. The effect varies with the size of the machine and whether the HP, IP or LP cylinder is considered. For a given degree of roughness the HP cylinder is worst affected, the IP next and the LP least. For example, consider a 300 MW and a 600 MW machine whose average roughness is 30 μm (about the equivalent of 600 grade emery paper).

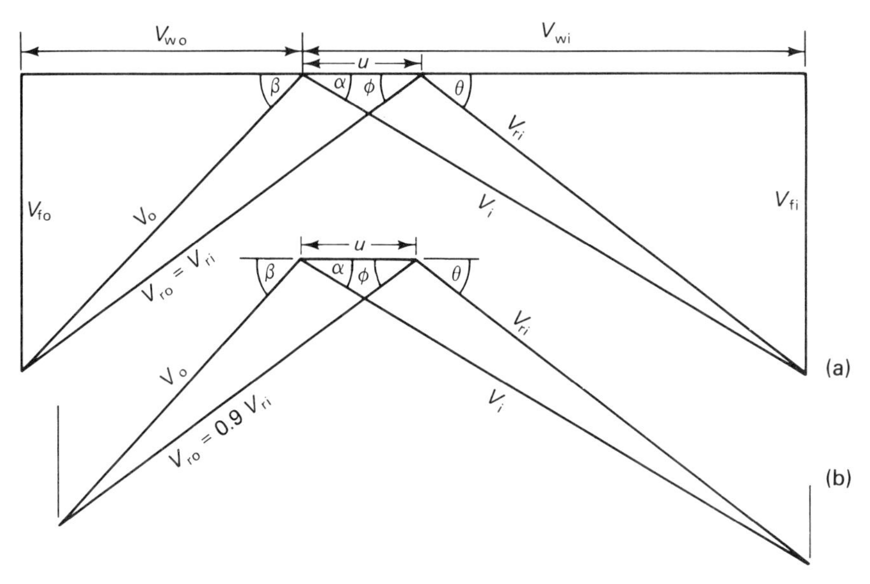

Figure 10.38 Effect of blade friction

Figure 10.38(c) Deposition on IP blading (CEGB)

Cylinder	HR% *(300 MW)*	HR% *(600MW)*
HP	5.6	4.2
IP	4.5	3.7
LP	1.6	1.5

The smaller machine is affected to a greater extent than the larger one.

Figure 10.39 shows the approximate effect on the turbine heat rate of various degrees of roughness. It is apparent that substantial losses can be attributed to blading that is roughened to only a small extent. Consequently it is good practice to carefully check the blading whenever the cylinders are opened.

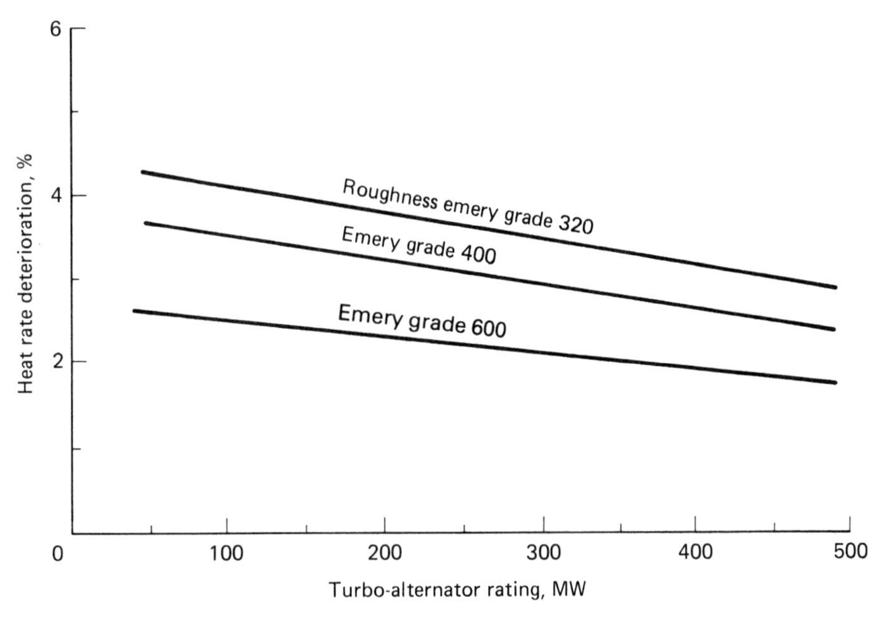

Figure 10.39 Approximate variation of overall turbine heat rate for various size machines and different degrees of roughness

Turbine pressure survey

A very useful indication of the internal condition of a turbine is achieved very simply by carrying out a pressure survey. In *Figure 10.40* a sloping line is drawn as shown and the pressure scale is from zero to any convenient pressure above that of the TSV. From acceptance test results or design details, determine the pressure at each tapping point on the turbine for full load, and mark these points with a line. Thus, in *Figure 10.40* the 'reaction' pressure at 120 MW was 54 bar abs. at the time the acceptance tests were carried out and so a line is drawn accordingly.

If, at some later date the pressures are noted at each of the points while the machine is doing 120 MW, and if the condition of the turbine is no different to before, then when the points are plotted they will all lie exactly on the sloping line at the appropriate intersections. On the other hand, if the turbine has not deteriorated in any way but the loading has changed, the points will now plot on a straight line *below* the one for 120 MW and converging with it at the bottom right-hand corner as shown in *Figure 10.41*, where the load is assumed to be 100 MW. The optimum pressure at 100 MW at any point *after* the throttle valves will be 100/120 of the full load pressure. Thus, the 'impulse' pressure will be $95 \times 100/120 = 79.2$ bar abs. The proportion of full-load pressure will be the same for all the other downstream measuring points. The TSV pressure, of course, does not alter

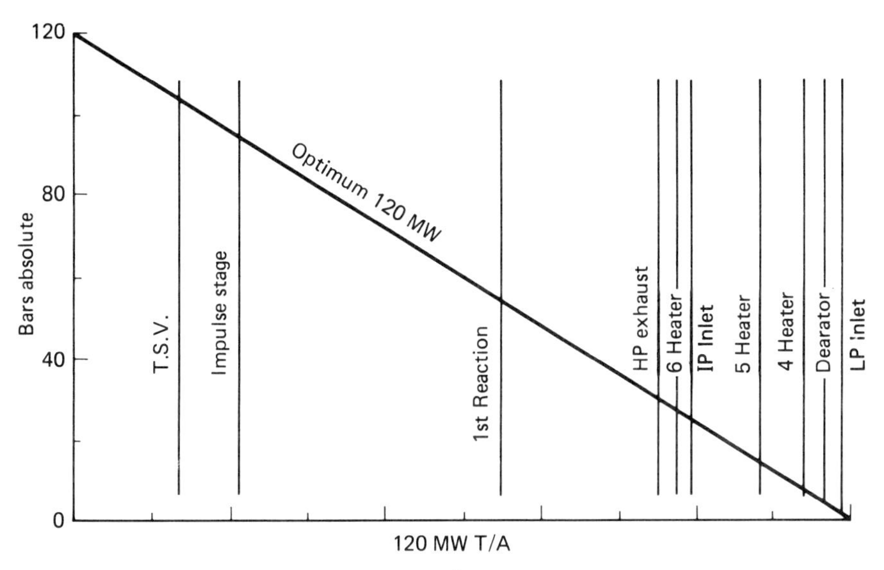

Figure 10.40 Basic turbine pressure survey diagram

irrespective of the loading.

The linear relationship between stage pressure and output is shown in *Figure 10.42* for a 120 MW turbine – a similar linear relationship will apply between stage pressures and throttle valve steam flow. Thus the optimum line for a pressure survey at 100 MW will be as shown in *Figure 10.43* plus optimum lines for 80 and 60 MW load.

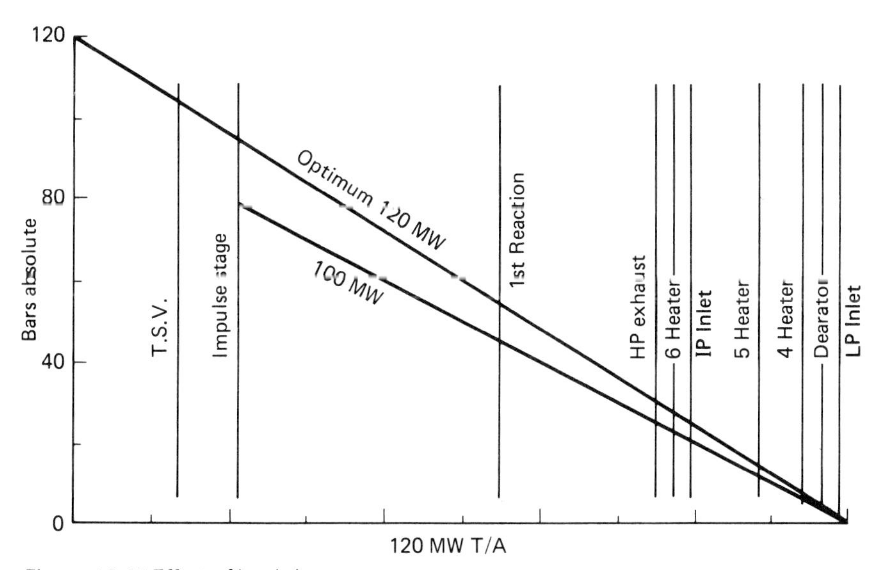

Figure 10.41 Effect of load change

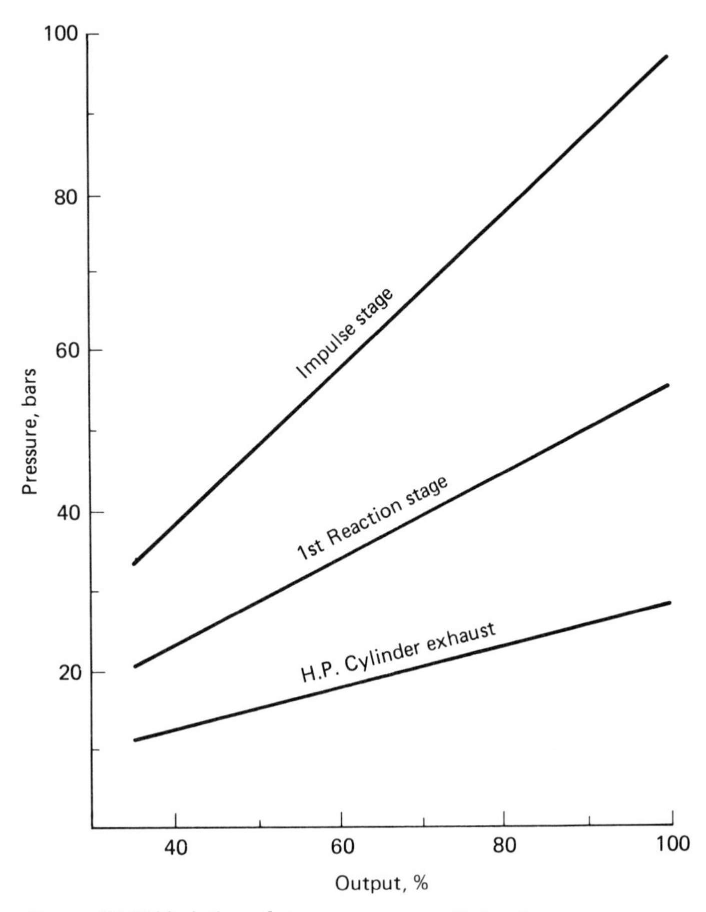

Figure 10.42 Variation of stage pressures with loading

If the turbine pressures are noted and, when plotted, lie on a straight line but above the optimum line for the particular load, then this is indicative of general wear throughout the turbine due to such things as worn diaphragm seals or blade tip seals; this condition is shown in *Figure 10.44*. On the other hand, if there is no general wear but at one location there is some restriction to steam flow, the effect will be to cause a 'kink' in the pressure line as shown in *Figure 10.45*. Pressures upstream of the restriction will be high. Notice that the results indicate only a restriction to flow *somewhere* between the two pressure tapping points – the line does not necessarily indicate a general restriction between the points.

Of course, it is of paramount importance that the pressure gauges used are accurate and that all the readings are obtained quickly while the load is steady. A pressure survey should be carried out on each running machine each month. It will be appreciated that a particular machine may have

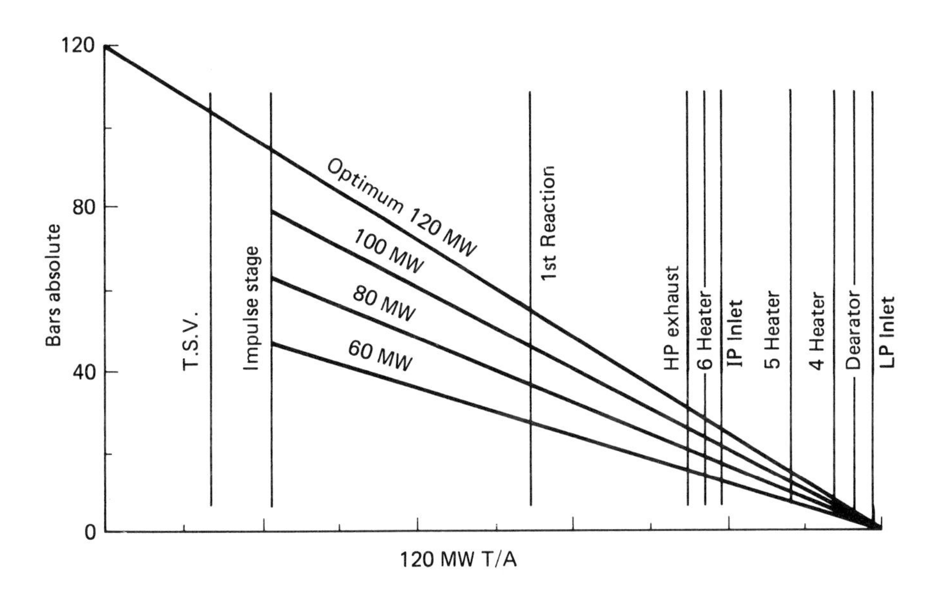

Figure 10.43 Effect of range of loadings on pressure survey diagrams

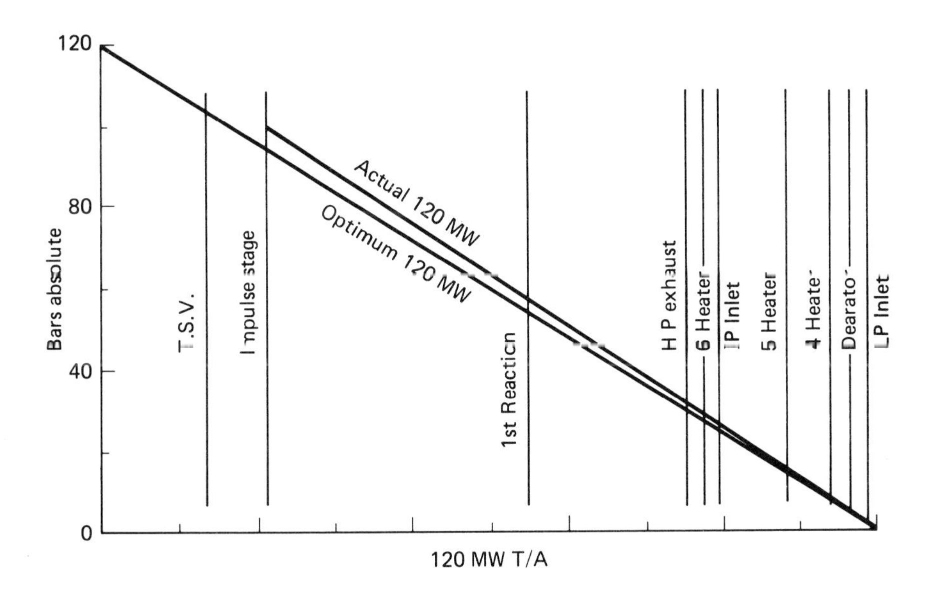

Figure 10.44 Effect of internal wear on pressure survey diagrams

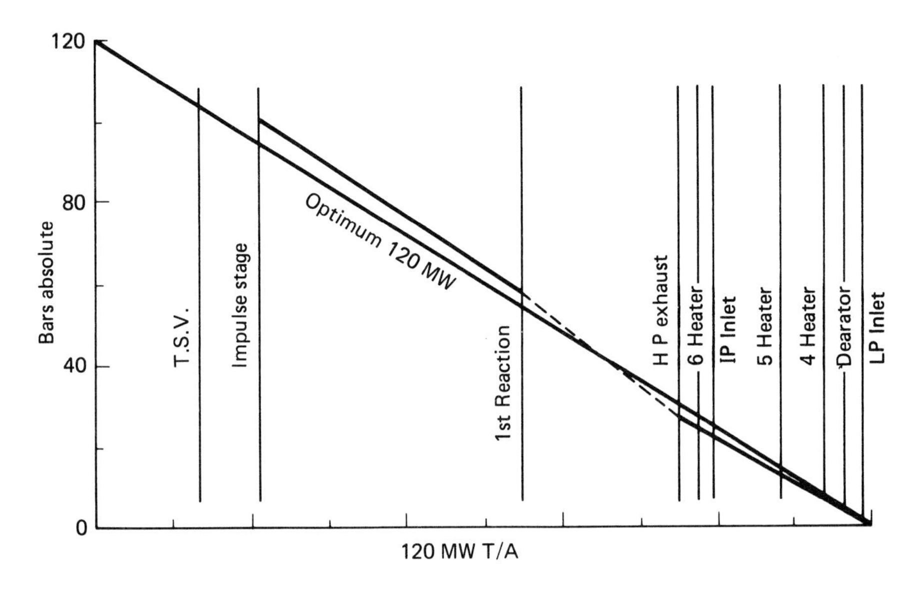

Figure 10.45 Effect of internal restriction to flow on pressure survey diagrams

various defects simultaneously. For example, it is common for a machine which has general wear to have also, say, a restriction to flow at the first stages of the HP or IP cylinder due to damage from debris getting past the strainers.

At the bottom end of the pressure survey scale (say from the LP cylinder inlet onwards) it is not possible to plot the pressures accurately. Fortunately, clearances are so liberal in the LP cylinder that the chances of damage due to rubs are not very great, but there remains the possibility of silica deposition. Therefore, the LP inlet and LP bled steam pressures should be checked against optimum at the time of the pressure survey.

Another important point to remember when plotting the pressures is that all the heaters should be in service. If they are not there will be a discontinuity in the best line through the points. For example, the drawing in *Figure 10.46* shows the results of having D and E heaters out of service on a 60 MW machine; E heater bled steam is tapped from the HP cylinder exhaust and D is tapped from stage 7 of the IP cylinder. The HP cylinder steam flow is what one would expect for a certain output, say 58 MW, if the machine were normal. However, because the top two heaters are out of service the actual output is 61 MW. Also the extra steam flow through the IP/LP cylinders is considerably more than would normally be associated with 61 MW loading – in fact it is probably of the order of 68 MW. Hence the plotted line for the HP cylinder is below the optimum line and that for the IP/LP is above it.

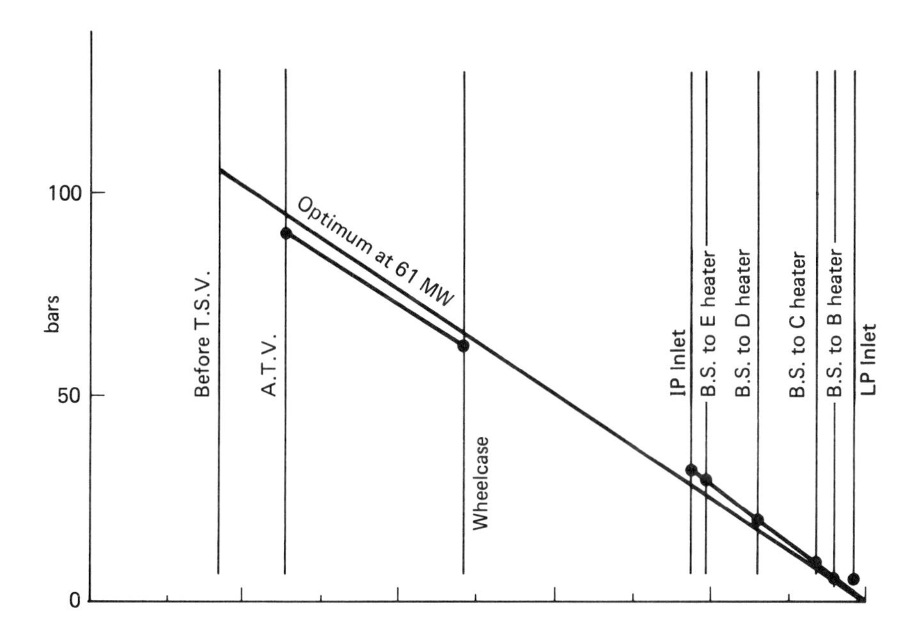

Figure 10.46 Effect of feed heaters out of service on pressure survey diagrams

Silica deposition

Silica deposition, if allowed to continue, will cause the passage areas to be progressively reduced. The silica is deposited in the form of silica compounds, some of which are water soluble and some not.

At a particular station the turbines were found to be severely contaminated. Deposition had occurred at the last few rows of the IP cylinder plus the first three of the LP cylinder. That in the IP was largely water soluble while that in the LP was not. Investigations revealed that there had been a continuous, though slow, rate of pressure increase of the steam at the LP cylinder inlet for several years, see *Figure 10.47*; the average rate was about 0.14 bar per year. This highlights the importance of checking small pressure changes at the LP end of the machine; for example, note the pressure of the LP inlet in *Figure 10.46*. Two-shift operation adversely affects the rate of deposition.

Of course, the best way to prevent this trouble is to remove the silica in the first place. With modern water treatment plants this is not much of a problem. Even so, silica compounds can get into the condensate and feed systems from dust which has entered items such as feed pumps, feed heaters,

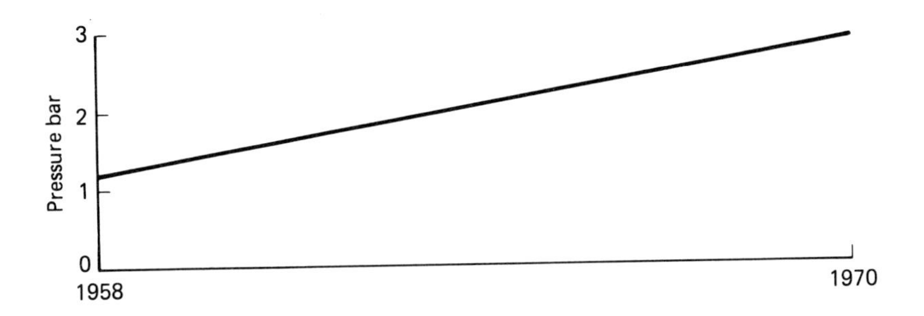

Figure 10.47 Effect of silica deposition on LP cylinder inlet pressure

etc., when they are opened for maintenance. Another source of contamination occurs when there are reheater leaks – when the unit is taken off load the reheater goes under vacuum and so dust is drawn in through the hole. Such contamination will usually require at least heavy blowdown and at worst will cause deposition on the turbine (*Figure 10.48*).

Shaft glands

Main shaft gland wear can cause a significant loss of performance of a turbine and so it is necessary to monitor the condition of the glands periodically. Of course, if they are damaged there is normally nothing that can be done until a suitable outage occurs. But at least if their condition can be predicted it will enable suitable arrangements to be made beforehand. *Figure 10.49* shows a typical gland sealing arrangement on a small turbine, the one illustrated being a 120 MW unit high-pressure gland. Steam is leaked-off to join the bled steam supply to Nos. 1 and 4 feed heaters. As the glands wear the temperature after the junction of the bled and leak-off steam supplies will rise thus providing a convenient way to monitor the state of the glands. Ideally it should be possible to measure the temperature of every gland leak-off line but this is not normally available.

On modern machines the arrangement is simpler as there are normally no leak-offs to heaters except to the deaerator. Instead, the steam leaks off into an exhauster line which is common to all. Typical of this arrangement is that shown in *Figure 10.50*. All the leak-off steam is passed to a gland condenser, so changes in the total quantity of steam due to gland wear will result in an increased temperature rise of the condensate at the gland steam condenser. *Figure 10.51* shows a typical design.

The clearances in glands are small and the fins are of thin metal, so it only requires one 'rough' start on a machine to cause considerable damage, and

Figure 10.48 Deposit on turbine LP rotor (CEGB)

this, in its turn, will greatly increase the amount of steam leaking-off. *Figure 10.52* shows some typical arrangements of glands. If glands are found to be damaged it should be borne in mind that one possible cause is that they have not been packed sufficiently with steam. This can result in cooling of the area by air inleakage which, in its turn, may distort the shaft as shown in *Figure 10.53*. The steam flow through glands is quite high. For example, the steam flow from the HP cylinder alone on a 350 MW unit is about 8.5 kg/s, even with the glands in good condition.

Determination of gland steam flows to exhauster line

Reference to the gland system shown in *Figure 10.50* reveals a fairly common situation with gland exhauster layouts. A simplified version of *Figure 10.50* is shown in *Figure 10.54*. Several different quantities feed into a common line and the whole of the gland leak-off system is at about the same pressure. Thus, if the total exhauster line steam flow is established by measuring the drain outlet flow at the gland steam condenser, or by carrying out a heat balance, the individual flows can be estimated by the following method:

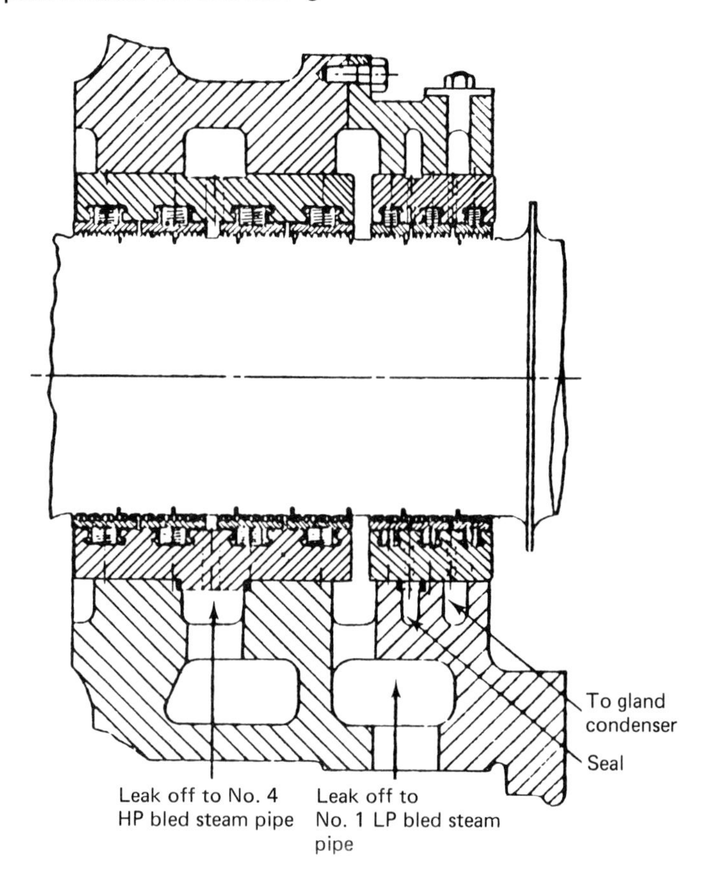

Figure 10.49 120–MW turbine high pressure shaft gland (CEGB)

Thermocouples are fitted to each line and so the temperature of the steam can be determined for each of the locations denoted by *F*. Knowing the temperature and the pressure it is a simple matter to determine the corresponding heat *h*.

Consider the section showing flows F_1, F_2, and F_3, as shown in *Figure 10.55*.

$$F_1 = F_2 + F_3$$
$$F_1h_1 = F_2h_2 + F_3h_3$$
$$\text{But } F_3 = F_1 - F_2$$
$$\therefore F_1h_1 = (F_1 - F_2)\,h_3 + F_2h_2$$
$$F_1h_1 = F_1h_3 - F_2h_3 + F_2h_2$$
$$= F_1h_3 - F_2(h_3 - h_2)$$
$$F_1h_1 = F_1h_3 + F_2\,(h_2 - h_3)$$

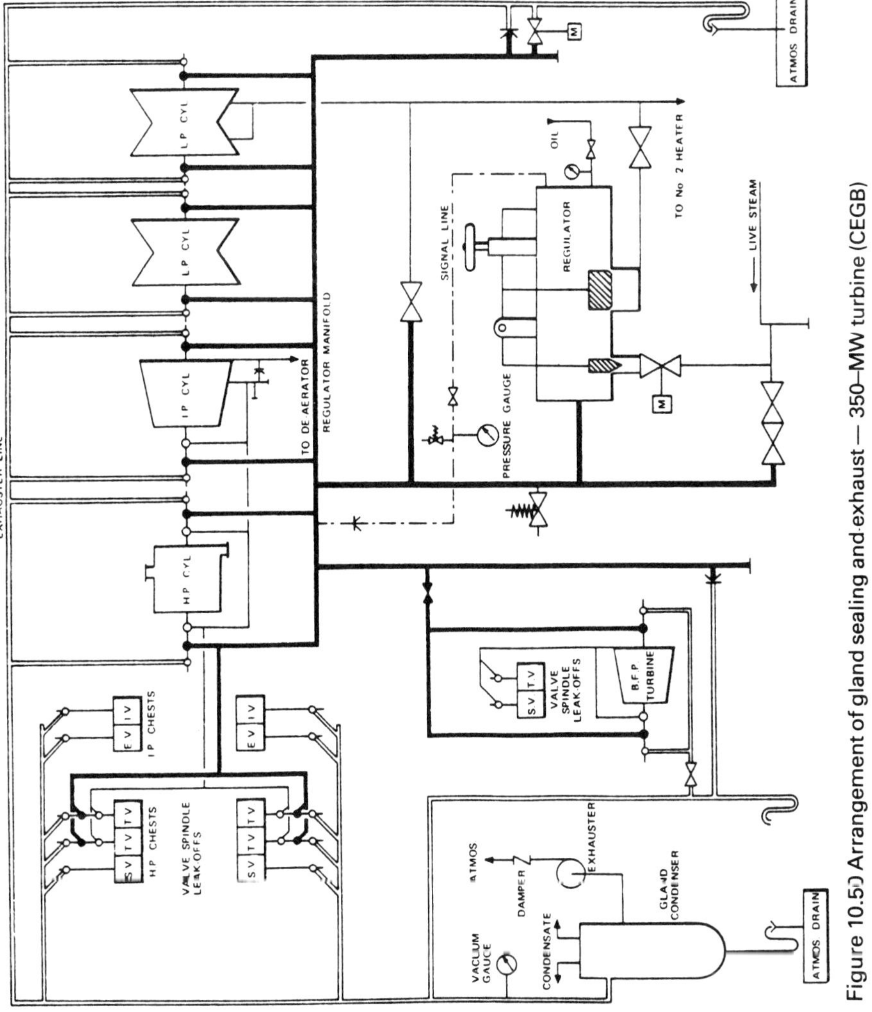

Figure 10.50 Arrangement of gland sealing and exhaust — 350-MW turbine (CEGB)

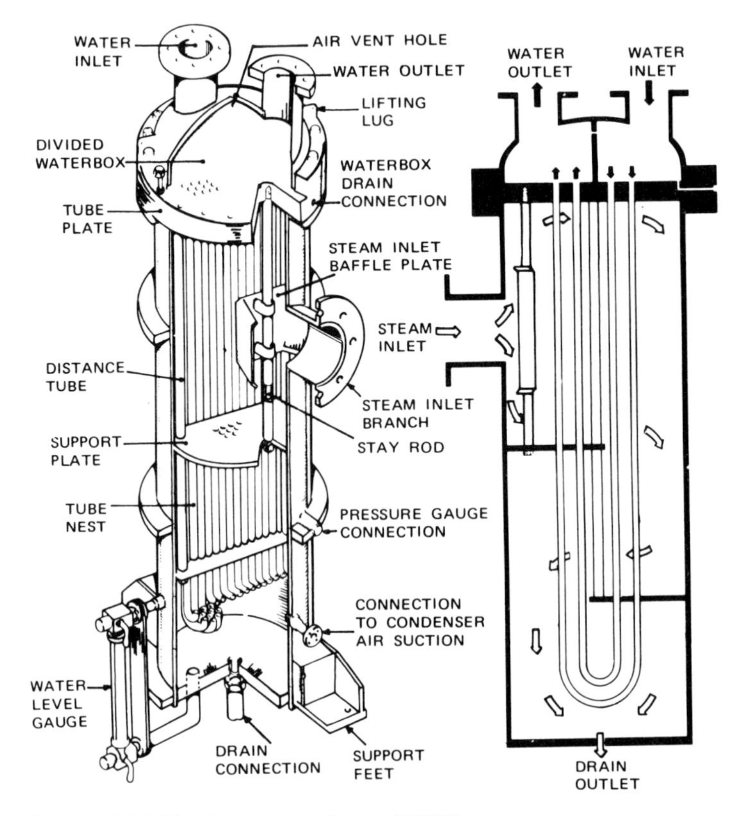

Figure 10.51 Gland steam condenser (CEGB)

$$\text{So } F_2 = \frac{F_1 h_1 - F_1 h_3}{h_2 - h_3}$$

$$\therefore F_2 = \frac{F_1 (h_1 - h_3)}{h_2 - h_3}$$

Thus flow F_2 can be determined if F_1 is known. F_3 is given by:

$$F_3 = F_1 - F_2$$

The procedure can now be repeated, for flows F_3, F_4 and F_5. F_3 is already known and the other two are given by:

$$F_4 = \frac{F_3 (h_3 - h_5)}{h_4 - h_5}$$

$$F_5 = F_3 - F_4$$

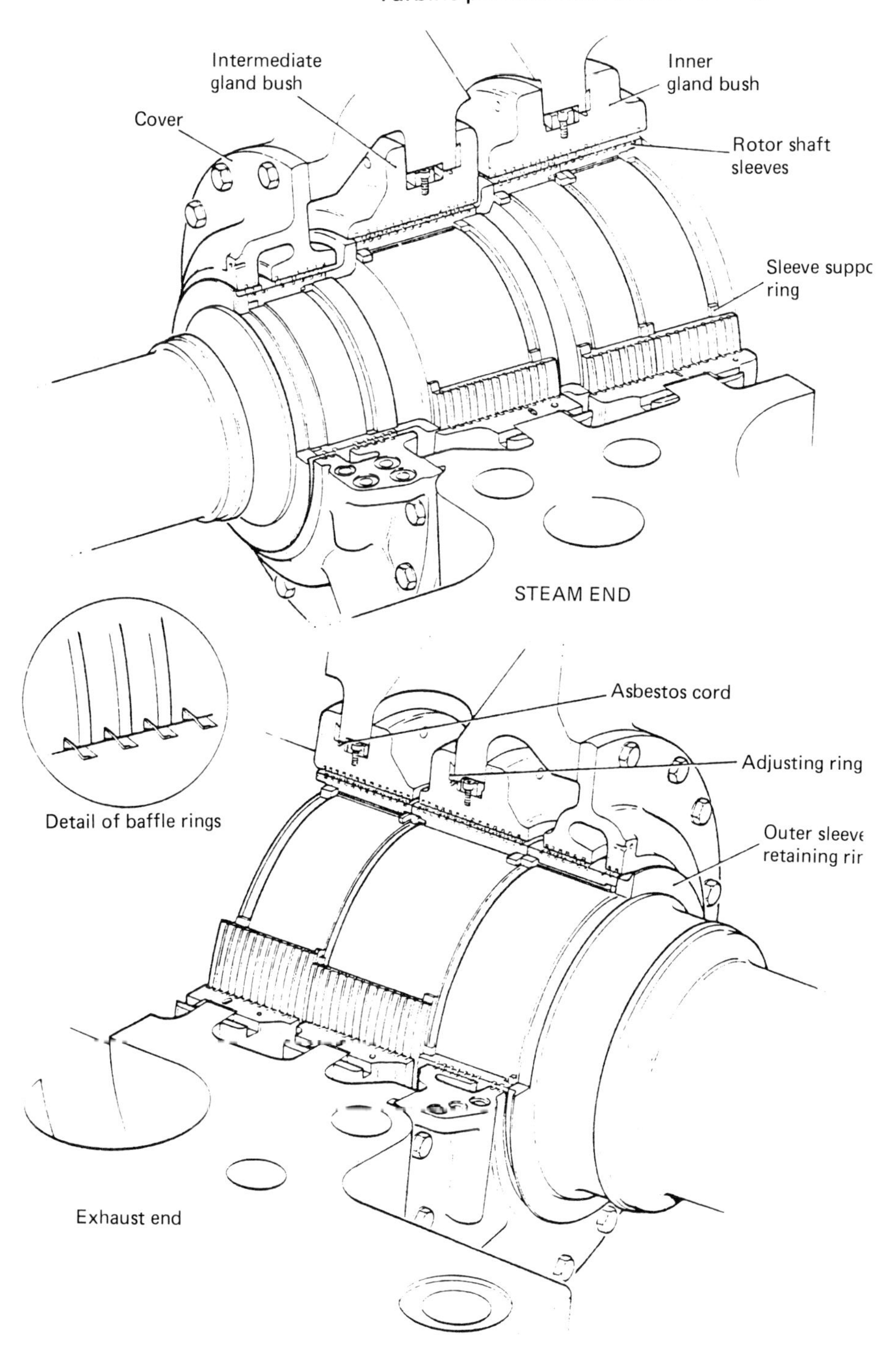

Figure 10.52 HP turbine glands (CEGB)

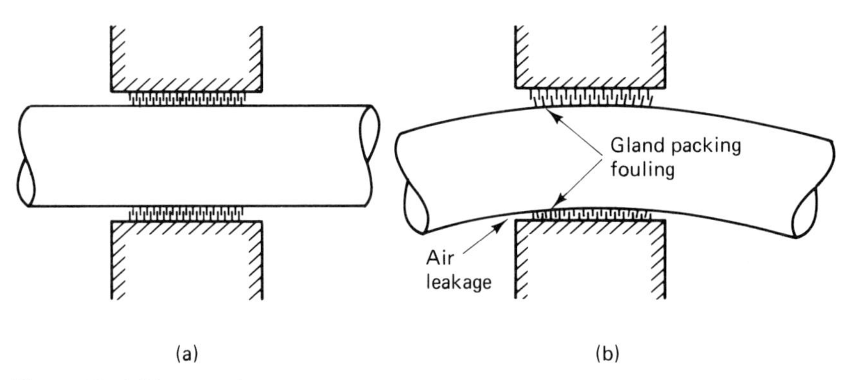

Figure 10.53 Diagram showing effects of undersealing glands (CEGB)

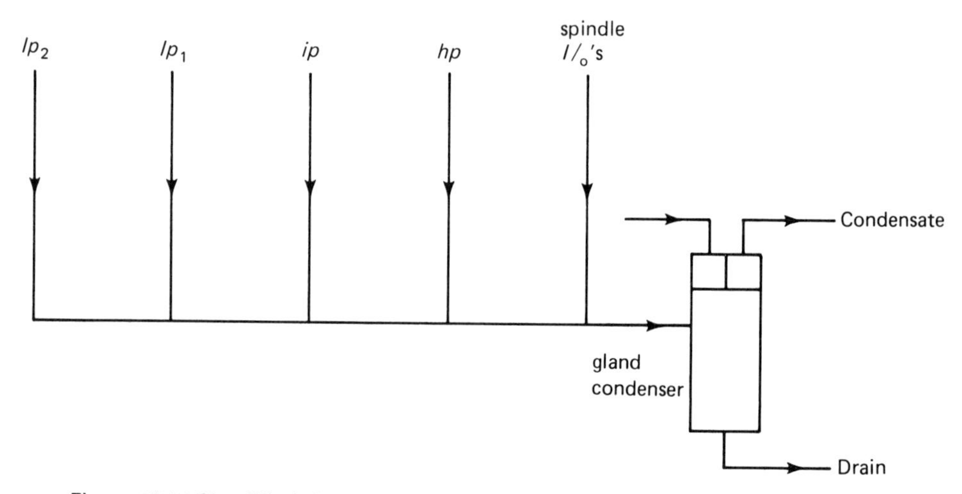

Figure 10.54 Simplified gland leak-offs flows

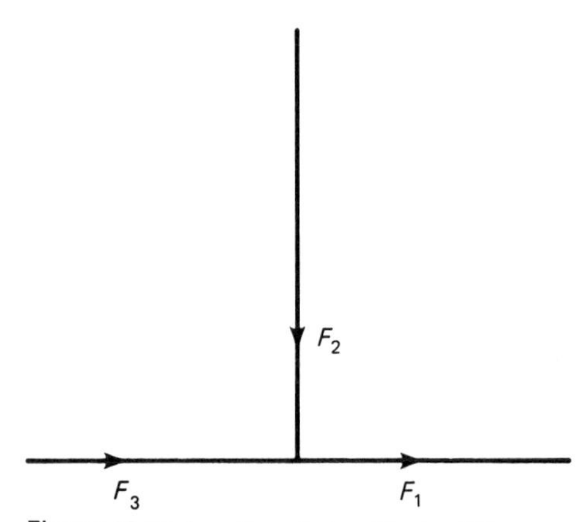

Figure 10.55 Junctionof gland leak-off flows

Knowing F_5, flows F_6 and F_7 can now be found, and so on for the remaining flows.

Example

Suppose the data in *Figure 10.56* was obtained from a gland exhaust system which operated at 1.0 bar absolute:

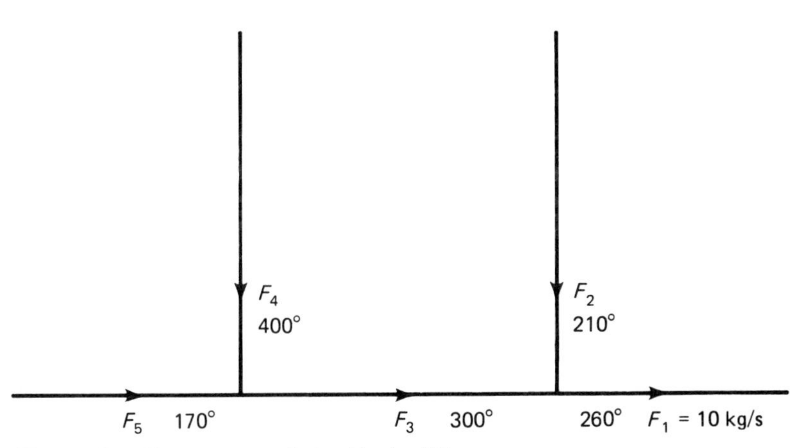

Figure 10.56 Temperature of gland leak-off flows

Flow F_1 is measured and found to be 10 kg/s. The corresponding heats in kJ/kg are determined from steam tables:

h_1	h_2	h_3	h_4	h_5
2994.4	2895.2	3074.5	3278.2	2816.0

$$F_2 = \frac{F_1 (h_1 - h_3)}{h_2 - h_3} = \frac{10\,(2994.4 - 3074.5)}{2895.2 - 3074.5}$$

$$= \frac{(-)\,801.0}{(-)\,179.3} = 4.47 \text{ kg/s}$$

$$F_3 = 10.0 - 4.47 = 5.53 \text{ kg/s}$$

$$F_4 = \frac{F_3 (h_3 - h_5)}{h_4 - h_5} = \frac{5.53\,(3074.5 - 2816.0)}{3278.2 - 2816.0}$$

$$= \frac{1429.5}{462.2} = 3.1 \text{ kg/s}$$

So $F_5 = F_3 - F_4 = 5.53 - 3.1 = 2.43$ kg/s

Effect on heat rate of using reheater spray water

Although facilities are normally provided for controlling the reheat outlet temperature by means of spray injection it should not be used unless absolutely necessary. The basic objection to using the sprays is that the steam formed from the spray water does work only in the IP and LP cylinders of the turbine. Because the HP cylinder has been bypassed by the steam formed, there is a reduction in the efficiency of the turbine. The method of calculation is shown in the following example.

Example (see *Figure 10.57*)

A 350 MW unit has the following design conditions. What is the change in heat rate with a R/H spray flow of 6.39 kg/s?

TSV steam flow	Q_s = 282.4 kg/s (1 016 640 kg/h)
TSV pressure	P_0 = 159.6 bar abs.
TSV temperature	t_o = 566°C
TSV enthalpy	H_o = 3482 kJ/kg
TSV entropy	S = 6.5335 kJ/kgK
R/H inlet pressure	P_{ri} = 42.0 bar abs.
R/H inlet enthalpy	H_{ri} = 3133 kJ/kg (3078 if expansion is isentropic in HP cyl.)
R/H outlet pressure	P_{ro} = 41.6 bar abs.
R/H outlet temperature	t_{ro} = 566°C
R/H outlet entropy	S_{ro} = 7.2601 kJ/kgK
R/H outlet enthalpy	H_{ro} = 3594 kJ/kg
Condensate temperature	T_c = (30.6°C) 303.6 K
Final feed temperature	t_f = 252°C
Final feed pressure	P_f = 206 bar abs.
Final feed entropy	S_f = 2.7353 kJ/kgK
Final feed enthalpy	h_f = 1094.4 kJ/kg
HP heater feed flow	Q_f = 282.4 kg/s (1 016 640 kg/h)
Spray water temperature	t_s = 139°C
Spray water pressure	P_s = 69 bar abs.
Spray water enthalpy	h_s = 588.7 kJ/kg
Spray water entropy	S_s = 1.7388 kJ/kgK
Back pressure	P_b = 44 mbar
T/A heat rate (without spray)	HR = 8467 kJ/kWh at 350 MW

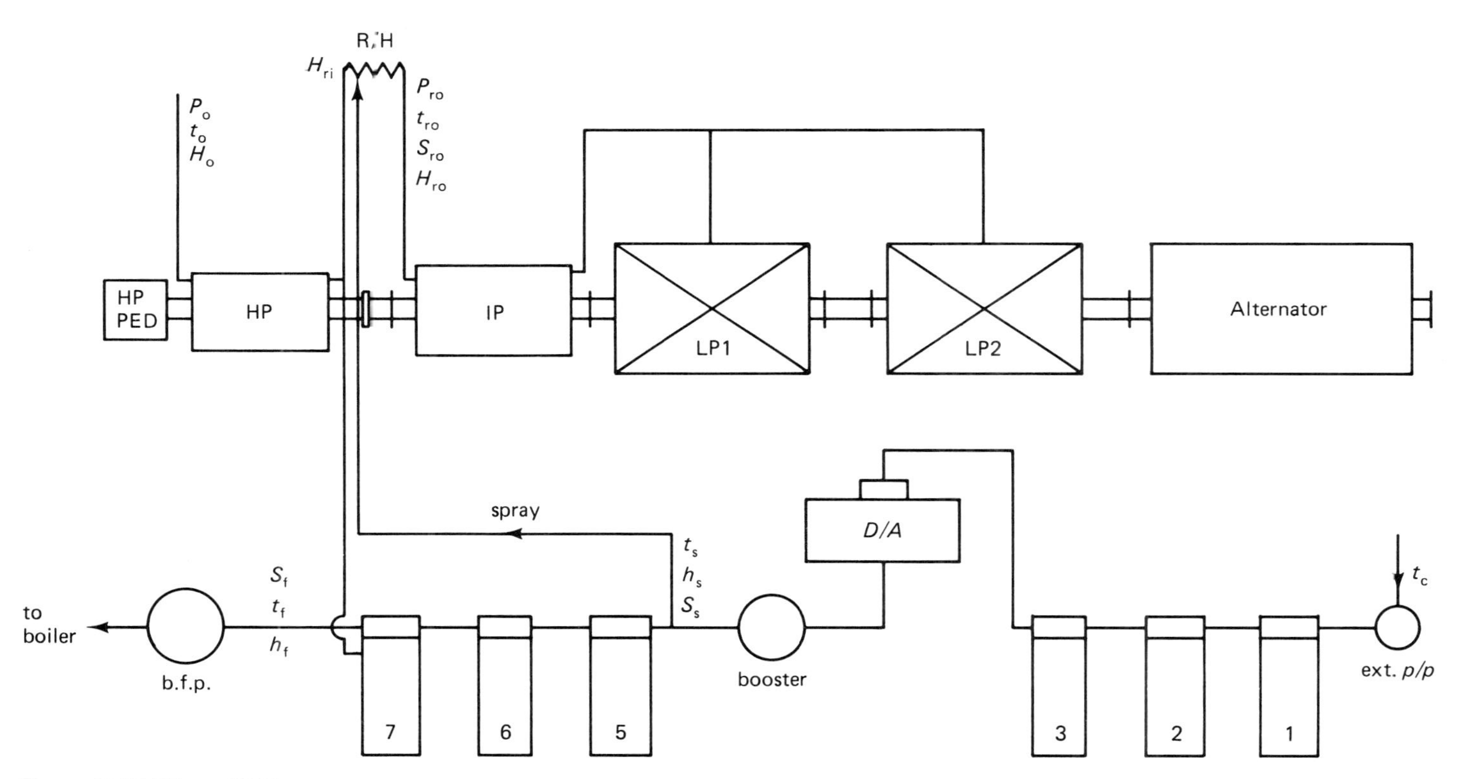

Figure 10.57 Effect of R/H spray on turbine performance

$$\text{Thermal efficiency} = \frac{\text{output heat}}{\text{input heat}}$$

$$= \frac{\text{input heat} - \text{rejected heat}}{\text{input heat}}$$

$$= 1 - \frac{\text{rejected heat}}{\text{input heat}}$$

So the ideal cycle efficiency of a reheat cycle without spray water (*Figure 10.58*) is given by:

$$\text{Ideal cycle efficiency} = 1 - \frac{T_{\text{c}}\,(S_{\text{ro}} - S_{\text{f}})}{(H_o - h_f) \times (H_{ro} - H_{ri})}$$

$$= 1 - \frac{303.6\,(7.2601 - 2.7353)}{(3482 - 1094.4) + (3594 - 3078)}$$

$$= 1 - \frac{1373.7}{2906.6}$$

$$= 0.5269 \text{ or } \mathbf{52.69\%}$$

The spray water ideal cycle efficiency (*Figure 10.59*) is given by:

$$\text{Ideal cycle efficiency (spray water)} = 1 - \frac{T_{\text{c}}\,(S_{\text{ro}} - S_{\text{s}})}{(H_{\text{ro}} - h_{\text{s}})}$$

$$= 1 - \frac{303.6\,(7.2601 - 1.7388)}{(3594 - 588.7)}$$

$$= 1 - \frac{1676.3}{3005.3}$$

$$= 0.4422 \text{ or } \mathbf{44.22\%}$$

Now ideal cycle efficiency × turbine design efficiency = actual efficiency

$$\text{Also the actual efficiency} = \frac{3600}{\text{Heat rate}} = \frac{3600}{8467}$$

$$= 0.4252 \text{ or } \mathbf{42.52\%}$$

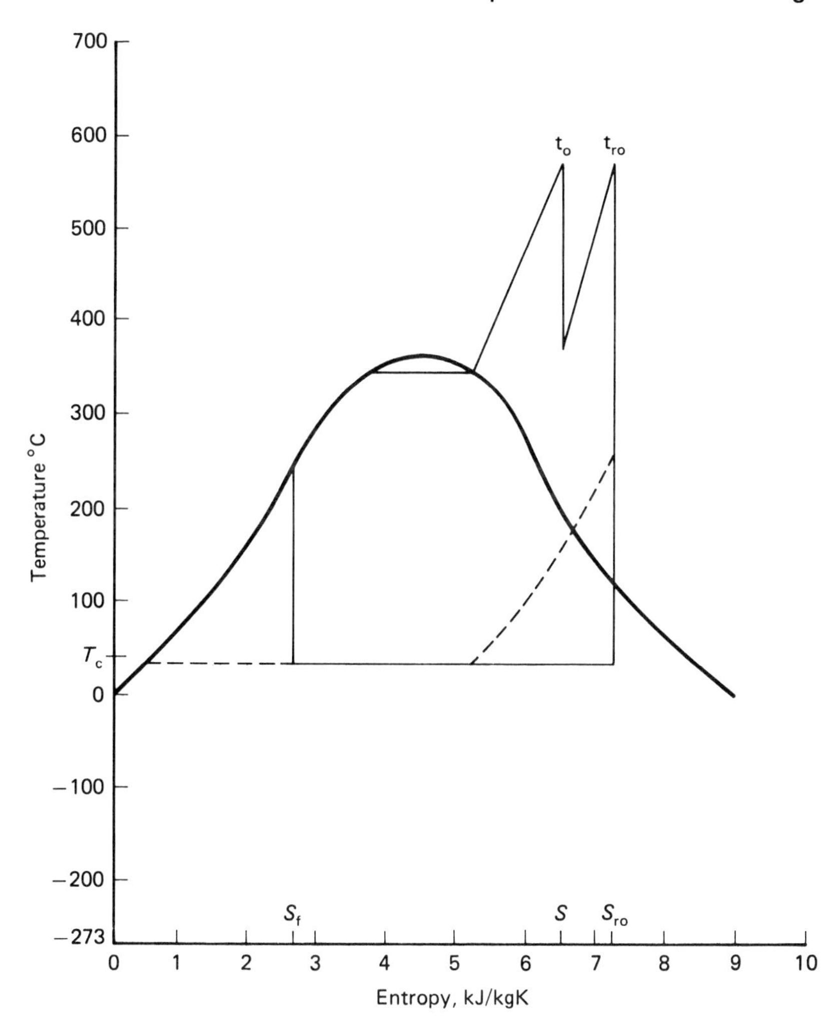

Figure 10.58 Ideal cycle without spray

$$\text{And the turbine design efficiency} = \frac{\text{Actual efficiency}}{\text{Ideal efficiency}} = \frac{42.52}{52.69}$$

$$= 0.807 \text{ or } \mathbf{80.7\%}$$

The actual cycle efficiency when using spray is given by:

actual cycle efficiency (with spray) = Turbine design efficiency × ideal cycle efficiency (spray)

$$= 80.7 \times 44.22$$

$$= \mathbf{35.69\%}$$

$$\text{Actual heat rate (with spray) } HR_S = \frac{3600 \times 100}{35.69} = 10\,087 \text{ kJ/kWh}$$

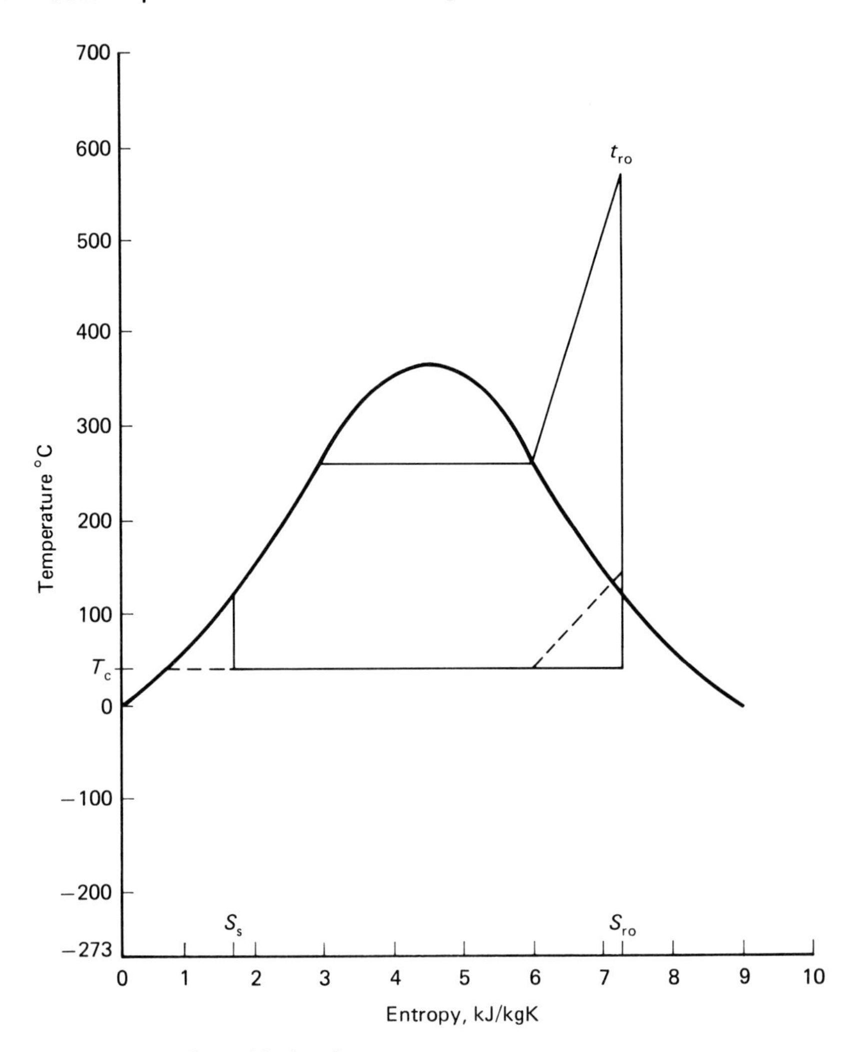

Figure 10.59 Spray ideal cycle

The spray water flow is 6.39 kg/s, i.e. 23 000 kg/h

$$\text{So the combined heat rate} = \frac{[(Q_S - 23\ 000)\ HR] + (23\ 000 \times HRs)}{Q_s}$$

$$= \frac{[(1\ 016\ 640 - 23\ 000) \times 8467] + (23\ 000 \times 10\ 087)}{1\ 016\ 640}$$

$$= \mathbf{8504\ kJ/kWh}$$

So percentage increase in heat rate when using 23 000 kg/h of spray water is:

$$\frac{(8504 - 8467) \times 100}{8467} = \mathbf{0.44\%}$$

Expressed another way, the efficiency without spray would be

$$\frac{3600}{8467} \times 100 \qquad = 42.52\%$$

and would become $\dfrac{3600 \times 100}{8504} = 42.34\%$

when using 23 000 kg/h of spray.

Changes which occur inside the turbine due to R/H spray

Up to now only the cycle changes have been discussed, but the effects of reheater spray flow can also be assessed by considering the various physical changes which occur. This method is given below.

Effects of reheat spray injection

The changes which occur to bring about the deterioration in performance are mainly:

(a) A reduction of power output from the HP cylinder because of the reduced steam flow, as every kilogram of spray water flow results in a comparable reduction of HP cylinder steam flow.
(b) A reduction of feed flow through the HP feed heaters, if the spray water is tapped off the feed system before the HP heaters. This will result in a reduction of bled steam flow to the heaters, and hence there will be an increased steam flow through the IP and LP cylinders. Consequently there will be an increase in the power output from these cylinders.
(c) A change in the heat added to the feed water in the boiler because of the difference in the heat given to the spray compared to that given to the feed.

In addition, the last heater will have a reduced quantity of bled steam as mentioned in (b), and this will cause an increased steam flow through the reheater, so necessitating extra heat supply from the boiler.

Consider each item in turn, using the same data as before:

(a) *Loss of power from HP cylinder*

Enthalpy at turbine stop valve = 3482 kJ/kg
Enthalpy at HP cylinder exhaust = 3133 kJ/kg

Available heat drop = 349 kJ/kg

So with 23 000 kg/h of spray the loss of electrical power

$$= \frac{23\ 000 \text{ kg/h} \times 349 \text{ kJ/kg}}{3600} = \mathbf{2\ 230\ kW}$$

The above assumes that there is 23 000 kg/h spray flow, all of which bypasses the HP cylinder, so reducing the flow of steam through the cylinder by the same amount.

(b) *Increased output from IP and LP cylinders*

The design feed quantity through the HP feed heaters (Q_f) is 282.4 kg/s
Now heat lost by the bled steam = heat gained by feed water.

Let Q_B = quantity of bled steam, kg/s
H_B = enthalpy of bled steam, kJ/kg
h_i = enthalpy of feed water at heater inlet, kJ/kg
h_o = enthalpy of feed water at heater outlet, kJ/kg
Q_f = quantity of feed water, kg/s
h_c = enthalpy of heater drain water, kJ/kg
Then $Q_B (H_B - h_c) = Q_f (h_o - h_i)$

$$\text{So } Q_B = \frac{Q_f (h_o - h_i)}{H_B - h_c}$$

Assume the heat surrendered per kilogram of steam and the heat accepted per kilogram of feed water remains constant.

$$\text{Then } Q_B \quad Q_f, \text{ and } \frac{Q_{B1}}{Q_{B2}} = \frac{Q_{f1}}{Q_{f2}}$$

where the subscripts 1 and 2 refer to design and actual conditions respectively.

$$\text{Then } Q_{B2} = Q_{B1} \times \frac{Q_{f2}}{Q_{f1}}$$

where Q_{f1} = 282.4 kg/s
Q_{f2} = 282.4 − 6.39 kg/s spray = 276.0 kg/s

$$\text{So } Q_{B2} = Q_{B1} \times \frac{276.0}{282.4} = Q_{B1} \times 0.9773$$

Therefore the bled steam to each HP heater will be reduced to 0.9773 of its design value, as shown in *Table 10.10*.

Hence the total extra electrical output because of reduced bled steam flow is **977.5 kW**

Table 10.10

			HP heaters		
			5	*6*	*7*
1	Design bled steam flow	kg/s	18.166	10.251	29.467
2	Reduced bled steam flow	kg/s	17.754	10.018	28.798
3	Reduction in BS flow (1) – (2)	kg/s	0.412	0.233	0.669
4	Enthalpy of bled steam	kJ/kg	2907.5	3336.9	3132.0
5	Enthalpy of steam at exhaust	kJ/kg	2353.9	2353.9	2353.9
6	Heat drop available (4) – (5)	kJ/kg	553.6	983.0	778.1
7	Extra generator output (3) × (6)	kW	228.0	229.0	520.5

(c) *Change in boiler heat supplied to steam*

(i) *Change due to extra steam flow through reheater*
The reduced flow of steam to No. 7 heater (0.669 kg/s) will now pass through the reheater. The extra heat required to raise this steam from HP exhaust conditions to reheater outlet conditions is given by:

$0.669\,(H_{ro} - H_{ri}) = 0.669\,(3594 - 3133)$
$= \mathbf{308.4\ kJ/s} = \mathbf{1\ 110\ 240\ kJ/h}$

(ii) *Change due to heating reheater spray water*

First consider the heat required to raise the final feed water to TSV conditions, i.e.

$H_o - h_f = 3482 - 1094.4 = 2387.6$ kJ/kg

Next, consider how much heat is required to raise the spray water to reheat inlet steam conditions, i.e.

$H_{ri} - h_s = 3133 - 588.7 = 2\ 544.3$ kJ/kg
Hence, the extra heat required is 2544.3 – 2387.6 = 156.7 kJ/kg
So extra heat required to heat 6.39 kg/s of spray water is equal to 6.39 × 156.7 = **1001.3 kJ/s** = 3 604 680 kJ/h
The total heat in the steam supplied to the turbine will be
(350 000 kW × design *HR*) + (i) + (ii) kJ/h
= (350 000 × 8467) + 1 110 240 + 3 604 680 kJ/h
= **2 968 164 820 kJ/h**
Also the output of the machine will be
350 000 kW – (a) + (b) = 350 000 – 2230 + 977.5 kW
= **348 747 kW**
So turbine heat rate when using R/H spray is

$$\frac{2\ 968\ 164\ 820\ \text{kJ/h}}{348\ 747\ \text{kW}} = \mathbf{8510\ kJ/kWh}$$

This is in very close agreement with the value calculated earlier, i.e. 8504 kJ/kWh.

Questions

1 Where is the motive power obtained from that acts on a blade?
2 What is the formula for the blade efficiency of an ideal blade?
3 What is the maximum efficiency and u/V_1 ratio for an ideal stage?
4 Name a common use of velocity compounding in modern plant.
5 What is the most important parameter for efficiency in a turbine design?
6 How many stages are required on a 3000 r/min machine compared to one at 3600 rev/min which is identical in other respects?
7 Define cylinder efficiency.
8 What are typical values for HP, IP and LP cylinder efficiency?
9 What does a kink in a pressure survey line indicate?
10 What is the effect of roughness of blades and nozzles?
11 Would the cylinder efficiency be affected by excessive gland leak-off?
12 Why are Curtis stages often used at turbine inlets?
13 What is the on-load manifestation of silica deposition?
14 Which blades are affected by silica deposition?
15 How would you determine gland leak-off flows?

Exercise 1 – Turbine monitoring

Figure 10.60 shows the steam path and design steam conditions in the HP

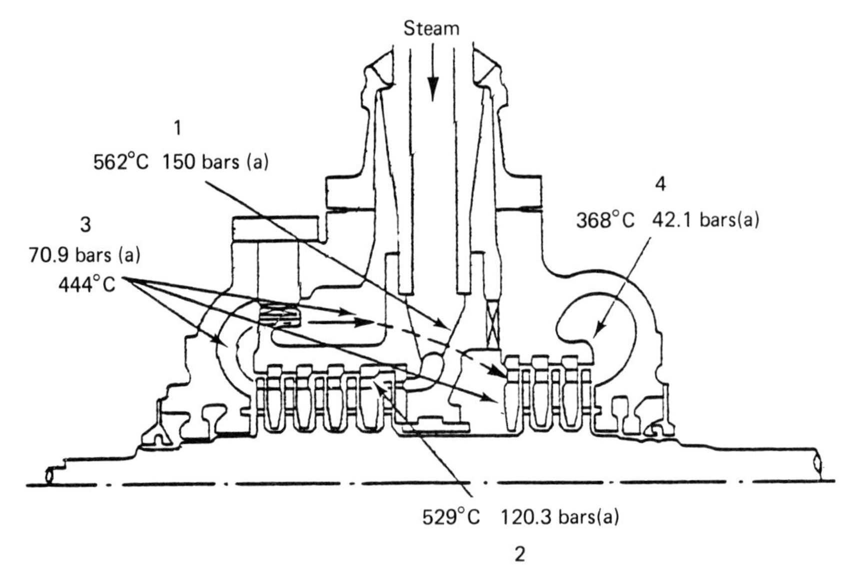

Figure 10.60 Diagram of reverse flow HP cylinder. Exercise 1 (CEGB)

cylinder of a 350 MW turbine at full load. The efficiencies of the individual sections were calculated and the results are:

Point (1) to (2)	72.76%
Point (2) to (3)	90.21%
Point (3) to (4)	91.66%
Point (1) to (3)	85.65%
Point (1) to (4)	88.84%

Account for the variation of efficiency.

Exercise 2 – Turbine pressure survey

A new HP cylinder inlet nozzle block was fitted to a 60 MW machine. The intention was to increase the load capability from its previous 62 MW to 65 MW. However, when the unit was returned to service the maximum output was 59.3 MW. Work carried out on the turbine when it was out of service for the block to be fitted included:

1 HP rotor replaced by a refurbished spare.
2 HP nozzle block replaced by new one made at the manufacturers' works.
3 Turbine stop valves and throttle valves replaced.
4 Curtis wheel first-row moving blades dressed and second-row moving blades renewed.
5 Curtis stage fixed blades dressed.
6 HP turbine main shaft glands replaced.
7 Alignment check carried out.

Upon return to service a pressure survey was carried out and the results are shown in *Figure 10.61*. The full line marked 'actual at 59.3 MW (max. load)' joins the pressures obtained as indicated. The dashed portion of the line indicates where the full line would lie if it were straight. The line marked 'optimum at 59.3 MW' is derived from acceptance test data.

Questions

1 Comment upon the general state of the turbine.
2 What is the cause of the turbine load limitation and why?
3 Why is the pressure drop from 'before TSV' to 'ATV' less than optimum?

Exercise 2 – Turbine pressure survey (Answers)

1 The kink in the 'actual at 59.3 MW' line from the ATV to wheelcase indicates a restriction to flow. There is a restricted output of 59.3 MW.

Reference to the work carried out indicates that items 1, 2, 3, 4 and 5 could have a connection with the problem. However, of these items, 1, 4 and 5 are fairly routine occurrences. This does not exonerate them automatically, but it does make any of them being the cause of the trouble

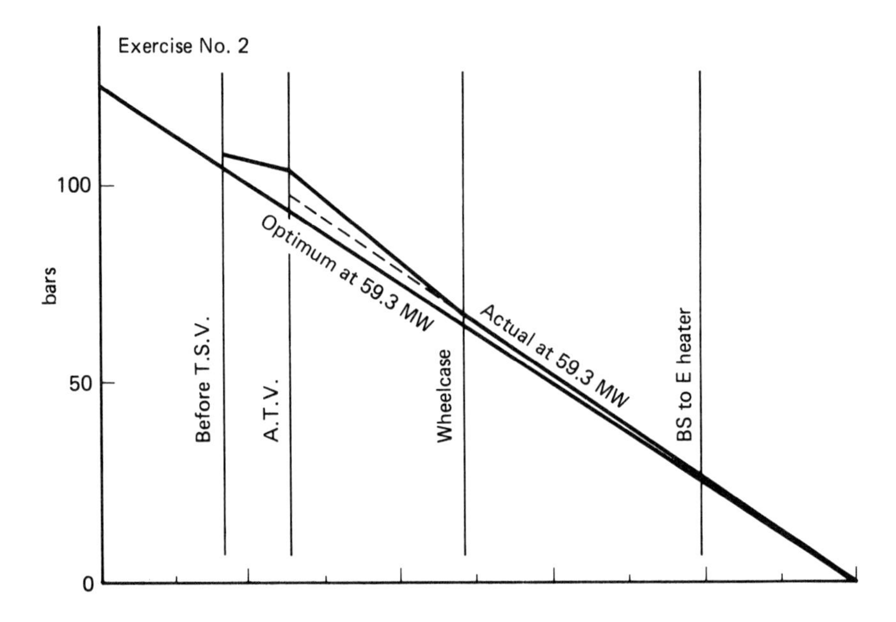

Figure 10.61 Pressure survey diagram. Exercise 2

unlikely.

The 'actual' line from the wheelcase onward is above the optimum line but straight – this indicates general wear throughout the turbine. The pressure at the wheelcase is 64.5 bar optimum and 69.0 bar actual, so the load capability without the general wear is of the order of 59.3 MW × 69.0/64.5 = 63.4 MW.

2 The actual cause of the turbine limitation is somewhere between the ATV and wheelcase. When that is removed there will then be the additional, but smaller, source of limitation due to general wear.

The wheelcase pressure is the same for the whole Curtis stage from the HP nozzle outlet to the outlet of the second row of moving blades. Hence there is a restriction either at the nozzle block or the Curtis blading. If it is at the blading it will probably be at the first moving row because of damage from debris getting through the steam strainers.

3 The low pressure drop from 'before TSV' to 'ATV' is because the throttle

valves are as wide open as they will go, so the throttling loss is a minimum. In addition the rate of flow is limited by the restriction, item 2. This indicates that the section from 'before TSV' to 'ATV' is free of obstruction.

Addendum

In the event, the turbine HP cylinder covers were lifted later and the nozzles and blading checked. The Curtis blading was found to be satisfactory. The nozzle block was the cause of the restriction because the nozzle openings had been made too small. The nozzles were modified and the machine could thereafter achieve its anticipated loading.

Project 1

A supercritical pressure boiler has sustained severe damage and it is unlikely that it will be economic to repair it. The conditions on the unit are:

TSV pressure and temperature 241.3 bar, 593°C
IP inlet temperature, 566°C
Turbine rating 375 MW
Full load steam flow 315 kg/s
HP cylinder exhaust pressure and temperature at full load 49.6 bar, 538°C
Back pressure 40 mbar
Final feed temperature 270°C

Various possibilities are being considered about what to do with the plant. One idea is to use the existing turbo-alternator but install a new boiler operating at 158.6 bar TSV pressure, 566°C reheating to 566°C. The final feed would be 240°C and the back pressure 40 mbar. In such a case what would be:

1 The new full-load rating of the T/A?
2 The wetness at the turbine exhaust compared to original? (i.e. would it be higher or lower?)
3 The new HP cylinder exhaust pressure?
4 The new full-load efficiency compared with the original? (Higher or lower?)
5 The full load steam flow?

Project 1 (Answer)

1 The turbine MCR will be in proportion to the original and new pressures, i.e.

$$375 \text{ MW} \times \frac{158.6}{241.3} = 246 \text{ MW}$$

Actually it will be a little higher because the pressure drop across the throttles will be a little less than originally.

2 The wetness of the exhaust will be less at the new MCR than the old.

3 With 158.6 bar inlet pressure the HP cylinder exhaust pressure on full load will be:

$$\frac{158.6}{241.3} \times 49.6 = 32.6 \text{ bar}$$

4 The two ideal cycles are shown in *Figures 10.62* and *10.63*. Hence the new cycle will be less efficient. In addition, the new full-load turbine efficiency will be less than before.

5 Steam flow is proportional to load and so the new MCR flow will be about

$$\frac{246}{375} \times 315 \text{ kg/s} = 206.6 \text{ kg/s}$$

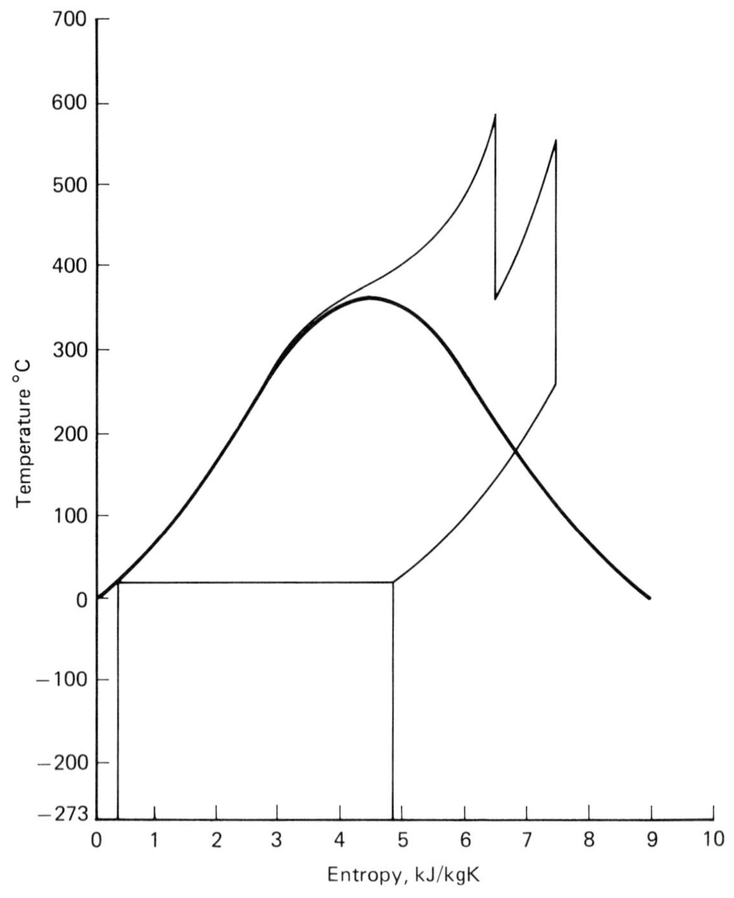

Figure 10.62 Supercritical cycle. Project No 1 (Efficiency 56.3%)

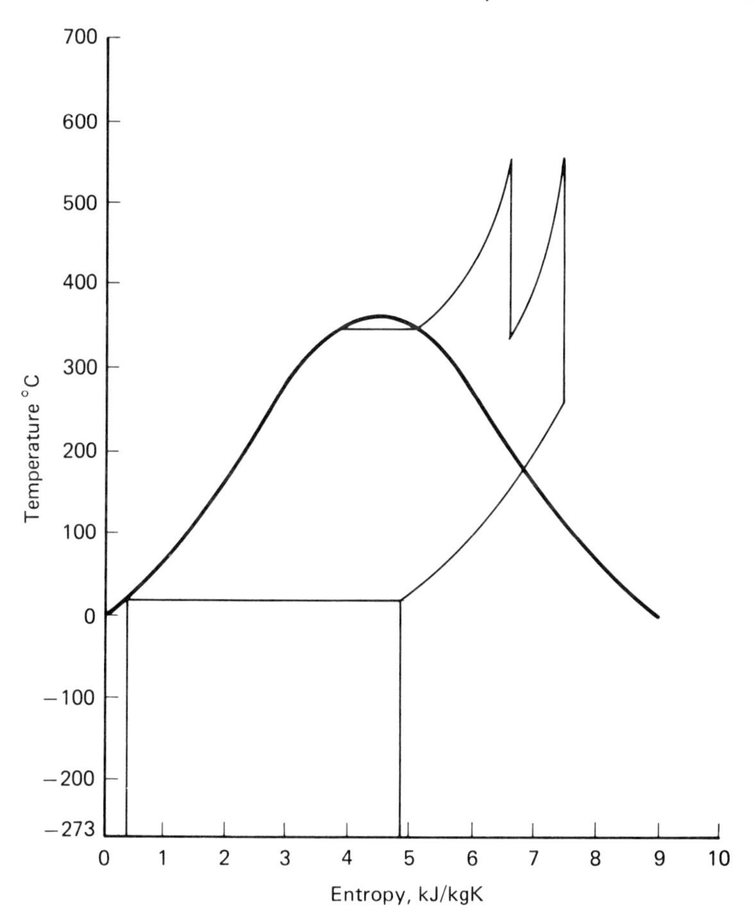

Figure 10.63 Modified cycle. Project No 1 (Efficiency 44.9%)

Project 2

Incident on No. 7 T/A at Drakelow 'B' Power Station (120 MW Parsons turbine) on 15 October

Sequence of events

On 9 October the machine (*Figure 10.64*) was running at 65 MW. A routine pressure survey was carried out by the Efficiency Department Staff (see *Figure 10.65*).

2 On 15 October the machine was running at 90 MW. At 12.30 hours the load fell to 81 MW and there was a 'kick' on the eccentricity and differential expansion charts.

3 While the loading was still at 81 MW, a pressure survey was carried out at 14.00 hours on 15 October (*Figure 10.66*)

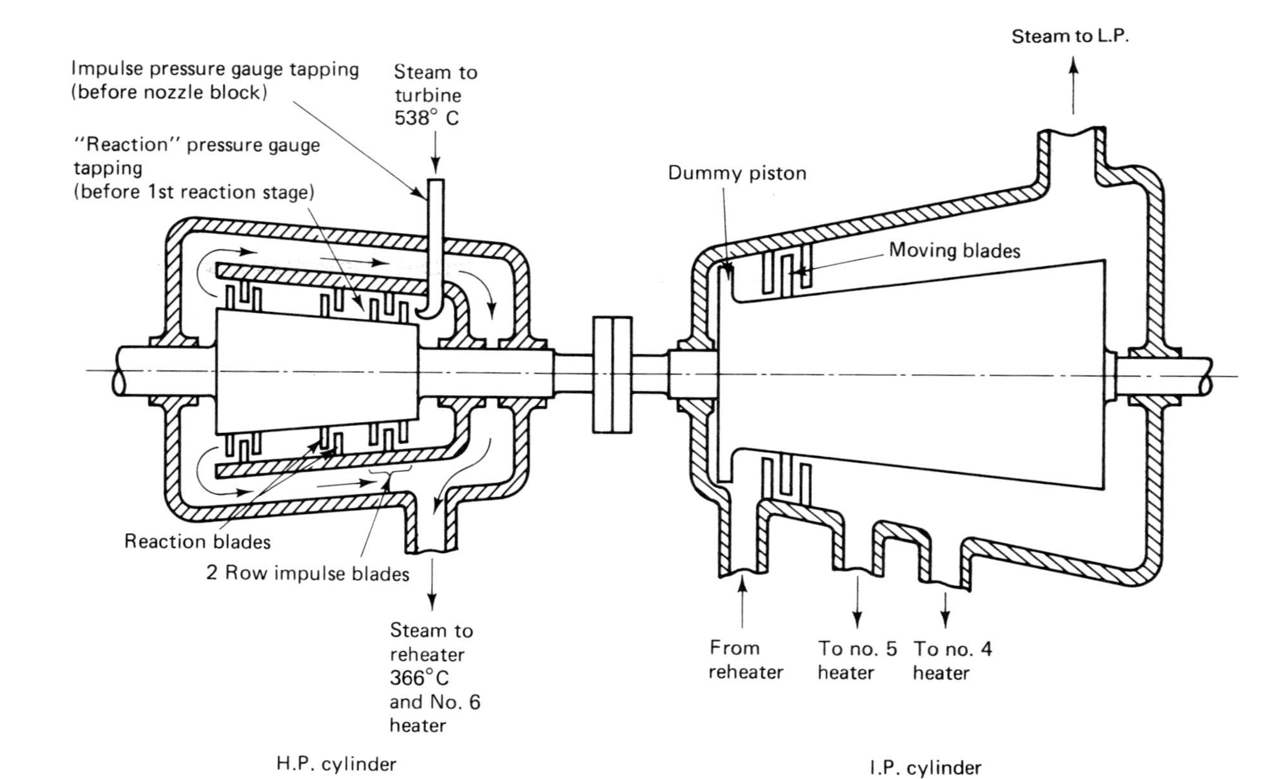

Figure 10.64 Drakelow No. 7 T/A. impulse — reaction HP and IP cylinders (diagrammatic). Project No 2

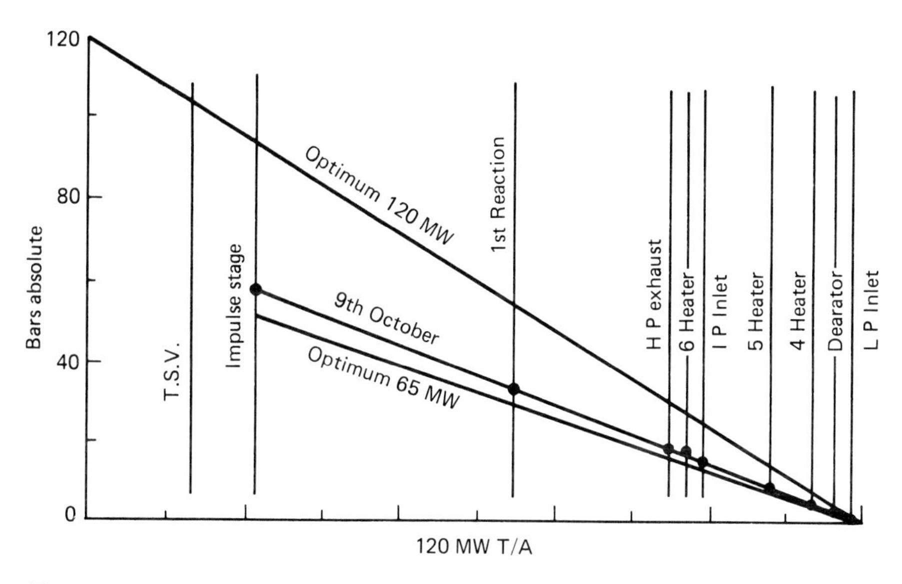

Figure 10.65 Routine pressure survey on No 7 T/A. Project No 2

4 Machine taken off-load at 16.00 hours.

5 Machine came to rest quickly when taken off load and difficulty was experienced in getting the turning gear to turn the shaft. Noises came from the IP cylinder inlet end.

6 The pressure gauges used in the pressure survey were subsequently checked for accuracy and found to be satisfactory.

Note: The machine was running with the LHS IP steam chest blanked off.

Question

The Station Manager wants to know what the probable trouble is and the extent of the damage. Should cylinder covers be lifted and if so, which ones? Note: To lift a cover unnecessarily will extend the outage for several days so do not recommend it unless there is a definite reason.

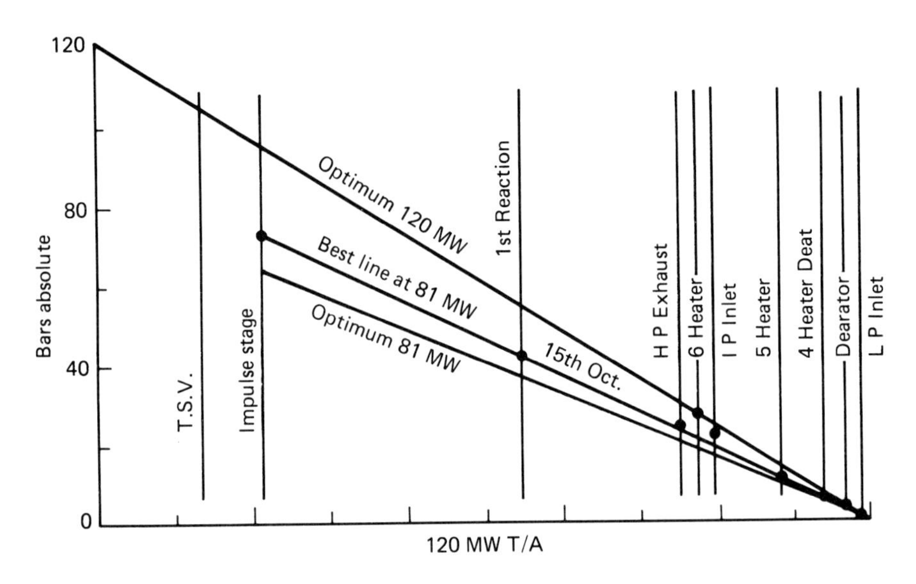

Figure 10.66 Pressure survey after incident. Project No 2

Project 2 (Answer)

The recommendations made to Management on the day the incident happened were:

1 Some IP blading located between the cylinder inlet and the tapping to No. 5 bled steam line is damaged, i.e. between the 1st and 8th row of blades.

2 The trouble is probably due to one of the following:

(a) Debris from, say, reheater repairs. However, any pieces that got into the turbine would have to be small enough to get past the steam strainers, and so this is not a very likely cause.

(b) Something coming adrift inside the cylinder such as a nozzle-plate fixing bolt.

(c) A blade failure on an early row causing subsequent damage to further rows.

(d) IP cylinder distortion due to the unbalanced steam admission caused by having the left-hand IP steam chest blanked off, so allowing blading to touch stationary parts.

3 Threre is no reason to believe that the HP cylinder is seriously affected. Possibly the moving blade radial sealing pieces may have been worn due to the shaft eccentricity at the time of the incident. However, this would have no adverse effect except to lower the cylinder efficiency a little.

Therefore it is recommended that the HP cylinder cover is not lifted.

Subsequent sequence of events

The IP cylinder cover was lifted on 21 October. It was found that the first two rows of moving blades were completely stripped and extensive damage had been caused to the third row. There was no extensive damage to the remaining rows, but several of them had damaged axial seals and were 'blued'. The intermediate blades up to the third stage were badly damaged.

Question

In view of the above information Management wish to know whether the previous recommendation not to open the HP cylinder still stands?

Answer

The HP cylinder should not be opened.

As several rows of blades have been shed in the IP cylinder, the thrust towards the LP end of the machine has been reduced. On the other hand the dummy piston is intact so there is an increased net thrust towards the HP cylinder and so the shafts would physically move in that direction (which was confirmed by reference to the differential expansion chart). The effect would be to increase the axial clearance between the fixed and moving blades in the HP cylinder. Blade tip leakage would increase and all the 'reaction' stage pressures would be higher than normal.

However, the 'impulse' pressure gauge reading would be unaffected because it is tapped-off immediately after the impulse stage and the pressure at that point is determined by the HP cylinder inlet nozzles.

Therefore the original recommendation remains unaltered.

Footnote

The HP cylinder was eventually opened for other work about two years later. The condition of the internals was as predicted – radial seals worn but no other damage.

Project 3 – Steam turbines

A non-reheat 100 MW turbine operates at 3000 rev/min and has one double-flow LP cylinder. If the leaving loss is 2.5%, what length of last-row blade is required, given the following data?

Steam pressure and temperature at TSV	= 103.4 bar 566°C
Steam enthalpy at TSV	= 3534 kJ/kg
Back pressure	= 40 mbar
Steam enthalpy at exhaust	= 2353 kJ/kg
Steam flow at TSV	= 100.0 kg/s
Steam flow to condenser	= 64.0 kg/s
Diameter of disc on last wheel, d	= 1.5 m
Steam at exhaust	= 12% wet

Project 3 (Answer)

$$\%\text{ leaving loss} = \frac{\text{loss per kg TSV flow} \times 100}{\text{work done per kg TSV flow}}$$

$\therefore$ loss per kg TSV flow = leaving loss × work done per kg TSV flow
So loss = 0.025 × (3534 − 2353) = 29.5 kJ/kg flow at TSV

$$\therefore \text{ loss per kg of flow to condenser} = \frac{29.5 \times 100}{64}$$

$$= 46.1\text{ kJ} = 46\ 100\text{ J}$$

$$\text{So leaving loss} = \frac{mV^2}{2}\text{J} = 46\ 100\text{ J}$$

$\therefore V = \surd(46\ 100 \times 2) = 303.6$ m/s

$$\text{Also } V = \frac{\text{Steam flow} \times \text{volume per kg at 40 mbar}}{\text{Area of last row annulus}}$$

Volume of steam at 40 mbar = Dryness fraction × dry saturated volume
= 0.88 × 34802.2 = 30 626 litre/kg
= 30.6 m³/kg

$$\text{So area of last row annulus} = \frac{64.0 \times 30.6}{303.6} = 6.45\text{ m}^2$$

There are two exhausts, so each = 3.225 m²
Let D = tip diameter of last row of blades

$$\text{Then } 3.225 = \frac{\pi}{4}(D^2 - d^2) = \frac{\pi}{4}(D^2 - 1.5^2)$$

$$\text{So } D = \sqrt{\left(\frac{3.225 \times 4}{\pi} + 1.5^2\right)} = \sqrt{6.36} = 2.5 \text{ m}$$

$$\therefore \text{Blade length} = \frac{2.5 - 1.5}{2} = 0.5 \text{ m}$$

Additional Reading

1 GARDNER, C.C., 'Events leading to erosion in the steam turbine', *Proc. I. Mech. E.* (1964)
2 FORSTER, V.T., 'Performance loss of modern steam-turbine plant due to surface roughness', *Proc. I. Mech. E.,* **181**, Part 1 (1967)
3 WOOD, B., 'Wetness in steam cycles', *Proc. I. Mech. E.*, **174**, No. 14 (1960)
4 TRAUPEL, W., 'Steam turbines, yesterday, today and tomorrow', *Proc. I. Mech. E.*, **193**, No. 38 (1979)
5 BS 132, *Steam Turbines*
6 CHURCH, E.F., *Steam Turbines*, McGraw-Hill
7 PACE, E.L., 'Integration of turbine driven boiler feed pumps in large power plants', *A.S.M.E.* Paper No. 59 – A – 196
8 SALISBURY, J.K., *Steam Turbines and Their Cycles*, John Wiley
9 McCRAE, R.U., 'The influence of the modern boiler feed pump turbine on modern reheat steam cycles', Paper presented to the South African I. Mech. E., Johannesburg 1965
10 *Applied Thermodynamics in Steam Power Stations* Brown-Boveri
11 TOMALIN, P., APPLEGATE, R. and McBIRNIEIS.C., 'The English Electric 375 MW supercritical steam turbine at Drakelow 'C' Power Station', *English Electric Journal*, Vol. 22 No. 6 (1967)
12 WELCH, C.P. and HOFFMAN, H.J., 'The application of the deviation concept in turbine cycle monitoring', *Jour. of Engineering for Power* (October 1961)
13 SALISBURY, K., 'Power plant performance monitoring', *A.S.M.E.* Paper No. 60 – WA – 222
14 COTTON, K.C. and SCHOFIELD, P., 'Analysis of changes in the performance characteristics of steam turbines', *Jour. of Engineering for Power* (April 1971)
15 SALISBURY, K., 'A new performance criterion for steam turbine regenerative cycles', *Jour. of Engineering for Power* (October 1959)

11 Condensers and back pressure

To illustrate the important contribution made to the work done by operating at a vacuum, consider *Figure 11.1*. Steam is admitted to a turbine at a

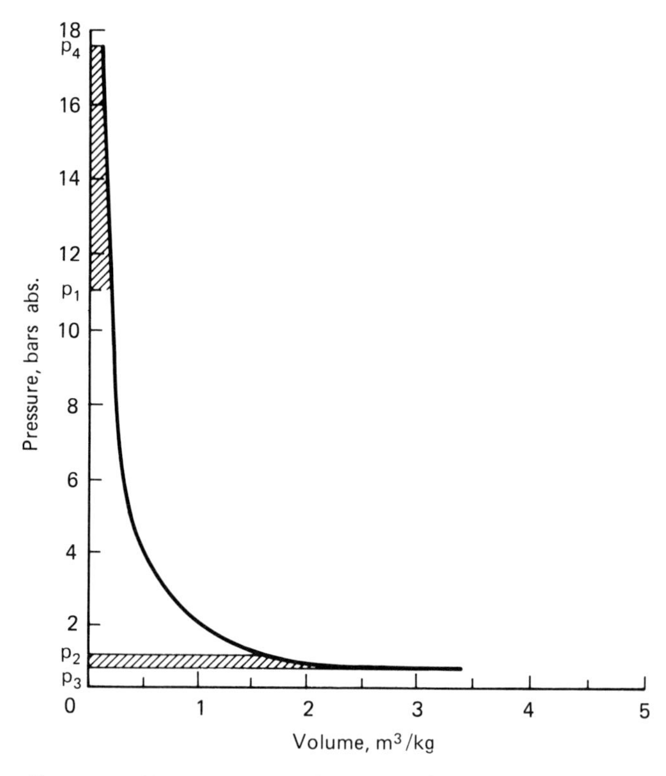

Figure 11.1 Pressure *vs* specific volume for dry saturated steam

pressure of 11 bar absolute as shown by P_1. The volume of the steam is 0.177 m^3/kg. If, after expansion in the turbine, it is rejected at a pressure P_2 of 1 bar absolute the volume will have become 1.7 m^3/kg and the work done will be represented by the area under the curve between the limits shown by P_1 and P_2.

If, now, the final pressure is reduced to 0.5 bar absolute the expansion will continue to P_3 and the volume will be 3.3 m^3/kg. Thus, the extra work obtained per kilogram of steam is represented by the shaded area. This is a considerable amount of extra work, obtained by improving the back pressure by 0.5 bar. To achieve a comparable amount of extra work at the inlet to the turbine the steam pressure would have to be lifted from P_1 to P_4, i.e. from 11 to 17.5 bars as shown by the cross-hatched area.

Of course, in practice it is normal to operate with considerably lower back pressures than depicted in *Figure 11.1.* It is easy to see that even small changes in back pressure can cause considerable changes in the work done per kilogram of steam – and remember there are over a million kilograms of steam entering the condenser per hour on large units. So it is easy to see why turbine back pressure is the most important terminal condition of all. Therefore it is important to the efficient operation of a unit that its back pressure is always maintained at the optimum level.

Effect of varying the back pressure

From what has already been said it follows that a large amount of extra work is done by the steam when the back pressure is reduced. If this were the whole story then lowering the back pressure would always result in increased output from a unit. The trouble is that as the back pressure improves certain losses increase. These are mainly:

1 CW pumping power.
2 Leaving loss.
3 Reduced condensate temperature.
4 Wetness of the steam.

Consider each item in turn.

Increased CW pumping power. Assuming that the CW inlet temperature is low enough the back pressure can be reduced by putting more and more CW through the condenser tubes. However, this will require more and more CW pumping power and the gain from improved back pressure must be offset against the extra power absorbed by the pumps. Therefore CW pumps should be run only when the cost of running them is less than the resulting benefit from increased unit output. In other words, the pump operation should always be optimized (see under 'Works Power', Chapter 14, page 651).

Increased leaving loss. Consider the last row of blades in a turbine. These present to the steam a fixed annulus through which it must pass to get to the condenser. Now, the steam leaves the last row at a velocity which depends upon the conditions prevailing at that point. As this velocity is not utilized usefully it represents a loss of possible work. This is known as the 'Leaving Loss'. There is always a leaving loss but as the back pressure is reduced its magnitude increases rapidly. For example, if the back pressure is 60 mbar the loss would be a certain value. If the back pressure is reduced to 30 mbar the specific volume of the steam will be approximately doubled, and so the velocity of the steam through the fixed annulus must also double. But the leaving loss varies as the square of the velocity, and consequently will increase four times.

Reduced condensate temperature. If the condensate in the condenser is at the saturation temperature corresponding to the back pressure it will be 36°C at 60 mbar. Reducing the back pressure to 30 mbar will cause the temperature to drop to 24°C. Hence, when it enters No. 1 LP heater it will be cooler than before. Consequently more steam will automatically be bled to the heater because of the increased condensation rate of the steam. It follows that the extra steam being bled to the heater is no longer available to do work in the turbine downstream of the tapping point, and so the turbine will be deprived of some work.

Increased wetness of steam. The lower the back pressure the greater the wetness of the steam. The extra moisture could result in damage to the moving blades. In addition the volume of steam is reduced. Thus at 30 mbar back pressure the volume of the steam without wetness would be 45.7 m^3/kg. If there were 10% wetness the steam volume per kg would be reduced to 41.1 m^3. As a rough guide it can be assumed that every 1% wetness will reduce the efficiency of the associated stage by 1%.

The losses mentioned will eventually significantly affect the result. Continued reduction of the back pressure will result in the net improvement in heat consumption becoming progressively less until a point is reached at which the benefit due to improved back pressure is exactly neutralized by the losses, and this is the point of minimum heat consumption, as shown in *Figure 11.2*. Further reduction of the back pressure will cause the heat consumption to increase, and so there is no point in operating at a lower value. It should be noted, though, that the back pressure for minimum heat consumption varies with load and so the operations staff should be supplied with a curve such as shown in *Figure 11.3* to enable them to determine the minimum back pressure for any loading for their particular machines.

From the foregoing notes it is obvious that every effort should be made to operate the plant at the optimum back pressure.

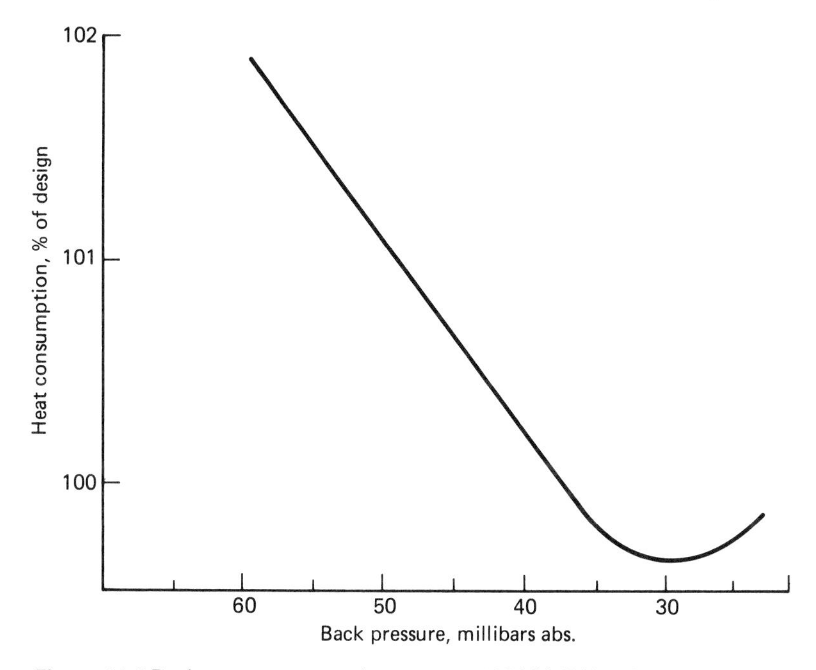

Figure 11.2 Back pressure correction curve — 120 MW T/A at full load

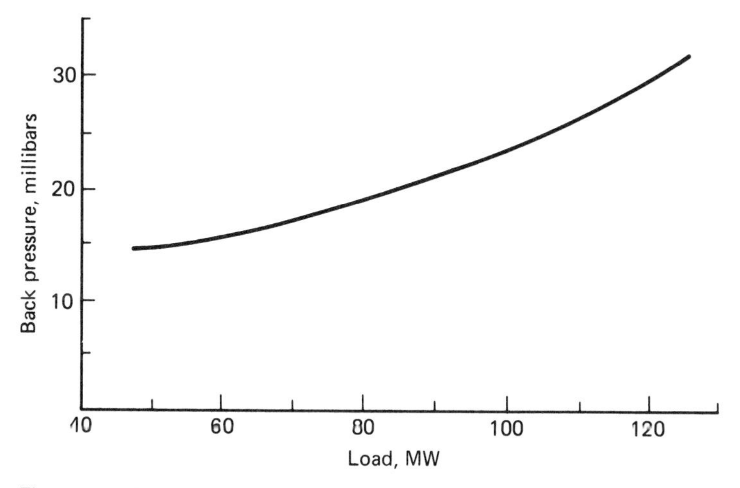

Figure 11.3 Minimum back pressure for various loads — 120 MW T/A

Graphical determination of losses contributing to departure of back pressure from optimum

The usual reasons for departure of condenser conditions from optimum are:

1 CW inlet temperature different from design.

2 CW quantity flowing through condenser incorrect.
3 Fouled tube plates.
4 Dirty tubes.
5 Air ingress into system under vacuum.

The contribution of some factors to a given departure of back pressure from optimum may be determined graphically. Consider a condenser with the following optimum and actual conditions at, say, full load.

Condition		*Unit*	*Optimum*	*Actual*
1	CW inlet temperature	°C	16.5	18.2
2	CW outlet temperature	°C	25.0	28.2
3	CW temperature rise (2) – (1)	°C	8.5	10
4	Saturated steam temp. corresponding to back pressure	°C	30.5	35.0
5	Terminal temp. difference (4) – (2)	°C	5.5	6.8
6	Air suction temperature	°C	26.0	27.0
7	Air suction depression (4) – (6)	°C	4.5	8.0
8	Back pressure	mbar	43.65	56.22

Refer to the 'Condenser Condition Graph', *Figure 11.4*.

Deviation due to CW inlet temperature. Plot a line vertically from the actual CW inlet temperature of 18.2°C to the intersection with the optimum 'CW rise' of 8.5°C. Thence plot horizontally to the intersection with the optimum 'terminal temperature difference' (TTD) line, and then vertically downward to cut the 'saturated steam temperature' line. The corresponding back pressure is 47.2 mbar. Hence, the loss due to the high CW inlet temperature is the difference in back pressure between 47.7 mbar and the optimum value of 43.65, i.e. 4.05 mbar.

Deviation due to CW flow. Plot a line from the actual CW inlet temperature vertically to the intersection with the *actual* CW rise of 10.0°C. Thence plot horizontally to the optimum TTD, then vertically downward to the saturation temperature of 33.7°C. The corresponding back pressure is 52.0 mbar so the loss due to incorrect CW flow is given by 52.0 – 47.7 = 4.30 mbar.

Deviation due to air/dirty tubes. The effect of air and dirty tubes on heat transfer is to increase the TTD above optimum. As they both give the same effect they are lumped together in this exercise. (Note: They can be segregated, as will be shown later). Plot from the actual CW inlet temperature to the actual CW rise and thence across to the actual TTD line of 7°C. Plotting vertically downward the saturated steam temperature is 35.1°C, and the back pressure is 56.22 mbar. So the deviation due to air/dirty tubes is given by 56.22 – 52.0 mbar = 4.22 mbar.

The effect of air ingress into the condenser is to increase the value of the

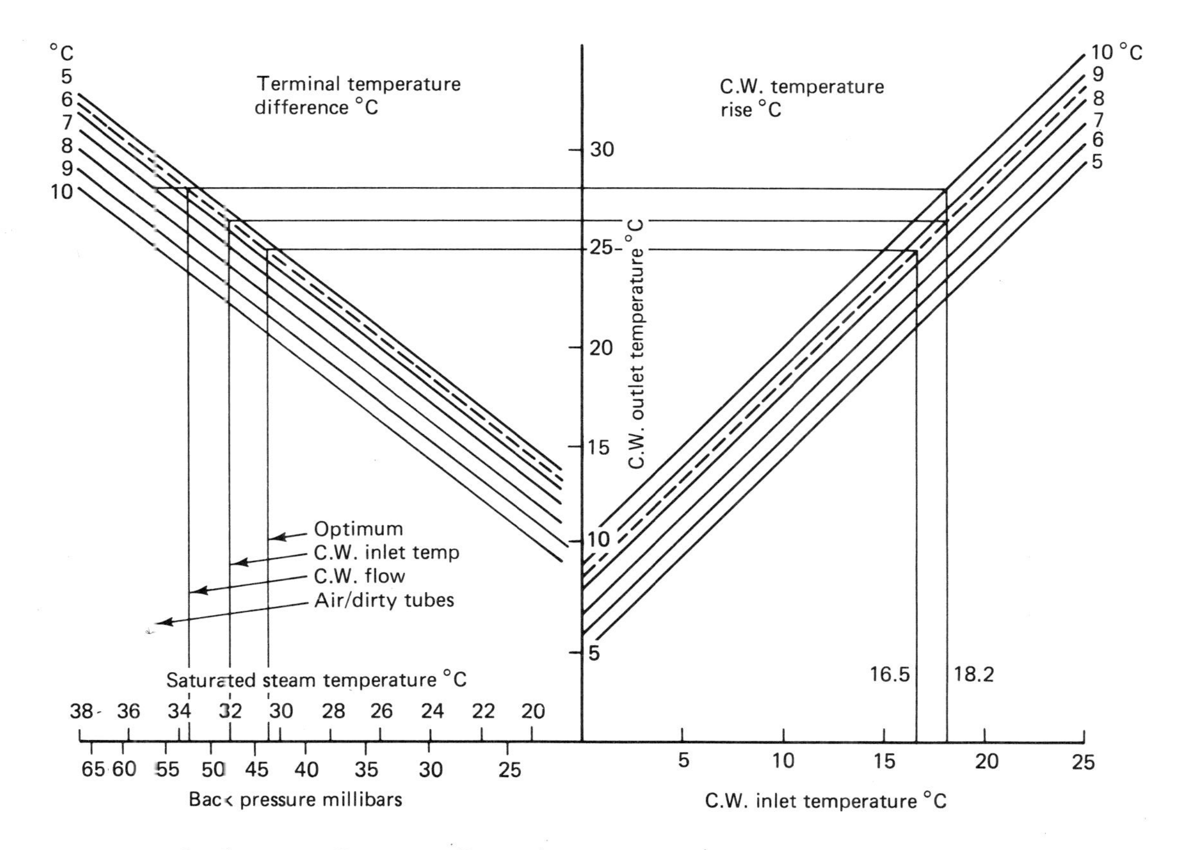

Figure 11.4 Condenser condition graph (full load)

'air suction depression' from optimum. In the case being considered the optimum value, obtained from the acceptance tests, is 4.5°C, but it is actually 8°C, so there must be air present. Action should be taken to locate and stop the ingress. Then a new set of readings can be obtained and all the deviation due to 'air/dirty tubes' can be attributed to dirty tubes. Incidentally, when condenser tubes are cleaned it is only the 'dirty tube' component which is eliminated.

Calculation of back pressure deviation

The graphical means of determining the extent of the deviations is useful for demonstrating the *method* of calculation. However, it is not particularly convenient for investigations on actual plant as each load requires the determination of the optimum conditions as a preliminary to calculations of the deviations. It is better to have curves to cover all the conditions likely to be met in practice. Curve 1 (*Figure 11.5*) enables the optimum back pressure

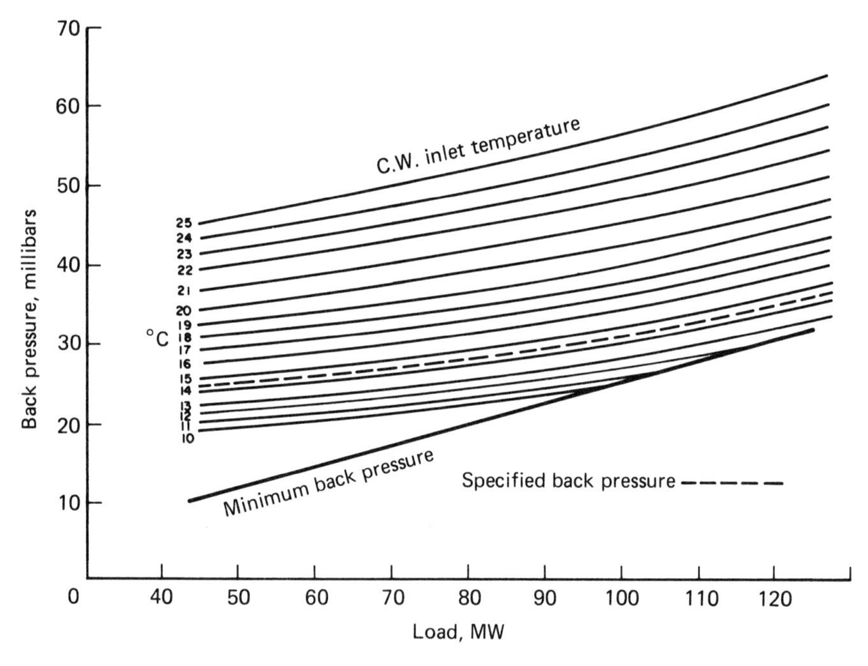

Figure 11.5 Target back pressure — 120 MW T/A. (Curve No 1)

to be determined for any load and for any probable CW inlet temperature. Thus, with a loading of 100 MW and a CW inlet temperature of 20°C the optimum back pressure would be 43.6 mbar.

Also shown on the curve is the specified back pressure for any load, i.e. the optimum back pressure when the CW inlet temperature is at the design value (in this case 14.5°C), and shown by the dotted line. To derive the curves in *Figure 11.5* proceed as follows:

From design data determine the optimum CW rise and terminal temperature difference for a range of loads as in curve 2 (*Figure 11.6*). Thus, at 100

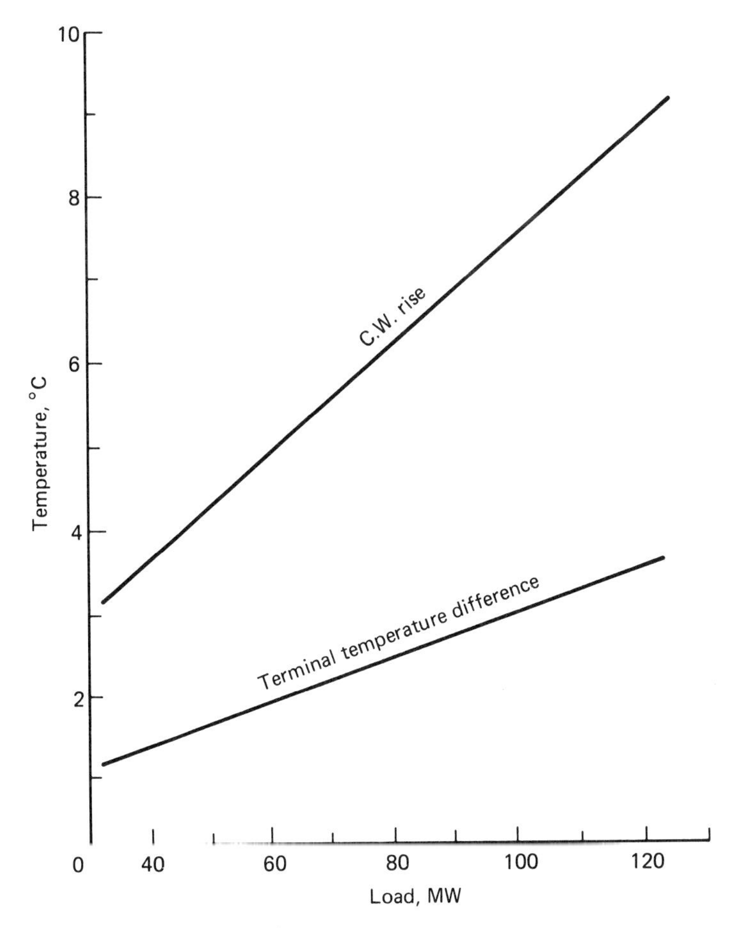

Figure 11.6 Optimum C.W. temperature rise and terminal temeperature difference — 120–MW T/A. (Curve No 2)

MW the CW rise is 7.5°C and the TTD is 3°C. Hence the saturation temperature will be 10.5°C above the CW inlet temperature. So with a CW inlet temperature of, say, 20°C the saturation temperature of the condensate will be 30.5°C, which corresponds to a back pressure of 43.65 mbar. Similarly, if the CW inlet temperature is 16°C the saturation temperature will be 26.5°C and the corresponding back pressure 34.6 mbar. Proceeding in this manner the family of curves were plotted.

There is one further item required – that of saturation temperature against back pressure, as shown in *Figure 11.7* The deviations can now be deter-

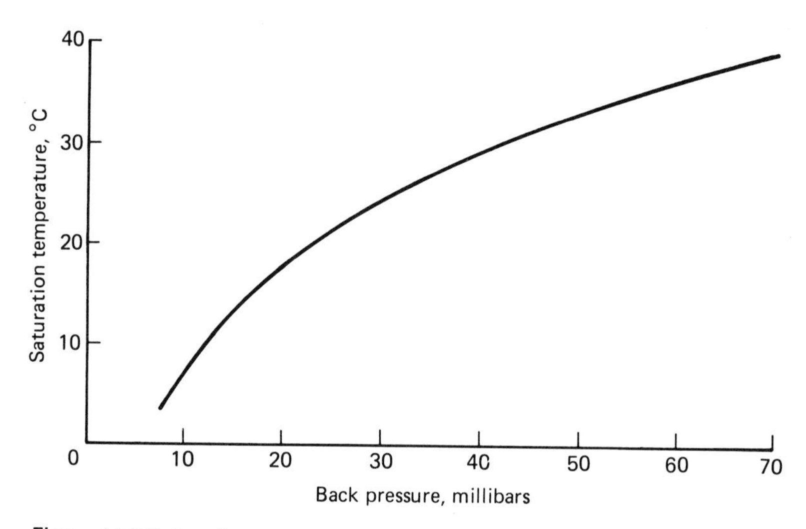

Figure 11.7 Saturation temperature *vs* back pressure (Curve No 3)

mined for any load. As with so many monitoring exercises it is convenient to use a pro-forma for the calculations such as that on page 501.

For example, in Test 1 a check was carried out on a 120 MW unit with three condensers, A, B and C. Items 1–9 are obvious and do not require any comment. Item 10 is determined from curve 1. At the intersection of the 'specified' back pressure and 100 MW read the back pressure 30.2 mbar.

Lines 11 and 12 are obtained directly from curve 2. Line 13 is the back pressure corresponding to a saturation temperature equal to the sum of the temperatures in lines 3, 11 and 12. In this case it is 21.5°C and the back pressure, from curve 3, is 25.6 mbar. Line 14 is calculated in a similar manner, but the temperature is given by line 5 and line 12. The back pressure corresponding to 23.9°C is 29.8 mbar. Lines 15 to 19 are self-explanatory.

Spot back pressure check

(+) = higher, (−) = lower back pressure.

	Date						
	Test			*1*	*2*	*3*	*4*
	Load MW			*100*	*80*	*120*	*118*
	Item	*Derivation*	*Unit*				
1	Back pressure	Plant	mbar	36.5	34.5	37.1	48.0
2	Corresp. sat. steam temp.	Figure 11.7	°C	27.6	26.4	27.5	32.2
3	CW inlet temp.	Plant	°C	11.0	7.0	8.0	18.7
4	CW outlet temp. 'A'	Plant	°C	20.9	10.3	21.6	30.2
	'B'	Plant	°C	22.7	14.0	23.8	27.0
	'C'	Plant	°C	19.2	12.0	20.0	27.0
5	(Mean)	Mean of (4)	°C	20.9	12.1	21.8	28.1
6	'A' exhaust steam temp.	Plant	°C	28.0	26.0	27.0	36.0
	'B'	Plant	°C	27.0	26.0	27.5	38.0
	'C'	Plant	°C	21.0	28.0	21.0	36.0
7	'A' condensate temp.	Plant	°C	25.4	26.5	27.5	35.0
	'B'	Plant	°C	25.4	26.5	27.5	35.0
	'C'	Plant	°C	21.7	24.5	27.0	26.5
8	'A' air suction temp.	Plant	°C	25.5	24.0	26.5	31.0
	'B'	Plant	°C	24.0	18.0	22.0	31.0
	'C'	Plant	°C	17.0	23.5	23.0	30.5
9	'A' CW outlet valve	Plant	Wide = 91 cm	30	36	33	38
	'B'	Plant		28	40	36	35
	'C'	Plant		23	31	33	34
10	Specified back press.	Figure 11.5	mbar	30.2			
11	Optimum CW rise	Figure 11.6	°C	7.2			
12	Optimum TTD	Figure 11.6	°C	3.0			
13	Back press. due to CW inlet temp.	(3)+(11)+(12)	mbar	25.6			
14	Back press. due to CW flow	(5)+(12)	mbar	29.8			
15	Variation due to CW inlet temp.	(13)−(10)	mbar	(-)4.6			
16	Variation due to CW flow	(14)−(13)	mbar	(+)4.2			
17	Variation due to air/dirty tubes	(1)−(14)	mbar	(+)6.7			
18	Total variation	(1)−(13)	mbar	(+)10.9			
19	Target back pressure	Figure 11.5	mbar	27			
20	Variation from target	(1)−(19)	mbar	(+)9.5			
21	No. of air pumps i/s (maximum 3)	Plant	—	2	2	3	1

Line 20 is determined by reference to curve 1. The target back pressure is read against the intersection of 100 MW and the actual CW inlet temperature of 11.0°C, i.e. 20.7 mbar. However, if the CW inlet temperature and the load lines intersect below the line of 'Minimum back pressure' then the target value to use is located from the intersection of the load and minimum back pressure lines. Thus, in the case quoted, if the CW inlet temperature had been 8°C then the target back pressure would be 25.5 mbar. Line 21 is self-explanatory.

Exercise 1 (Answers on page 533)

Calculate the deviations for checks 2, 3 and 4.

Notes on the results

Loss due to high CW inlet temperature. Provided the cooling towers (where appropriate) are performing satisfactorily this loss must be accepted. It is possible, of course, to minimize the loss by having an abnormal quantity of CW flowing through the condenser, thus giving a smaller CW rise across the condenser than optimum. However, the potential gain is reduced by the extra CW pumping power required. Therefore the increased turbine output due to improved vacuum must be greater than the increased CW pumping power required to justify this means of reducing the loss.

Deviation due to incorrect CW flow. This is normally a loss which can be eliminated. If the CW rise across the condenser is less than optimum the flow is excessive and the CW outlet valve opening should be reduced. Excessive CW flow may cause undercooling of the condensate, in which case the condensate temperature will be lower than that of the saturated steam temperature. If the rise is greater than optimum then the valve should be opened further. But if the CW temperature rise is unaffected by even an abnormal opening of the CW outlet valve, then the condenser tube plates are probably fouled with leaves or other debris, assuming there is no shortage of CW.

Deviation due to air ingress. This is an entirely preventable loss and steps should be taken to locate and stop any air ingress into the system under vacuum as soon as the condition is detected. Remember, the resistance to heat transfer of a layer of air 1.0 mm thick is equal to that of a slab of copper 16.5 m thick. Excessive air in the condenser may lead to an increased reading on the condensate oxygen meter. On the other hand there are times when the air ingress is so small that only one 50% air pump or steam ejector is required to handle it. In such a case it is a waste of energy to run two 50% pumps or ejectors 'just to be safe'.

Deviation due to dirty tubes. Operationally little can be done to eliminate the cause of the loss, as the tubes must be cleaned when the condenser is out of service. However, as soon as the loss is detected it should be ascertained that the chlorine injection to the affected plant is satisfactory. It may be that the Station Chemist will have the dosage increased. The effect of this loss on back pressure can be reduced by increasing the flow of CW but, as stated earlier, operation of the pumps must be optimized.

Notes on the effect of air ingress on back pressure

The capacity of the air pumps is determined empirically. Some idea of the relationship between air pump capacity and unit size is given in *Figure 11.8.*

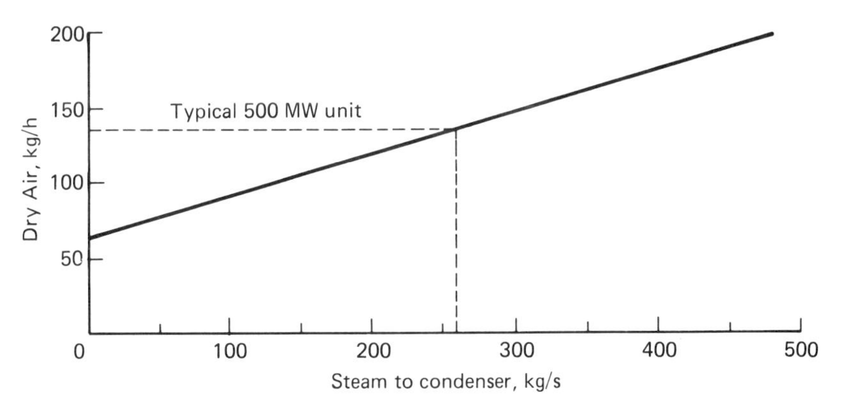

Figure 11.8 Air extraction plant capacity

When air mixes with steam it has very little effect on the absolute pressure. For example, mixing saturated steam with 1/2000 of its weight of air will increase the back pressure by only about one quarter of one per cent (0.25%) if the back pressure is 34 mbar, when only Dalton's law of partial pressures is considered. The real trouble with air is that it is incondensable, and so, when the steam condenses on the CW tubes, the air remains, and may form a film on the tube surface. As stated above, air is such an excellent insulator that it only requires a film a few molecules thick to interfere seriously with the heat transfer, and as a result the back pressure suffers.

Fortunately it is easy to determine whether air is present merely by measuring the temperature of the contents of the air suction pipe to the air pumps. When there is only a little air present the temperature is very little below the saturated steam temperature (say within 4.5°C). As more and more air is present the temperature falls – the more air present the greater the depression of the air suction compared to the saturated steam temperature. Preferably the thermometer should be in direct contact with the contents of the air suction pipe.

It may happen that at very low back pressures there is an accumulation of air in the condenser. This could be because the specific volume of the air becomes greater the lower the back pressure. Consequently the total volume to be handled by the air removal equipment may increase to such an extent that the equipment cannot cope. Therefore, if the condenser performance falls off sharply at low back pressures but returns to normal at higher pressures (for example going from part-load to full-load operation) then air-removal limitations should be considered a possibility.

Suggested modifications to back pressure indicators

It will be apparent that often it is necessary to determine both the back pressure and the corresponding saturation temperature. To avoid the necessity of referring to steam tables the back pressure indicator can be given an auxiliary scale. For example, consider the Vacumeter and Kenotometer instruments; they have the usual pressure scale on the left-hand side of the mercury column and a scale graduated in 'Percentage perfect vacuum' on the right-hand side. This latter scale is of no use in power stations so the author has had them replaced at the stations where he works with one graduated in steam saturation temperature, so the back pressure and saturation temperature are indicated as shown in *Figure 11.9*. Thus, when a reading of back pressure is obtained from the instrument, the corresponding temperature can also be determined.

Representative back pressure

Normally there is a significant variation of pressure across the plane of the turbine exhaust/condenser inlet, which is further complicated by the fact that there are now several different condenser configurations in common use. Therefore, it is necessary to have provision for a number of pressure-sensing tappings which should be about 10 mm diameter and preferably flush with the wall. Each exhaust should have tappings on all four sides, or two sides if that is all that are accessible, and there should be at least eight per condenser. The holes in individual condensers should be connected by a manifold although it is an advantage if individual measurements can also be obtained if required. Complete details are given in CEGB Site Test Code No. 3, *Performance of Surface-Type Steam Condensers.* On smaller machines with underslung condensers it was common to fit a vacuum grid such as shown in *Figure 11.10.*

When carrying out precise back-pressure measurements, use precision test mercury columns such as shown in *Figure 11.11* although suitable pressure transducers are now also very popular. Whatever instrument is used it should be accurate to within 0.3 millibar. Normally it is necessary to correct the readings obtained from a mercury column to those that would have been obtained at standard conditions. The method is shown later. When pressure transducers are used they have the considerable advantage

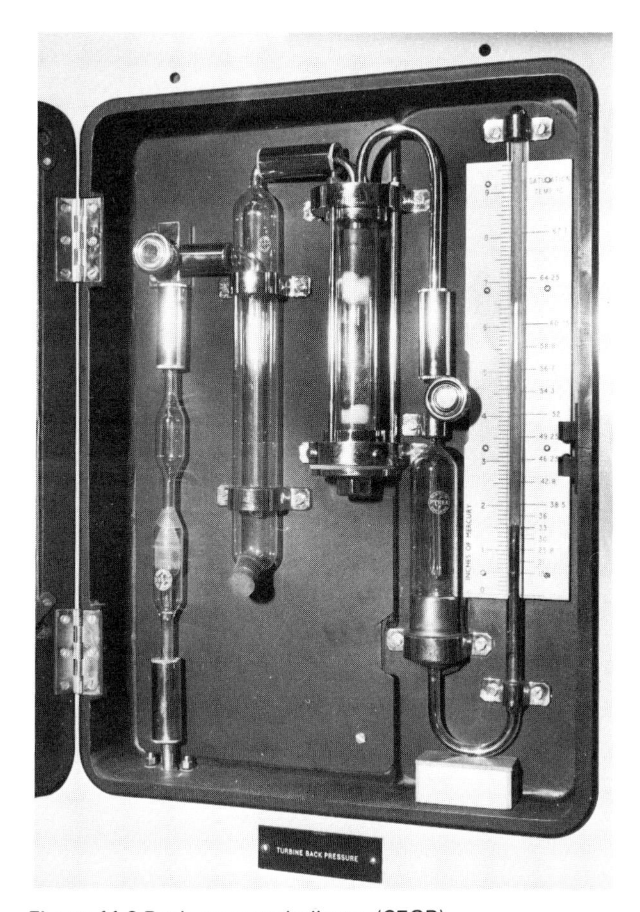

Figure 11.9 Back pressure indicator (CEGB)

of being capable of use in conjunction with automatic data aquisition equipment.

Representative CW temperature

The temperature of the inlet circulating water is usually sufficiently uniform for single point measurement. A thermometer pocket containing some oil and projecting at least 150 mm into the pipe should be adequate. The outlet circulating water, though, will almost certainly have significant variations of temperature and so some form of temperature averaging is required. Several possibilities exist to achieve this, one of which is to have four cantilevered sampling probes as shown in *Figure 11.12*. Details of this and others are given in the CEGB Site Test Code No. 3.

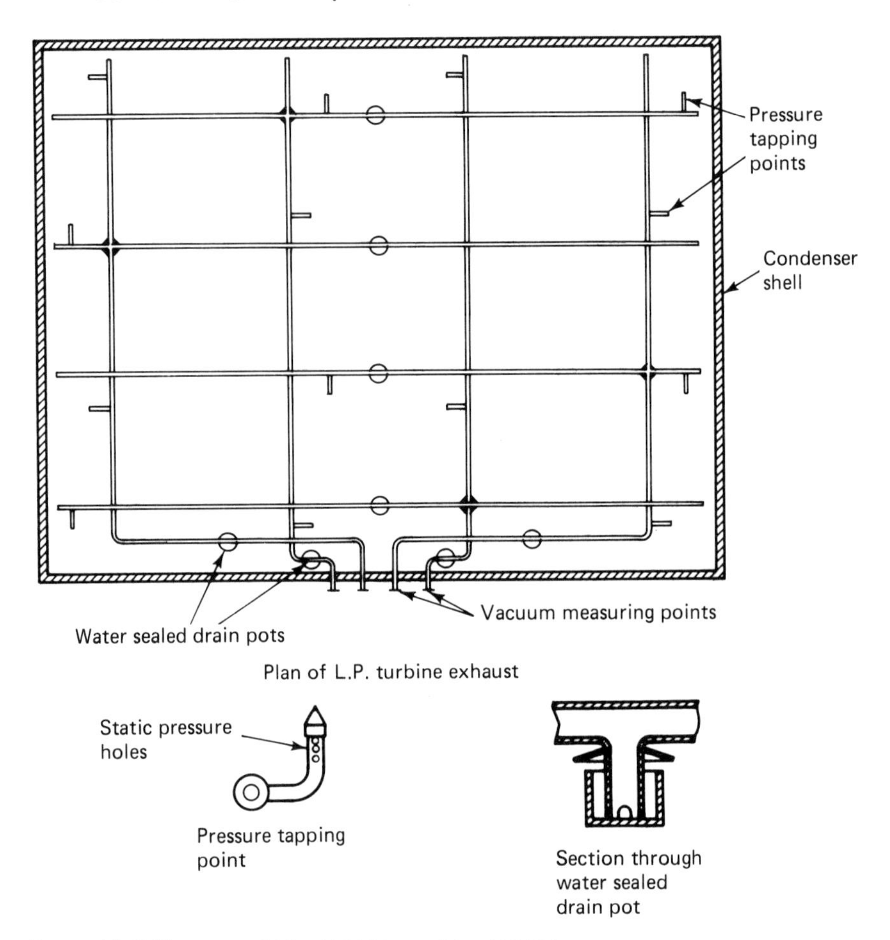

Figure 11.10 Vacuum grid for 120 MW machine (CEGB)

Correction of mercury column reading to 1013 mbar barometer

This is best shown by an example. The corrections are obtained from those used for the Fortin barometer.

Example

1 Average of mercury column readings	1000.000 mbar vacuum
2 Correction for ambient temperature (say 20°C)	(−) 3.26 mbar
3 Corrected reading (1) + (2)	996.740 mbar
4 Latitude correction (say 60°N)	(+) 1.270 mbar
5 Fully corrected manometer	998.010 mbar
6 Fully corrected barometer reading, say (see section on Fortin barometer)	1015.320 mbar

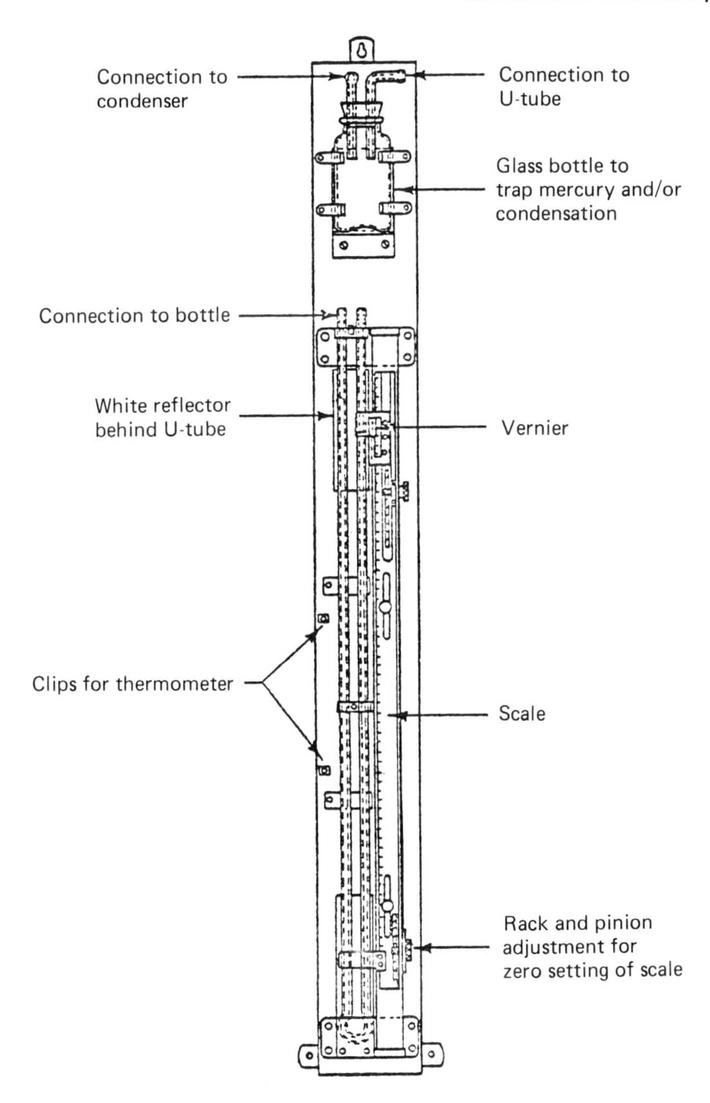

Figure 11.11 Precision test mercury column (CEGB)

7 Condenser back pressure (6) − (5)	17.31 mbar
8 Condenser vacuum corrected to 1013 mbar = (1013 − 17.31)	995.69 mbar

Detection of points of air ingress

It has already been mentioned that one method of determining that air is present is to note the air suction depression in the pipe leading to the air pumps. *Figure 11.13* shows typical air extraction baffling. Another common

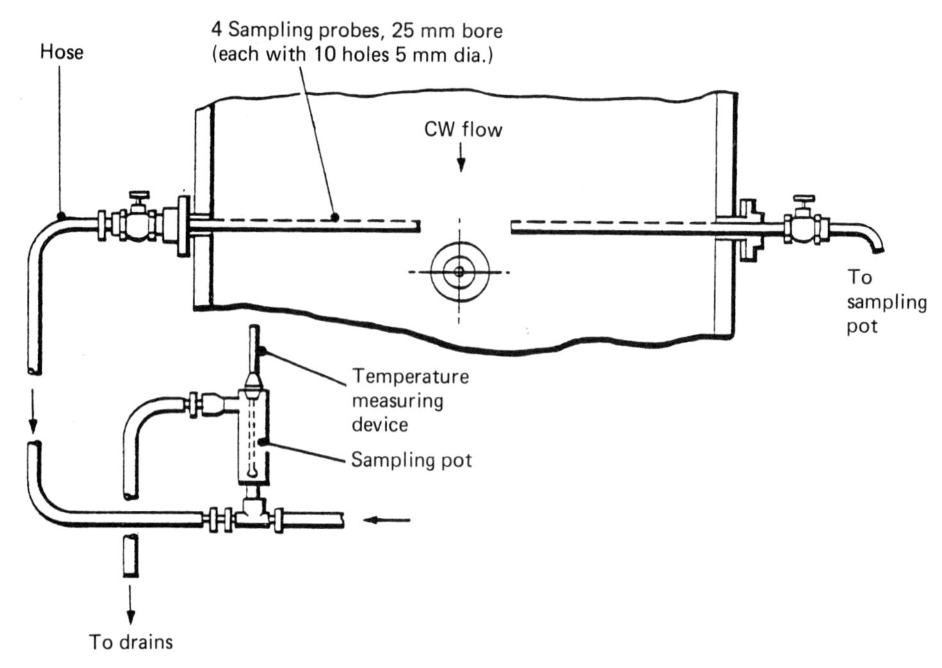

Figure 11.12 Method of measuring circulating water mean outlet temperature (CEGB)

method is to shut the air suction valves on the air pumps and note the time it takes for the back pressure to rise by a set amount – say 30 millibars. Comparison of the time obtained when the condenser was known to be 'tight' will indicate the severity of the air ingress. Sometimes metering orifices are provided which enable the actual quantity of air being handled by the air pump to be determined.

Whatever method is used, once it has been determined that air is present the main task is then to determine where it is leaking into the system and to rectify the trouble. However, it is often a sound idea to first of all try various combinations of the air pumps or ejectors, as it is not unheard of for the standby ejector or pump to have inleakage itself such that the running air removal equipment can barely cope. Thus there is no spare capacity for the normal inleakage into the main condenser.

To 'search' the main plant for leakage, a very convenient piece of apparatus is the 'Leybold leak detector' (*Figure 11.14*). It is electrically operated and has a sensing head located in the air suction pipe. One of the halogen family of fluids, say 'Isceon 12' or 'Arklone P', is sprayed on the suspect area. Should there be air ingress, the gas enters the condenser and is carried through the air suction pipe to the air pumps. During its passage through the pipe it passes over the sensing head which sends an electrical signal to the equipment, and the movement of a pointer indicates the presence of the gas. Of course, the condenser must be under vacuum when

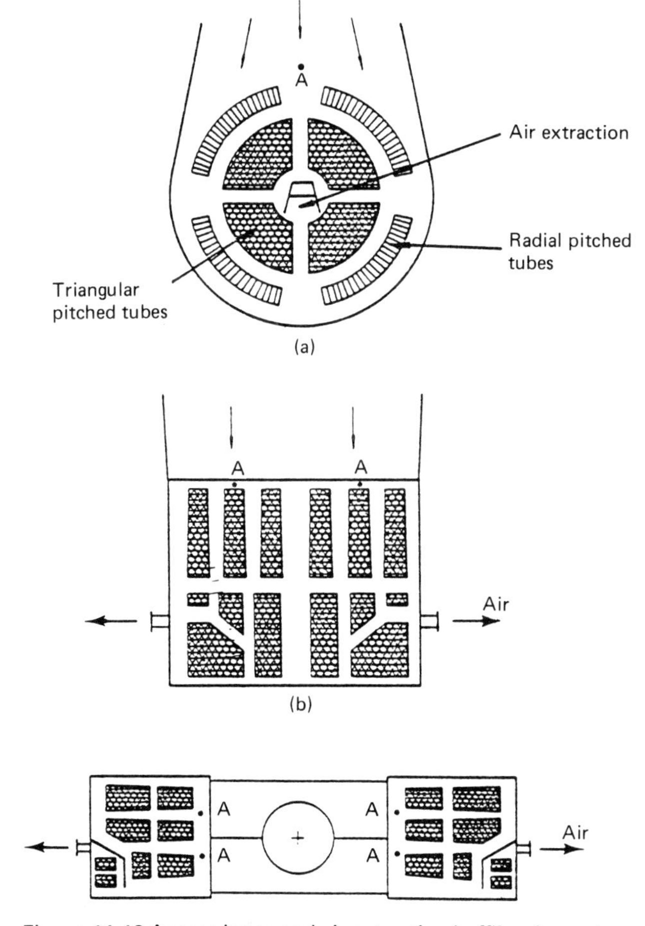

Figure 11.13 Access lanes and air extraction baffling for various configurations (CEGB)

this equipment is used.

Common locations for sources of air ingress include the atmospheric valve; explosion vents on the LP turbine; glands and gland housings; low-pressure bled steam lines and heaters; water-sealed glands on valves and pumps which operate below atmospheric pressure; condenser gauge glass packings and so on. Joints on the low-pressure, bled-steam pipes are large and often are not very accessible, so they may not be well 'made'. Should leakage occur in such a location a cure can be effected by 'Furmaniting' the joint. This is a process whereby a firm will send a team to inject a special compound into the joint to seal it while the unit remains on load. Pressure joints can also be sealed by this process and so it is obviously of great benefit for base load plant. The photographs in *Figure 11.15* show a pressure joint being repaired by Furmaniting.

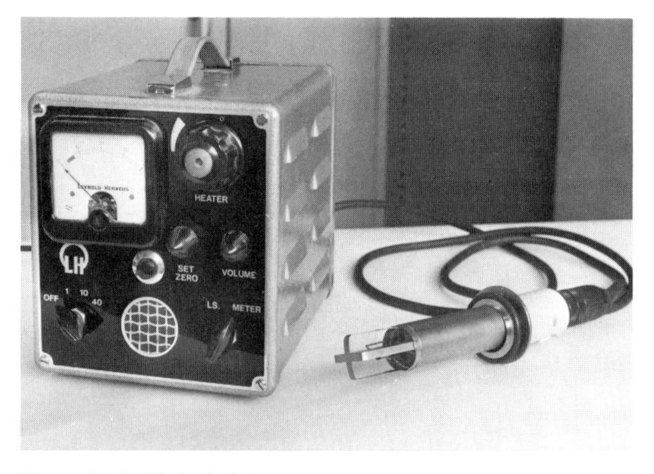

Figure 11.14 Air leak detector apparatus

Figure 11.15(a) 'Furmaniting' a steam leak from a valve (Furmanite Ltd.)

Double tube plates

Since the early 1960s it has been common to build condensers with double tube plates. With this type of construction the inlet and outlet ends of the

Figure 11.15(b) After 'Furmaniting' (Furmanite Ltd.)

condenser each have two tube plates separated by a gap of about one centimetre. The basic idea is that in the event of a ferrule or tube-expansion leaking the circulating water will drip into the space between the tube plates instead of contaminating the condensate. Any leakage is piped to a small collecting tank via a conductivity measuring unit. Provided the conductivity is acceptable the drains are pumped back to the condenser. However, if the conductivity level is unacceptable because of leakage of circulating water then the drains are pumped to waste.

Detection of small leaks in condensers

Double tube plates, as mentioned above, provide an excellent means of detecting a small CW leak at the tube ends. However, other leaks are possible and there are various ways of locating them. The old-established method of location is to fill the steam side of the condenser with water to above the tubes and add fluorescene – about 2 kg for a 350 MW unit. Leakage is located by scanning the tube ends in ultra-violet light, the idea being that any leakage will drip from the tubes and be easily visible because it will fluoresce. However, although this method is satisfactory in many cases, there are some disadvantages, namely:

1. Very small leaks are difficult to detect.
2 If there are a number of leaks it is difficult to segregate sound tubes from faulty ones.
3 The cold water used to flood the condenser often causes small tube leaks to contract and seal. The leakage will re-appear, of course, when the tubes are warmed-up in service.
4 The unit must be off load.

Therefore, various alternative methods have been developed including the following:

(a) *Foam.* This consists of spraying a layer of foam on the tube plates at both ends of the condenser while a vacuum is maintained on the steam side. If there is a leak, the associated tube will be put under vacuum and the foam will enter the tube, thus easily identifying it. Of course, it is absolutely vital for the success of this method that the foam should be stable, i.e. it should adhere to the tube plate for a considerable time as a thick layer.

(b) *Bubbler leak.* A tedious but positive method. One end of the condenser has its tubes plugged, a vacuum is maintained on the steam side and the bubbler is connected to each tube in turn at the other end. Should there be a faulty tube, air bubbles will pass through the bubbler. The objections to this method are:

1 the steam side must be under vacuum;
2 it is laborious;
3 if there is an obstruction in the tube (say, a bullet stuck part way along), then only the tube between the bubbler and the obstruction will be tested;
4 it is not much good for detecting leaks at tube ends.

An alternative to the conventional bubbler, shown in *Figure 11.16*, was developed at the Marchwood Engineering Laboratories of the CEGB. The arrangement is shown in *Figure 11.17*, and the equipment can be used whether the turbine is on or off load. The off-load method of operation is as follows:

With the vent valve shut, the apparatus is brought under vacuum from the vacuum pump. The pump isolating valve is then shut and, shortly after, the balance valve is also shut. Any leakage into the tube will be indicated by a stream of bubbles in the bubbler jar.

(c) *Indiplugs.* A similar effect to the bubbler is obtained by using Indiplugs. These are tapered rubber plugs which have a hole along their length. A very thin rubber diaphragm fits over the end of the plug. The method of use is simple. The suspect tubes are sealed at one end and the rubber plugs inserted in the other. A vacuum is maintained

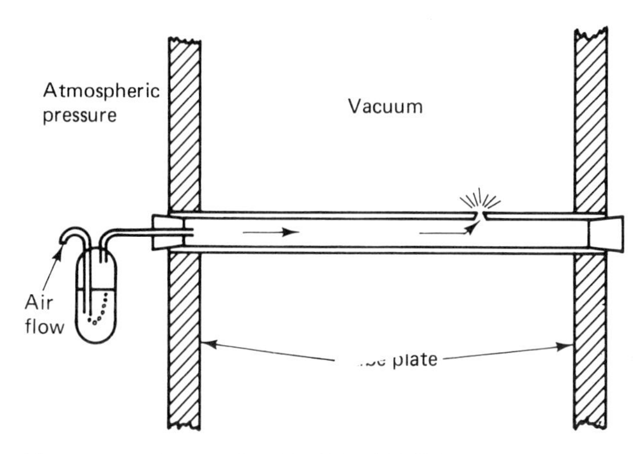

Figure 11.16 Conventional bubbler (CEGB)

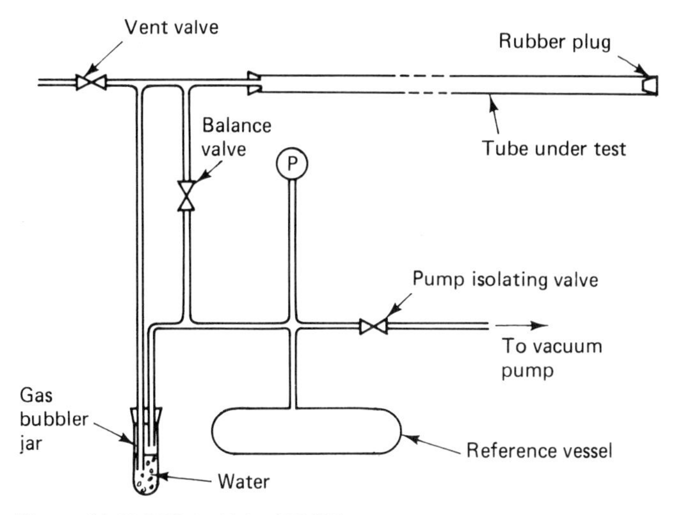

Figure 11.17 MEL bubbler (CEGB)

in the condenser and, if there is a leak in a tube, the diaphragm is distorted thus clearly indicating the presence of the leak.

(d) *Furmanite guns*. Another method utilizes Furmanite guns. These can be used to seal the ends of the tubes and the tube is pressurized by air. The rate of decay of the air pressure is a measure of the soundness of the tube. The method is laborious but can be used without the condenser being under vacuum. Other Furmanite guns are available to check for ferrule or expanded joint leaks. This is a very important application, as such leaks are often very troublesome to locate.

The equipment can be used also to detect leaks in feed heater and cooler tube nests. When the handle is squeezed the neoprene seal is expanded and seals the tube. The tube is sealed at either end and it is then pressurized with air. Leakage is indicated by the decay of the pressure.

For checking tube end ferrules a special gun is used. A seal is made against the tube plate around the ferrule and a second is made a short distance inside the tube by an expanded neoprene seal. Thus, the ferrule and short length of tube can be pressurized with air and leakage is determined by the rate of pressure decay.

(e) *Halogen Gas*. This method will indicate the level of the faulty tube in the condenser, so the number of individual tubes to be checked is considerably reduced. An indication of the level of the CW in the condenser is required, and the steam side must be under vacuum. The CW level is lowered slowly and a halogen gas is introduced into the air space above the CW level. When the faulty tube is exposed the gas will enter ths steam space and along the air suction pipe past the Leybold equipment sensing head.

On-load tube cleaning

The desirability of keeping the condenser tubes clean on the CW side is obvious, as dirt is synonomous with interference with heat transfer. One particular source of trouble arises from slime deposition. River waters contain algae and other organisms which find the habitat inside a condenser tube amenable, and so they settle on the tube surface. As they are jelly-like creatures, they provide a suitable bonding agent for mud and silt, thus seriously interfering with heat transfer.

The solution to the problem is to make the environment inhospitable, which is done by intermittently dosing the CW going to the condenser with chlorine. The residual free chlorine at the CW outlet must be carefully monitored to ensure that no contamination occurs if it is returned to a river. Chlorination is very effective, although quite expensive. At coastal stations there are often additional problems due to mussel growth, see *Figure 11.18*. Here again the normal cure is to inject chlorine into the CW.

An alternative to chlorine injection for keeping the tubes clean is to use on-load mechanical cleaning. In this system spongy balls are circulated through the tubes while the unit is in service, thus constantly keeping them clean. The general arrangement is shown in *Figure 11.19*. Many units have been fitted with this equipment. The costs involved with the system, besides capital, include the pumping power to recirculate the balls, make-up for the ball charge and the extra cost of the CW pumping power because of the increased system resistance. On the other hand there is no necessity for chlorine injection and, the manufacturers claim, the tubes are kept completely free of films from slime, dirt and scale.

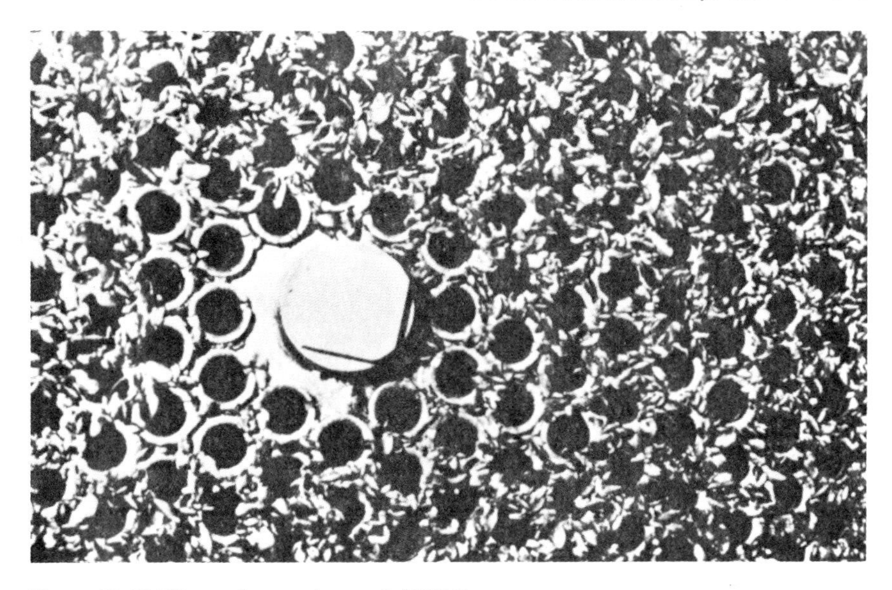

Figure 11.18 Effects of mussel growth (CEGB)

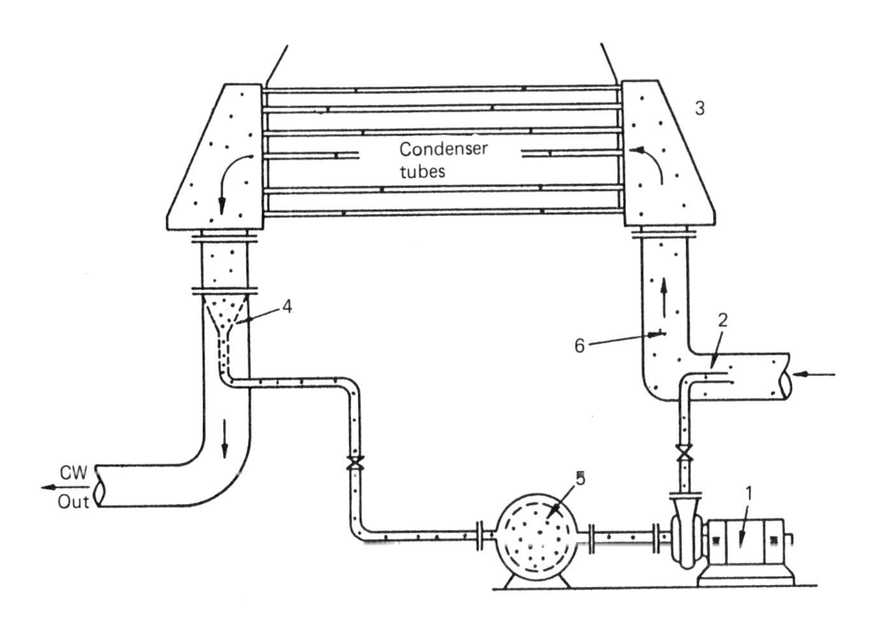

Figure 11.19 On-load condenser cleaning system (CEGB)

1. Pump/motor set for ball circulation
2. Injection/distribution point
3. Condenser waterbox
4. Strainer unit for ball recovery
5. Ball trap for collection and inspection purposes
6. Sponge rubber balls distributed in the circulating water

Scale formation

A common problem in Europe and America in recent years has been the deposition of phosphate scales on the CW side of condenser tubes. The trouble stems largely from the increasing use of washing powders, particularly in domestic washing machines. The water from many of the machines eventually discharges into rivers, thus increasing the phosphate level of the water. This undesirable trend will probably continue because of the increasing use of these machines.

When this water is used as power station CW the phosphate, under suitable conditions, forms a scale on the condenser tubes which interferes with the heat transfer and so worsens the back pressure. The measures taken to combat the problem include:

(a) *Scale prevention.* This is achieved by controlling the pH of the CW to 7.5 by dosing it with sulphuric acid. However, this can lead to acid attack of the concrete of the CW culverts.

(b) *Scale removal.* Periodically chemically clean the CW side of the condenser tubes to remove the deposition. The amount of deposit can be considerable – for example, over two tonnes were removed from a 350 MW unit condenser.

Asiatic clam fouling

This type of fouling is common in the USA, and the history of the problem is quite interesting. Asiatic clams are a popular food with Chinese people and, in the 1930s, many Chinese labourers were working on projects on the Columbia River. Some live clams got into the river and multiplied rapidly, so much so that now they are to be found in the rivers of over half the states in the USA.

The clams find the environment inside condensers hospitable and have an adverse effect on turbine back pressure, as they can grow to 35 mm in three years and some become even larger. No really effective solution to the problem has yet been found but some of the means of controlling the pests include:

(a) massive doses of chlorine;
(b) regular condenser cleaning;
(c) reverse flow condensers in which the direction of water flow through the tubes can be changed;
(d) operating at elevated temperatures of over 40°C.

Variations of condenser operating conditions

The three main conditions to consider are:

(a) change of CW inlet temperature;

(b) change of CW flow;
(c) change of heat rejected to the condenser.

Before proceeding it is important to appreciate that the amount of heat transferred in a heat exchanger usually depends upon the log mean temperature difference (LMTD) between the two fluids. The numerical value of the log mean temperature difference is given by:

$$\text{LMTD} = \frac{\theta_1 - \theta_2}{2.3 \log_{10} \dfrac{\theta_1}{\theta_2}}$$

where $\theta_1 = t_3 - t_1$
$\theta_2 = t_3 - t_2$
t_1 = CW inlet temperature
t_2 = CW outlet temperature
t_3 = saturated steam temperature

The value can be calculated or read from *Figure 11.20*.

The log mean temperature difference formula is due to Grashof and was related to contraflow heat exchangers. Condensers, though, are usually of the crossflow type and so the temperature difference is often taken as the arithmetic mean, i.e.

$$\text{Mean temperature} = \frac{\theta_1 + \theta_2}{2}$$

The following calculations use the LMTD and the reader should recalculate them using the arithmetic mean to see what difference is made.

(a) *Effect of variation of CW inlet temperature on back pressure*

There are two effects caused by a change of CW inlet temperature. The primary one is to alter the steam saturation temperature by the same amount as the CW change, assuming all the other factors remain constant. This, in its turn, will change the corresponding back pressure. The secondary effect is caused by the fact that the heat transfer of the CW water film in contact with the condenser tubes changes with the temperature of the water. The primary and secondary changes are in opposite directions. The magnitude of the secondary effect is approximately equal to the fourth root of the mean CW temperature.

For example, consider a condenser with the following conditions:

CW inlet temperature t_1 = 10°C
CW outlet temperature t_2 = 20°C
Steam saturation temperature t_3 = 25°C

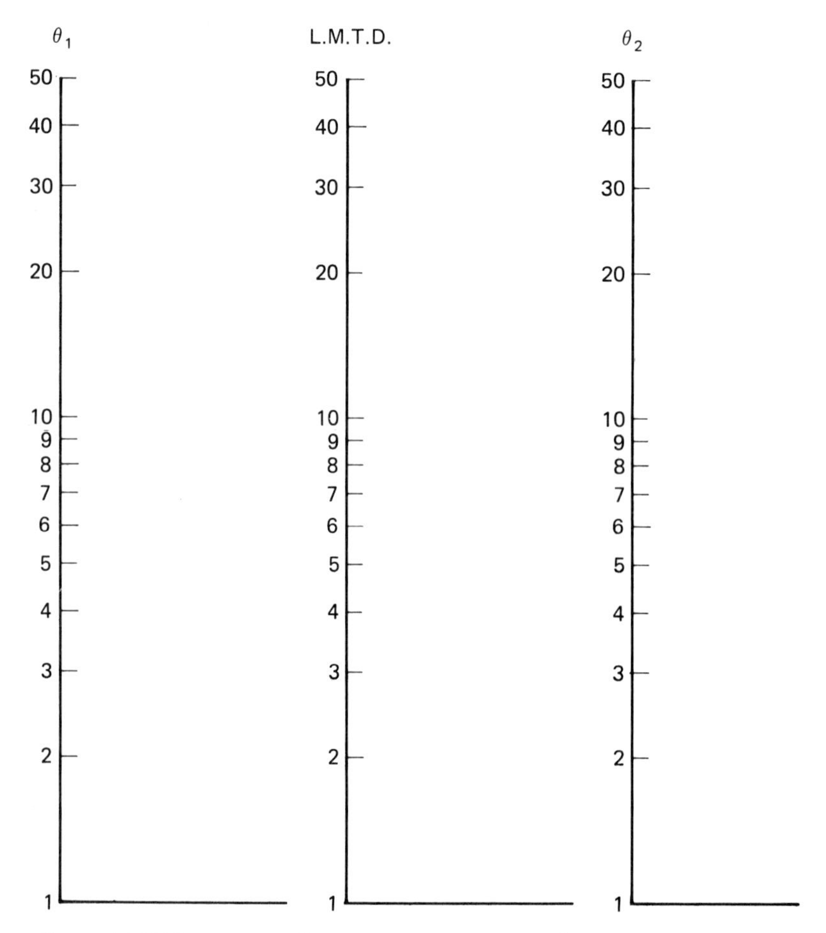

Figure 11.20 Nomogram of log mean temperature difference

Corresponding back pressure = 31.66 mbar
Mean CW temperature = 15°C
Log mean temperature difference = 8.5°C

If the CW inlet temperature is increased to 15°C the primary effect will be to increase the saturation temperature of the steam to 30°C. The corresponding back pressure is 42.41 mbar.

The secondary effect depends upon the change of mean CW temperature from 15°C to 20°C; the new log mean temperature difference will be:

$$\text{New LMTD} = 8.5\sqrt[4]{\left(\frac{15}{20}\right)} = 8.5 \times 0.93$$

$$= 7.9°\text{C}$$

$$\text{But LMTD} = \frac{\theta_1 - \theta_2}{2.3 \log_{10} \frac{\theta_1}{\theta_2}}$$

$$\therefore 7.9 = \frac{10}{2.3 \log_{10} \frac{t_3 - t_1}{t_3 - t_2}}$$

$$\log_{10} \frac{t_3 - t_1}{t_3 - t_2} = \frac{10}{7.9 \times 2.3} = 0.55$$

$$\frac{t_3 - t_1}{t_3 - t_2} = \text{antilog } 0.55 = 3.548$$

$t_3 - 15 = 3.548\,(t_3 - 25)$
$73.7 = 2.548t_3$
So $t_3 = 28.92$
Equivalent back pressure = 40.0 mbar

So the final conditions are:

CW inlet temperature t_1 = 15°C
CW outlet temperature t_2 = 25°C
Steam saturation temperature t_3 = 28.92°C
Equivalent back pressure = 40.0 mbar

(b) *Effect of variation of CW flow on back pressure*

The primary effect of a change of CW flow is to alter the CW temperature rise. Thus, if the flow is halved the temperature rise will double, other things being equal. The secondary effect, which operates in the same direction as the primary, results from the change of heat transfer rate, due to the changed thickness of the CW boundary film. It is approximately proportional to the square root of the flow. Consider a system with the following initial conditions:

CW inlet temperature t_1 = 10°C
CW outlet temperature t_2 = 20°C
CW temperature rise = 10°C
Steam saturation temperature t_3 = 25°C
Corresponding back pressure = 31.66 mbar
Log mean temperature difference = 8.5°C
CW flow = 10 000 kg/s

If the flow increases to 12 000 kg/s the CW rise will become

10 000/12 000 = 8.3°C due to the primary effect. The mean CW temperature will thus be 14.1°C and the saturation temperature of the steam 18.3 + 5 = 23.3°C. The corresponding back pressure is 28.6 mbar.

Secondly, the increased flow will increase the heat transfer rate by reducing the stagnant water film adjacent to the condenser tubes and this will result in a log mean temperature difference as follows:

$$\text{LMTD} = 8.5\sqrt{\frac{10\,000}{12\,000}} = 7.76°\text{C}$$

So the new conditions will be:

CW inlet temperature t_1	= 10°C
CW outlet temperature t_2	= 18.3°C
Log mean temperature difference	= 7.76°C
CW flow	= 12 000 kg/s

$$\text{Thus } 7.76 = \frac{8.3}{2.3 \log_{10} \frac{t_3 - t_1}{t_3 - t_2}}$$

$$\text{Log}_{10} \frac{t_3 - t_1}{t_3 - t_1} = \frac{8.3}{2.3 \times 7.76} = 0.465$$

$$\frac{t_3 - t_1}{t_3 - t_2} = 2.917$$

$$t_3 - 10 = 2.917\,(t_3 - 18.3)$$

$$43.38 = 1.917\,t_3$$

$$\therefore t_3 = 22.6°\text{C}$$

The corresponding back pressure = 27.32 mbar

(c) *Effect of variation of heat transferred to the CW*

If the heat rejected to the condenser changes the CW temperature rise and the log mean temperature difference will also change. For example, consider a condenser with the following conditions:

CW inlet temperature t_1	= 10°
CW outlet temperature t_2	= 20°C
CW temperature rise	= 10°C
Steam saturation temperature t_3	= 25°C
Corresponding back pressure	= 31.66 mbar
Log mean temperature difference	= 8.5°C
Heat rejected to CW	= 100%

If the heat rejected is increased to 105% the CW temperature rise will become

$$10 \times \frac{105}{100} = 10.5°\text{C}$$

Also, the log mean temperature difference will become

$$8.5 \times \frac{105}{100} = 8.9°\text{C}$$

$$\therefore 8.9 = \frac{10.5}{2.3 \log_{10} \dfrac{t_3 - t_1}{t_3 - t_2}}$$

$$\log \frac{t_3 - t_1}{t_3 - t_2} = \frac{10.5}{2.3 \times 8.9} = 0.513$$

$$\frac{t_3 - t_1}{t_3 - t_2} = 3.258$$

$$t_3 - 10 = 3.258\,(t_3 - 20.5)$$

$$56.789 = 2.258 t_3$$

$$\therefore t_3 = 25.15°\text{C}$$

The corresponding back pressure = 31.95 mbar

So the final conditions are:

CW inlet temperature	= 10°C
CW outlet temperature	= 20.5°C
Steam saturation temperature	= 25.15°C
Corresponding back pressure	= 31.95 mbar
Heat rejection to condenser	= 105%

It should be remembered that much of the above is also applicable to other heat exchangers such as feed heaters.

In the example that follows, *Figures 11.22* and *11.23* give heat transfer corrections to the log mean temperature difference as an alternative to calculating the values.

Example

A power station is operating at full load with all six of its cooling towers in service. It is a closed CW system so there is no supply of cooling water from the river except for a small amount of make-up which can be disregarded.

By how much would the back pressure change if one cooling tower was taken out of service but the total station load remained the same and the water loading on the remaining towers was unchanged? The initial conditions are:

Condenser CW inlet temperature t_1	= 20.25°C
Condenser CW outlet temperature t_2	= 30.40°C
CW temperature rise	= 10.15°C
Terminal temperature difference	= 3.6°C
Saturated steam temperature t_3	= 34°C
Corresponding back pressure	= 53.18mbar
Velocity of CW in condenser tubes	= 1.5 m/s
Cooling tower dry bulb temperature	= 10°C
Cooling tower wet bulb temperature	= 7.5°C
Condenser tube diameter	= 25 mm
$\theta_1 = t_3 - t_1$	= 13.75°C
$\theta_2 = t_3 - t_2$	= 3.6°C

$$\text{LMTD} = \frac{13.75 - 3.6}{2.3 \log_{10} \dfrac{13.75}{3.6}}$$

$$= \frac{10.15}{2.3 \log 3.82}$$

$$= \frac{10.15}{2.3 \times 0.5821}$$

So LMTD = 7.58°C

Taking one cooling tower out of service will cause the original heat abstraction in the condensers to be accomplished in the new circumstances by only 5/6 of the quantity of water. Therefore the CW rise will become:

$$10.15 \times \frac{6}{5} = 12.18°\text{C}$$

So the CW outlet temperature would become 32.43°C if the CW inlet temperature remained as before. However, as it is a closed CW system this will not be the case, and so it is necessary to refer to the Universal Performance Chart (*Figure 11.21*) to determine the new conditions.

The initial conditions are shown on the chart. When the cooling tower is taken out of service the CW rise will become 12.18°C and reference to the chart shows that at 12.18°C cooling range the re-cooled temperature t_1 = 21°C

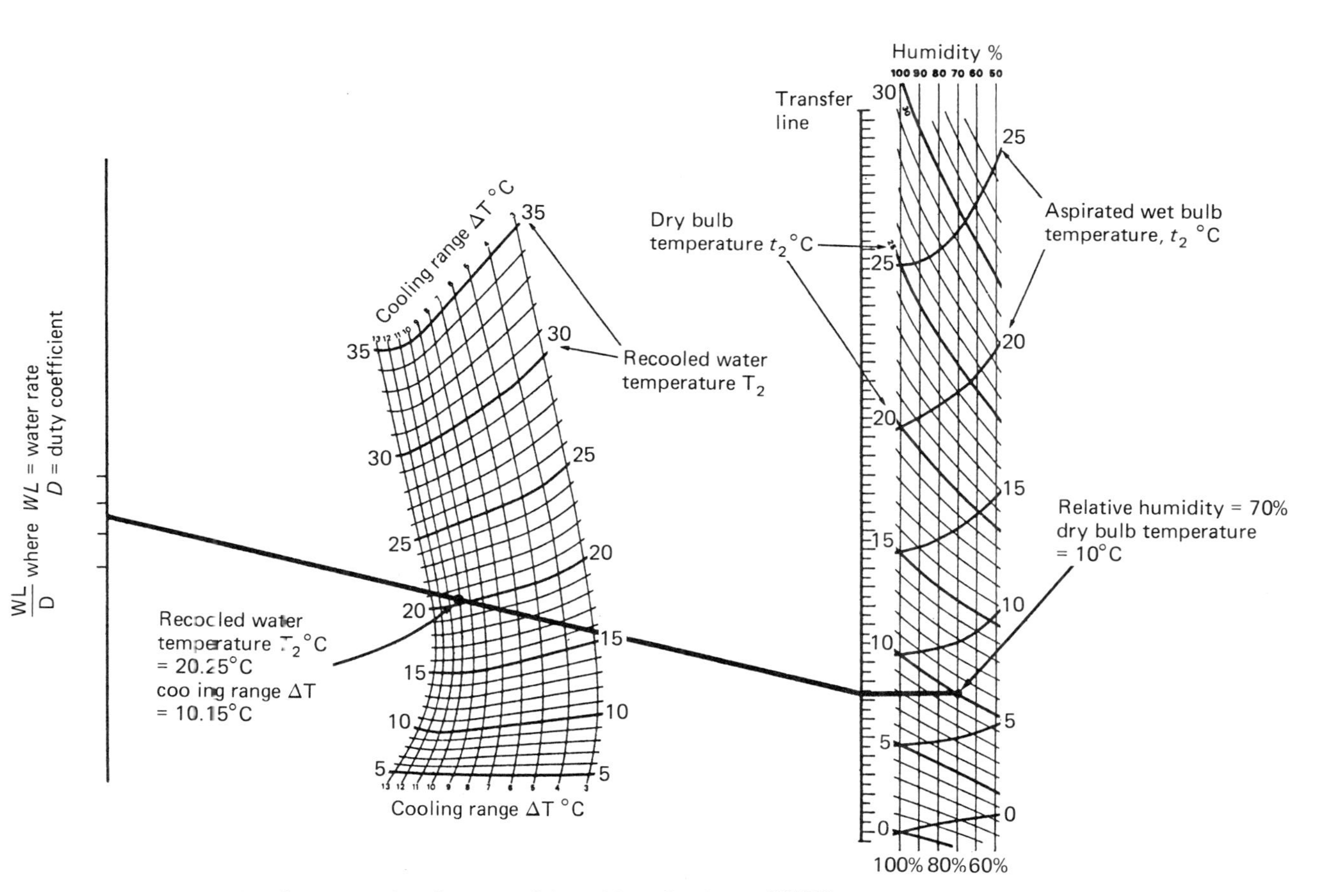

Figure 11.21 Universal performance chart for natural draught cooling tower (CEGB)

Hence the new value of $t_2 = 21.0 + 12.18 = 33.18°C$
Therefore the mean CW temperature has gone from

$$\frac{20.25 + 30.40}{2} = 25.31°C, \text{ to}$$

$$\frac{21.0 + 33.18}{2} = 27.09°C$$

Because of the higher average temperature the log mean temperature difference will reduce as follows (see *Figure 11.22*):

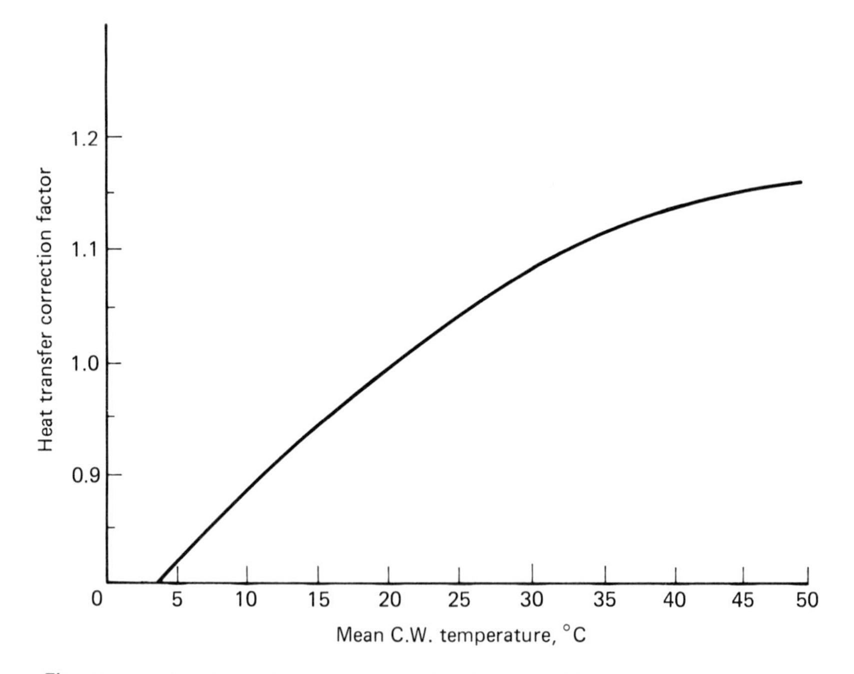

Figure 11.22 Heat transfer correction factor for mean CW temperature

Factor from curve for mean temperature 25.31°C = 1.05
Factor for mean temperature of 27.09°C = 1.07

$$\text{So factor } K_1 = \frac{1.05}{1.07} = 0.982$$

Also the velocity of the CW through the tubes will be less, the new velocity being 1.5 × 5/6 = 1.25 m/s. This will cause the heat transfer to reduce as shown in the curve in *Figure 11.23*.

Factor for velocity 1.5 m/s = 3.13

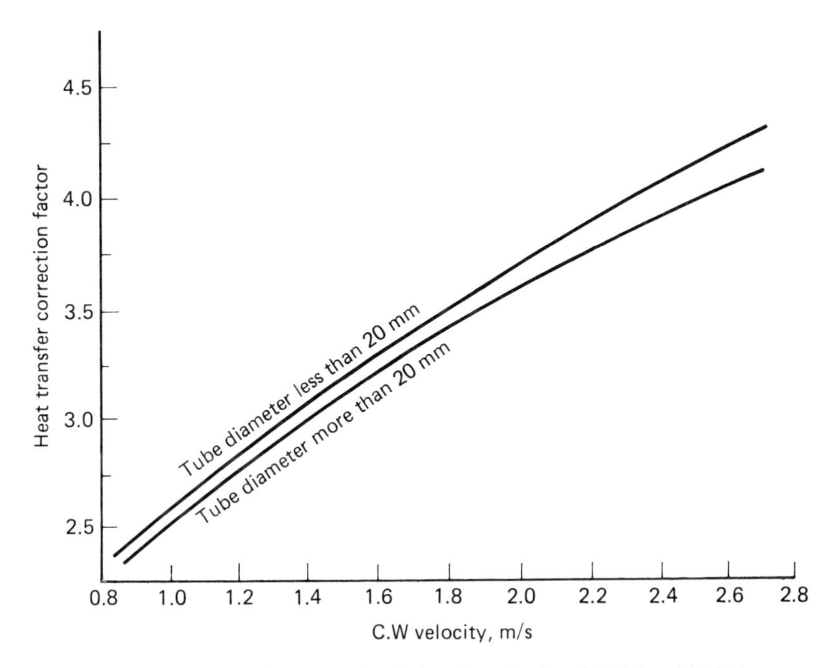

Figure 11.23 Heat transfer correction factor for velocity of CW flow (CEGB)

Factor for velocity 1.25 m/s = 2.85

$$\text{So factor } K_2 = \frac{3.13}{2.85} = 1.098$$

Because of factors K_1 and K_2 the original log mean temperature will change from 7.58°C to

$$7.58 \times K_1 \times K_2 = 7.58 \times 0.982 \times 1.098$$
$$\text{So LMTD} = 8.2°\text{C}$$

So with five cooling towers in service:

$$8.2 = \frac{12.18}{2.3 \log \dfrac{\theta_1}{\theta_2}}$$

$$\log \frac{\theta_1}{\theta_2} = \frac{12.18}{2.3 \times 8.2} = 0.65$$

$$\frac{\theta_1}{\theta_2} = 4.467$$

$$\theta_1 = 4.467\,\theta_2$$

$(t_3 - t_1) = 4.467\,(t_3 - t_2)$
$t_3 - 21 = 4.467\,(t_3 - 33.18)$
$127.2 = 3.467 t_3$
$t_3 = 36.7°\text{C}$
Corresponding back pressure = 61.7 mbar

Hence the back pressure will go from 53.18 mbar to 61.7 mbar by taking one cooling tower out of service.

Condenser layouts

Traditionally, condensers were always located beneath the low-pressure cylinder, normally in a transverse direction. Since the 1960s a change has been made to other dispositions.

Axial condensers

With the advent of multi low-pressure cylinders the axial condenser became feasible, see *Figure 11.24*. A disadvantage of this type is that it requires a deep basement and so building costs are increased. On the other hand the condenser design is such that a continuous support wall is provided along the sides of the LP cylinders.

Bridge condensers

This type is shown in *Figure 11.25*. The condenser and the support beam for the low-pressure cylinder are integral and span the gap between the foundation blocks at the steam and generator ends.

Radial condensers

As the name implies, the condenser tubes are located all round the LP turbine except for space for the IP/LP steam pipes and access to bearings (*Figure 11.26*). This arrangement offers some thermodynamic advantages in that the leaving loss is reduced and there is a reduced hood loss. The weight of the structure is less than other types and the height of the basement is reduced, so leading to lower building costs. The foundation block is simplified and so this is a big advantage.

Pannier condensers

These are similar to radial condensers in some respects, but the condenser tubes are only located at the sides of the turbine (*Figure 11.27*). There is only limited space below the operating floor which is something of a disadvantage.

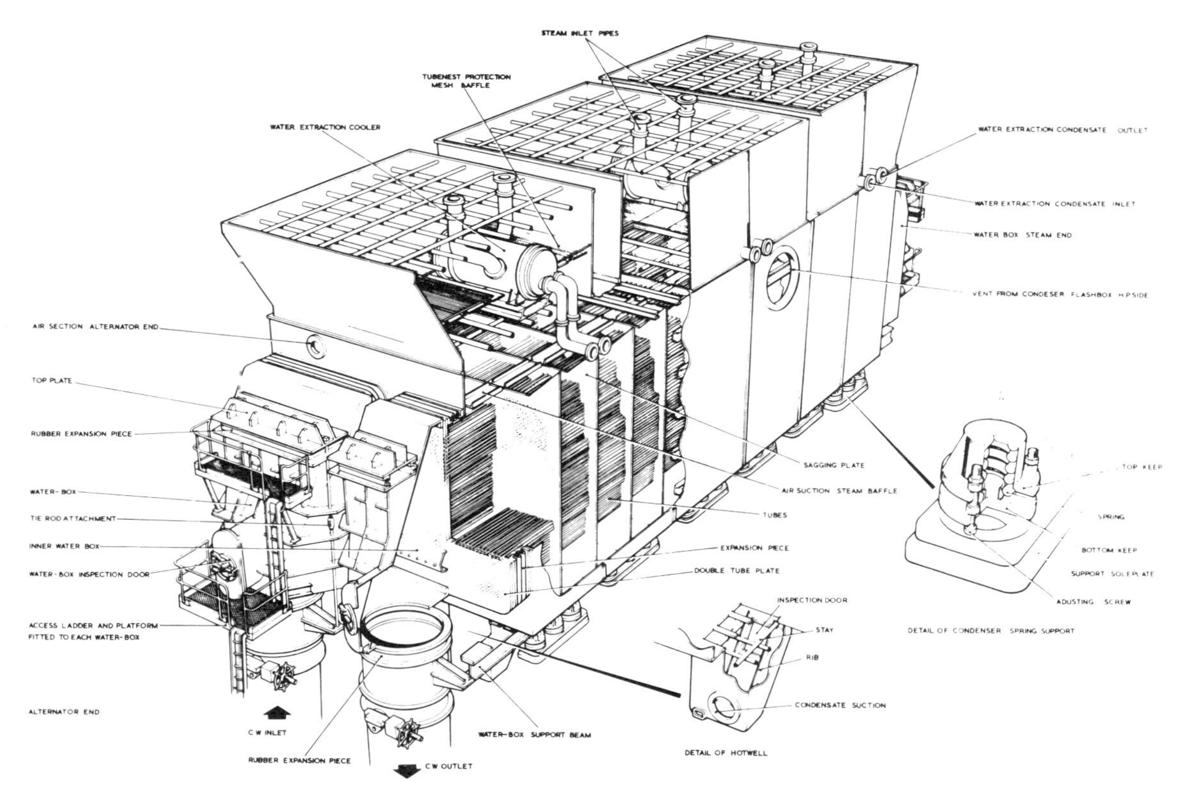

Figure 11.24 Axial condenser (CEGB)

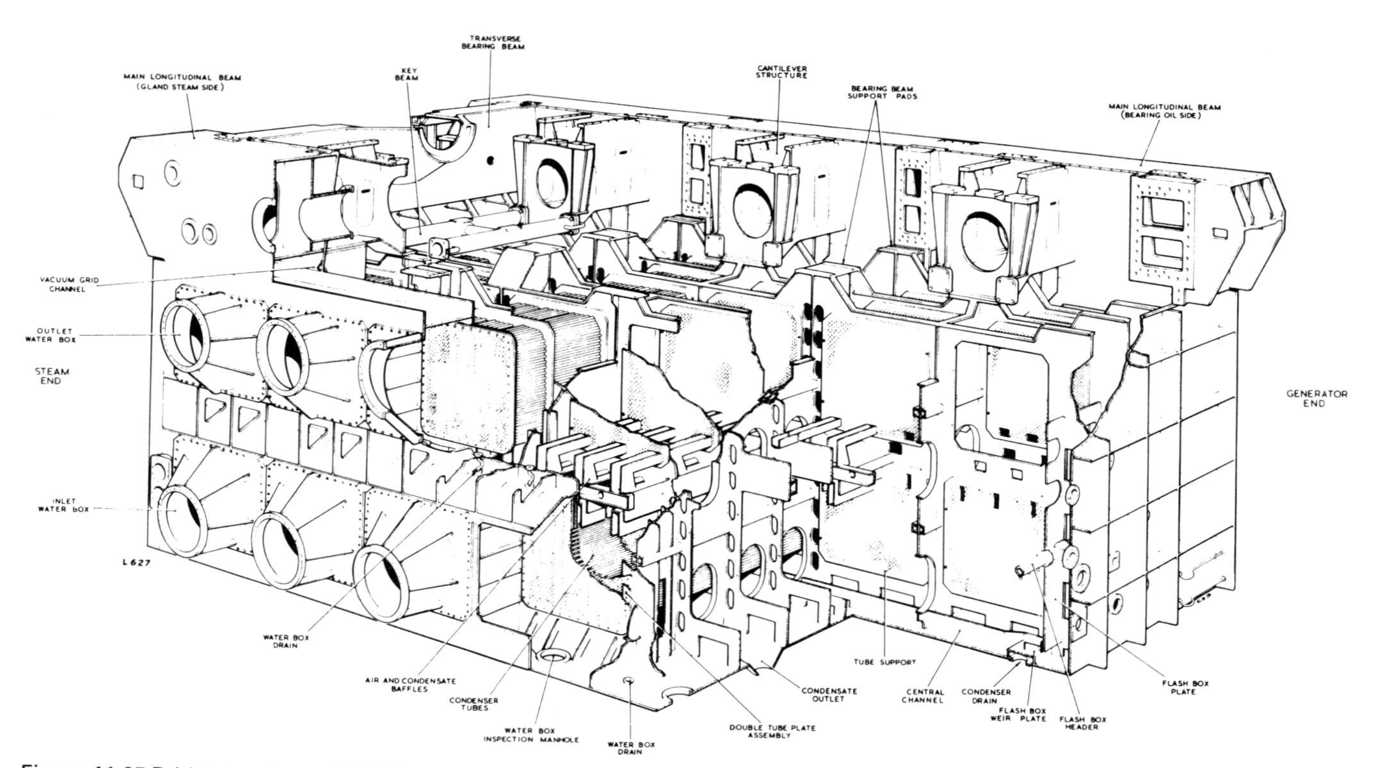

Figure 11.25 Bridge condenser (CEGB)

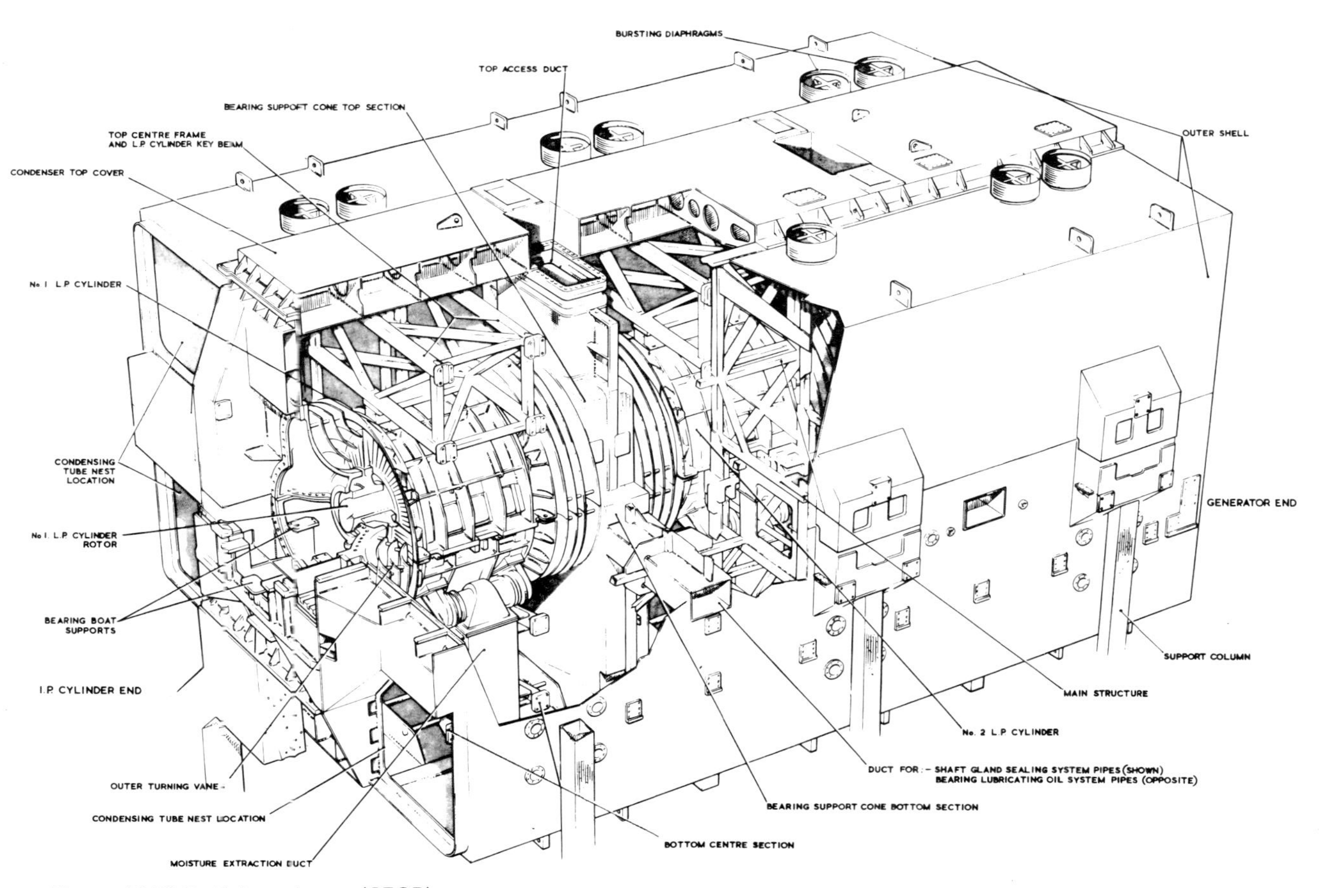

Figure 11.26 Radial condenser (CEGB)

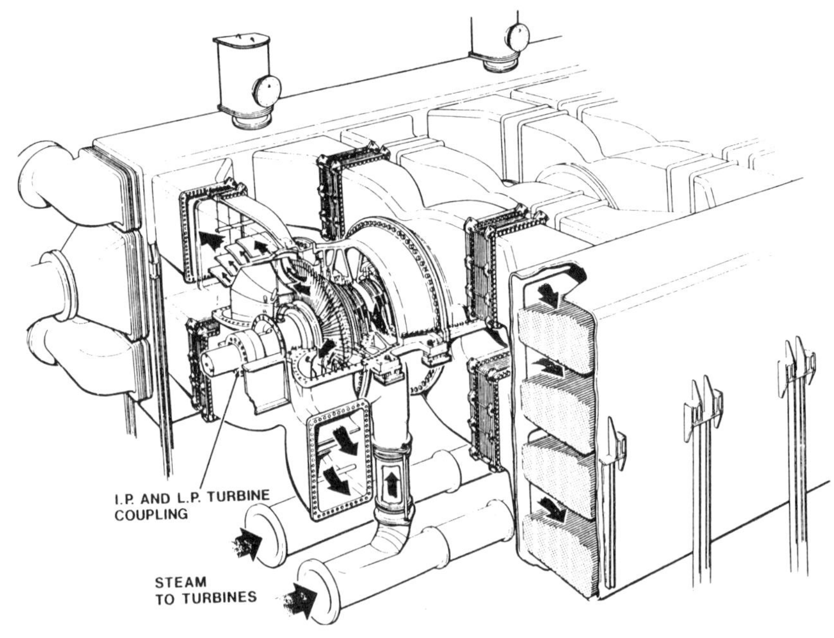

Figure 11.27 Pannier condenser (CEGB)

Condenser performance

Condenser performance tests are normally incorporated as a part of turbine heat consumption tests. Consequently various items of information such as the 'as-run' heat consumption at a given loading are readily available. Basically a condenser is guaranteed by the manufacturer to deal with a specified quantity of steam and maintain a specified back pressure when supplied with a fixed CW flow at a given inlet temperature. Also the cleanliness of the tubes is specified as is the number of air pumps required.

Therefore, before comparing a condenser test performance with its guarantee it is necessary to correct for deviations of the above parameters from those specified. For this it is best to use a working sheet such as that on the next page. For detailed information about condenser performance reference should be made to the CEGB Site Test Code No. 3, *Surface-Type Steam Condensers*, published in 1981.

Working Sheet For Condenser Tests Date

T/A No. at Power Station

No.	Conditions	Units	Specified	Test
1	Gross load on set	kW	500 000	496 650
2	Heat equivalent of load = (1) × 3600 × 10^{-6}	GJ/h	1800.00	1787.94
3	Generator efficiency (from test, or assume 99.0%)	%	—	99.0
4	Mechanical efficiency (from test, or assume 30–100 MW is 99%; 100 MW and above is 99.5%)	%	—	99.5
5	Heat coverted to work = (2) × (10) ÷ [(3) × (4)]	GJ/h	1827.32	1815.08
6	Heat consumption of set ('as-run' for test)	KJ/kWh		8462.64
7	Total heat supplied to set = (1) × (6) × 10^{-6}	GJ/h		4202.97
8	Heat rejected to condenser = (7) − (5)	GJ/h	2095.16	2387.89
9	Fully corected back pressure	mbar	37.1	41.3
10	Temperature corresponding to back pressure	°C	27.8	29.6
11	CW inlet temperature	°C	14.0	5.0
12	CW outlet temperature	°C	24.2	15.4
13	Initial temperature difference ϕ_1 = (10) − (11)	°C	13.8	24.6
14	Terminal temperature difference ϕ_2 = (10) − (12)	°C	3.6	14.2
15	CW temperature rise = (12) − (11)	°C	10.2	10.4
16	ϕ_1/ϕ_2 = (13)/(14)	—	3.8	1.7
17	$\log_{10} \phi_1/\phi_2 = \log_{10}$ (16)	—	0.5798	0.2304
18	Log e (16) = (17) × 2.3026	—	1.3350	0.5305
19	LMTD = (15)/(18)	°C	7.6	19.6
20	Surface area of tubes	m^2	28 400	–
21	Heat rejected = [(8)/(20)] × 10^6	kJ/hm^2	73 773	84 080
22	Heat transmission rate (21)/(19)	kJ/hm^2 °C	9707.0	4289.8
23	Quantity of CW = ((8) × 10^6)/(3600 *Cw* × (15)) where *Cw* = 4.2 kJ/kgK	kg/s	13 585.2	15 185.5
24	CW flow = (23) × specific vol. × 10^{-3} = (23) × 1.0017 × 10^{-3}	m^3/s	13.61	15.21
25	CW velocity through tubes = [(24) test/ (24) spec] × 2	m/s	2.0	2.24
26	Back pressure temp. − LMTD = (10) − (19)	°C	20.2	10.0
27	Test LMTD corrected for mean water temperature = $(19)\ \text{test} \times \left(\dfrac{26\ \text{test}}{26\ \text{specified}}\right)^{1/4}$	°C	—	16.44
28	Test LMTD corrected to specified heat rejection and CW quantity = $(27) \times \dfrac{(8)\ \text{specified}}{(8)\ \text{test}} \times \left(\dfrac{(24)\ \text{test}}{(24)\ \text{specified}}\right)^{1/2}$	°C	—	15.23
29	Exhaust temperature for comparison with guarantee = (26) Specified + (28)	°C	–	35.4
30	Back pressure corresponding to (29)	mbar	—	57.5
31	Corrected back pressure compared to specified = (9) spec − (30)	mbar	—	(−)20.4

Questions

1 Why is back pressure such an important terminal condition on a unit?
2 Does reducing the back pressure always result in more work being available per kilogram of steam?
3 What determines the minimum practical back pressure?
4 Does the minimum practical back pressure vary with load?
5 Does it vary month by month?
6 What components of a total deviation are usually determined?
7 Which are reducible by cleaning the condenser tubes?
8 Which are reducible by cleaning the tube plates?
9 Which are reducible by stopping air ingress?
10 Comment on the 'high CW temperature' loss.
11 Comment on 'correct CW flow' loss.
12 Comment on air ingress.
13 Comment on the 'dirty tubes' loss.
14 Why is air ingress so detrimental to back pressure?
15 What precautions are desirable when determining the CW temperature? Back pressure?
16 Name some methods of monitoring condensers for air ingress.
17 How would you locate sources of air ingress?
18 Name some common sources of inleakage.
19 Why are CW leaks undesirable in condensers?
20 Name some methods of detecting leaking tubes.
21 Name some means of preventing slime accumulating in tubes.
22 What is the cause of phosphate scaling in condensers?

Exercise 2

(a) Name the various condenser arrangements in use on modern plant. Comment upon each, giving any advantages and disadvantages that you know.
(b) Describe a double tube-plate installation and say why they were introduced.

Project 1

Refer to the 'Working Sheet for Condenser Tests'.
Calculate the 'corrected back pressure compared to specified' for these conditions:

Gross load on set	499 000 kW
'As-run' heat consumption	7846 kJ/kWh
Fully corrected back pressure	31.66 mbar
CW inlet temperature	10°C
CW outlet temperature	20°C

Exercise 1 (Answers) Refer to page 501.

		Test	1	2	3	4
		Load MW	100	80	120	118
Back pressure	Plant	mbar	36.5	34.5	37.1	48.0
Corresponding sat. steam	Curve 3	°C	27.6	26.4	27.5	32.2
CW inlet temp.	Plant	°C	11.0	7.0	8.0	18.7
CW outlet temp. 'A'	Plant	°C	20.9	10.3	21.6	30.2
CW outlet temp 'B'	Plant	°C	22.7	14.0	23.8	27.0
CW outlet temp 'C'	Plant	°C	19.2	12.0	20.0	27.0
Mean CW outlet temp	Average of (4)	°C	20.9	12.1	12.1	28.1
Exhaust temp. 'A'	Plant	°C	28.0	26.0	27.0	36.0
Exhaust temp. 'B'	Plant	°C	27.0	26.0	O/C	38.0
Exhaust temp. 'C'	Plant	°C	21.0	28.0	21.0	36.0
Condensate temp. 'A'	Plant	°C	25.4	26.5	27.5	35.0
Condensate temp. 'B'	Plant	°C	25.4	26.5	27.5	35.0
Condensate temp 'C'	Plant	°C	21.7	24.5	27.0	26.5
Air suction temp. 'A'	Plant	°C	25.5	24.0	26.5	31.0
Air suction temp. 'B'	Plant	°C	24.0	18.0	22.0	31.0
Air suction temp. 'C'	Plant	°C	17.0	23.5	23.0	30.5
'A' C.W. outlet valve posn.	Plant	Wide = 91 cm	30	36	33	38
'B' C.W. outlet valve posn.			28	40	36	35
'C' C.W. outlet valve posn.			23	31	33	34
Specified back press.	Curve 1	mbar	30.2	29	35.5	35
Optimum C.W. rise	Curve 2	°C	7.2	6.2	8.8	8.7
Optimum TTD	Curve 2	°C	3.0	2.5	3.5	3.5
Back pressure due to C.W. inlet temp.	(3)+(11)+(12)	mbar	25.6	10.0 (min)	31.0 (min)	44.8
Back pressure due to C.W. flow	(5)+(12)	mbar	29.8	16.6	32.2	47.0
Variation due to C.W.in.	(13)−(10)	mbar	(−)4.6	(−)9.0	(−)4.5	9.8
Variation due to C.W. flow	(14)−(13)	mbar	(+)4.2	(−)3.4	1.2	2.2
Variation due to air/ dirty tubes	(1)−(14)	mbar	(+)6.7	17.0	4.9	1.0
Total variation	(1)−(13)	mbar	(+)10.9	14.5	6.1	3.2
Target, back pressure	Curve 1	mbar	27	20.0 (min)	31.0 (min)	44.0
Variation from target	(1)−(19)	mbar	(+)9.5	(+)14.5	(+)6.1	(+)4.6
No. of air pumps i/s	Plant	—	2	2	3	1

Project 1 (Answer)

Item No.	*Value*	*Item No.*	*Value*
1	499 000	17	0.4771
2	1 796.4	18	1.0986
3	99.0	19	9.10
4	99.5	20	—
5	1 823.66	21	73 644
6	7 846	22	8 092.75
7	3 915.15	23	13 832.6
8	2 091.49	24	13.86
9	31.66	25	2.04
10	25	26	15.9
11	10	27	8.57
12	20	28	8.66
13	15	29	28.86
14	5	30	39.7
15	10	31	(−) 2.6
16	3		

Project 2

The condensers on a 350 MW unit have the following optimum and actual conditions. The back pressure correction curve is shown in *Figure 11.28*.

Condition	*Unit*	*Optimum*	*Actual*
1 CW inlet temperature	°C	16.5	18.0
2 CW outlet temperature	°C	25.1	28.0
3 Saturated steam temperature	°C	30.5	35.77
4 Air suction temperature	°C	28.0	33.0
5 Back pressure	mbar	44.0	58.0

(a) What back pressure improvement could be obtained by cleaning the condenser tubes?

(b) Determine the cost of sustaining the tube fouling condition at full load, given:

Full load heat consumption = 0.777 GJ/s
Boiler efficiency (GCV basis) = 85%
Fuel cost = 96p/GJ

Project 2 (Answer)

(a) Back pressure with clean tubes = 44 mbar
BP due to high CW inlet temp. (18 + 8.6 + 5.4 = 32.0°C) = 47.5 mbar
BP due to high CW inlet and flow (28 + 5.4 = 33.4°C) = 51.5 mbar
BP due to high CW inlet and flow plus dirty tubes = 58.0 mbar

Hence effect on back pressure of dirty tubes = 58.0 − 51.5 = 6.5 mbar

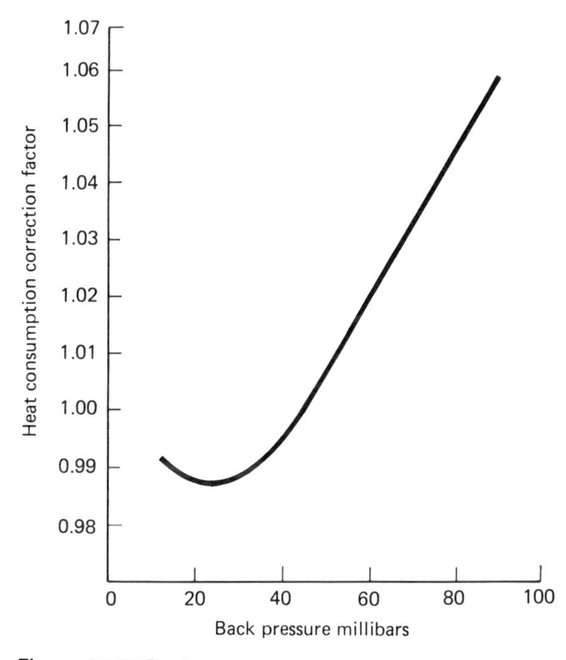

Figure 11.28 Back pressure correction curve for a 350–MW turbo-alternator at full load

(b) Reference to the heat consumption graph shows that over the range above (47–60 mbar), the graph is a straight line.

At 44.0 mbar the correction is 1.0; at 60.0 mbar it is 1.02

∴ Heat correction factor change is 0.02 for 16 mbar
= 0.00125/mbar
So extra heat at FL with dirty tubes = $0.777 \times 0.00125 \times 6.5$
= 0.0064 GJ/s
∴ extra boiler input heat = 0.0064/0.85 = 0.0076 GJ/s
Cost of extra heat = 0.0076×0.96
= £0.0073/s = £26.8/h = £4415/week at FL

Additional Reading

1 DRUMMOND, G., 'Steam side pressure gradients in surface condensers', *Proc. I. Mech. E.*, **186**, No. 10/72 (1977)
2 SILVER, R.S., 'An approach to a general theory of surface condensers', *Proc. I. Mech. E.*, **178**, No. 14 (1963/64)
3 CHRISTOPHER, P.J. and FORSTER, V.T., 'Rugeley dry cooling tower system', *Proc. I. Mech. E.*, **184**, Part 1 (1969/70)
4 Site Test Code No. 3, *Performance of Surface-Type Steam Condensers*, CEGB (1981)
5 GRANT, I.D.R., 'The effects of air and of condensate drainage on condenser performance', NEL Report No. 294.
6 BS 4485: Pt. 2 (1969) *Water Cooling Towers* (4 Parts).

12 Feed-water heating

A non-reheat cycle incorporating a turbine with three stages of feed heating is illustrated in *Figure 12.1*. The temperature of the condensate leaving the condenser is shown as point A. Because of feed heating the temperature is raised to that shown at point B. Consequently, the enthalpy change of the feed due to feed heating is represented by the area under the curve AB.

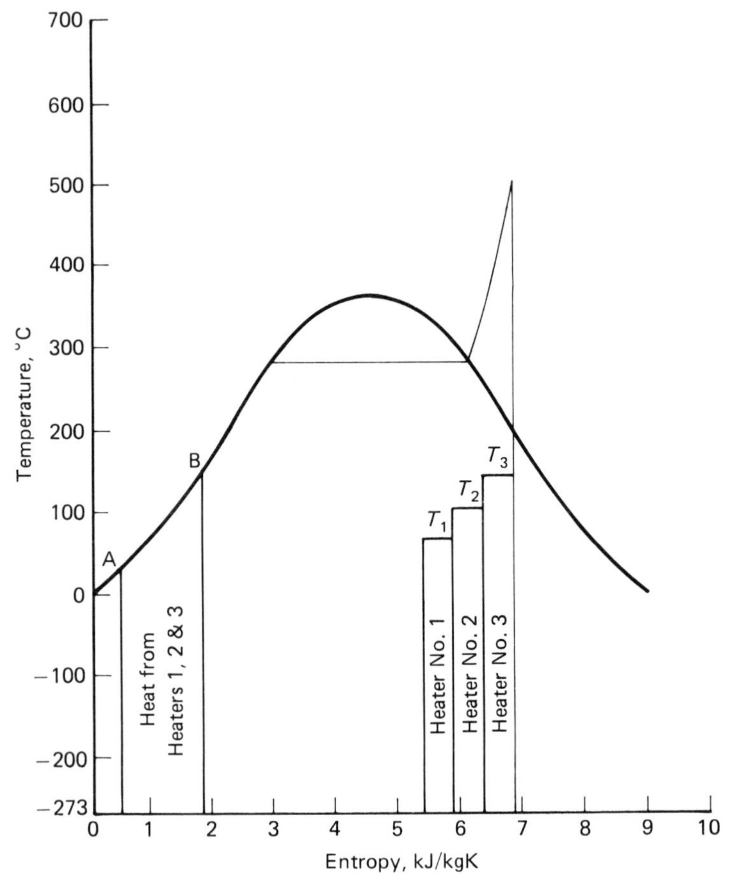

Figure 12.1 Idealised representation of feed heating

The source of the heat is steam bled from the turbine. That bled to heater number 1 is at temperature T_1 absolute and the heat it contains is equal to T_1 multiplied by the entropy change of the strip. Similar considerations apply to the steam bled to heaters 2 and 3. The total heat represented by the three strips is equal to the total heat given to the feed, i.e. to the area under AB.

As steam conditions have progressed there has been an increase in the number of stages of feed heating on units. Thus, modern plants often have eight or even nine heaters. Of course, feed heaters are very expensive items of equipment and so the actual number used for a particular plant will be decided on economic grounds. *Table 12.1* shows some information on typical installations. *Figure 12.2* shows the order of improvement that results from using various numbers of heaters. There is a diminishing return from using more than one, and the gain by going from, say, ten, to a huge number, is seen to be quite small. Therefore, the number of heaters in use on modern machines will probably remain about the economic maximum for some time.

Table 12.1 Number of feed heaters on various plants

Output (MW)	*Steam at TSV (bar)*	*(°C)*	*R/H Temp. (°C)*	*Final feed (°C)*	*No. of heaters*	*Country*
120	103.4	538	538	224	6	UK
200	162.0	566	538	238	6 or 7	UK
250	172.4	538	538	257	6	USA
300	158.6	566	566	252	7 or 8	UK
375	241.3	593	566	266	8	UK
500	158.6	566	566	252	7 or 8	UK
600	158.6	566	566	278	9	UK
800	158.6	538	538	254	8	USA
860	172.4	538	538	254	7	USA

An important consideration with non-contact heaters is the amount of heat exchange surface to provide. The greater the surface area the higher the outlet feed temperature, but the cost will be greater. The economic limit is usually when the outlet feed temperature is within about 5°C of the steam saturation temperature; in other words when the terminal temperature difference is about 5°C.

Types of feed heater

Low pressure

These are either of the non-contact or direct-contact type. *Figure 12.3* shows a typical non-contact heater. The bled-steam is at a low pressure and may be

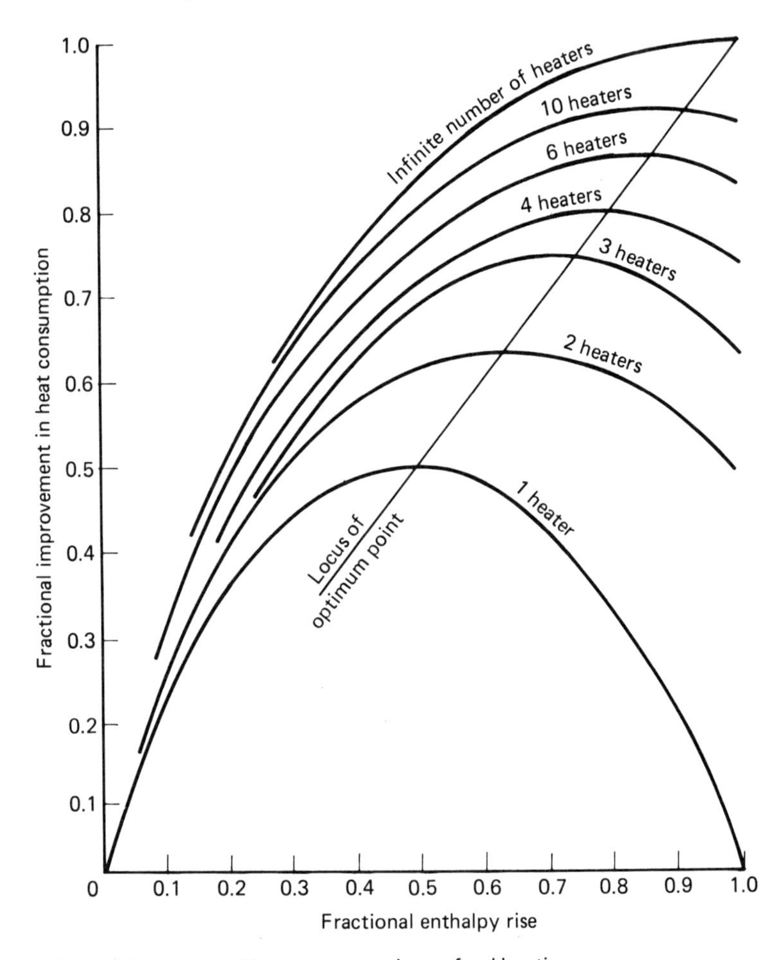

Figure 12.2 Thermal improvement due to feed heating

sub-atmospheric. All installations have at least one DC (direct contact) low-pressure heater, i.e. the deaerator. In this, as with all DC heaters, the bled steam is in direct contact with the condensate and so the condensate and the steam are at the same pressure in the shell. The condensate is raised to saturation temperature and so the terminal temperature difference is zero. *Figure 12.4* shows a typical layout.

On some of the recent large units the whole LP heater train comprises DC heaters. A typical layout is shown in *Figure 12.5*. The condensate in No. 1 heater is raised to saturation temperature. Therefore, for it to attain a higher temperature still in No. 2 heater, it must be raised to a higher pressure. This is achieved by cascading the outlet of No. 1 heater downwards through a suitable distance to give the condensate at No. 2 the required extra head. The condensate is then cascaded to No. 3 heater and then to No. 4.

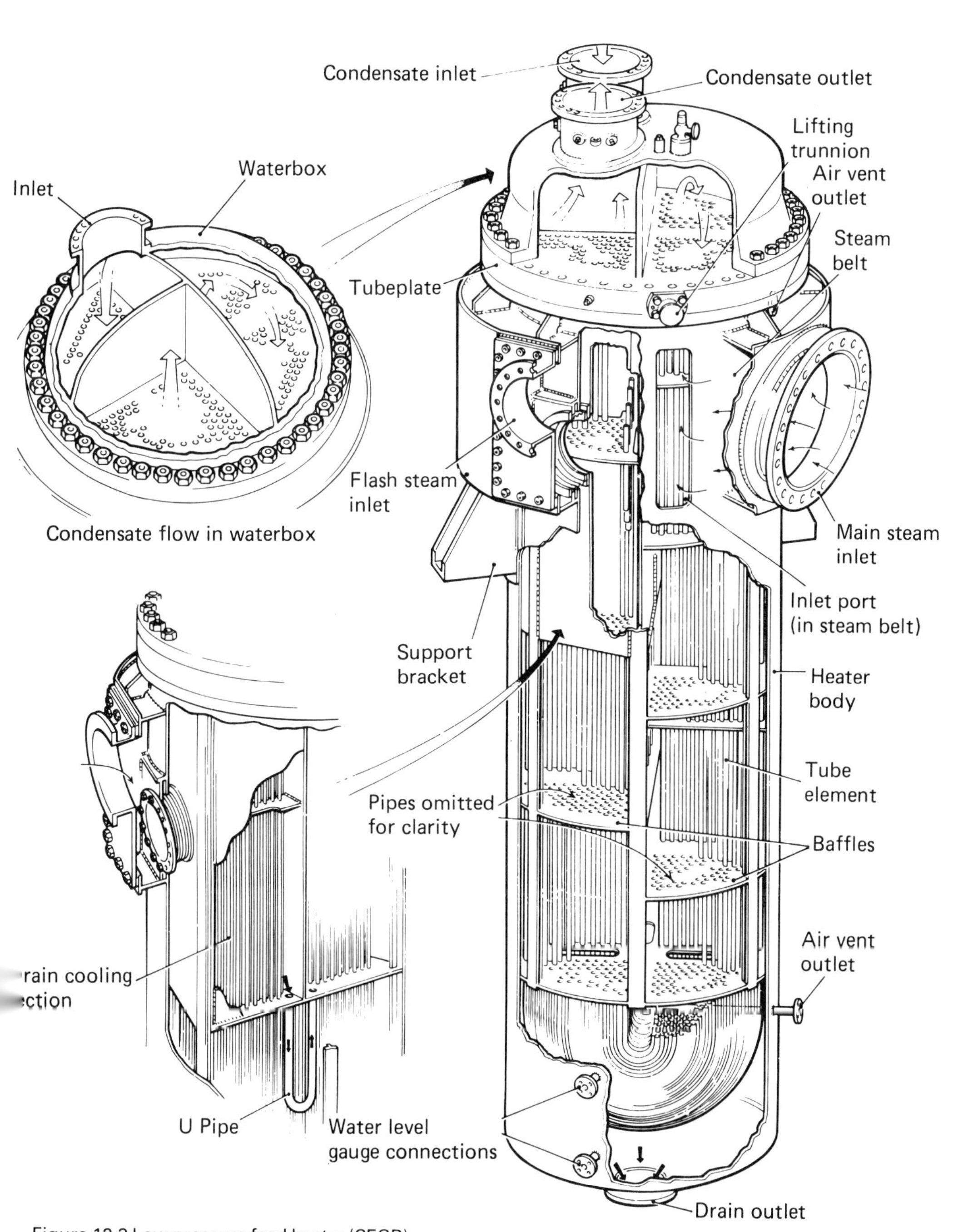

Figure 12.3 Low pressure feed heater (CEGB)

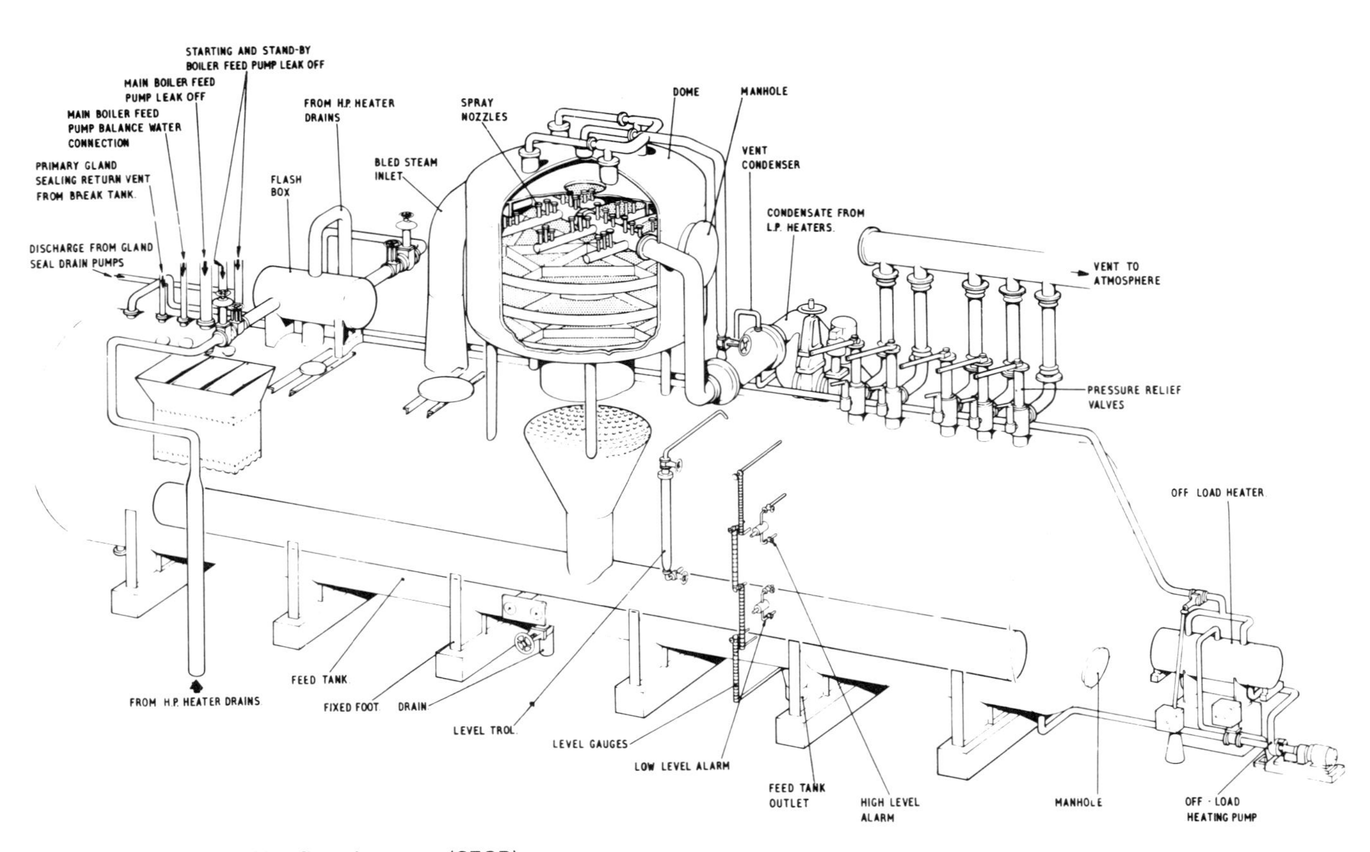

Figure 12.4 Diagram of full flow deaerator (CEGB)

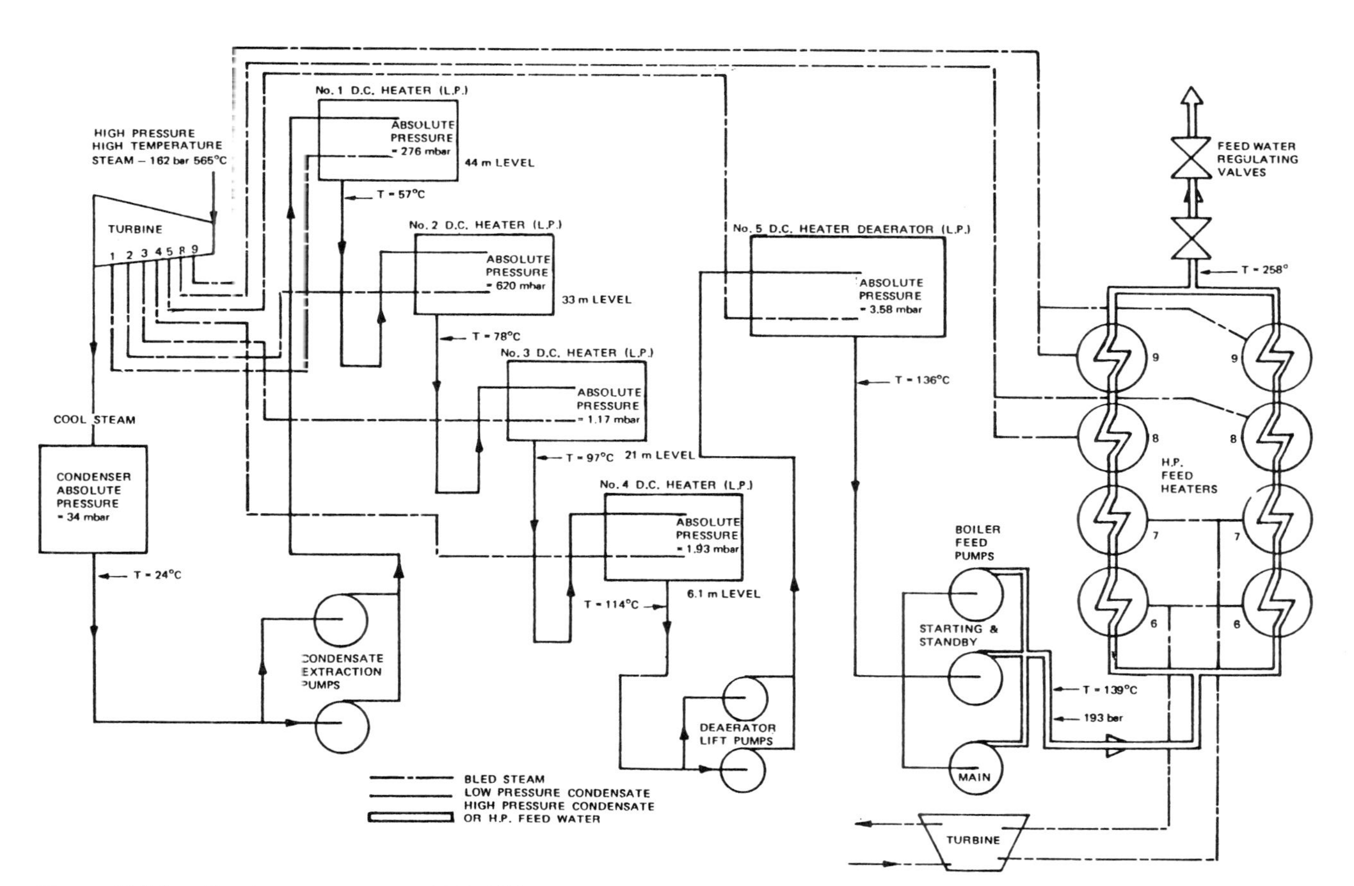

Figure 12.5 Feed heater arrangement of 600–MW unit (CEGB)

Thermodynamically the only advantage of using DC heaters is that the TTD is zero, whereas with non-contact heaters it would be between 1 and 5°C. *Figure 12.6* shows the construction of a direct-contact heater. Of course, these heaters are often operating at sub-atmospheric pressure and so it is important that they, and the associated pipework, are assembled so that air cannot leak into the system.

High-pressure non-contact heaters

All the feed heaters after the booster pump or feed pump are termed 'high pressure'. The bled steam supply often contains a substantial quantity of superheat. On units without bled-steam driven boiler feed-pump turbines, the bled steam for feed heating is tapped off the main turbine at suitable locations. Normally the highest pressure heater is supplied from the HP cylinder exhaust and the next highest is supplied from an early stage of the IP cylinder. Thus, on a reheat turbine the penultimate heater steam temperature is considerably higher than that of the final heater.

On the other hand, a bled-steam turbine may receive its steam from the HP cylinder exhaust and appropriate tappings from the bled-steam turbine provide the steam for heat feeding, see *Figure 12.7(a)*. The bled steam tapped from such a source, while at the same pressure as would be obtained from the main turbine, is at a much lower temperature. Therefore, it is desirable to obtain the steam for the heaters from the bled-steam turbine where possible. Sometimes such turbines exhaust their steam to a suitable feed heater, such as the deaerator, but a common alternative is for them to exhaust to a condenser or to the main turbine.

Figure 12.7(b) shows the layout of a high-pressure heater. This particular type consists of a number of small bore tubes connected to tubular headers. Alternative types are shown in *Figure 12.7(c)*. They incorporate an integral desuperheating, condensing and, usually, drains cooling section. The sections are clearly marked.

Feed heater trains

Figures 12.8, 12.9 and *12.10* show feed heater layouts on some modern plant. *Figure 12.8* shows the layout on a 375 MW once-through supercritical pressure unit. The layout is complicated somewhat by the necessity to provide recirculation facilities external to the boiler while pressure-raising. *Figure 12.9* illustrates a 500 MW unit layout incorporating non-contact heaters except for the deaerator, whereas in that shown in *Figure 12.10* there are direct-contact LP heaters.

Up to the 1950s a common material for HP heater tube nests was 70/30 cupro-nickel. However, this proved to be unsuitable because the tube metal flaked off (i.e. it exfoliated). So a change was made to other materials. For feed water up to 240°C, 90/10 cupro-nickel is satisfactory and for higher

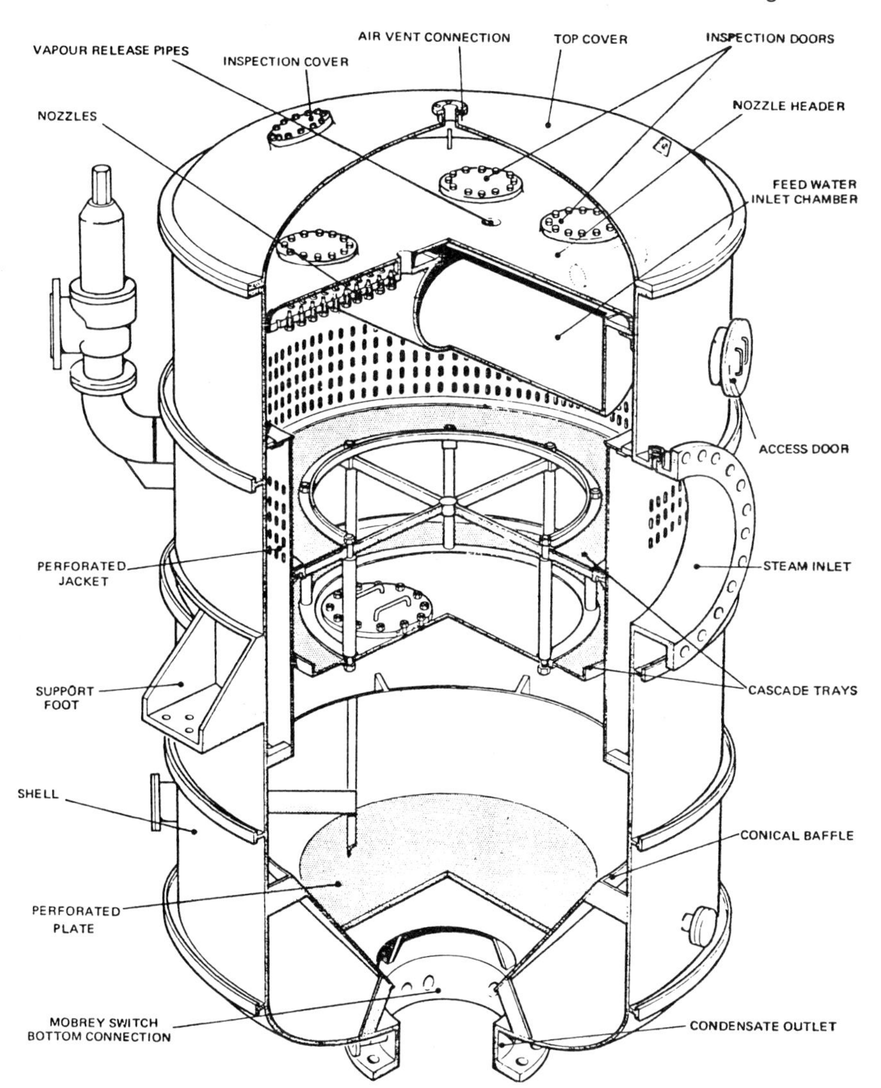

Figure 12.6 Direct contact feed heater construction (CEGB)

temperatures steel is commonly used. This is free from corrosion because of the oxygen-free operating conditions on modern plant. It also has the advantage that the use of welding for tube joints is facilitated and also the chemical control of the water is simplified. On the other hand, modern HP heaters usually have a drains cooling section and so, with steel tubes, corrosion at the water level is aggravated by air ingress during shut-down periods. Therefore, it is necessary to ensure complete drainage of the steam side of the heaters by some form of automatic emptying device every time the unit is shut down.

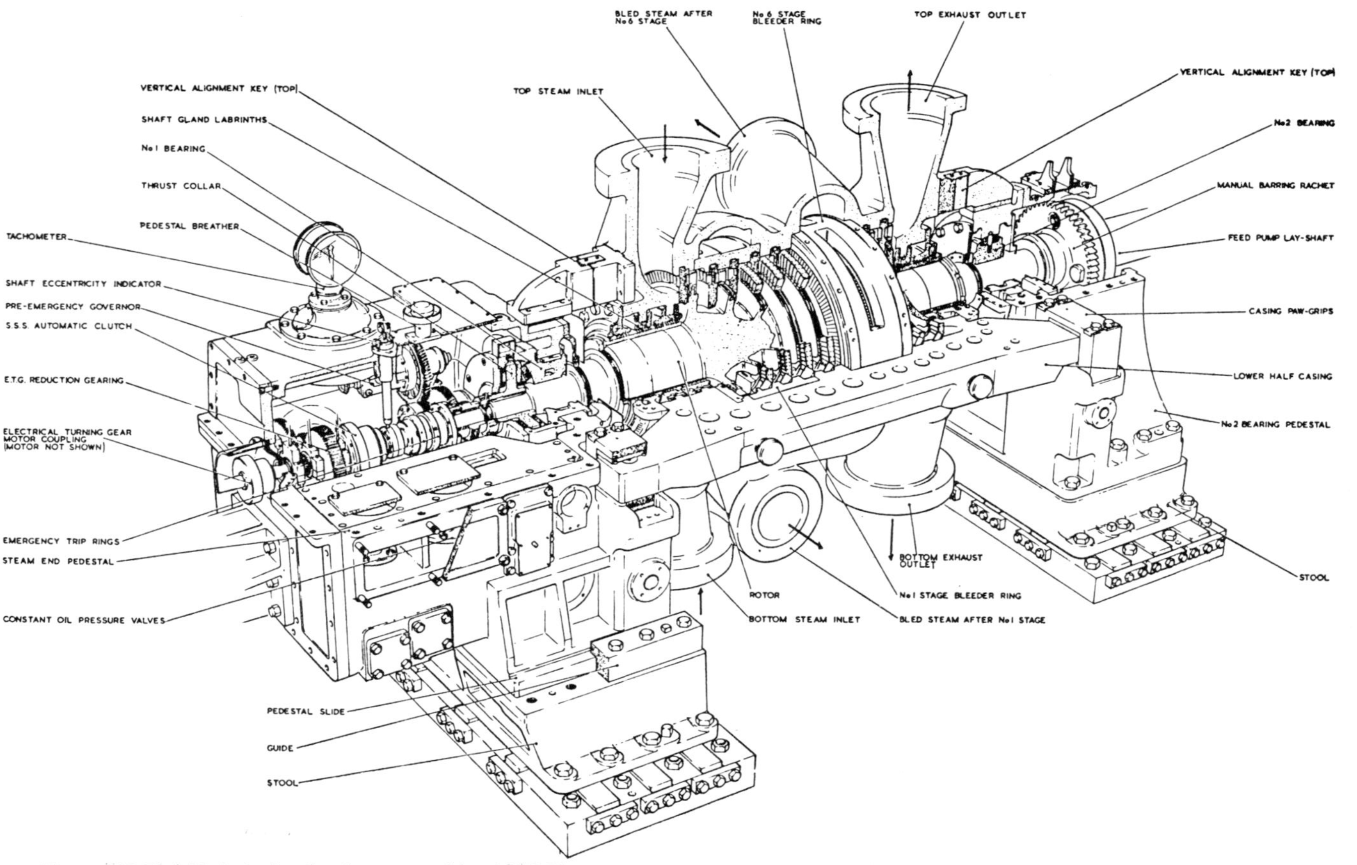

Figure 12.7(a) Main boiler feed pump turbine (CEGB)

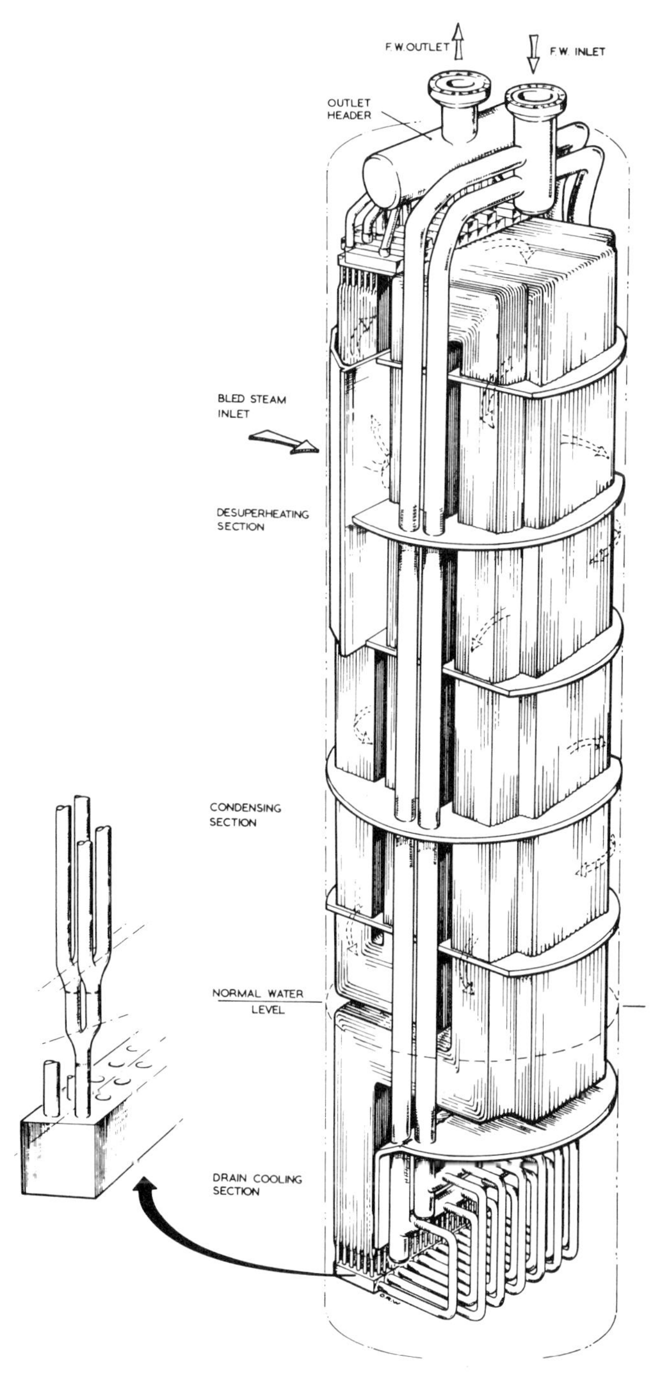

Figure 12.7(b) HP feed heater with tubular headers (CEGB)

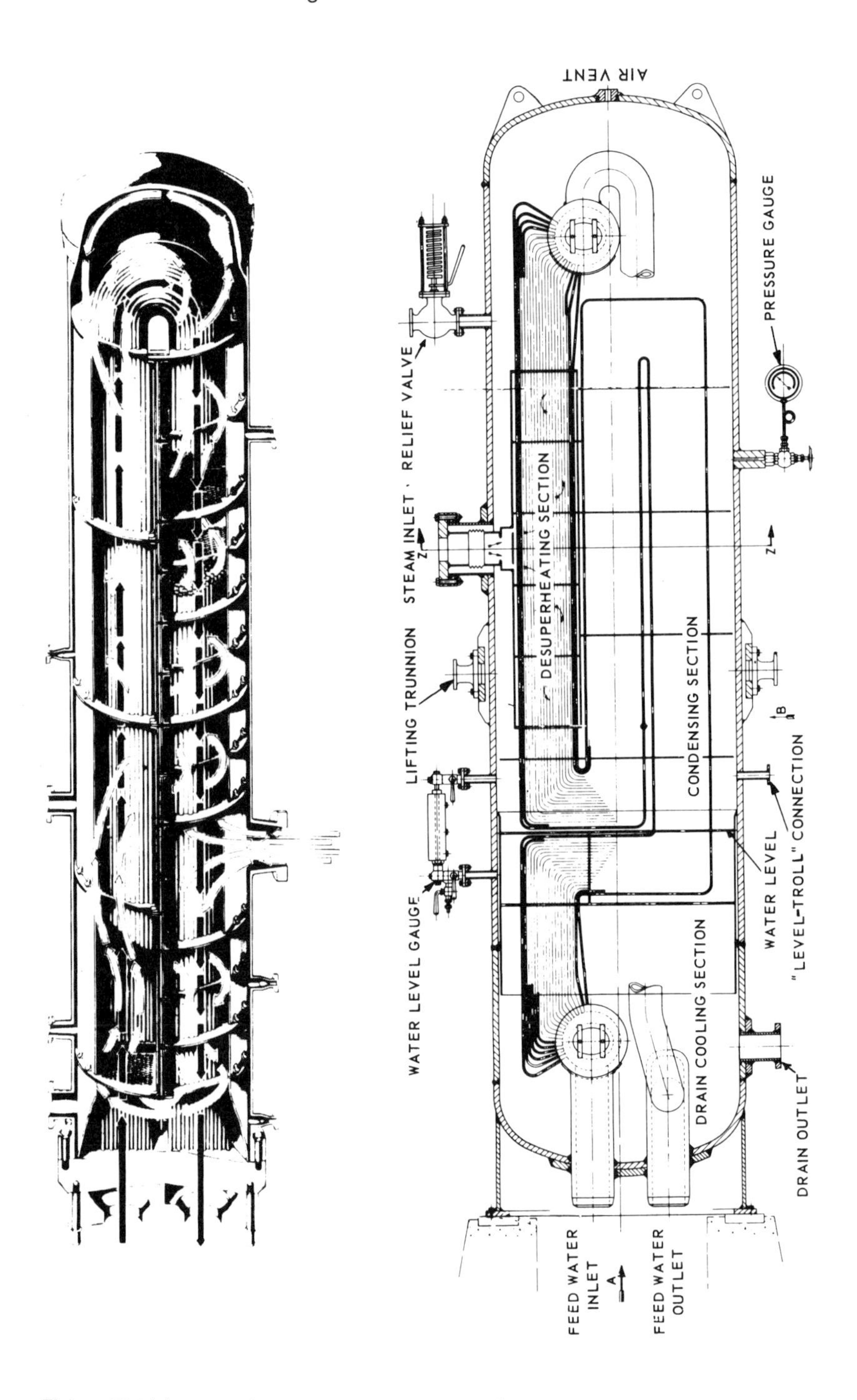

Figure 12.7(c) HP feed heaters — other types

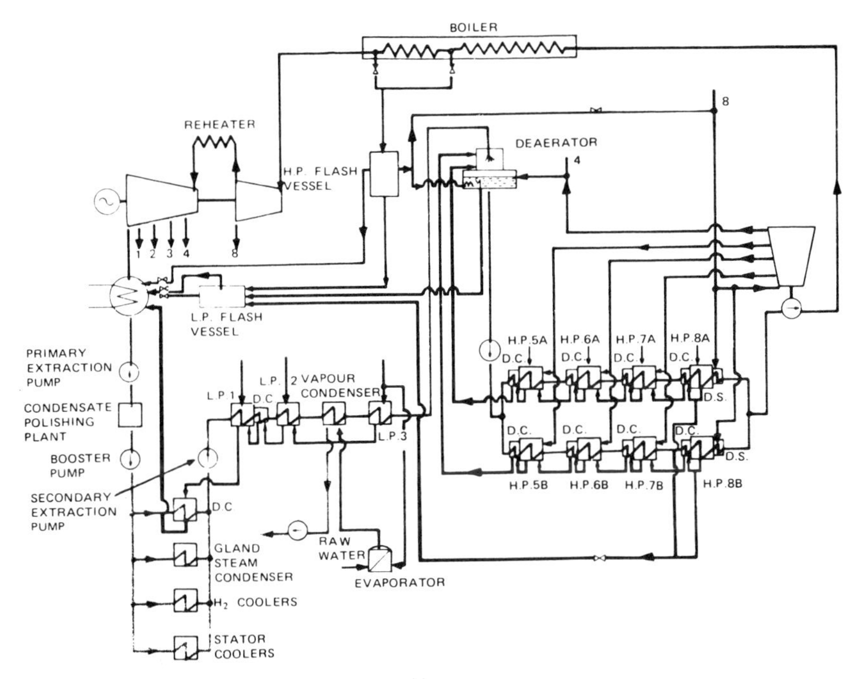

Figure 12.8 Diagrammatic arrangement of a feed heating system for a 375 MW unit (CEGB)

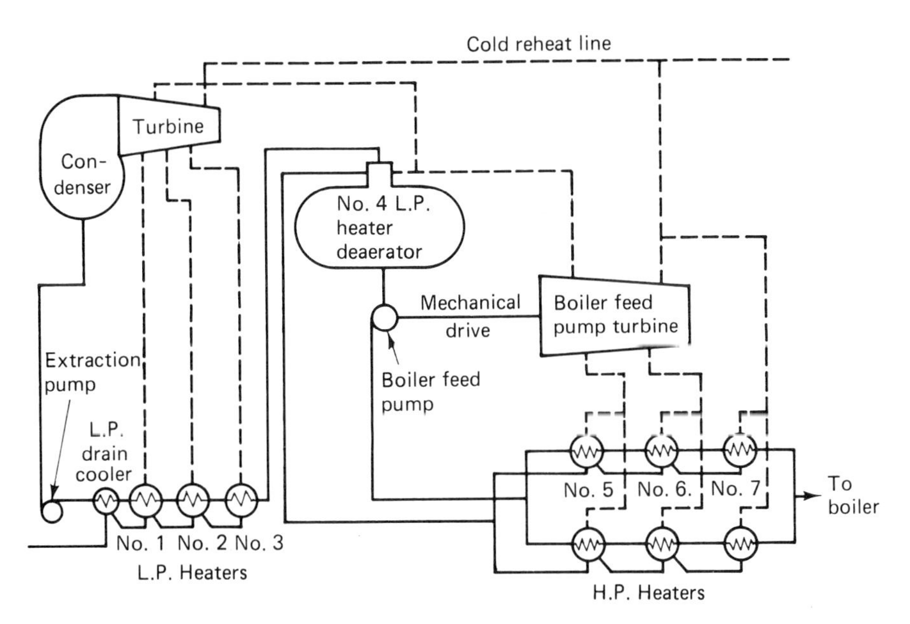

Figure 12.9 Diagrammatic arrangement of a feed heating system for a 500–MW unit (CEGB)

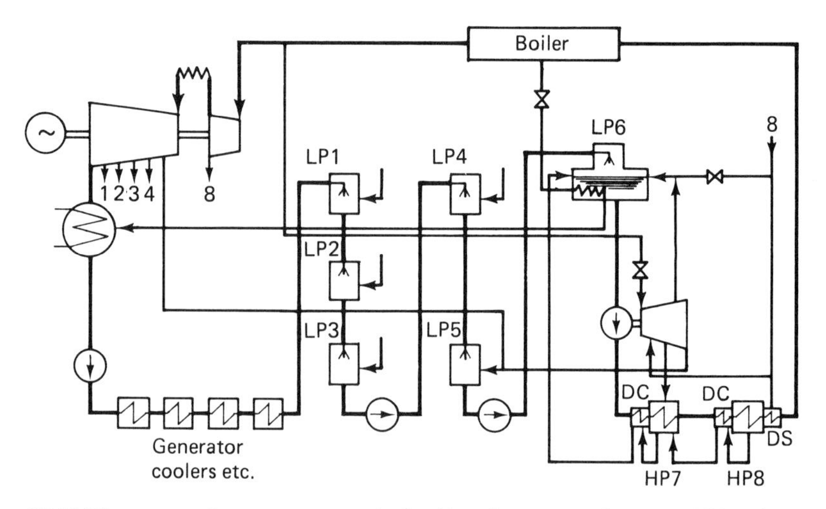

Figure 12.10 Diagrammatic arrangement of a feed heating system for a 660–MW unit (CEGB)

Heater spacing

Normally heaters each give approximately the same rise in feed temperature – usually in the range 25–35°C. However, the last heater on reheat units (i.e. the one supplied with cold reheat steam) will usually have a substantially greater heat transfer.

Heater drainage

Flash boxes

The normal method of drainage is by cascading the drain water from one heater to another lower down the train. Often flash boxes are provided such as shown in *Figure 12.11*. An orifice is located at the drain inlet to the flash

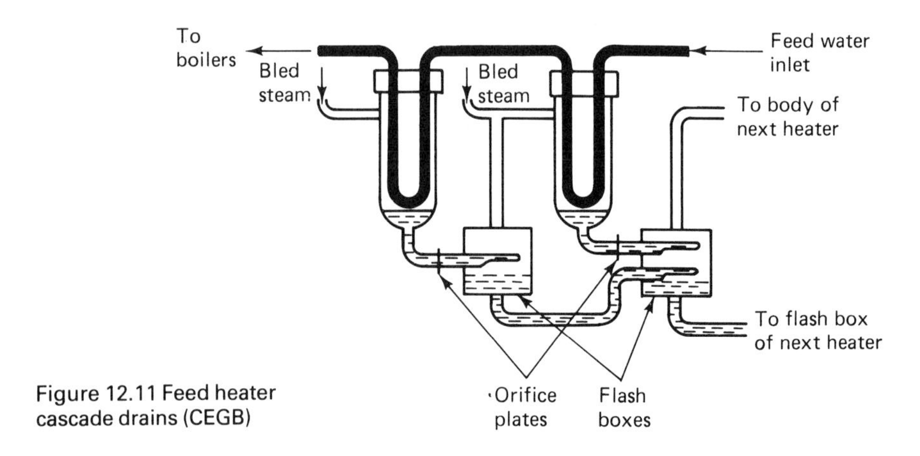

Figure 12.11 Feed heater cascade drains (CEGB)

box to ensure that flashing takes place inside the box. The orifice size determines the maximum quantity of drain water that it will pass and so this also controls the maximum steam quantity to the upstream heater. It is important that an orifice is not changed for one of different size unless the manufacturers have been consulted. Worn orifice plates should be replaced. Each line going to a flash box has its own orifice plate. Inside the box the supply pipe terminates with a diffuser. This has a slot on the underside to allow the flashing steam/water to be discharged downward and thus minimize the quantity of moisture entrained with the flash steam which passes to the heater. *Figure 12.12* shows an orifice plate and diffuser assembly.

Figure 12.12 Orifice plate and diffuser assembly (CEGB)

Calculation of flash steam quantity

The quantity of flash steam is easily calculated. Consider the flash box shown in *Figure 12.13*. Assume 1 kg of water is supplied to the orifice, and the water is at 18 bar abs. and 205°C. Reference to the steam tables shows the heat content to be 875 kJ/kg of water. The pressure inside the flash box is determined by the bled steam pressure to the associated heater. For example, if we are considering, say, No. 5 flash box then the associated heater will be No. 5. Suppose the bled steam pressure is 10 bar abs., then the flash steam will be at the saturation temperature corresponding to 10 bar, i.e. 180°C, and its enthalpy will be 2776.2 kJ/kg. The water in the flash box will be at saturation temperature also, i.e. 180°C, and the heat content will be 762.6 kJ/kg.

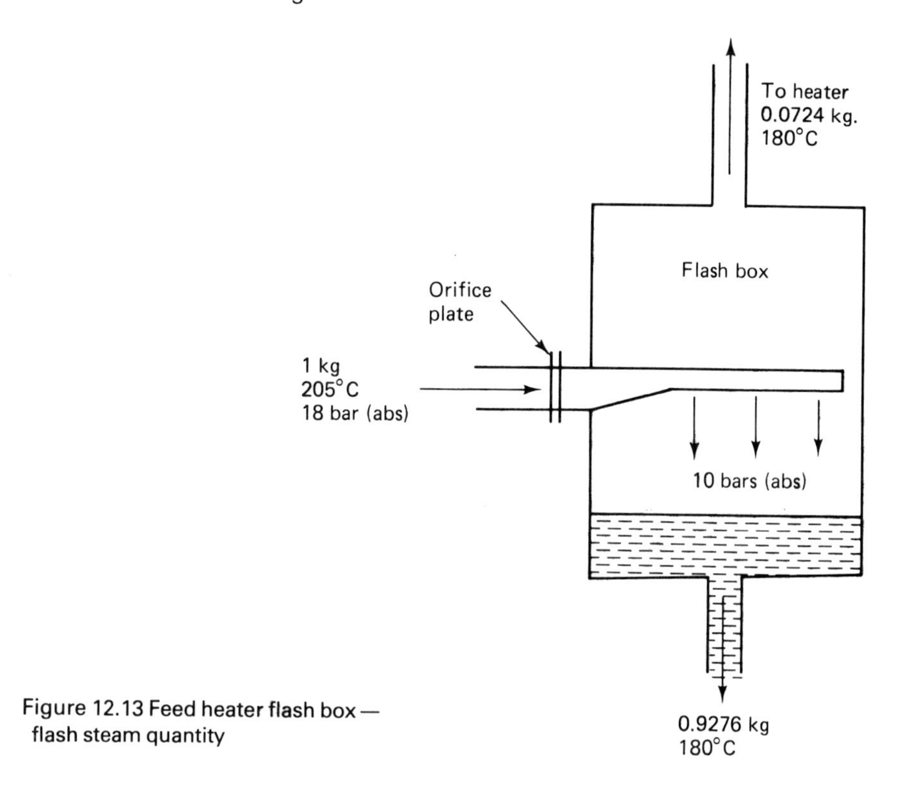

Figure 12.13 Feed heater flash box—flash steam quantity

The difference in the heat content of the water entering the flash box and that inside is 875 − 726.6 = 148.4 kJ/kg and this must be given to the flash steam. The latent heat of the flash steam is 2776.2 − 726.6 = 2049.6 kJ/kg. Consequently there is only enough heat available to produce

$$\frac{148.4}{2049.6} = 0.0724 \text{ kg or } 7.24\%$$

of flash steam per kg of cascade drain water entering the box.

In general terms the quantity of flash steam =

$$\frac{\text{(Heat in inlet water)} - \text{(Heat in outlet water)}}{\text{Latent heat at F/B pressure}}$$

Heater forward drains pumps

Sometimes, instead of cascading the heater drains they are passed to a forward drains pump whose function is to receive the drain water and discharge it into the feed line upstream of the heater. The arrangement is shown in *Figure 12.14*. The benefit of doing this is that the drain water temperature is higher than that of the feed. Consequently the feed water

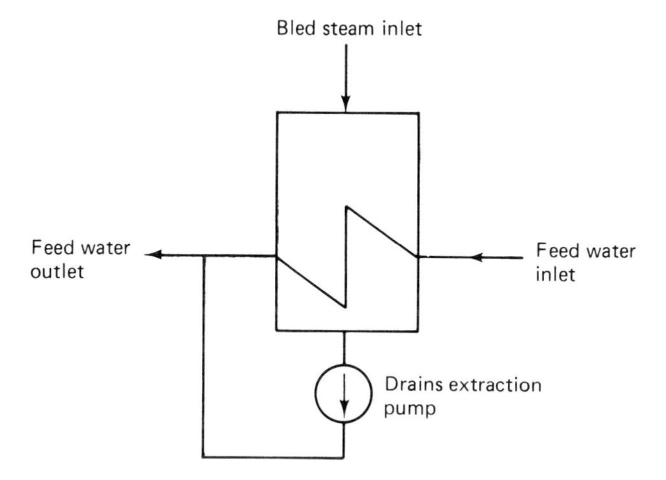

Figure 12.14 Feed heater forward drains pump (CEGB)

temperature is raised slightly by mixing the two. On the other hand the cost of supplying and operating the pump must be less than the resulting benefit if this arrangement is to be economic. The duty imposed on heater drains pumps is arduous because the water is at or very near boiling temperature. Consequently a slight reduction of pressure will cause some water to flash off. Therefore the pump must be located at a suitable distance below the heater to provide the necessary head to prevent flashing.

Heater drains pumps

The more usual arrangement is for the heater drainage to be cascaded from the highest pressure heater to the next highest and so on. When it leaves the last of the HP heaters the drainage is passed to a flash vessel from which the flash steam is passed directly to the deaerator, and the water is passed to a drains pump. The pump discharges the water to the deaerator. A typical arrangement is shown in *Figure 12.15*.

Emergency operation

If the system demand is considerably in excess of the capacity of the plant available, 'Emergency Operation' may be called for by the System Control Engineers. This means that the plant is operated at its maximum capacity consistent with safety requirements but irrespective of efficiency. In these circumstances it is common to shut off the steam to the last feed heater, with the result that the output is increased by several per cent. The associated boiler, of course, must be able to cope with the colder feed water. Also, the

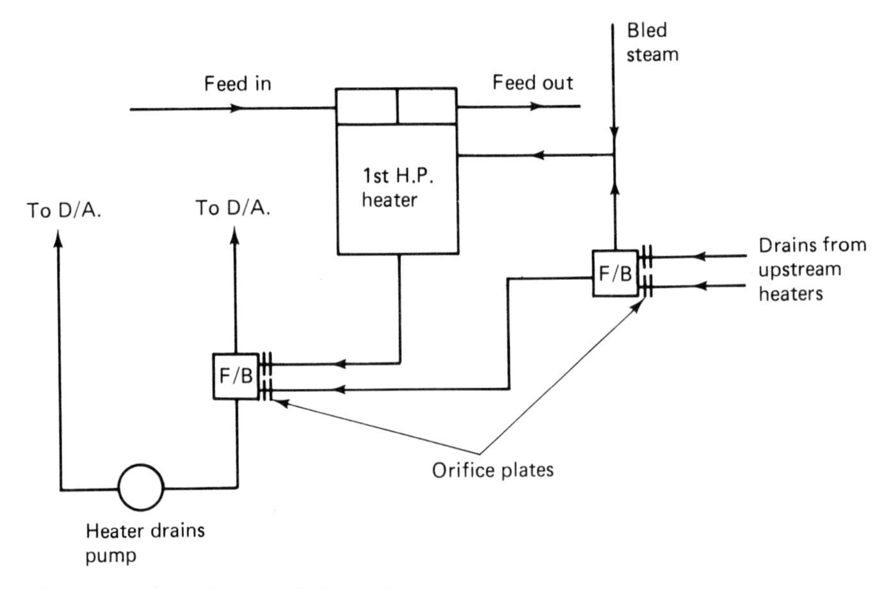

Figure 12.15 Feed heater HP drains disposal

alternator, generator transformer and ancillary equipment must be capable of carrying the extra burden.

The change of heat rate of the turbo-alternator is quite pronounced. Consider a 500 MW unit whose heat rate is, say, 7842 kJ/kWh at 520 MW. (In normal circumstances machines are capable of outputs higher than that shown on the nameplate.) So at 520 MW the heat consumption will be $7842 \times 520\,000 \times 10^{-6} = 4077.84$ GJ/h. Operation with the last heater out of service will increase the output to, say, 540 MW and the heat rate to 7948 kJ/kWh. So the heat consumption at 540 MW is given by:

$7948 \times 540\,000 \times 10^{-6} = 4291.92$ GJ/h
So to generate the last 20 MW it has been necessary to supply
$4291.92 - 4077.84 = 214.08$ GJ/h extra heat
The corresponding heat rate of the last 20 MW is:

$$\frac{214\,080\,000}{20\,000} = 10\,704 \text{ kJ/kWh, so the extra output is very expensive.}$$

Typical figures for heaters out of service are:

(a) Lowest pressure heater about 0.5%;
(b) Highest pressure heater about 1.5%.

Feed heater heat balance

In feed heater investigations it is assumed that all the heat abstracted from the bled steam is transferred to the feed water.

Thus $Q_b(h_s - h_f) = Q_f(h_{f,o} - h_{f,i})$

Where Q_b = quantity of bled steam, kg/s
h_s = enthalpy of bled steam, kJ/kg
h_f = enthalpy of drain water, kJ/kg
Q_F = quantity of feed water, kg/s
$h_{f,o}$ = enthalpy of feed water at heater outlet, kJ/kg
$h_{f,i}$ = enthalpy of feed water at heater inlet, kJ/kg

For example, consider the LP heaters in *Figure 12.16*. What is the feed outlet temperature from No. 3 heater?

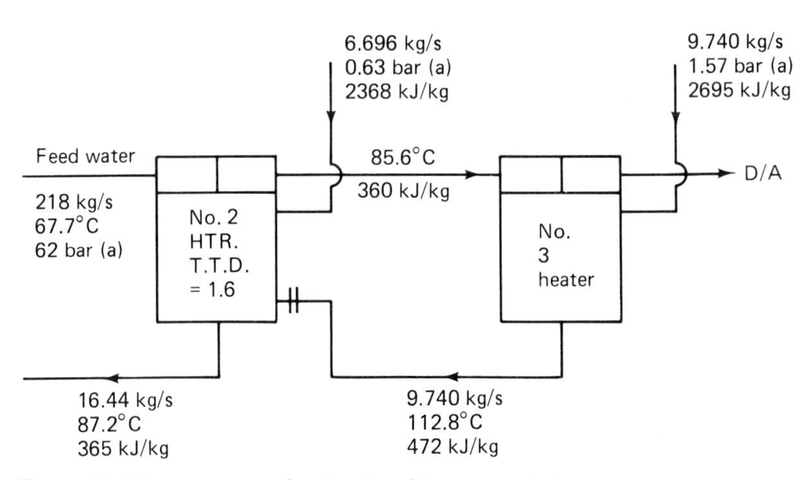

Figure 12.16 Low pressure feed heaters (diagrammatic)

$$Q_b(h_s - h_f) = Q_F(h_{f,o} - h_{f,i})$$

$$9.74\,(2695 - 472) = 218\,(h_{f,o} - 360.0)$$

$$\text{So } h_{f,o} = \frac{9.74\,(2695 - 472)}{218} + 360 \text{ kJ/k}$$

$$= 99.3 + 360 \text{ kJ/kg} = 459.7 \text{ kJ/kg}$$

The corresponding temperature is 109°C (from steam tables).

Effect of increased TTD

If there is an increase in the resistance to heat transfer in a heater (e.g. if the tubes are dirty) the bled steam saturation temperature will be unaffected but the feed outlet temperature will be reduced. Accordingly the TTD will increase and this will cause a reduction of the bled steam flow.

Consider No. 2 LP heater in *Figure 12.16*. The TTD is 1.6°C and feed temperature rise 17.9°C. The corresponding bled steam flow is 6.696 kg/s. Suppose now that the heater becomes dirty so that the TTD increases to 6.5°C, then the feed rise will be 13.0°C. The heat given up per kilogram of bled steam ($h_S - h_f$) will be unaltered, as will the quantity of feed flow.

So $Q_B \propto$ Feed temperature rise

$$\therefore \frac{Q_B}{Q_{B_2}} = \frac{\text{Feed temp. rise}_1}{\text{Feed temp. rise}_2}$$

Let suffix 1 represent the original conditions and suffix 2 the final ones.

$$\frac{6.696}{Q_B} = \frac{17.9}{13.0}$$

$$\therefore Q_{B_2} = \frac{6.696 \times 13.0}{17.9}$$

Hence new bled steam flow = 4.86 kg/s

The feed outlet from No. 2 heater will be 67.7 + 13.0 = 80.7°C and this will also be the temperature entering No. 3 heater. Consequently the feed temperature rise in No. 3 will be 28.3°C instead of 23.4°C, assuming the feed temperature at No. 3 heater outlet remains at its normal value.

So the bled steam flow will be $\frac{28.3}{23.4}$ times its original flow,

i.e. it will be 1.209 × 9.74 = 11.776 kg/s

Consequently a heater deficiency has three effects:

(a) That on the heater concerned;
(b) That on subsequent heaters;
(c) That on the steam flow in the turbine.

The loss of efficiency due to poor heater performance is about 0.027% for each degree Celsius by which the TTD increases.

Thus, if there is a group of three heaters whose TTDs are respectively 5°C, 4°C and 1°C above normal, the effect on efficiency will be about:

$(5 + 4 + 1)\,0.027 = 0.27\%$

Heat exchange in feed heaters

It should be established clearly that, whatever the type of heater, the greatest heat transfer by far is by the action of condensing the steam. Even if a heater is supplied with bled steam which has a considerable degree of superheat it will still be the condensing section which does most of the work. *Figure 12.17* shows a typical temperature/heat transferred diagram. The

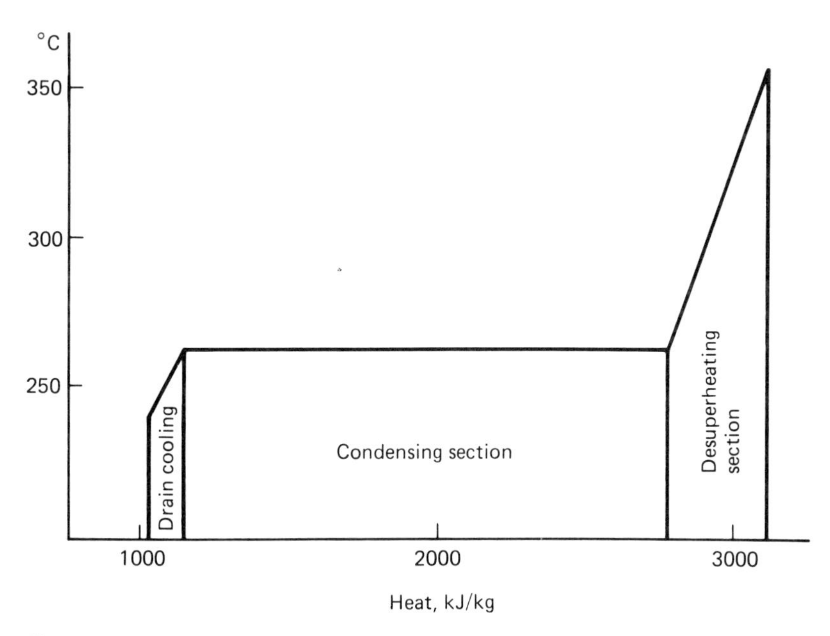

Figure 12.17 Heat surrendered in each section of last HP heater

saturation temperature is that of the condensing steam. This is not the same as that of the steam before the heater because there is some pressure drop in the desuperheating section.

Figure 12.18 shows the steam and water conditions for the high-pressure feed heaters on a 375 MW supercritical pressure turbine. Consider the last heater, i.e. No. 8:

> 'Steam to heater' inlet pressure/temperature = 49.5 bar abs./358°C;
> 'Steam to heater' heat content = 3100 kJ/kg;
> 'Steam to heater' dry saturated heat = 2792 kJ/kg;
> 'Steam to heater' wet saturated heat = 1150 kJ/kg;
> Enthalpy of drain water = 1027 kJ/kg.

So for every kilogram of steam supplied to the heater:

> The superheat component surrenders 3100 − 2792 = 308 kJ of heat;
> The condensing component surrenders 2792 − 1150 = 1642 kJ;
> The drains cooling component surrenders 1150 − 1027 = 123 kJ.

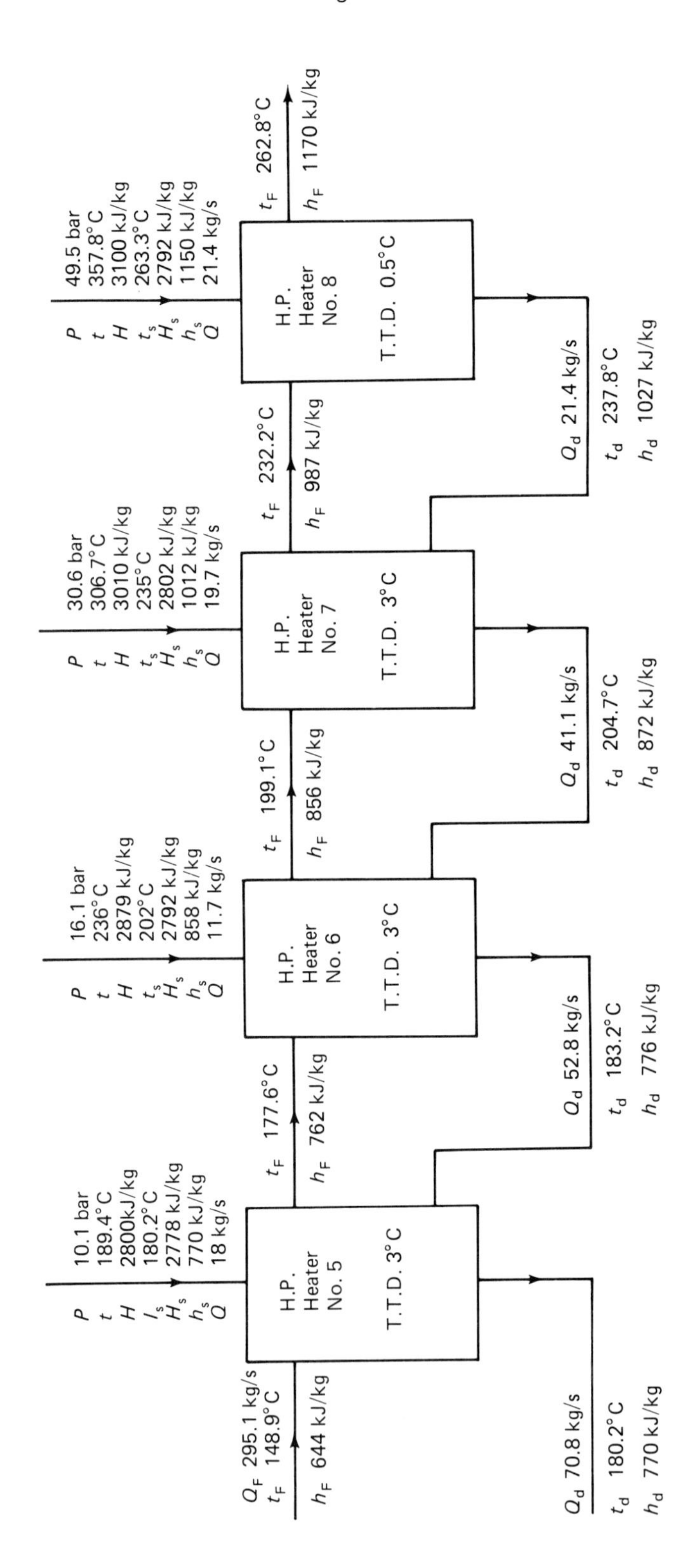

Figure 12.18 HP feed heater conditions for a 375–MW supercritical pressure unit (CEGB)

Figure 12.19 shows representations of various types of heat exchange used in feed heaters.

Deterioration of heater performance

This can be caused by various things, but the main ones to consider are:

(a) Air blanketing;
(b) Water-side contamination of the tubes;
(c) Steam-side contamination of the tubes;
(d) Drainage defects

Consider each in turn.

(a) Air blanketing

Air can get into a heater while it is on load if it operates at sub-atmospheric steam pressure. The usual points of entry are at leaking bled-steam line joints or heater fittings. On heaters which operate normally above atmospheric pressure air can get in while the unit is off load or on very low loads.

Any air that does get in should be discharged to the condenser via the air vent lines. These lines have an isolating valve near the heater body and often also a restricting orifice to prevent excessive quantities of steam being vented. Normally about 0.5% of the steam is vented. Some operations staff isolate the vent lines when the heaters are on load except for a short period each shift. This is satisfactory on heaters which are always substantially above atmospheric pressure when the turbine is on load, provided they are adequately vented when the turbine is brought on load. The lower pressure heaters, though, should be continuously vented.

The location of the air vent connections at the shell of the heater is most important. If difficulty is being experienced in achieving adequate air removal it may be that the take-offs need to be re-located. Ideally the air vent take-offs should be at the 'remote' end of the steam flow but the difficulty is to decide just where that is. Typically they are as shown in *Figure 12.20)a)*, *(b)* and *(c)*.

Figure 12.20(a) shows the case of a heater with no cascade drainage going into it. The best location for the vent is at the remote end from the steam inlet just above the level of the condensate. *Figure 12.20(b)* shows the case where the bled steam enters the heater at about the middle. Thus there are two remote ends and a vent is located at each. For heaters receiving bled steam and flash steam separately the vent should be positioned so that between a quarter and a third of the heating surface is below the vent. This ensures that the vent will not be swamped by flashing drain water, thus obstructing air removal, see *Figure 12.20(c)*.

Should air accumulate in a heater it will blanket the tubes. It is such an

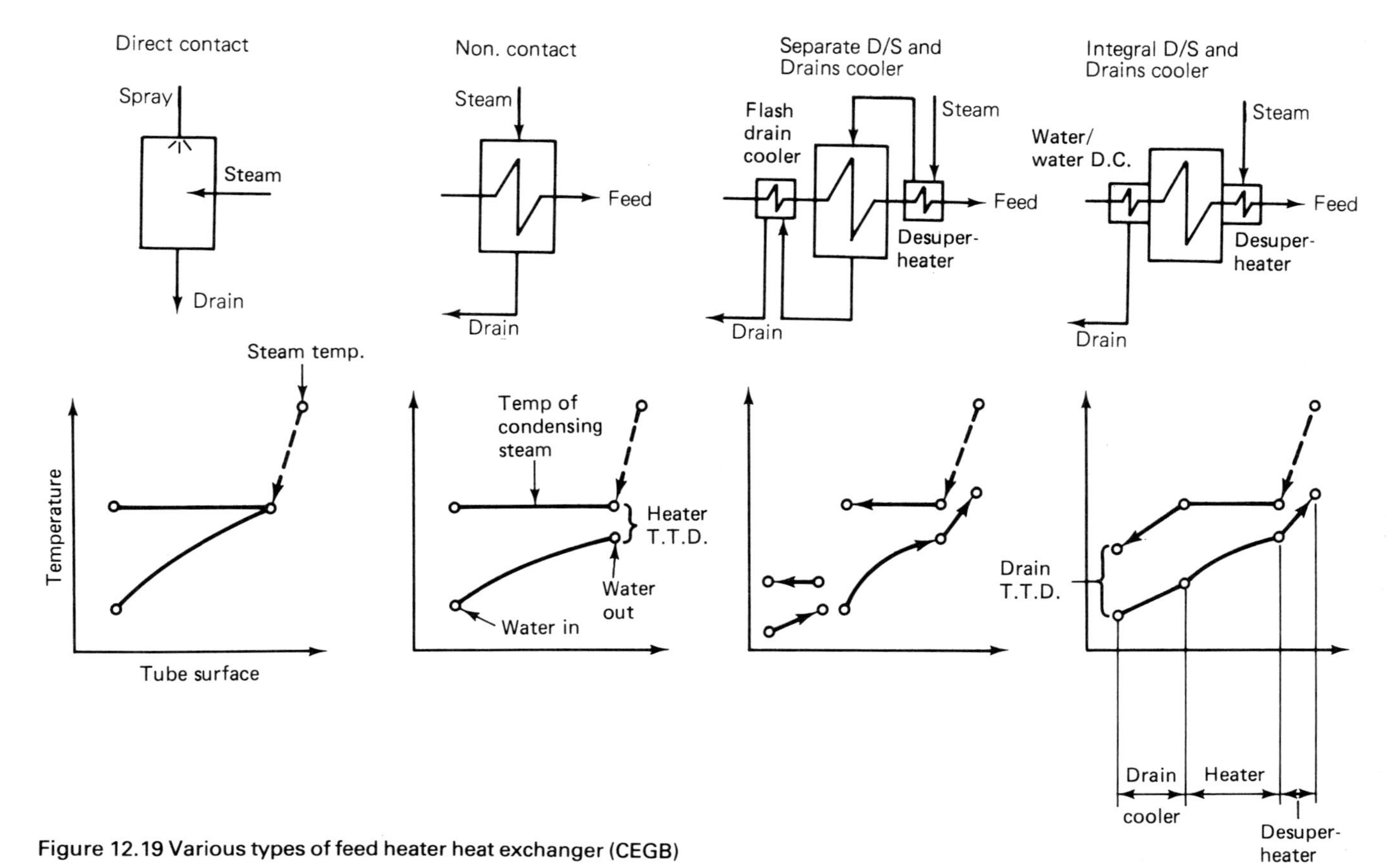

Figure 12.19 Various types of feed heater heat exchanger (CEGB)

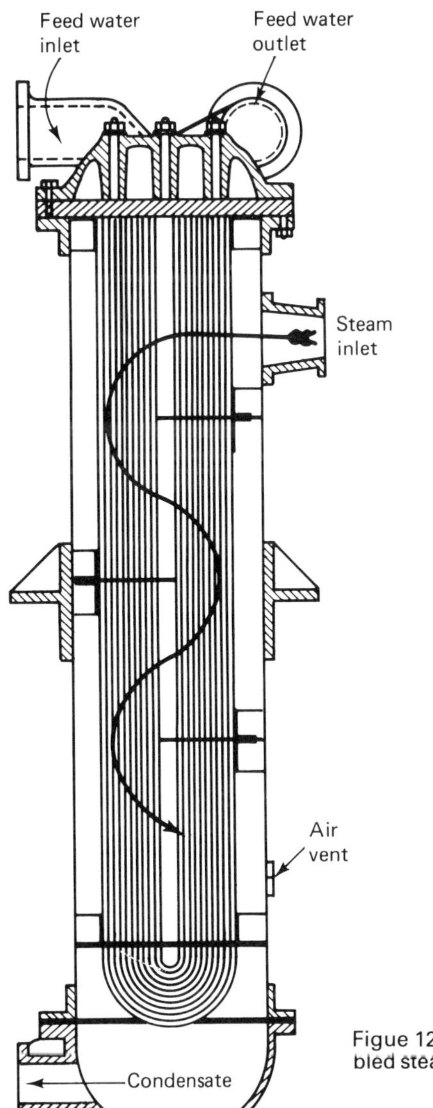

Figue 12.20(a) Location of feed heater air vents — bled steam only (CEGB)

excellent insulator that it will interfere seriously with heat transfer to the feed water. Consequently the outlet feed temperature will be reduced and the drain water temperature will be lowered.

(b) Water-side contamination of the tubes

A common cause of this type of contamination is oil which finds its way into

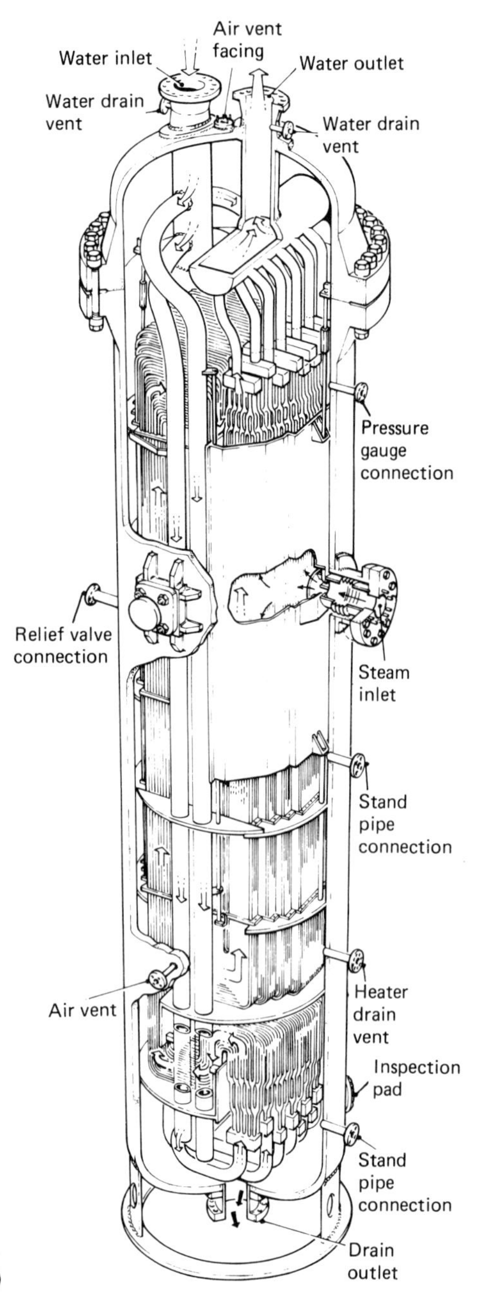

Figure 12.20(b) Location of feed heater air vents— mid level steam inlet (CEGB)

the condenser and, hence, into the condensate. From there it is pumped through the heaters along with the feed water. Some of the oil is deposited on the inside of the heater tubes and so causes interference with the heat

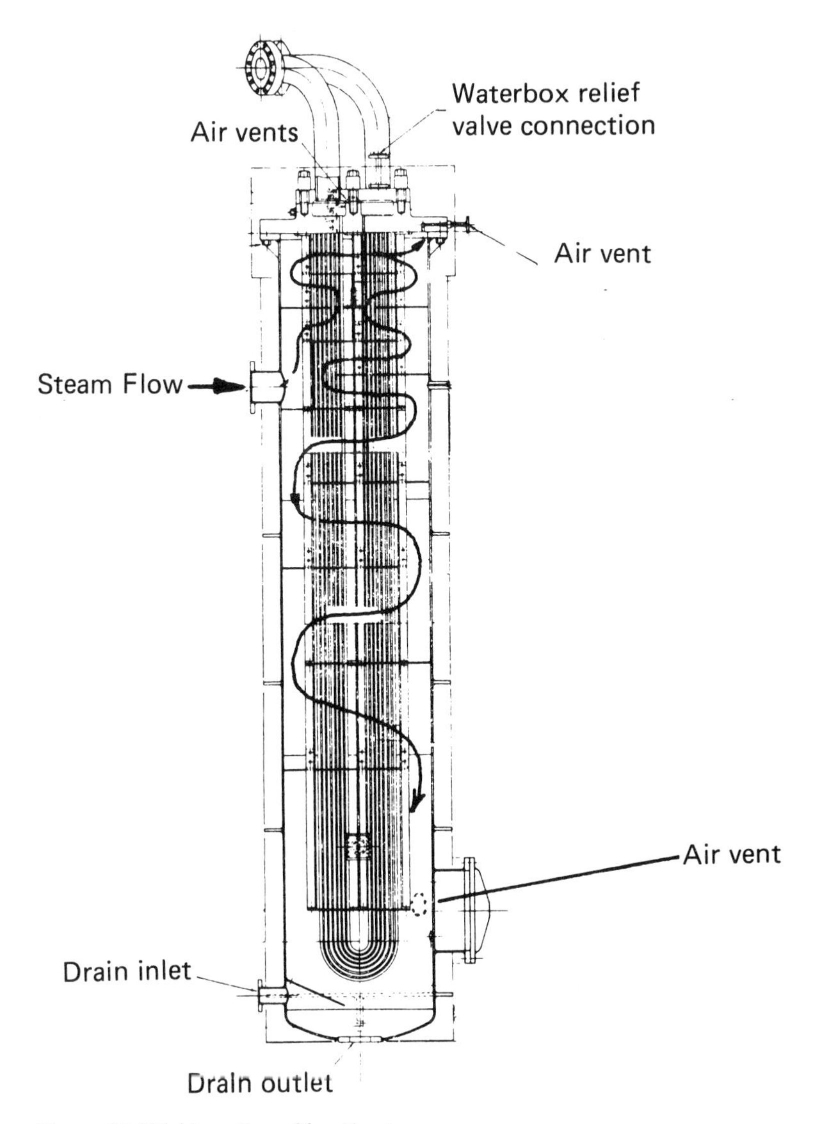

Figure 12.20(c) Location of feed heater air vents — flash steam plus bled steam (CEGB)

transfer. As with air contamination the effect is to lower the outlet feed temperature while the steam temperature and pressure remains unaffected. However, unlike the case of air ingress, the condensate is not undercooled.

Serious oil contamination occurred on a 120 MW unit when one of the turbine LP cylinder bearings leaked oil which got into the condenser and thence into the feed. *Figure 12.21* shows how dramatically the TTD was affected. Actually all the HP heaters were badly affected but No. 6 heater

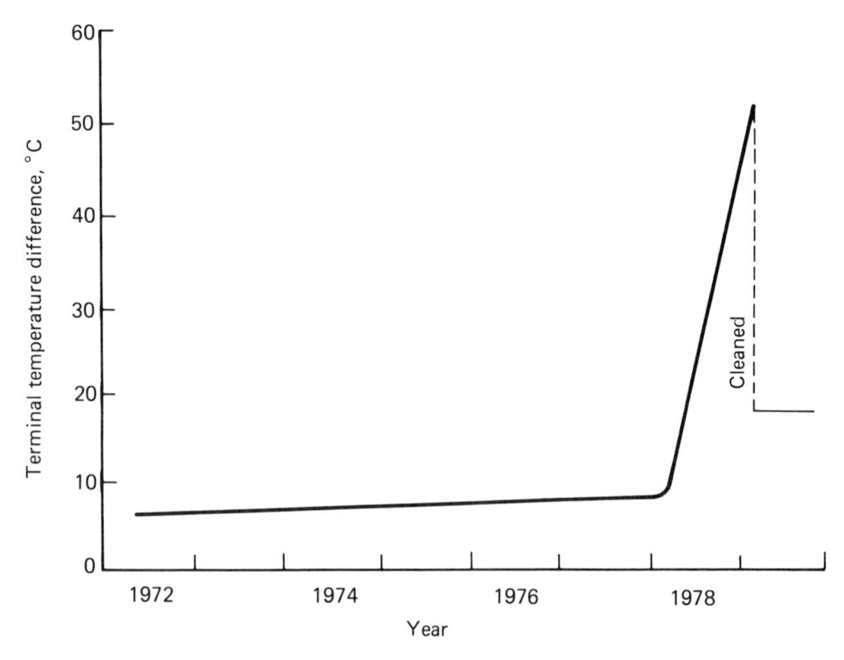

Figure 12.21 No. 6 HP feed heater— effect of fouling

was the worst. Several chemical cleans failed to remove the deposit and finally the only partial cure that could be found was to use a high-pressure (620 bar) jet of water down each individual tube. This reduced the TTD to about one third of the contaminated condition.

(c) Steam-side contamination of the tubes

In the 1950s it was common to use 70/30 cupro-nickel for heater tubes. After some years' experience it became clear that this was an unsuitable material because the tubes exfoliated – that is, the metal flaked off like dead skin. The result was that the exfoliated material blocked the spaces between the tubes and, of course, the tube thickness was progressively reduced until eventually the tubes failed mechanically. The rate of exfoliation is enhanced by frequent two-shifting.

Figure 12.22 shows how the terminal temperature difference increased on a particular heater as exfoliation progressed. Note that the rate of rise is slow over a number of years, unlike the case of oil contamination where the increase occurred at a specific time, after which it was rapid. The heater to which *Figure 12.22* refers was so badly affected that the tube thickness had been halved and the space between the tubes was almost blocked solidly. Some idea of the effects of exfoliation can be seen from *Figure 12.23*.

In the late 1950s, after the discovery of problems with 70/30 Cu–Ni tubes,

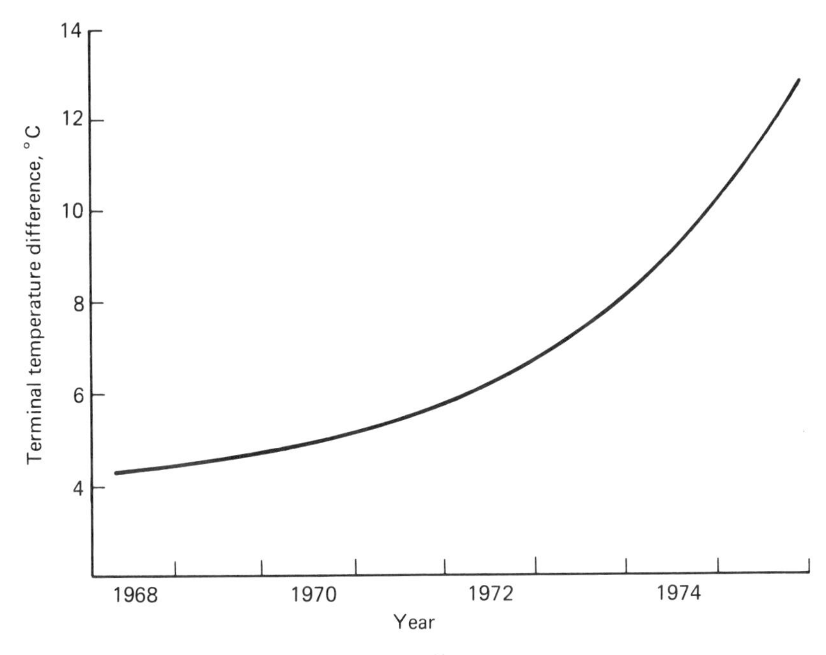

Figure 12.22 Effect on TTD of exfoliated HP heater

Figure 12.23 Exfoliated tube nest (CEGB)

a change was made to other materials such as 90/10 Cu–Ni, mild steel and Monel. Plants with 70/30 cupro-nickel tube nests should be protected from oxygen as far as possible, because exfoliation can proceed only when free oxygen is in contact with the tubes – a level of oxygen of little over 100 ppm is sufficient.

(d) Drainage defects

If a drain line orifice becomes fouled, say with copper oxide, it will cause the upstream water level to increase. Alternatively if an orifice becomes enlarged due to, say, erosion it will be capable of passing extra drainage which may cause flooding of the flash box. Similarly if the slotted discharge pipe inside the flash box should disintegrate it could cause flooding by obstructing the flash box discharge pipe. The water level in heaters with drains cooling is determined by the configuration of the drain pipework or by level actuated drain valves.

Operation with heaters out of service

If, because of some defect, it is necessary to take a heater out of service then the steam flow to the next higher pressure heater will be increased considerably. For example, consider the two heaters in a feed train as illustrated in *Figure 12.24(a)*. Suppose the relevant data for normal operation is as shown. The total volume of steam flowing to No. 6 heater is 22.46 × 51.9 = 1165.67 litre/s.

If No. 5 heater is now taken out of service, the feed temperature entering

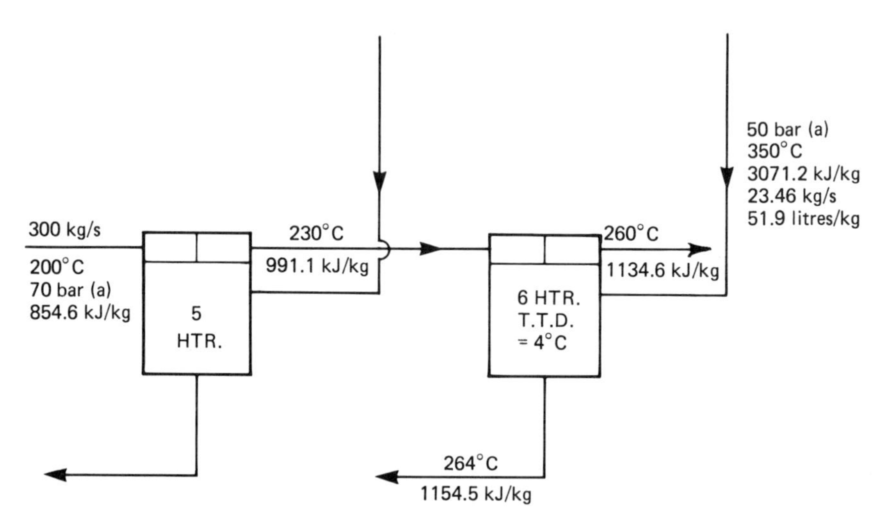

Figure 12.24(a) Normal heater operation

No. 6 heater will be 200°C, and the heat content will be 854.6 kJ/kg. So the steam flow to No. 6 heater will become (assuming the outlet temperature remains at 260°C):

$$Q = \frac{300\,(1134.6 - 854.6)}{(3071.2 - 1154.5)} = \frac{84000}{1916.7} = 43.8 \text{ kg/s}$$

In other words the steam flow will about double and, therefore, so will the velocity of the steam. This could result in damaging the heater tubes or the steam impingement baffle. Therefore the manufacturers normally recommend in such a case that the steam supply to the heater should be throttled to permit only the design feed temperature pick-up across the heater.

Thus, in the case being considered the temperature rise across No. 6 heater will be limited to 30°C. As the temperature of the inlet feed will be 200°C then the outlet will be 230°C. The TTD will remain as before (i.e. 4°C), and so the saturation temperature of the steam supply will be 234°C. The enthalpy of the steam will remain at its former value because it will only be throttled at the bled steam valve. Inspection of the steam tables reveals that for steam at 234°C saturation temperature the pressure is 30 bar abs. The temperature corresponding to the required enthalpy of 3071.2 kJ/kg is found by inspection to be 330°C and the specific volume is 86.874 litre/kg. So the conditions shown in *Figure 12.24(b)* will then pertain at No. 6 heater.

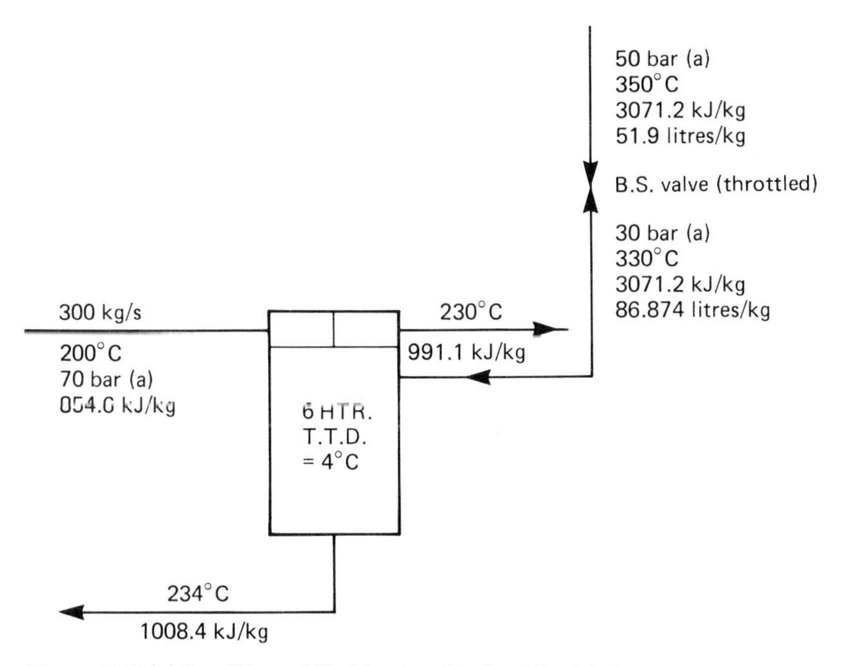

Figure 12.24(b) Conditions at No 6 heater after throttling bled steam

$$\text{So the steam flow to No. 6 heater} = \frac{300\,(991.1 - 854.6)}{(30761.2 - 1008.4)} = \frac{4\,0950}{2062.8}$$

$$= 19.8 \text{ kg/s}$$

And the total volume of steam flowing will be $19.8 \times 86.874 = 1720$ litre/s.

So, by throttling the steam, the flow has been reduced from 43.8 to 19.8 kg/s. Also the volume flow has been reduced from $(43.8 \times 51.9) = 2273$ to 1720 litre/s and, of course, the velocity will be reduced in the same proportion.

Further, the specific volume of the steam has gone from 51.9 to 86.9 litre/kg, and consequently the steam is not only reduced in quantity and velocity but also in density, all of which factors are desirable for safeguarding the heater tubes.

Boiler feed pump gland sealing

It is common to seal the glands of feed pumps from another pump such as shown in *Figure 12.25(a)* which refers to a 120 MW unit. The conditions

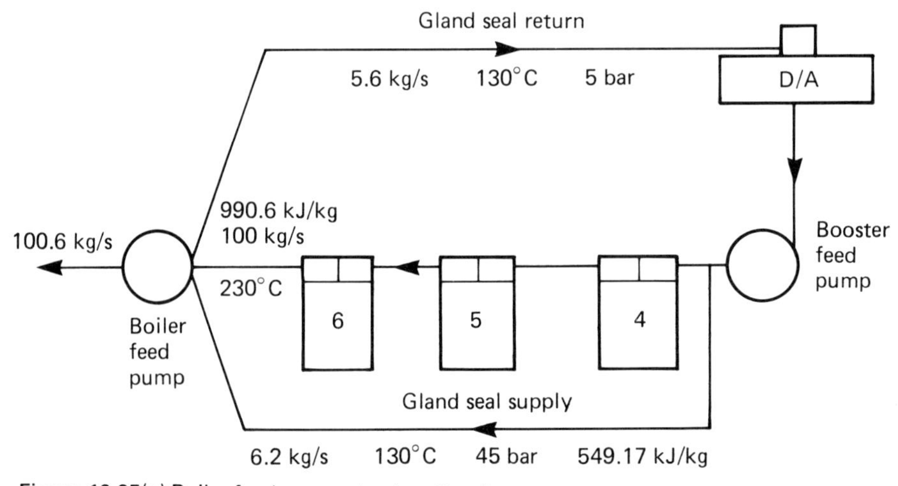

Figure 12.25(a) Boiler feed pump gland sealing flows

during a particular test were as indicated. As can be seen, 6.2 kg/s of water bypasses the HP heaters, of which 5.6 kg/s is returned to the deaerator. So 0.6 kg/s enters the boiler feed pump and mixes with 100 kg/s of water at 230°C.

$$\text{So the combined heat} = \frac{(0.6 \times 549.17) + (100 \times 990.6)}{100.6} = 988.0 \text{ kJ/kg}$$

and the equivalent temperature is 229°C.

Therefore the feed water is reduced in temperature by 1°C because of the gland sealing, so it is not a significant loss. Of course, heaters ripping and so bypassing will give a similar effect but on a much greater scale, such as shown in *Figure 12.25(b)*.

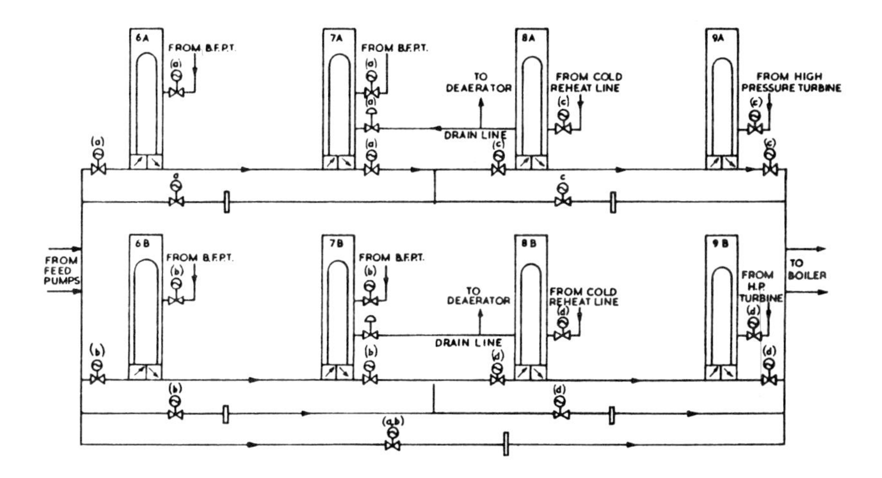

Figure 12.25(b) HP heater bypass system (CEGB)

For example, suppose on a 500 MW unit the discharge from the feed pump is 416.0 kg/s at 170°C, and that the final feed temperature with all the feed heaters in service is 254°C. Assume that if a bank of heaters tripped, half of the total feed flow would be via the bypass valve.

Then the final feed temperature would be reduced from 254°C to about

$$\frac{(208 \times 254) + (208 \times 170)}{416} = 212°\text{C}$$

Monitoring the feed heater system

As with so many aspects of monitoring power station plant, it is important to have comprehensive data on the optimum operation of the heater system. Such information will be available from the acceptance tests. Failing this, reliable tests by station staff at a time when the plant is known to be in good condition will do. If necessary it is always possible to use design data. Having got the data for optimum operation it is then only necessary to carry out a 'feed heater temperature survey' every six months, say. This consists of noting all the relevant data on each heater and comparing it with optimum. The data required for each heater is:

(a) Steam temperature entering the heater;
(b) Drain water temperature;
(c) Inlet feed water temperature;
(d) Outlet feed water temperature;
(e) Inlet feed temperature of next higher heater. This should be the same as (d), and serves to check whether any feed is bypassing the heater;
(f) Steam pressure in heater shell.

With direct contact heaters the data required is only:

(a) Shell pressure (and thus the corresponding saturation temperature);
(b) The outgoing water temperature.

The two temperatures should be the same. If they are not it may be that the venting is ineffective or there may be damage to the internal fittings of the heater.

Example of a feed heater investigation

A routine feed investigation was carried out on a particular unit. The high-pressure heaters are designated B, C, D and E and the tube nests are made of 70/30 cupro-nickel. The results of the heater survey are shown in *Table 12.2*, along with the corresponding acceptance test data.

Table 12.2 Feed heater survey

ACC = Acceptance test   **GLO = Gland leak-off**

S = Survey   **BS = Bled steam**

Heater		*A*		*B*		*C*		*D*		*E*	
		ACC	*S*	*ACC*	*S*	*ACC*	*S*	*ACC*	*S*	*ACC*	*S*
Saturation	°C	65.6	66.0	147.3	149.9	173.6	174.7	202.1	201.1	230.0	230.0
BS before GLO	°C		68.5	—	—	—	—	—	—	—	—
BS at heater	°C	76.0	133.6	205.1	181.1	344.2	357.0	335.4	330.6	401.6	394.7
Feed in	°C	33.5	38.5	114.0	108.6	141.6	139.5	168.2	161.7	194.9	190.3
Feed out	°C	62.1	60.8	141.6	139.5	168.2	161.7	194.9	190.3	225.3	215.0
Drain	°C	62.9	62.8	144.6	143.7	173.2	171.4	202.1	200.8	229.9	230.8
Feed rise	°C	28.6	22.3	27.6	30.9	26.6	22.2	26.7	28.6	30.4	24.7
TTD	°C	3.5	3.3	5.7	10.4	5.4	13.0	7.2	10.9	4.7	15.0
BS pressure	bar	0.756	0.753	3.5	3.7	7.7	7.9	15.2	15.4	26.8	27.0

Comments

The TTDs in each case are high except for ‘A’ heater. In the case of ‘E’ heater the TTD is three hundred per cent above optimum. The usual causes of high TTD are:

1 Contamination of the water side of the tubes due to, say, oil.
2 Air blanketing on the steam side.
3 Deposits on the steam side.

The condensate was checked for traces of oil contamination. The equipment will detect even minute quantities of oil in the water, but in this case none was detected. Therefore, oil contamination was not probable.

Air could get into the HP heater shells only during shut-down periods and would normally be continuously vented when the plant was started. The air vent cocks were checked and found to be correctly set and the vent lines were hot. Therefore there was at least some venting taking place. In addition, air would probably cause under cooling of the drain water and this was not happening. Therefore air contamination was ruled out.

That left deposits on the steam side as the probable cause. (Note that the trouble could not be a partially closed BS valve or other interference with the steam supply as this would not affect the TTD, even though it would affect the feed rise). As the tubes are made of 70/30 Cu–Ni and the plant had been in service since the mid 1950s trouble due to exfoliation was a distinct possibility. This was particularly so as the plant was beginning to be two-shifted regularly. Also earlier results suggest a continuous worsening of the situation and in addition some slight exfoliation had been experienced in the past.

Of course, the implications would be very serious if the trouble were found to be exfoliation, as probably every HP heater in the station (16 altogether) would be affected just as seriously in the fairly near future as they all had similar materials, similar life and similar operating regimes. The following recommendations were therefore made to Management:

1 As soon as possible remove an HP heater tube nest for examination, preferably from 'E' Heater shell.
2 When the nest is removed, take the opportunity to check for oil deposition inside the tubes, although it is not anticipated that any will be found.
3 If exfoliation is present to a serious degree (and this will probably be the case) then all the HP heaters should be examined as soon as possible with a view to determining their remaining useful life.

Addendum

When a tube nest was examined it was found to be badly exfoliated. The tube wastage was considerable and the debris had almost blocked the spaces between the tubes, see *Figure 12.26*. The nests have now been re-tubed in mild steel.

Figure 12.26 Exfoliated tube nest (CEGB)

Questions

1 What is the purpose of feed heating?
2 What is the measure of the work lost to the turbine?
3 What is the ideal number of feed heaters?
4 What is the temperature of the drain water in a DC heater?

Table 12.3 Feed heater fault finding chart

Effect / Possible Cause	Heater by-pass valve passing	One or more heaters have poor heat transfer	Lower pressure heater tripped or by-passed	Gland leak-off excessive	Cascade drain line defects	Reduced steam press., e.g. BS valve throttled	Air in steam space	Internal deposits on tubes, e.g. oil	External deposits on tubes, e.g. exfoliktion	Vent shut	Reduced bled steam flow to heater	Unsuitable tube material, e.g. 70/30 Cu-Ni	Cascade drains by-passing heater
TTD high		X					X	X	X	X		X	
Low feed temp. rise		X			X	X	X	X	X	X	X	X	
Drains undercooled					X		X			X			
Low 'steam-to-heater' temp.					X	X							
High inlet steam temp.				X			X						X
Feed inlet temp. low	X		X										
Final feed tsmp. low	X	X	X				X	X	X	X	X	X	
Heater body pressure low						X					X		

5 Is 70/30 cupro-nickel a good material for heater tubes?
6 What is the formula for the flash steam quantity produced in a flash-box?
7 Why are heater drains pumps used?
8 What are the causes of an increased TTD at a heater?
9 The largest proportion of heat transfer occurs in what part of a heater?
10 What are the manifestations of air accumulation inside a heater?
11 Where would the vents be located on a heater supplied with bled steam plus drains from an upstream heater?
12 What are the indications of oil contamination?
13 What are the indications of exfoliation?
14 What information should be recorded during a feed heater survey?
15 How frequently should feed heater surveys be carried out?
16 What increase in power output will be achieved by shutting off the steam to the last heater?
17 What is the approximate effect of 1°C increased TTD on efficiency?
18 What is the justification for using DC heaters?
19 What are the manifestations of a partly closed BS valve on heater operation?
20 What information is required to carry out a heat balance across a heater?

Exercise 1

Upon return to service after the routine survey of a turbine it was observed that the temperature of the steam entering No. 1 LP heater was becoming progressively higher. Within four weeks it was up to 379°C whereas the optimum value was 174°C. *Figure 12.27* shows the general layout of the

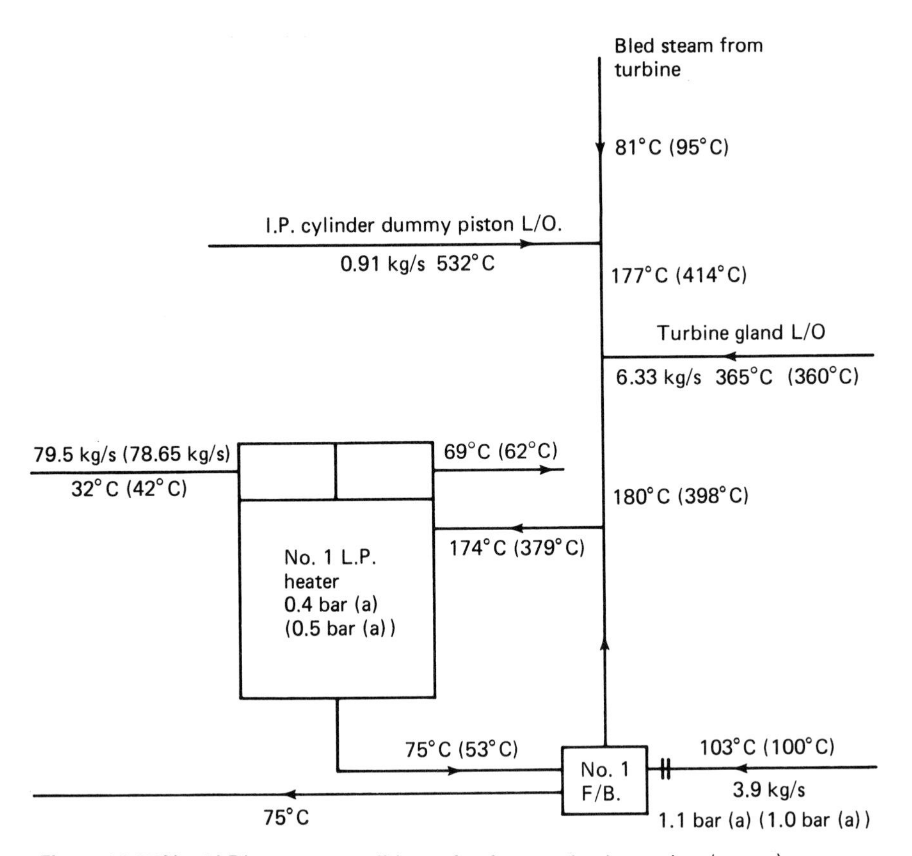

Figure 12.27 No. 1 LP heater— conditions after four weeks shown thus ( ). Exercise 1

heater and its connections. The leak-off steam from the second stage glands of the dummy piston discharges into the bled steam pipe as does the gland leak-off steam from the turbine shaft. The optimum values are shown and also the values after four weeks' operation, the latter being in brackets.

The temperature of the steam at the heater is completely unacceptable, so it is important to determine:

(a) The cause of the high temperature.
(b) Recommendations to remedy the situation.

Note: No. 2 LP heater and all the other heaters in the train are operating satisfactorily. For example, when the unit is on full load the condensate flow is 78.65 kg/s and the temperature rise of the condensate across No. 2 heater is 26°C, i.e. at optimum. The inlet steam conditions to the IP cylinder are 26.0 bar abs., 538°C.

Exercise 1 (Answer)

Optimum conditions (see Figure 12.28(a))

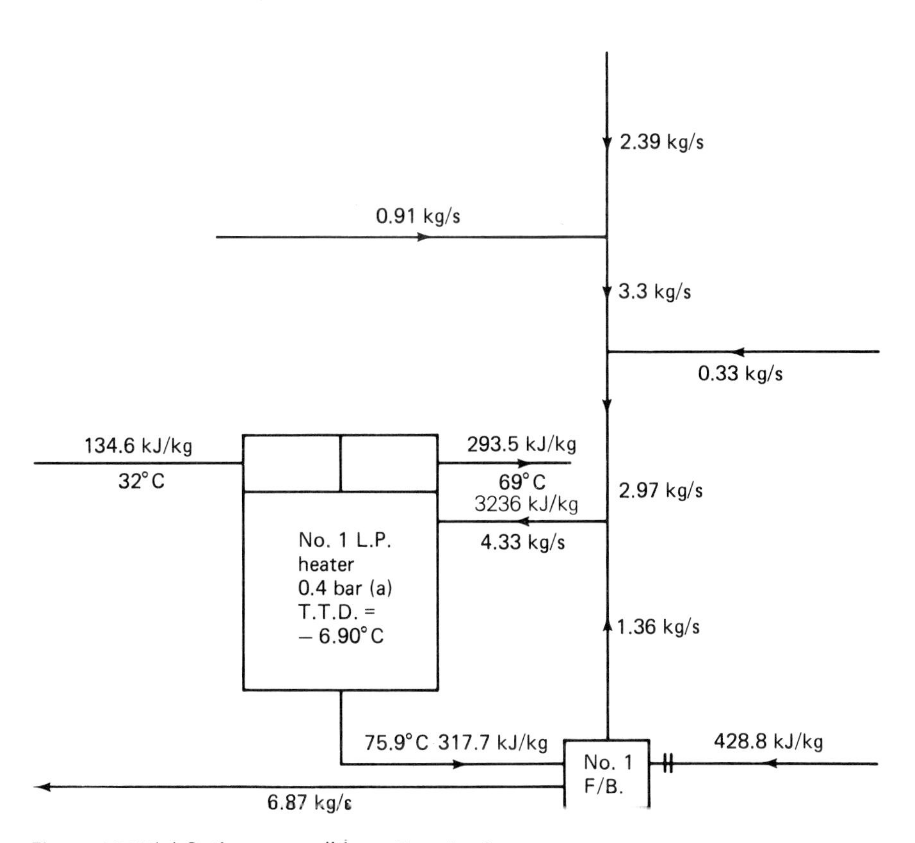

Figure 12.28(a) Optimum conditions. Exercise 1

$$\text{Steam to heater} = \frac{79.5(293.5 - 134.6)}{3236 - 317.7} = 4.33 \text{ kg/s}$$

$$\text{Flash steam} = \frac{(428.8 - 317.7) \times 3.9}{2319.2} = 1.36 \text{ kg/s}$$

The remaining flows can now easily be established as shown in *Figure 12.28(a)*.

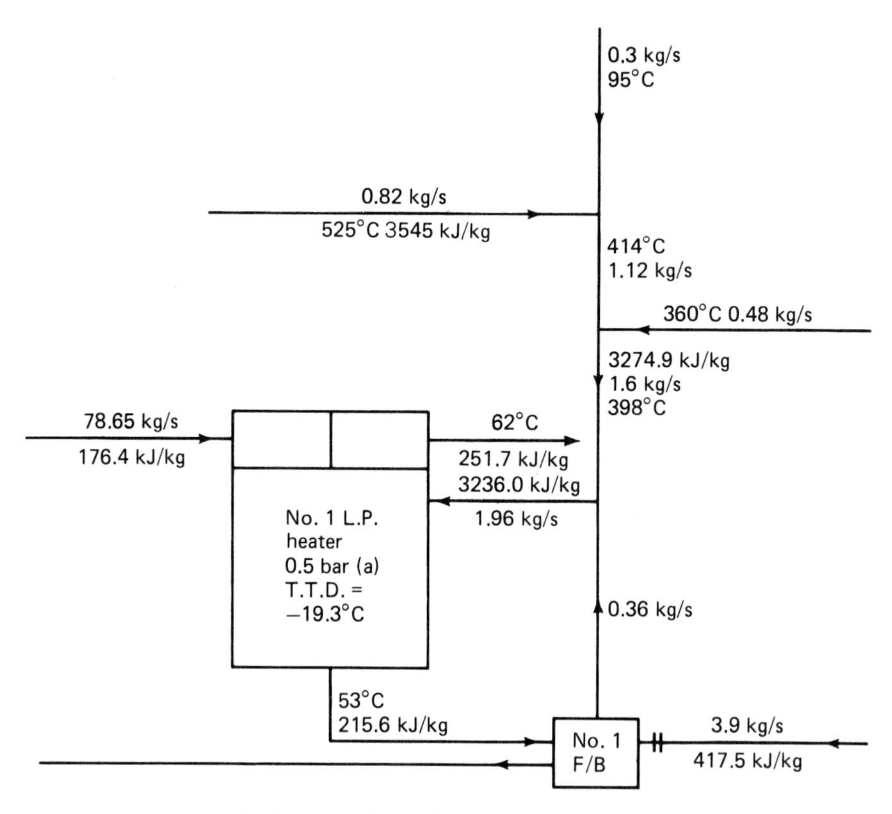

Figure 12.28(b) Conditions after four weeks. Exercise 1

Conditions after four weeks' operation (see Figure 12.28(b))

$$\text{Drainage from No. 2 heater to No. 1 F/B} = \frac{78.65 \times 3.9}{79.5} = 3.86\text{, say } 3.9 \text{ kg}$$

$$\text{Flash steam} = \frac{417.5 - 215.6}{2305.4} = 0.092 \text{ or } 9.2\%$$

$$\text{So flash steam quantity} = 0.092 \times 3.9 = 0.36 \text{ kg/s}$$

$$\text{Steam to heater} = \frac{78.65(251.7 - 176.4)}{(3236 - 215.6)} = 1.96 \text{ kg/s}$$

The heat in the steam at the dummy piston leak-off (*Figure 12.28(b)*) is the same as that at IP cylinder inlet, because it has merely been throttled at the dummy piston glands, i.e. 3545 kJ/kg and temperature 525°C.

The unknown flows remaining are:

Shaft gland L/O; Dummy piston L/O; Bled steam from turbine

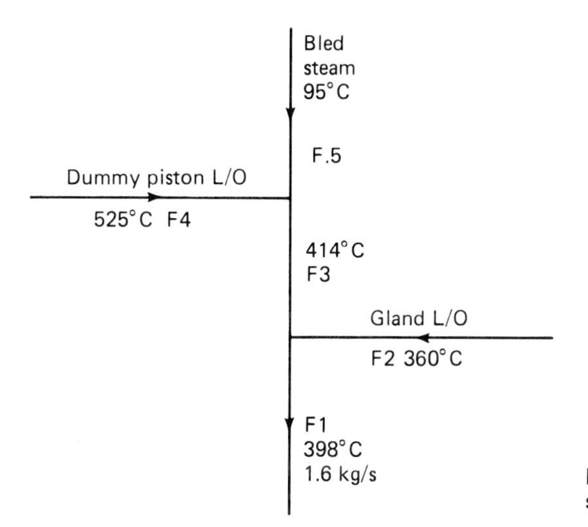

Figure 12.29 Determination of steam flows. Exercise 1

Use the formula derived for gland flows (see Chapter 10, Turbine Monitoring). The corresponding heats, assuming a constant pressure of 0.5 bar, are:

$$h_1 = 3274.9 \text{ kJ/kg}$$
$$h_2 = 3197.0 \text{ kJ/kg}$$
$$h_3 = 3308.0 \text{ kJ/kg}$$
$$h_4 = 3545.0 \text{ kJ/kg}$$
$$h_5 = 2673.0 \text{ kJ/kg}$$

$$\text{So } F_2 = \frac{1.6\,(3274.9 - 3308)}{(3197.0 - 3308)} = 0.48 \text{ kg/s}$$

$$F_3 = F_1 - F_2 = 1.12 \text{ kg/s}$$

$$F_4 = \frac{1.12\,(3308 - 2673)}{(3545 - 2673)} = 0.82 \text{ kg/s}$$

$$F_5 = F_3 - F_4 = 1.12 - 0.82 = 0.3 \text{ kg/s}$$

Comparing the various flows for optimum conditions with those after four weeks' service, it is seen that:

1 The bled steam flow has been reduced to 13% of its optimum flow.
2 The dummy piston L/O is about the same.
3 The shaft gland L/O is now about 150% of its optimum flow.
4 The steam to heater flow is now about 50% of its optimum flow.
5 The flash steam is now about 25% of its optimum flow.

Also, the TTD has gone from (−)6.9°C to (−)19.3°C.

The increased TTD and reduced steam flow to heater indicate a severe reduction of heat transfer in the heater, which could be due to:

1 External tube deposits (e.g. exfoliation)
2 Internal tube deposits (e.g. oil contamination)
3 Air in the steam space.

The first two items would not affect the condensate temperature, but the third would cause undercooling. In fact the condensate temperature is 28°C below the saturation temperature. Thus, the basic cause of the trouble being experienced is air ingress to the heater shell.

The flows being experienced may seem puzzling, but the reason is as follows:

The factors which determine the rate of flow from the dummy piston are the difference of pressure between the IP cylinder inlet and dummy piston outlet steam pressures, plus the state of the dummy piston glands. Similarly, the shaft gland leak-off steam is determined by the gland inlet and outlet pressures plus the state of the glands. In both cases, if the glands are at optimum condition the flows will be about optimum. So the dummy piston glands seem to be satisfactory while there is some wear on the shaft glands.

The flows from the dummy piston and shaft glands account for almost all the demand for steam at the heater. Consequently, the bled steam is reduced to a tiny proportion of its normal flow.

Note: A thorough search for sources of air ingress was carried out by Efficiency Department staff using Leybold leak detector apparatus. Four flange joints were found to be leaking. Two of them were particularly bad and were on the bled steam line from the turbine before the junction with the dummy piston leak-off line. The other two were not so bad, and were located at flanges on the line between the junctions with the dummy piston and shaft gland leak-offs.

Exercise 2

A feed heater survey was carried out in 1977 on a 120 MW unit. The optimum values and the 1977 results are listed below. The tube material for the Nos. 4, 5 and 6 HP heaters is 70/30 cupro-nickel. The LP heaters are not listed as they were in a satisfactory condition. *Figure 12.30* shows how the terminal temperature differences changed with time.

Analyse the results.

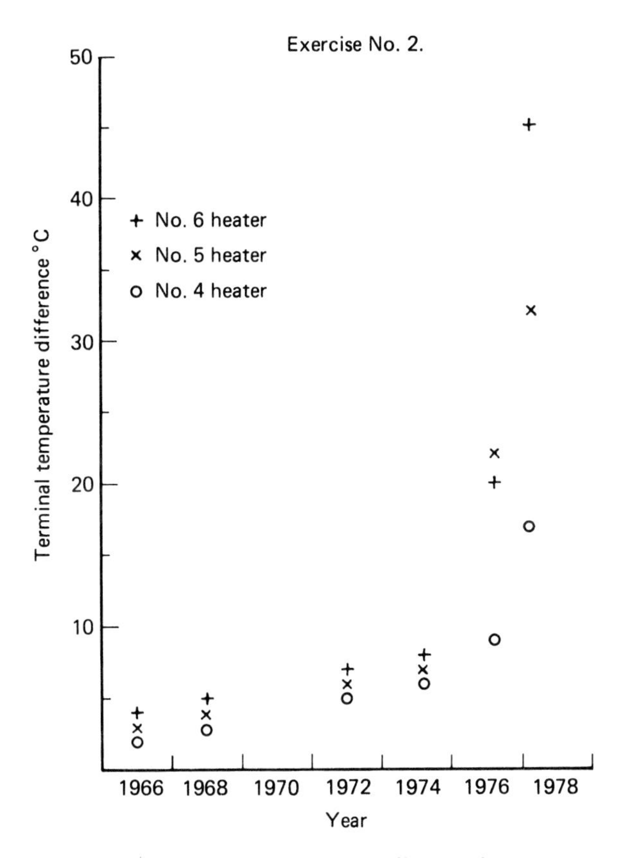

Figure 12.30 Terminal temperature difference for 4, 5 and 6 heaters *vs* time. Exercise 2

		Heater number					
		4		*5*		*6*	
		Opt	1977	Opt	1977	Opt	1977
Steam pressure at heater	bar (a)	6.5	6.5	13.0	13.0	27.0	28.0
Steam temp. at heater	°C	320	240	445	440	380	370
Feed water inlet temp.	°C	126	126	160	145	190	160
Feed water outlet temp.	°C	160	145	190	160	227	185
Drain temp.	°C	162	162	192	o/c	228	226

Exercise 2 (Answer)

The following information is derived from that given.

		Heater number					
		4		*5*		*6*	
		Opt	1977	Opt	1977	Opt	1977
Saturation temp. of steam at heater	°C	162	162	192	192	228	230
Feed temp. rise	°C	34	19	30	15	37	25
TTD	°C	(+)2	(+)17	(+)2	(+)32	(+)1	(+)45
Sat. temp. – drain temp.	°C	0	0	0	—	0	4

The feed temperature rise on each heater is low and the TTDs are much removed from optimum (*Figure 12.31*). Thus, there is significant inter-

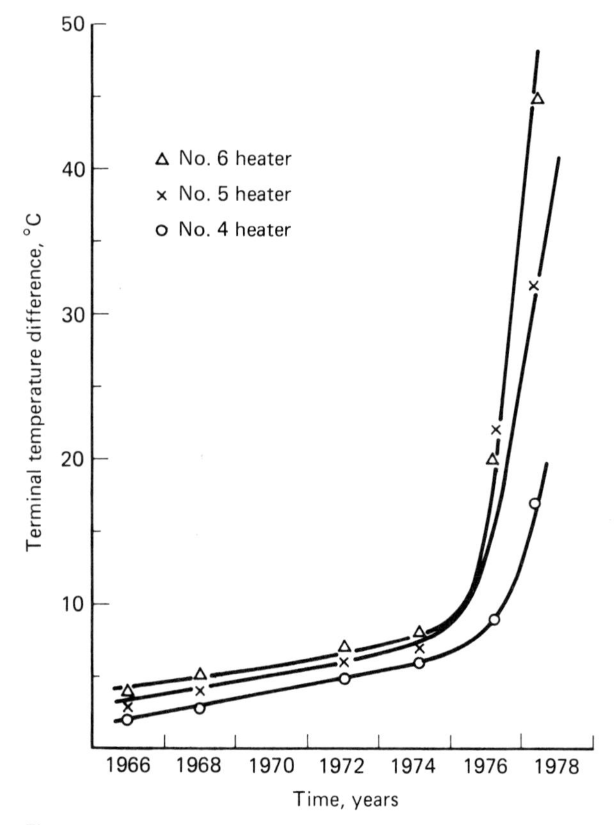

Figure 12.31 Curves of TTD for Nos. 4, 5 and 6 heaters. Exercise 2

ference with the heat transfer in each of the heaters. There is no under-cooling of the drain water and so the trouble is not due to excessive air accumulation in the heater shells. Thus, the interference with heat transfer could be due to such things as:

(a) Water-side deposits, e.g. oil contamination;
(b) Steam-side deposits, e.g. exfoliation.

The tube material is one which is prone to exfoliation and so this must be considered to be a real possibility. Also, one would expect exfoliation effects to be most severe in the highest heater and be less severe on No. 5 and then No. 4, and this is, in fact, the case. Also the deterioration would be gradual. On the other hand the onset of the rapid rise of TTD in 1975 seems too sudden for exfoliation, and would indicate that the trouble is due to water-side deposition. Thus there seems to be two distinct phases of deterioration. The gradually worsening situation up to 1974 has all the hallmarks of exfoliation and this is what it was attributed to, although a nest had not been removed for confirmation. But in 1975 the dramatic change in the rate of deterioration implies oil deposition.

Recommendations to management

There is a possibility that the heaters are seriously exfoliated in which case the nests will need to be replaced in the near future. Also there is probably serious water-side contamination. Recommendations:

(a) The heater nest on at least No. 6 heater be removed for examination and a tube be cut out for detailed examination.
(b) Meanwhile the Station Chemist be requested to take samples of the feed water to see if there is any indication of oil contamination.
(c) If there is oil contamination clean all the heater tubes thoroughly as a matter of urgency. Also locate and stop the source of the contamination.
(d) If there is exfoliation check the tube thickness to assess the remaining useful life.
(e) Prepare an economic appraisal for possible tube nest replacement.

Addendum

In the event, the nests were found to have exfoliation when they were inspected and also, much more seriously, severe oil contamination. Three chemical cleans failed to remove the deposition and eventually they were partly cleaned with a high-pressure water jet. New techniques of chemical cleaning are now being devised.

The source of the contamination was found to be oil leakage from a bearing adjacent to the LP cylinder from which it got into the condensate.

Project 1

In 1978 a routine feed heater survey was carried out on a 120 MW turbine (*Figure 12.32*). The results are tabulated along with the corresponding

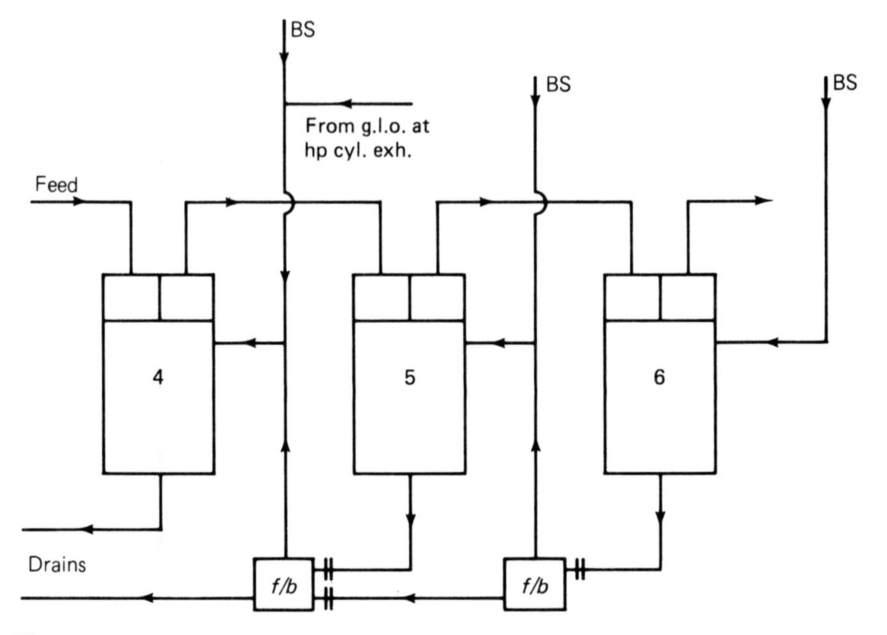

Figure 12.32 HP. heaters. Project No 1

results obtained at the time of the acceptance test. (Note: The figures have been 'rounded' to save tiresome interpolations when using the steam tables.)

The heat rate of the T/A at the time of the heater survey was 4.0% worse than on acceptance. The acceptance test feed flow was 102 kg/s. No. 1 heater results are not tabulated because there is insufficient room. Feed water pressure 40 bar abs.

Investigate the results and make appropriate recommendations.

Turbine Feed Heater Survey

Load 120 MW

AT = Acceptance Test

	2 Heater		*Deaerator*		*4 Heater*		*5 Heater*		*6 Heater*	
	A.T.	*1978*	*A.T.*	*1978*	*A.T.*	*1978*	*A.T.*	*1978*	*A.T.*	*1978*
Steam pressure bar at heater (abs.)	0.96	1.0	2.5	2.1	7.5	7.0	14.0	13.5	28.0	29.0
Steam temp. Before junction with gland leak-off °C	—	—	—	—	373	—	—	—	—	—
Steam temp. at heater inlet °C	160	160.0	256	—	325	165	460	450	380	385
Feed water inlet temp. °C	70.0	69.0	97.0	95.0	130	130	160	155	190	190
Feed water outlet temp. °C	97.0	95.0	128	130	160	155	190	190	230	230
Heater drain temp. °C	101.0	101.0	—	—	162	145	195	193	230	229

Project 1 (Answer)

The results indicate that No. 2 heater and the deaerator are performing satisfactorily. However, the HP heaters warrant further investigation. Insert all known temperatures, pressures and heats on the diagram and additional information as it is obtained.

Acceptance test

Steam flow to No. 6 heater $= \dfrac{102 \times (990.5 - 808.8)}{(3190.7 - 990.3)} = 8.4$ kg/s

Flash steam to No. 5 heater $= \dfrac{8.4\,(990.3 - 830.1)}{1957.7} = 0.69$ kg/s

Steam flow to No. 5 heater $= \dfrac{102\,(808.8 - 677.5)}{(3387.2 - 830.1)} = 5.2$ kg/s

Bled steam to No. 5 heater $= 5.2 - 0.69 = 4.51$ kg/s

Steam flow to No. 4 heater $= \dfrac{102\,(677.5 - 548.8)}{(3111.5 - 684.2)} = 5.4$ kg/s

Flash steam to No. 4 heater $= \dfrac{(7.71 + 4.51)\,(830.1 - 709.3)}{2055.5} = 0.72$

Bled steam plus GLO to No. 4 heater $= 5.4 - 0.72 = 4.68$ kg/s

Heat in steam plus GLO to No. 4 heater $= \dfrac{(5.4 \times 3111.5) - (0.72 \times 2065)}{4.68}$

$= 3272.5$ kJ/kg

Corresponding temperature $= 402°C$

Heat in bled steam before GLO $= 3211.6$ kJ/kg

Feed heater survey, February 1978

Feed flow $= 102 \times 1.04 = 106$ kg/s

Steam to No. 6 heater $= \dfrac{106\,(990.5 - 808)}{(3200 - 985.6)} = 8.7$ kg/s

Flash steam to No. 5 heater $= \dfrac{8.7\,(985.6 - 822.5)}{1964.1} = 0.72$ kg/s

Steam to No. 5 heater $= \dfrac{106\,(808.0 - 656.0)}{(3366.3 - 822.5)} = 6.33$ kg/s

Bled steam to No. 5 heater $= 6.33 - 0.72 = 5.61$ kg/s

Steam to No. 4 heater $= \dfrac{106\,(656.0 - 548.8)}{(2762.1 - 610.8)} = 5.28$ kg/s

Flash steam to No. 4 heater $= \dfrac{(6.33 \times 7.98)\,(822.5 - 709.3)}{2064.9}$

$= 0.78$ kg/s

Bled steam to No. 4 heater $= 5.28 - 0.78 = 4.5$ kg/s

Next compare the two heater diagrams that have been completed and compare one item at a time, thus:

TTDs

The changes from AT are: No. 6 (+)2°C; No. 5 (−)2°C; No. 4(+)2°C. These are not highly significant.

Drain temperature TD

These are: No. 6 (−)3°C; No. 5 0°C; No. 4 (−)20°C. So the drains at No. 4 heater are being seriously undercooled.

Steam flow to heater (compared to AT)

No. 6 (+) 0.3 kg/s; No. 5 (+) 1.13 kg/s; No. 4 (−) 0.12 kg/s.

Steam temperature at heater (compared to AT)

No. 6 (+) 5°C; No. 5 (−) 10°C; No. 4 (−) 160°C.

It is apparent that No. 4 heater has something wrong which will cause the heat transfer to be satisfactory, the drains undercooled, the inlet steam flow low and the steam temperature very low.

All of these factors could be the result of abnormal conditions at No. 4 flash box. In fact, it suggests that water is entrained with the flash steam. Such a situation could be the result of, say, a disintegrated diffuser obstructing the outlet or obstruction of the downstream orifice.

Therefore, it is recommended that the flash box internals and orifice plates be inspected as soon as possible.

Addendum

In the event the orifice on the line from No. 5 flash box to No. 4 was badly fouled and also that on the line from No. 4 to No. 3 flash box, both with copper oxide, see photographs in *Figure 12.33*.

Figure 12.33 Orifice plate before cleaning and after partial cleaning. (Note coin for comparison) Project No 1. (CEGB)
(a) Close-up before cleaning. Orifice size 19 mm

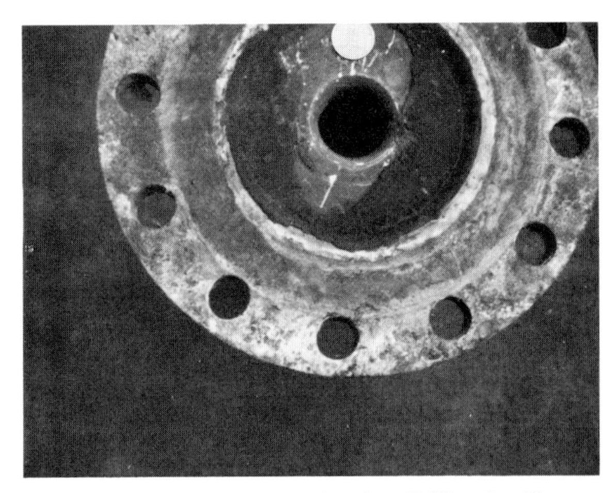

Figure 12.33(b) After partial cleaning. Orifice size 42 mm
Thickness of deposit on plate face about 3 mm

Project 2

A routine feed heater survey was carried out on No. 7 Unit at Drakelow 'B' (*Figure 12.34*). The results are tabulated along with some acceptance test

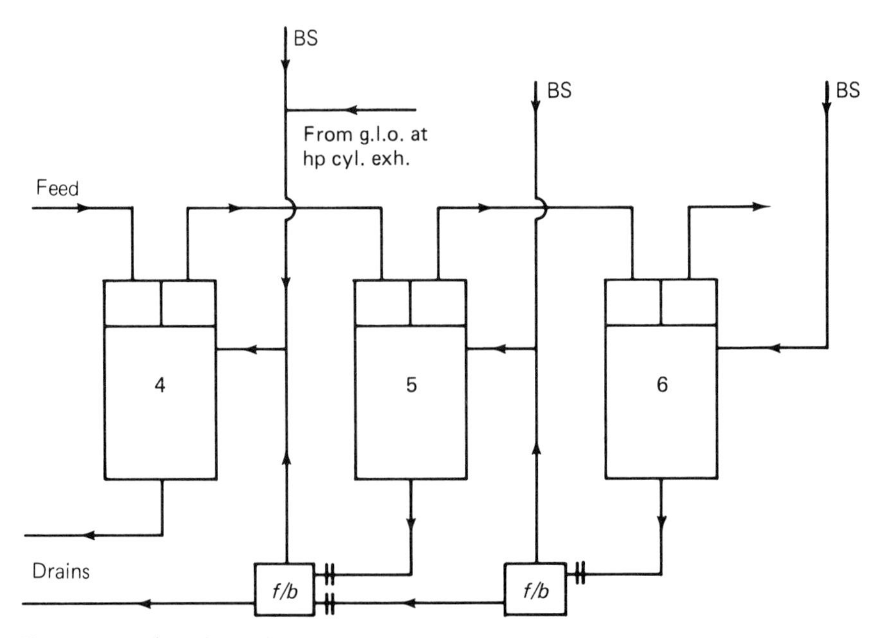

Figure 12.34 Drakelow 'B' No. 7 Unit HP heaters

data. No. 1 heater results have been omitted because of lack of space. The heater body vents were open and the pressure gauges accurate. The design tube materials are 70/30 cupro-nickel for the first two units (Nos. 5 and 6) and 90/10 cupro-nickel for the last two (Nos. 7 and 8). The feed flow at the time of the acceptance test was 103.8 kg/s at 40 bar absolute pressure. At the time of the routine check the turbine heat-rate was 2.0% worse than on acceptance test.

Note: Some of the results have been 'rounded-off' for convenience. Prepare a memorandum detailing your findings and recommendations.

No 7 Turbine Feed Heater Survey 8.2.78
Load 117.5 MW

	Units	*2 Heater*		*Deaerator*		*4 Heater*		*5 Heater*		*6 Heater*	
		A.T.	*1978*	*A.T.*	*1978*	*A.T.*	*1978*	*A.T.*	*1978*	*A.T.*	*1978*
Steam pressure at heater	bar (a)	0.96	1.0	2.4	2.0	6.0	7.0	14.0	14.0	28.0	28.0
Steam temperature at heater	°C	148	148	240	—	318	200	450	420	380	385
Steam temperature before junction with gland leak-off	°C	—	—	—	—	350	360	—	—	—	—
Feed water inlet temp.	°C	73	70	99	97	130	130	160	155	190	175
Feed water outlet temp.	°C	99	97	129	129	160	155	190	175	230	225
Heater drain temp.	°C	101.3	99.3	—	—	159	165	195	195	230	230

Project 2 (Answer)

Feed flow in 1978 = 103.8 × 1.02 = 105.9 kg/s

Acceptance test

$$\text{Steam to No. 6 heater} = \frac{103.8\,(990.5 - 808.8)}{(3190.7 - 990.5)} = 8.57\ \text{kg/s}$$

$$\text{Steam to No. 5 heater} = \frac{103.8\,(808.8 - 677.5)}{(3365.6 - 830.1)} = 5.38\ \text{kg/s}$$

$$\text{Flash steam to No. 5 heater} = \frac{8.57\,(990.5 - 830.1)}{1957.7} = 0.70\ \text{kg/s}$$

Bled steam to No. 5 heater = 5.38 − 0.70 = 4.68 kg/s

$$\text{Steam to No. 4 heater} = \frac{103.8\,(677.5 - 548.8)}{(3099 - 670.4)} = 5.5\ \text{kg/s}$$

$$\text{Flash steam to No. 4 heater} = \frac{(7.874 + 5.38)(830.1 - 670.4)}{2085.1} = 1.01\ \text{kg/s}$$

$$\text{Bled steam} + \text{GLO} = 5.5 - 1.01 = 4.49\ \text{kg/s}$$

Heat in steam before junction with flash is given by:

$$\frac{(5.5 \times 3099) - (1.01 \times 2755.5)}{4.49} = 3176.3\ \text{kJ/kg} = 355°\text{C}$$

February 1978

$$\text{Steam to No. 6 heater} = \frac{105.9\,(967.2 - 742.8)}{(3202.0 - 990.5)} = 10.75\ \text{kg/s}$$

$$\text{Steam to No. 5 heater} = \frac{105.9\,(742.8 - 655.9)}{(3301.1 - 830.1)} = 3.72\ \text{kg/s}$$

$$\text{Flash steam to No. 5 heater} = \frac{10.75\,(990.5 - 830.1)}{1957.7} = 0.88\ \text{kg/s}$$

$$\text{Bled steam to No. 5 heater} = 3.72 - 0.88 = 2.84\ \text{kg/s}$$

$$\text{Steam to No. 4 heater} = \frac{105.9\,(655.9 - 548.83)}{(2844.2 - 697.1)} = 5.28\ \text{kg/s}$$

$$\text{Flash steam to No. 4 heater} = \frac{(9.87 + 3.72)(830.1 - 697.1)}{2064.9} = 0.88\ \text{kg/s}$$

$$\text{Bled steam} + \text{GLO to No. 4 heater} = 5.28 - 0.88 = 4.4\ \text{kg/s}$$

Heat of BS + GLO steam

$$= \frac{(5.28 \times 2844.2) - (0.88 \times 2762)}{4.4} = 2860.64\ \text{kJ/kg}$$

Equivalent temperature = 207°C

This seems suspiciously low

It seems that some water is entrained with the flash steam, so the rest of the steam must, in fact, be much higher than 2860.6 kJ/kg. Its value cannot be determined until the temperature is measured in the pipe after the junction of the bled steam and gland leak-off steam.

Note: This was subsequently done and the temperature was found to be

Analysis of results

TTDs

Above optimum on each heater, the increases being 11°C on No. 4 heater; 15°C on No. 5 heater; 5°C on No. 6 heater.

Drain temperatures

Satisfactory on each heater.

Steam flows

Flow to No. 6 heater	125% of optimum
Flow to No. 5 heater	69% of optimum
Flow to No. 4 heater	96% of optimum

Steam temperatures

Steam temperature to No. 6 heater	5°C above optimum
Steam temperature to No. 5 heater	30°C below optimum
Steam temperature to No. 4 heater	118°C below optimum

It is apparent that there are probably several defects, i.e.:

1 The elevated TTDs on the whole HP heater train suggests water-side contamination such as oil.
2 The high steam flow to No. 6 heater is due to low feed inlet temperature, which in its turn, is due to poor heat transfer in No. 5 heater. No. 5 heater tubes should be made of 90/10 Cu–Ni, but the high TTD suggests that the material should be checked as there is possibly exfoliation present.
3 The very low steam inlet temperature to No. 4 heater is due to excessive wetness of the flash steam. The flow from 5 F/B to 4 F/B is 125% of normal and this could be overloading the orifice and diffuser at No. 4 F/B, possibly causing it to disintegrate.

Addendum

When the heater train was inspected the following defects were found:

1 The inside of the tube was coated with oil and magnetite deposits. The magnetite is of no particular significance.
2 The No. 5 heater tubes were made of 70/30 Cu–Ni and were exfoliated.
3 The No. 5 F/B to No. 4 F/B orifice plate was severely eroded although the F/B internals were satisfactory.
4 The No. 4 F/B to No. 3 F/B orifice was too small.

Additional Reading

1 SILVER, R.S., 'The energy balance in steam power plant feed systems', *Proc. I. Mech. E.*, **173**, No. 10 (1953)
2 HAYWOOD, R.W., 'Generalised analysis of the regenerative cycle', *Proc. I. Mech. E.*, **161**, p. 157 (1949)
3 CLEMMER, A.B. and LEMEZIO, S., 'Selection and design of closed feed water heaters', *Proc. A.S.M.E.* (1965)
4 BIGG, J.V., 'Design and construction of power station feed heaters', *Proc. I. Mech. E.* (1959)
5 OPLATKA, G., 'The optimum number of feed heating stages in steam power stations', from *Applied Thermodynamics in Steam Power Stations*, p. 12 Brown-Boveri
6 WEIR, C.D., 'A generalised analysis of regenerative feed heating trains', *Proc. I. Mech. E.*, **179**, Part 1, No. 15 (1964/65)

Part IV
Miscellaneous

13 Steam turbine heat consumption tests

14 Plant operating parameters

15 Economics of outages

13 Steam turbine heat consumption tests

General

Turbine heat consumption tests may be for acceptance purposes or for routine assessment of the performance of the machine. Acceptance testing is carried out as a contractual obligation when the machine is new. Its purpose is to enable the manufacturer to demonstrate the heat consumption of the turbine under specified operating conditions so that it can be compared to the guaranteed heat consumption under identical conditions. Routine testing is much more common, being carried out at intervals throughout the life of the machine. In the CEGB, every machine rated at 200 MW or more must be tested every year and machines whose output is less than 200 MW must be tested every two years. These are maximum periods between tests and if circumstances warrant it additional ones are carried out.

To ensure uniformity it is necessary for all the parties concerned in the tests to agree to a standard method of conducting them – this is particularly important in the case of acceptance testing. It has long been standard practice to comply with the requirements of British Standard 752 *Acceptance of Steam Turbines*. However, in 1978 the CEGB published Site Code No. 2 which deals with the requirements of both acceptance and routine testing. The publication is called *Steam Turbine-Generator Heat Rate Tests*, and it now forms the basis for testing within the CEGB, along with BS 752.

The object of either type of test is to determine the required heat input to the turbine for an output of one kilowatt hour at particular loadings. The relationship between the input heat and output electricity is called the 'Heat Rate' and its units are kJ/kWh.

Routine tests, although carried out regularly, are nevertheless conducted with care. However, some departures from the rigorous requirements of acceptance standards are permissible. For example, back pressure is determined from the Kenotometer or Vacumeter panel instrument; electrical output from the installed tariff metering; reheater spray flow from the panel instrument, and so on. Of course, these are only acceptable if the test team have no reason to suspect that any of the items is in error to an unacceptable extent. If any are suspect then standard test equipment should be substituted. For items other than those just considered, standard test equipment is used anyway. Thus, temperatures will be obtained from calibrated thermocouples, pressures from test pressure gauges, flows from precision mercury columns connected across calibrated pressure difference devices and so on.

Alternatively (and this is now common on larger plant), pressure and flow transducers are used. Transducers translate the input signal (say pressure) into an electrical output (*Figure 13.1*). Thus, the input pressure is detected

Figure 13.1
Pressure transducer *in-situ*

as an output voltage. It follows that testing is eased considerably because all the outputs from the pressure, flow and temperature devices can be translated into voltage signals and can be read on a digital voltmeter (DVM). This also applies to the alternator output.

From manually reading the DVM it is but a short step to arranging for the readings to be entered automatically on to punched-tape by a data logger. This permits much more rapid scanning of the test points and so gives more accurate average readings. A punch-tape code is shown in *Figure 13.2*. Upon completion of the test the taped results are calculated automatically. Thus,

1	0				0	0		0
2		0			0	0		0
3	0	0			0	0		
4			0		0	0		0
5	0		0		0	0		
6		0	0		0	0		
7	0	0	0		0	0		0
8				0	0	0		0
9	0		0	0	0	0		
0					0	0		
A	0						0	
B		0					0	
C	0	0					0	0
D			0				0	
E	0		0				0	0
F		0	0				0	0
G	0	0	0				0	
H				0			0	
I	0			0			0	0
J		0		0			0	0
K	0	0		0			0	
L			0	0			0	0
M	0		0	0			0	
N		0	0	0			0	
O	0	0	0	0			0	0
P					0		0	
Q	0				0		0	0
R		0			0		0	0
S	0	0			0		0	
T			0		0		0	0
U	0		0		0		0	
V		0	0		0		0	
W	0	0	0		0		0	0
X				0	0		0	0
Y	0			0	0		0	
Z		0		0	0		0	
FULL STOP		0	0	0		0		

Figure 13.2 Punched tape code

what was formerly a tedious process can now be accomplished with ease.

The trouble is, of course, that the equipment is expensive and so it requires more than the convenience of the test staff to justify it. The usual justification is that the number of people required to test a large machine manually is more than the number readily available. Furthermore, the time taken to run temporary wiring to test points, calibrate and fit transducers, set up mercury columns, and so on is considerable. In many stations permanent test wiring has been installed to reduce the time-consuming pre-test work.

Figure 13.3 shows the terminations in the turbine room of the data acquisition equipment and punched-tape printer for a turbine test using thermocouples and transducers. Each of 100 points can be scanned every 30

1. Voltage supplies
2. Scanner X
3. Cable terminal boxes
4. DVM
5. Data logger
6. Printer
7. Incoming cables

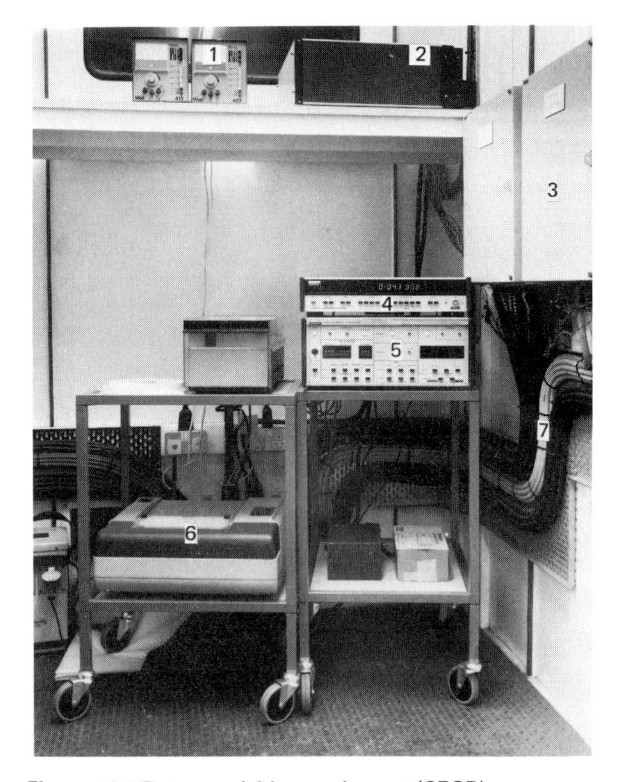

Figure 13.3 Data acquisition equipment (CEGB)

seconds and the information entered on punched paper tape. Upon completion of the test the tape is removed and put on a 'tape-reader' whose output is fed to a programmable calculator where the information is processed and the results printed on an impact typewriter. The data processing equipment is shown in *Figure 13.4.*

Preparations for a test

The success of a test is determined largely by the effort put in beforehand. The plant should be inspected thoroughly to see whether there is any reason why testing cannot take place – for example, there should be no significant loss of steam or water from the turbine system that cannot be measured; isolating valves should not 'pass'; heater tubes checked to ensure they do not leak; and so on. Where necessary the test equipment should be calibrated, which is particularly important with flow-measuring devices such as orifice plates and venturis. Thus, for example, orifice plates which are permanently 'in-line' should be calibrated at least every two years. If the plate is in a

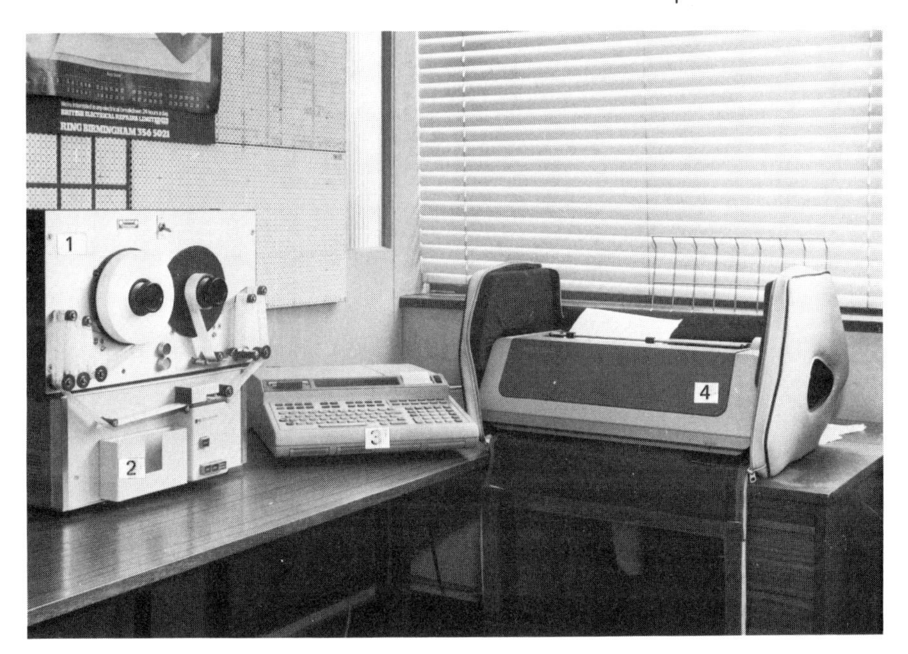

Figure 13.4 Data processing equipment (CEGB)
1. Paper tape handler
2. Paper tape reader
3. Programmable calculator
4. Impact typewriter

section of line which is capable of being isolated for normal operation, it should be calibrated every four years. The upstream and downstream sections of pipe should be included in the calibration.

Another essential item to be checked is that there is no bypassing or recirculation of water taking place which will result in either some water being measured twice or not at all. Pump gland sealing water supply and return flows must be measured and minor miscellaneous leakages (such as pump gland drips) should be assessed. All make-up to the system under test should be stopped before testing commences. On the boiler it is important that every care is taken to ensure that conditions can be kept steady during the test, so ashing and sootblowing should be carried out beforehand and blowdown stopped.

Effective isolation of the machine is a paramount requirement. To ensure that this is done in a workmanlike and efficient manner it is usual to prepare an isolation diagram and an isolation list which details every valve to be shut. Naturally, the isolation of the plant becomes more complicated the larger the machine. Typical isolation diagrams are shown in *Figures 13.5(a)* and *13.5(b)*. In addition to the isolation being applied before the test, the plant should be held on a steady loading at the test load for at least one hour to ensure that everything is thoroughly 'heat-soaked'.

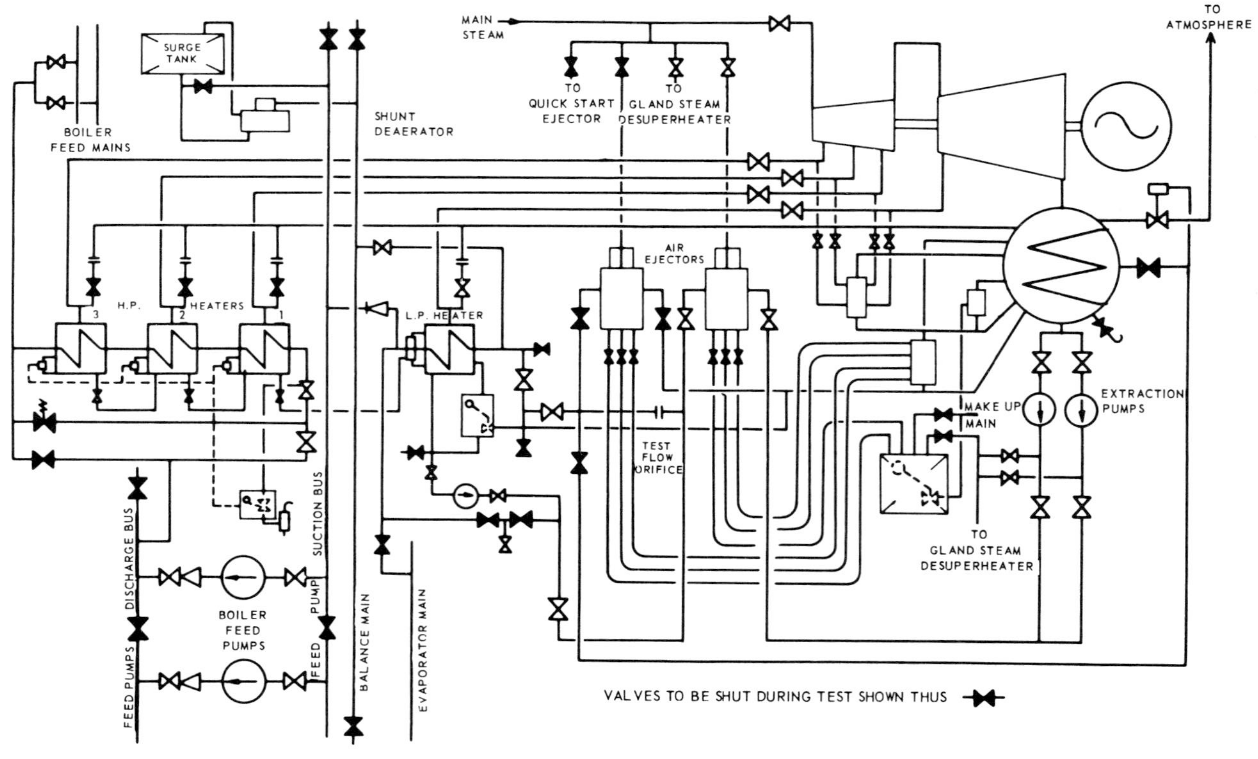

Figure 13.5(a) Isolation for small non-reheat turbine (CEGB

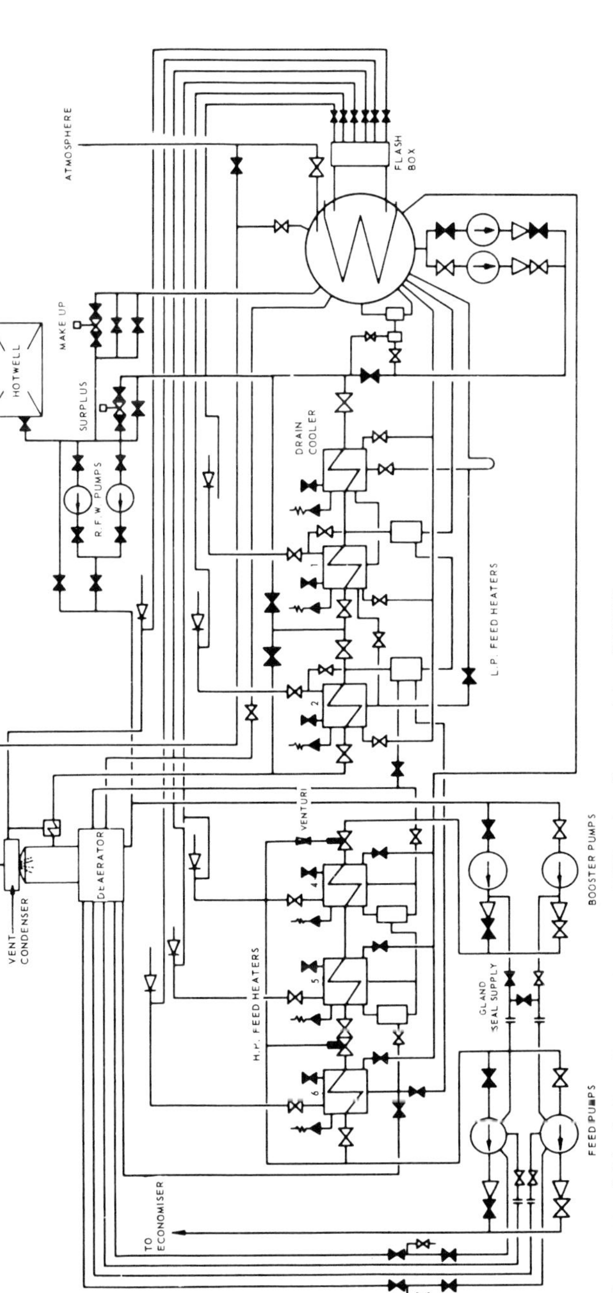

Figure 13.5(b) Isolation diagram for a 120 MW unit reheat turbine (CEGB)

Method of testing

Basically, all that heat consumption tests are designed to determine is the heat put into the turbine for 1 kWh of output at a particular loading. But the difficulties of measuring the heat input directly are so great that other means must be adopted to assess it. For example, *Figure 13.6* shows a fairly typical layout for a small (120 MW) reheat machine.

The necessary calculations to derive the heat input will be dealt with in detail later – for the present consider only the basic requirements:

1 The main flow of feed water is measured after the booster feed pump. Assuming that there is no leakage at the HP heaters, the same quantity of water will enter the feed pump. Meanwhile water is supplied to seal the pump glands, most of which is then returned to the deaerator, but some of which enters the pump. Therefore the gland seal supply and return water flows must be measured to determine the amount of in-leakage.
2 Reheat spray water flow should ideally be zero during a test. However, if there is a flow its value must be measured as it will detract from the quantity of steam flow to the HP turbine.
3 Before entering the HP cylinder some steam is tapped off the main line to supply LP gland sealing and spindle leak-off steam. Hence these two values must be assessed.
4 The steam entering the HP cylinder is thus equal to the measured main feed flow plus the feed pump gland in-leakage minus the reheat spray, LP gland seal and spindle leak-off flows.
5 The steam entering the IP cylinder is equal to that leaving the HP cylinder minus the bled steam supplied to No. 6 heater. If there is any reheat spray flow then it will add to the total steam entering the IP cylinder.
6 Allowance must also be made for variations of level during the test in storage vessels such as feed heater shells, condenser and deaerator. For example, if there is a substantial fall in the deaerator level (say, due to a boiler leak), during the test, then it represents a considerable quantity of extra water which will flow through the main venturi and HP feed heaters. This, in its turn, will cause a change in the bled steam flow to the heaters and so will change the steam flow in the turbine, thus affecting the turbine performance. Also, of course, the venturi flow reading will be higher.

During the test it is important that every effort is made to keep the plant conditions (loading, pressure, temperature, back pressure, etc.) as steady as possible. Even so, some variations are inevitable and so it is necessary to record those items that can affect the result as regularly as necessary. The feed flow should be measured at least every half-minute. On the other hand pressure and temperature need only be recorded every three minutes during

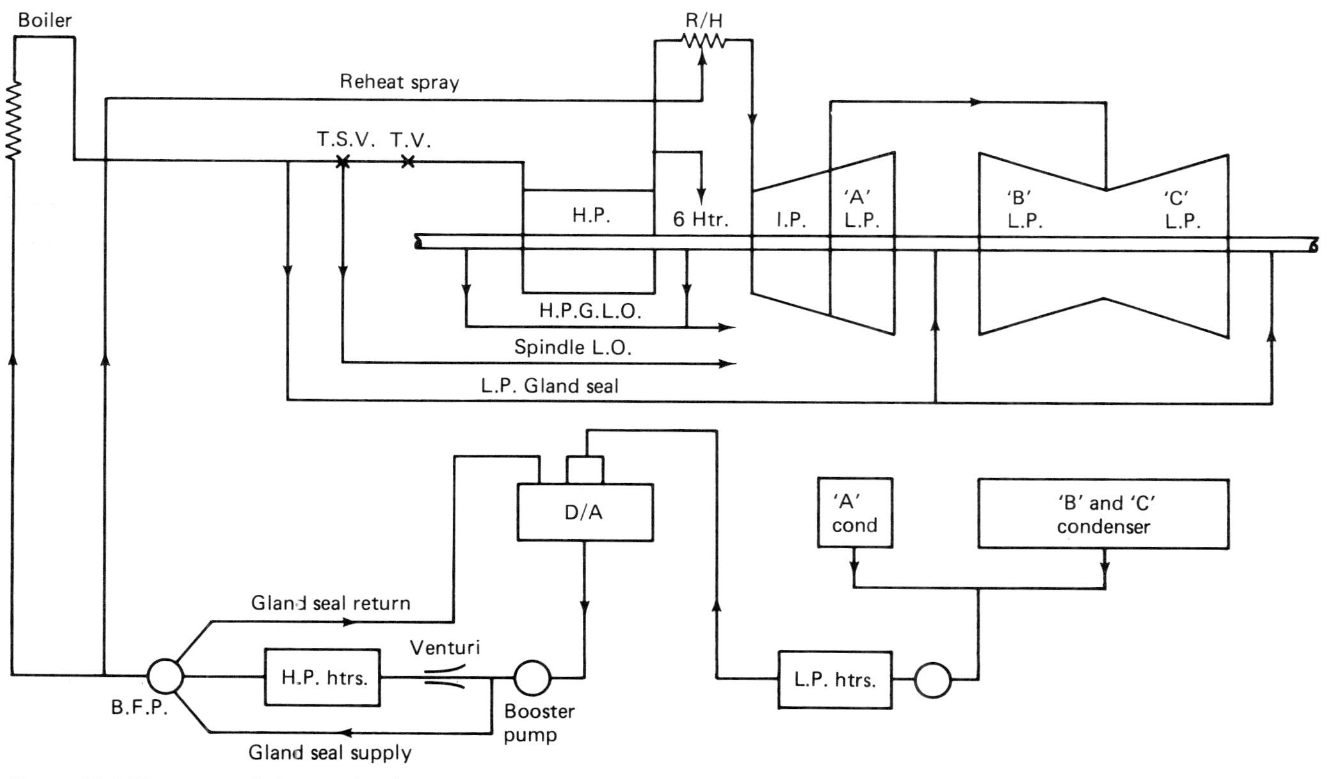

Figure 13.6 Diagrammatic layout of unit

a one-hour test, or every five minutes in a two-hour test. As mentioned earlier, one of the big advantages of automatic data acquisition is that all of the points can be scanned much more quickly and this leads to improved accuracy. *Figure 13.7* shows the test measuring points for a 500 MW machine. Several tests are carried out at each of several loadings, usually at about 100%, 80% and 60% MCR.

Results

The results of each test at a particular loading, when corrected to standard conditions, should be in very close agreement. In other words the 'test repeatability' should be clearly demonstrated. Failure to achieve this indicates either defects in the testing procedure or errors in the calculation. Suppose the 'corrected' results of a series of tests are as shown in *Table 13.1*.

Table 13.1 Heat consumption test results on a 350 MW T/A

Test No.		*1*	*2*	*3*	*4*	*5*	*6*	*7*	*8*	*9*	*10*	*11*
Load	(MW)	248	250	245	211	210	208	280	284	140	141	137
Heat	(GJ/h)	1990	2003	1996	1743	1700	1675	2224	2225	1195	1201	1185

Ideally the points, when plotted on a graph of heat consumption versus load, will lie in a straight line called a 'Willans line'. The results are plotted in *Figure 13.8*. Next it is necessary to determine the best straight line which will pass through the test points. This is done by 'regression analysis'. The method is tedious but simple; refer to *Table 13.2*. (Refer to Chapter 5 for discussion on regression analysis)

Table 31.2 Regression analysis of test points

(1)	(2)	(3)	(4)	(5)	(6)	(7)
Point No	X	Y	$x = X - \overline{X}$	$y = Y - \overline{Y}$	xy	x^2
	(MW)	(GJ/h)				
1	248	1 990	34	250.3	8 510.2	1156
2	250	2 003	36	263.3	9 478.8	1296
3	245	1 996	31	256.3	7 945.3	961
4	211	1 743	−3	3.3	−9.9	9
5	210	1 700	−4	−39.7	158.8	16
6	208	1 675	−6	−64.7	388.2	36
7	280	2 224	66	484.3	31 963.8	4 356
8	284	2 225	70	485.3	33 971.0	4 900
9	140	1 195	−74	−544.7	40 307.8	5 476
10	141	1201	−73	−538.7	39 325.1	5 329
11	137	1185	−77	−554	42 711.9	5 929
$n = 11$	ΣX = 2 354	ΣY = 19 137			Σxy = 214 751	Σx^2 = 29 464

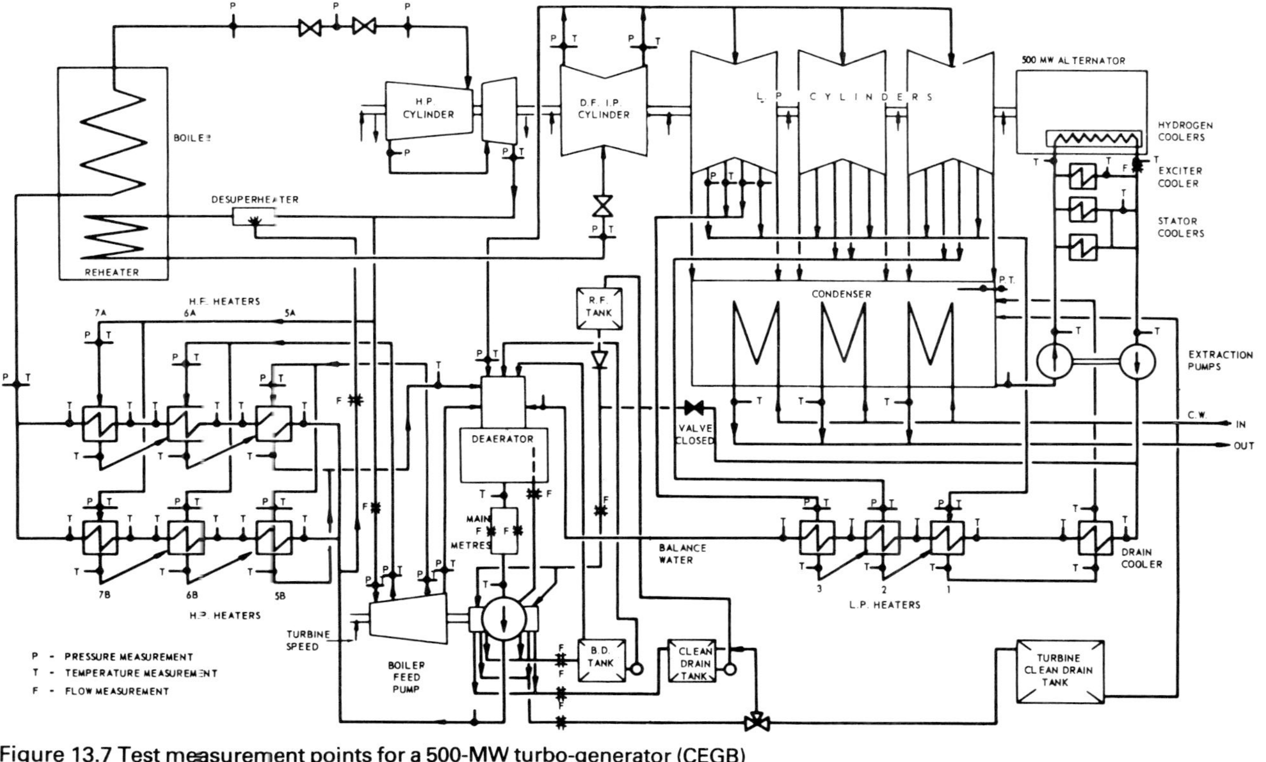

Figure 13.7 Test measurement points for a 500-MW turbo-generator (CEGB)

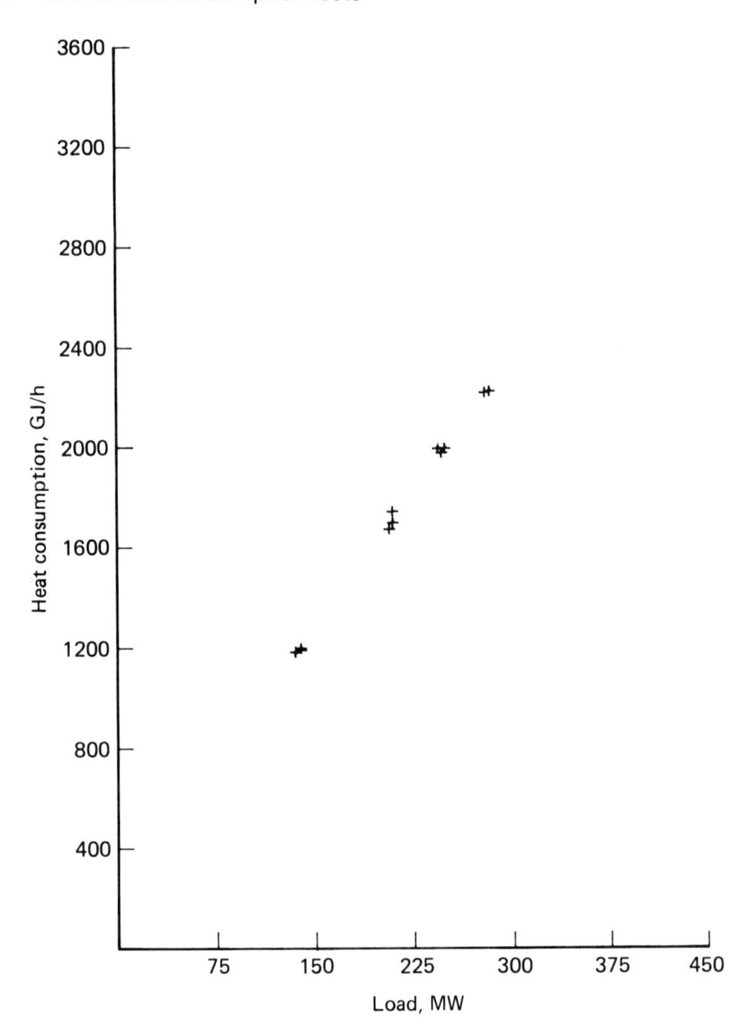

Figure 13.8 Plot of results of heat consumption tests (CEGB)

The line of best fit will pass through a point whose co-ordinates are $\overline{X}$, $\overline{Y}$

where $\overline{X} = \dfrac{\Sigma X}{\eta}$

$$\overline{Y} = \frac{\Sigma Y}{\eta}$$

and the slope of the line m is given by:

$$m = \frac{\Sigma xy}{\Sigma x^2}$$

where $x = X - \overline{X}$
and $y = Y - \overline{Y}$

$$\text{So } \overline{X} = \frac{\Sigma X}{11} = \frac{2354}{11} = 214 \text{ MW}$$

$$\overline{Y} = \frac{\Sigma Y}{11} = \frac{1\,9137}{11} = 1\,739.7 \text{ GJ/h}$$

$$\text{Slope of line} = \frac{\Sigma xy}{\Sigma x^2} = \frac{214\,751}{29\,464} = 7.289 \text{ GJ/h per MW}$$

or 7289 kJ/kWh

So the line of best fit (the Willans line) will pass through the points (214, 1739.7) and the slope m will be 7.289.

A computer print-out of the line is shown in *Figure 13.9* and it is seen that it intercepts the Y-axis at 180.0 GJ/h. This is called the 'Fixed Heat' and in this case is equal to 6.59% of the full-load heat consumption. Values of fixed heat of about 7% are usual for throttle-governed, and about 3½% for nozzle-governed machines. The slope of the line is called the 'Incremental Heat'.

Thus, the heat consumption at any load is given by the law:
Heat consumption = (7.289 × MW) + 180 GJ/h
For example, at 350 MW:

$$\text{Heat consumption} = (7.289 \times 350) + 180 = 2\,731.15 \text{ GJ/h}$$

$$\text{The heat rate at 350 MW} = \frac{2\,731.15 \times 10^6}{350\,000} = 7\,803.3 \text{ kJ/kWh}$$

The corresponding thermal efficiency is found from:

$$\text{Thermal efficiency \%} = \frac{3600 \times 100}{\text{Heat rate}}$$

$$\text{So at 350 MW the thermal efficiency} = \frac{360\,000}{7803.3} = 46.13\%$$

At lower loads the heat rate increases and so the thermal efficiency gets worse. This is because the fixed heat component represents an increasing proportion of the total heat consumption. *Table 13.3* shows the variations of heat, heat-rate and efficiency with load for the 350 MW machine being considered.

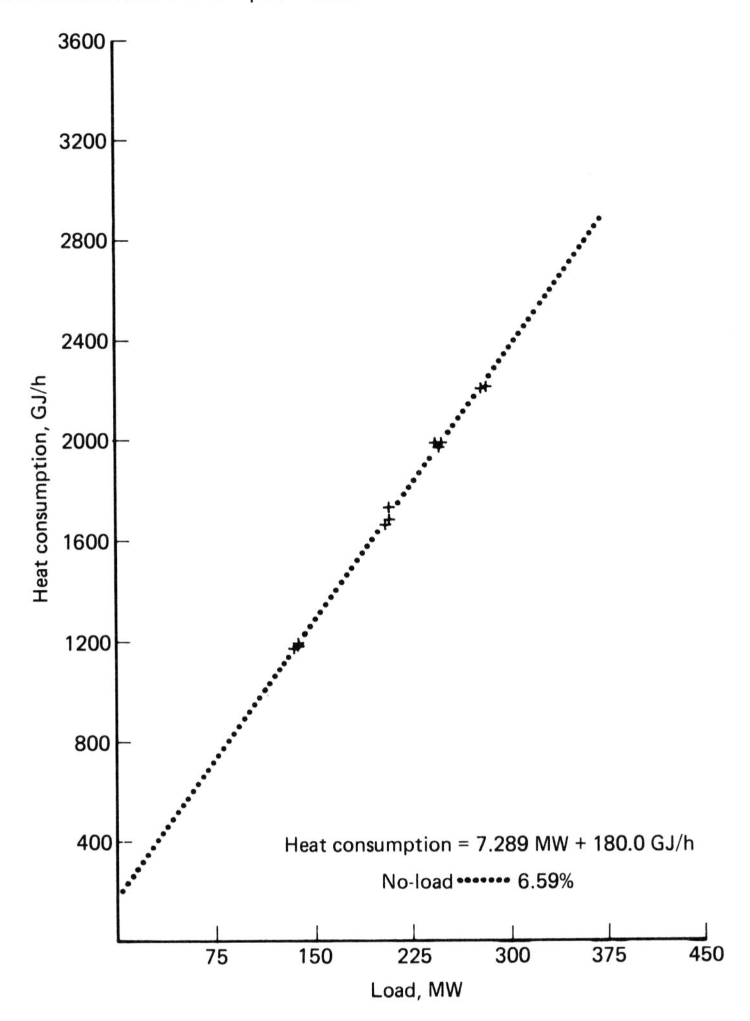

Figure 13.9 Turbine Willans line

Table 13.3

Load	MW	350	300	200	100
Heat consumption	GJ/h	2 731.15	2 366.70	1 637.80	908.90
Heat rate	kJ/kWh	7 803.3	7 889.0	8 189.0	9 089.0
Efficiency	%	46.13	45.63	43.96	39.61

Calculation of test results

Basically, all that is required to determine the heat consumption of a turbine is to add the heat flows from the turbine stop valve steam, the reheater to HP cylinder exhaust steam and from the reheater to the reheat spray water.

Consider the following, where the power generated is 251.949 MW.

TSV steam flow	= 225.361 kg/s
TSV steam enthalpy	= 3500.4 kJ/kg
Final feedwater enthalpy	= 1039.2 kJ/kg
	= 225.361 (3500.4 − 1039.2)
∴ Heat flow from TSV	= 554 658.5 kJ/s
IP cylinder inlet steam flow	= 192.831 kg/s
IP cylinder inlet steam enthalpy	= 3591.2 kJ/kg
HP cylinder exhaust steam enthalpy	= 3204.0 kJ/kg
∴ Heat flow from R/H to HP exhaust steam	= 192.831 (3591.2 − 3204.0)
	= 74 664.2 kJ/s
R/H spray water flow	= 2.1 kg/s
IP cylinder inlet steam enthalpy	= 3591.2 kJ/kg
R/H spray water enthalpy	= 535.1 kJ/kg
∴ Heat flow from R/H to spray water	= 2.1 (3591.2 − 535.1)
	= 6417.4 kJ/s
Hence total heat flow to turbine	= 635 740 kJ/s = 635.74 MJ/s
∴ 'As-run' heat rate at 251.949 MW	$= \frac{635\ 740 \times 3600}{251\ 949}$
	= 9084 kJ/kWh

However, while the above calculation is simple, it will be appreciated that the derivation of some of the information is quite complicated.

The comprehensive example which follows is for a 120 MW unit (i.e. it is a different machine from the one just considered). The layout is illustrated in *Figure 13.6*. A 120 MW machine has been selected because it illustrates all the main points of testing without the extra complications involved in testing larger plants such as IP shaft cooling; bled-steam boiler feed pump turbine, etc.

There are several pages of calculations which are split into individual sections. Thus, items 1–9 comprise one section dealing specifically with the derivation of the feed flow through the venturi. However, this is only the skeleton of the complete calculations, so a complete illustration of the method is given in a separate section after the heat consumption calculations, and similarly for the other sections, as indicated in the right-hand column.

Project 1 Calculate Test No. 4.

	Test No.		*1*	*4*	*Derived*
	Load	MW	120	96	*From*
1	Flow transducer output	mV	43.8597	24.7020	Notes 'Rate of flow using a flow transducer
2	Differential pressure	cm w.g.	461.1216		
3	$\sqrt{h} = \sqrt{(2)}$		21.4737		
4	Flow constant K	—	4.7018	4.7018	
5	Flow = (3) × (4)	kg/s	100.965		
6	Temp. at venturi (HP4 htr. inlet)	°C	128.1	119.1	
7	Press. at venturi (booster pump disch.)	bar(abs)	43.7	44.0	
8	Temp. and press. correction	—	0.9993		
9	Corrected flow through main venturi	kg/s	100.894		
	Boiler feed pump gland sealing water supply				
10	Average head (h) cm Hg under water	cm Hg/H_2O	60.476	51.868	Notes 'Rate of flow from manometer reading
11	Ambient temperature	°C	12.9	14.5	
12	Density of mercury minus water at 4°C	—	12.5642		
13	Corresp. manometer rdg. (10) × (12)	cm w.g.	759.83		
14	Square root of mano. rdg. $\sqrt{(13)}$	—	27.565		
15	Flow constant K	—	0.2265		
16	Sealing water flow (14) × (15)	kg/s	6.2434		
17	Press. of seal water at boost pump disch.	bar(abs)	46.5	44.0	
18	Temp. of seal water at No. 4 htr. inlet	°C	128.1	119.1	
19	Temp. and press. correction	—	0.9993		
20	True flow at 127°C/46.5 bar = (16) × (19)	kg/s	6.239		
	Boiler feed pump gland sealing water return				
21	Average head (h) cm Hg under water	cm Hg/H_2O	49.29	50.80	
22	Ambient temperature	°C	12.9	14.8	
23	Corresp. density of mercury minus water	—	12.5642		As above
24	Corresp. manometer rdg. (21) × (23)	cm w.g.	619.313		
25	Square root of mano. rdg. $\sqrt{(24)}$	—	24.886		
26	Flow constant K		0.2265		
27	Press. of seal water return	bar(abs)	4.2	5.1	
29	Temp. of seal water return	°C	128.1	119.1	
28	Temp. and press. correction	—	0.9997		
30	True flow to D/A at 127°C/5.2 bar (abs)	kg/s	5.635		
31	Inleakage to boiler feed pump (20) − (30)	kg/s	0.604		

	Test No.		1	4	Derived
	Load	MW	120	96	From
	Storage quantities and leaks				
32	2/3 Condenser shell	All in kg/h	0		See list of storage quantities and leaks
33	1/3 Condenser shell		0		
34	Stilling chamber		(−)4.990		
35	Turbine CD Tank		0		
36	Drains cooler shell		(−)4.082		
37	LP 1 heater shell		0		
38	Vapour condenser shell		0		
39	LP 2 heater shell		0		
40	LP 3 D/A shell		(−)1269 .605		
41	HP 4 heater shell		0		
42	HP 5 heater shell		0		
43	HP 6 heater shell		0		
44	RFT (866.1 kg/cm)		0		
45	Hydrogen cooling DW header tank		(−)7.711		
46	Hydrogen DW pump gland drips		0		
47	Unloading valve (atmospheric drain)		0		
48	Chemist's sample at extraction pumps		(+)2.722		
49	Extraction pumps gland drips		(+)7.25		
50	Heater drain pumps gland drips		(+)8.165		
51	Variation in flow through LP heaters Σ(32) to (39) + Σ(45) to (49)	kg/h	(−)6.811		See Note 1
52	Net corr. to flow Σ(40) to (44) −(50) +(51)	kg/h	(−)1284. 581		
53	Cold R/H desuperheat spray	kg/s	0	0	Spray take-off after boiler feed pump
	Steam flow to turbine				
54	$(9) + (31) + \frac{(52)}{3600} - (53)$ ε	kg/s	101.141		See Note 2
	Calculation of bled steam flow to HP 6 heater				
55	Feed water inlet temperature	°C	189.8	180.8	
56	Feed water inlet pressure	bar(abs)	28.6	21.6	
57	Feed water inlet enthalpy	kJ/kg	808.26		
58	Feed water outlet temperature	°C	226.6	214.7	
59	Feed water outlet pressure	bar (abs)	28.6	21.6	
60	Feed water outlet enthalpy	kJ/kg	974.41		
61	Heater drain temperature	°C	230.4	215.6	
62	Heater drain enthalpy	kJ/kg	992.3		
63	Bled steam temperature	°C	382.2	378.0	
64	Bled steam pressure	bar (abs)	28.6	21.6	
65	Bled steam enthalpy	kJ/kg	3194.6		
66	Feed flow through heater (9)	kg/s	100.894		

	Test No.		1	4	*Derived*
	Load	MW	120	96	*From*
67	BS flow = $\frac{(66)\,[(60) - (57)]}{(65) - (62)}$	kg/s	7.612		
	Calculation of turbine HP gland leak-off				
68	HP exhaust steam temp. (test)	°C	366.2	362.9	
69	HP exhaust steam press. (test)	bar (abs)	28.2	21.2	Notes 'Calculation of gland leak-off flows from HP turbine'
70	Specific volume of HP exhaust steam	dm^3/kg	99.385		
71	$\left(\frac{(69) \times 1000}{(70)}\right)^{1/2}$	—	16.845		
72	HP gland sealing steam $Q = \frac{1.366 \times (71)}{17.077}$	kg/s	1.347		
	Calculation of steam flow from R/H to IP turbine				
73	LP gland sealing steam supply (design)	all in kg/s	0.3780	0.3780	
74	Spindle leak-off steam (design)		0.3024	0.3024	
75	Steam flow from turbine HP gland leak-off (72)		1.347		
76	Steam bled to No. 6 HP heater (67)		7.612		
77	Total turbine steam flow (54)		101.141		
78	Steam from R/H to IP turbine (77) − (73) − (74) − (75) − (76)		91.5016		
	Electrical output				
79	Main kWh meter	kWh	121658	90289	
80	Correction	—	1.0	1.0	
81	Correction main kWh meter (79) × (80)	kWh	121658		
82	Check kWh meter	kWh	121628	90515	
83	Correction	—	1.0	1.0	
84	Corrected check kWh meter (82) × (83)	kWh	121628		
85	Reactive kVAr meter	kVAr	52525	32036	
86	Correction	—	1.0	1.0	
87	Corrected kVAr meter (85) × (86)	kVAr	52525		
88	Generator output = $\frac{(81) + (84)}{2}$	kWh	121643		
	Power factor				
89	P.F. = $(88) \div \sqrt{[(88)^2 + (87)^2]}$	—	0.918		Note: Preferably use 2-wattmeter method
90	Back pressure at LP exhaust	mbar	31.934	31.460	
	HP turbine heat rate				
91	Total turbine steam flow (54)	kg/s	101.141		
92	Steam to glands (LP) (design)	kg/s	0.3780	0.3780	
93	HP turbine throttle flow (91) − (92)	kg/s	100.763		

	Test No.		1	4	Derived
	Load	MW	120	96	*From*
94	HP throttle steam rate $\frac{3600 \times (93)}{(88)}$	kg/kWh	2.98206		
95	TSV steam temperature	°C	533.8	538.6	
96	TSV steam pressure	bar (abs)	106.8	107.4	
97	TSV steam enthalpy	kJ/kg	3448.8		
98	Final feed temp. after bypass	°C	226.6	214.7	
99	Final feed pressure	bar (abs)	40.6	41.6	
100	Final feed enthalpy	kJ/kg	974.8		
101	Nett heat input (97) − (100)	kJ/kg	2474.0		
102	HP throttle heat rate (101) × (94)	kJ/kWh	7377.6		
	Turbine gland supply heat rate				
103	LP sealing steam flow (design) (92) × 3600	kg/h	1360.8		
104	Gland sealing steam rate (103) ÷ (88)	kg/kWh	0.01119		
105	Enthalpy of sealing steam (97)	kJ/kg	3448.8		
106	Enthalpy of final feed water (100)	kJ/kg	974.8		
107	Net heat input (105) − (106)	kJ/kg	2474.0		
108	Gland supply heat rate (104) × (107)	kJ/kWh	27.684		
	IP turbine heat rate				
	Steam from R/H to IP turbine (78) × 3600	kg/h	329405.8		
109	IP steam rate $\frac{(78) \times 3600}{(88)}$	kg/kWh	2.708		
110	IP inlet steam press.	bar (abs)	26.5	20.1	
111	IP inlet steam temp.	°C	538.9	540.6	
112	IP inlet steam enthalpy	kJ/kg	3543.9		
113	HP exhaust steam temp.	°C	366.2	362.9	
114	HP exhaust steam press.	bar (abs)	28.2	21.2	
115	HP exhaust steam enthalpy	kJ/kg	3155.9		
116	Heat added to R/H steam (112) − (115)	kJ/kg	388.0		
117	IP heat rate (109) × (116)	kJ/kWh	1050.704		
	Reheat spray water heat rate				
118	R/H spray water flow	kg/h	0	0	
119	Water rate (118) ÷ (88)	kg/kWh			
120	IP inlet steam enthalpy (112)	kJ/kg			
121	Boiler feed pump disch. press.	bar (abs)			
122	Boiler feed pump disch. temp.	°C			
123	Enthalpy of spray water	kJ/kg			
124	Heat input (120) − (123)	kJ/kg			
125	R/H spray water heat rate (119) × (124)	kg/kWh	0		
	Total 'As-run' heat rate				
126	(102) + (108) + (117) + (125)	kJ/kWh	8455.0		
	Corrections to 'As-run' heat rate				
127	Total steam to turbine (54)	kg/s	101.141		

	Test No.		1	4	Derived
	Load	MW	120	96	From
128	Flow through HP heaters (9)	kg/s	100.894		
129	% devn. in HP flow $\frac{(128)-(127)}{(127)}$ × 100	%	(−)0.2442		
130	Correction rate ± 5%	±%	0.55	0.35	
131	Correction factor $\left[\frac{(130)}{5}\times\frac{(129)}{100}\right]+1$	—	1.0002		
132	Flow through LP heaters (design)	kg/h	290299.1		See figure 13.13
133	Variation in flow (51)	kg/h	(−)6.811		
134	% varn. in flow $\frac{(133)\times 100}{(132)}$	%	(−)0.002		
135	Correction rate ± 5% variation	±%	0.26	0.24	
136	Correction factor $\left[\frac{(135)}{5}\times\frac{(134)}{100}\right]+1$	—	1.0000		
137	Correction for TSV pressure		0.9997	0.9996	
138	Correction for TSV temp.		0.9991	1.0002	
139	Correction for IP temp.		1.0003	1.0008	
140	Correction for IP pressure drop		1.0044	1.0047	
141	Correction for back pressure		1.0026	1.0010	
142	Correction for final feed temp.		1.0008	1.0001	
143	Correction for power factor		1.0000	1.0004	
144	Total correction (131) × (136) × (137) × (138) × (139) × (140) × (141) × (142) × (143)		1.0071		
145	Corrected test heat rate (126) × (144)	kJ/kWh	8515.0		
146	Corrected test heat consumption (88) × (145)	GJ/h	1035.8		
147	Guaranteed heat rate at test loading	kJ/kWh	8651.5	8813.65	
148	% varn. from guarantee $\frac{(147)-(145)}{(147)}\times 100$	%	(+)1.58		

Note 1 Item 52 is the net change in storage quantities, the minus sign indicating a reduction in level, i.e. an increased flow.
Note 2 The feed flow exceeds the throttle flow by the change in storage quantity. Thus, the net change in storage capacity is assumed to be accounted for by variation of the boiler water level or boiler loss.

Rate of flow using a flow transducer

A flow transducer translates the differential pressure across a device such as a venturi or an orifice plate into an electrical output. The relationship between the differential pressure and voltage is linear, as shown in *Figure 13.10*.

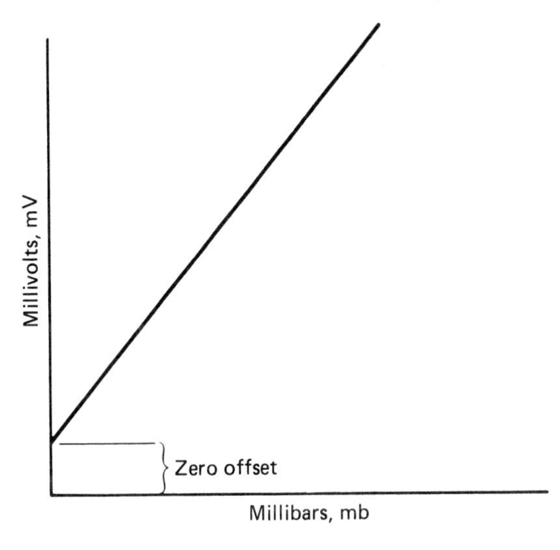

Figure 13.10 Law of flow transducer

Z = zero offset and m = slope of line

So $mV = (m - mb) + Z$

$$\text{Thus } mb = \frac{mV - z}{m}$$

$$\text{Let } \frac{1}{m} = S\text{; then } mb = S\,(mV - Z)$$

Example:

The law of the flow transducer is: $mb = 10.4359\,(mV - 0.54)$ (see *Figure 13.11.*)

Flow transducer output	= 43.8597 mV	(1)
So equivalent pressure	= 10.4359 (43.8597 − 0.54)	
	= 452.08 mbar	(2)
Equivalent head h, in cm w.g.	= (2) × 1.020 = 461.1216	
	(Note: mbar × 1.020 = cm w.g.)	
$\sqrt{h}$	= 21.4737	
Flow constant of DP device, K	= 4.7018	
Flow = $K\sqrt{h}$	= 100.965 kg/s	
Temp. of water at DP device	= 128.1°C	
Press. of water at DP device	= 43.7 bar abs.	
Temp. and press. correction factor	$= 0.9993 = \sqrt{\left(\dfrac{\text{Density at } t°\text{C}}{\text{Density at design temp.}}\right)}$	
Corrected flow	= 100.894 kg/s	

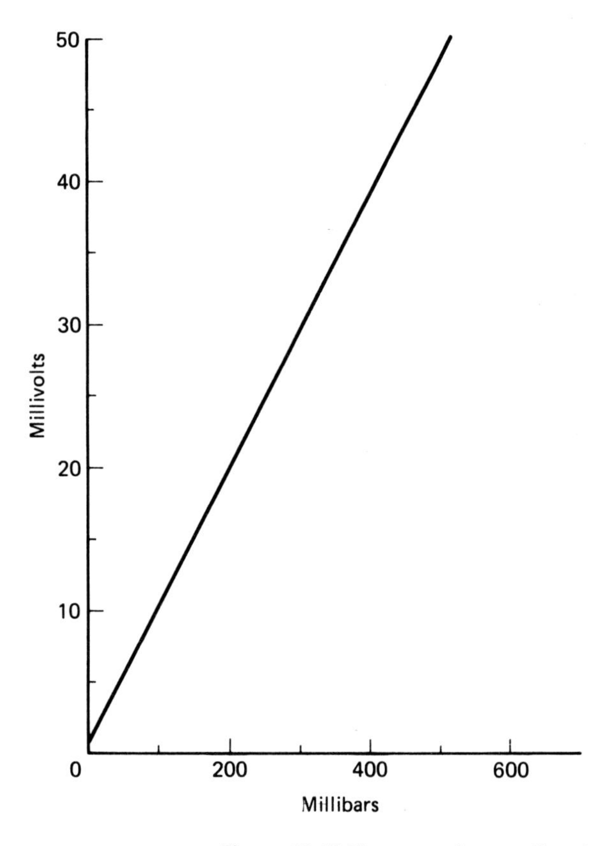

Figure 13.11 Flow transducer calibration

Rate of flow from a manometer reading

Consider the gland seal flow to the boiler feed pump. The design conditions are:

Flow at 127°C, 46.5 bar abs. = 7.56 kg/s
Head h = 1113.75 cm water gauge
1 Average manometer reading under water = 60.476 cm Hg
2 Ambient temperature = 12.9°C
3 Corresponding density of mercury minus water at 4°C (from *Figure 13.12*) = 12.5642
4 Corresponding manometer reading = (1) × (3) = 759.83 cm w.g.
5 Square root of manometer reading = $\sqrt{(4)}$ = 27.565
6 Flow constant (from design flow and head) = 0.2265
Thus 7.56 = $K\sqrt{1113.75}$, so K = 0.2265
7 Flow of sealing water = (5) × (6) = 6.2434 kg/s
8 Temperature of seal water at No. 4 heater inlet = 128.1°C
9 Pressure of seal water at booster pump discharge = 46.5 bar

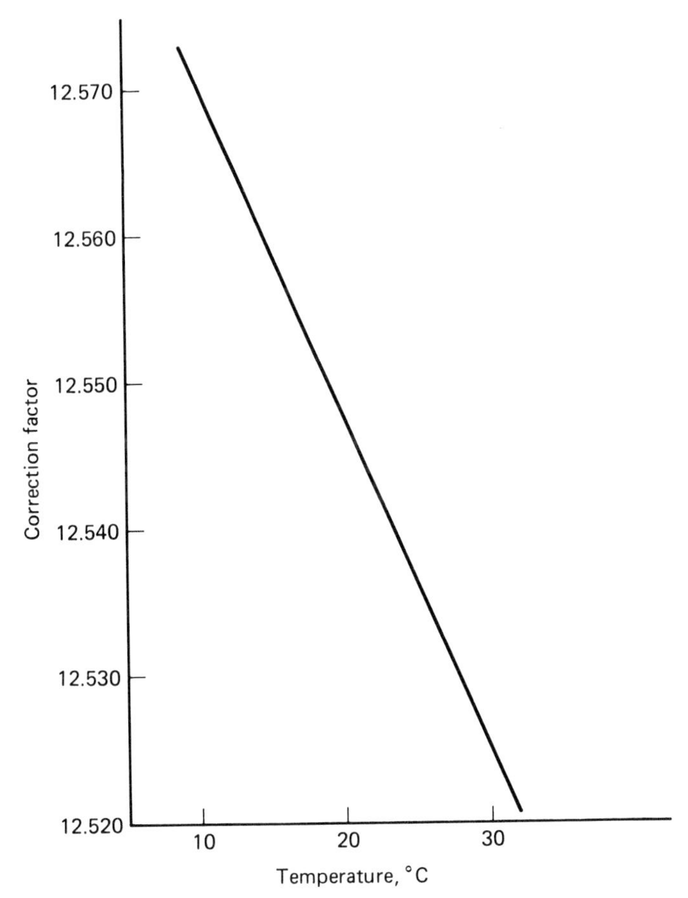

Figure 13.12 Manometer conversion (mm Hg under water to mm water at 4°C)

10 Temperature and pressure correction factor = 0.9993

$$\text{Factor} = \frac{\sqrt{\text{Density at } t°\text{C}}}{\sqrt{\text{Density at design temp.}}}$$

11 True flow of seal water at 127°C, 46.5 bar abs. = 6.239 kg/s

Gland seal flow return to deaerator

The design conditions are: Flow at 127°C, 5.2 bar abs. = 7.56 kg/s

Average manometer reading under water = 49.29 cm Hg
Ambient temperature = 12.9°C
Corresponding density of mercury = 12.5642
Corresponding manometer reading = 619.313 cm w.g.
Square root of manometer reading = 24.886
Flow constant = 0.2265
Temperature of water = 128.1°C
Pressure of water = 4.2 bar abs.

Temperature and pressure correction factor = 0.9997
True flow to D/A at 127°C, 5.2 bar abs. = 5.635 kg/s

Storage quantities – Variation

(in kg/h)

	Test Number	*1*	*4*
1	Nominal load (MW)	120	96
2	Duration of test (h)	2	1½h
3	'A' condenser	0	(+)4.082
4	'B' and 'C' condenser	0	(+)8.618
5	Condenser stilling chamber	(−)4.990	(−)14.051
6	Turbine clean drains tank	0	0
7	Drains cooler shell	(−)4.082	0
8	LP heater shell	0	(+)1.361
9	Vapour condenser shell	0	0
10	2 LP heater shell	0	(−)0.907
11	3 heater (D/A) shell	(−)1 269.605	(−)2 493.397
12	4 HP heater shell	0	0
13	5 HP heater shell	0	(−)3.175
14	6 HP heater shell	0	0
15	Gen. H_2 cooler DW header tank	(−)7.711	(+)11.793
16	Distilled water pump gland drips	0	0
17	In-leakage to condenser, from (15)	(+)7.7711	—
18	Extraction pump-sampling point	(+)2.722	(+)2.722
19	'A' Extraction pump gland drips	(+)3.629	(+)2.722
20	'B' Extraction pump gland drips	(+)3.629	(+)2.722
21	No. 1 heater drain pump gland drips	0	0
22	No. 2 heater drain pump gland drips	(+)8.165	(+)27.216
23	Unloading valve (atmospheric drain)	0	0

Notes:

1 Many of these items can be combined for routine tests. For example, items 16, 19, 20, 21, and 23 could be combined to give a 'miscellaneous' loss.

2 Storage vessels whose water level falls during a test (e.g. the deaerator) add to the water flow and are designated (−). Water that is lost from the system (e.g. gland drips) are designated (+).

3 The change of storage quantity is determined by noting the level of each storage vessel at the start and end of the test period. Reference to appropriate curves enables the change of storage quantity to be determined for the level change.

Gland leak-off flow from HP turbine

1 Design flow = 1.366 kg/s
2 Design cylinder exhaust steam pressure = 28.6 bar abs.
3 Design cylinder exhaust steam temperature = 365.6°C
4 Design cylinder exhaust specific volume = 98.074 dm^3/kg
5 Test cylinder exhaust steam pressure = 28.2 bar abs.
6 Test cylinder exhaust steam temperature = 366.2°C
7 Test cylinder exhaust specific volume = 99.385 dm^3/kg

8 $\dfrac{\sqrt{\text{Pressure}}}{\sqrt{\text{Specific vol.}}}$ design $= \sqrt{\dfrac{(2) \times 1000}{(4)}} = 17.077$

9 $\dfrac{\sqrt{\text{Pressure}}}{\sqrt{\text{Specific vol.}}}$ test $= \sqrt{\dfrac{(5) \times 1000}{(7)}} = 16.845$

10 Ratio of test to design $= \dfrac{(9)}{(10)} = 0.9864$

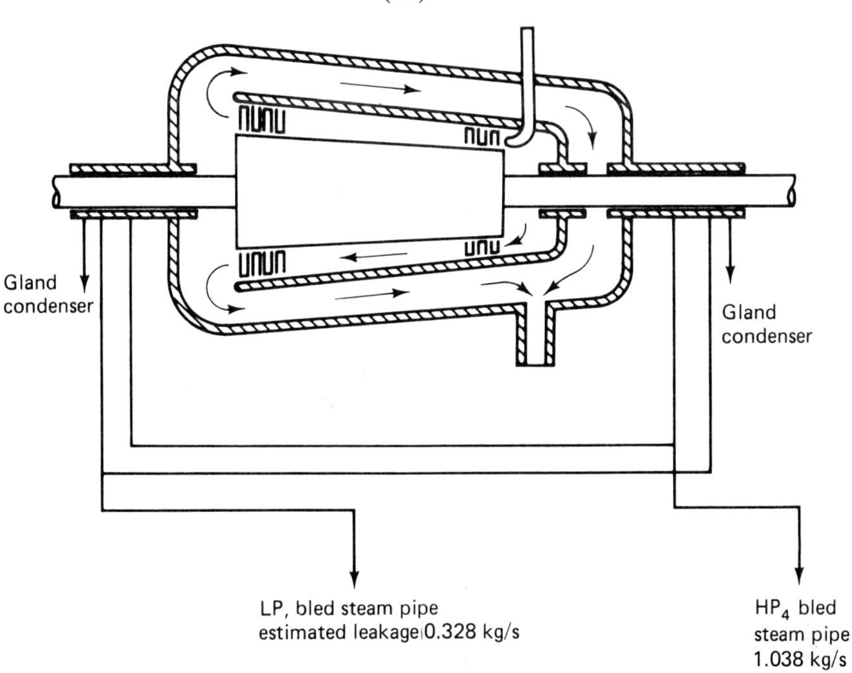

11 Design gland leak-off flow (from sketch) = 1.366 kg/s
12 Test gland leak-off flow = (10) × (11) = 1.347 kg/s

The reader is now in a position to appreciate the requirements of testing larger machines with the added complications of such things as a boiler feed pump turbine. *Figure 13.14* shows a typical layout of such plant and also the measurements required. Of course, normally boiler blowdown would be suspended during turbine testing and so item W_9 would be zero. The necessary calculations are listed in *Table 13.4* for the calculation of the turbo-alternator heat rate and no elaboration is required.

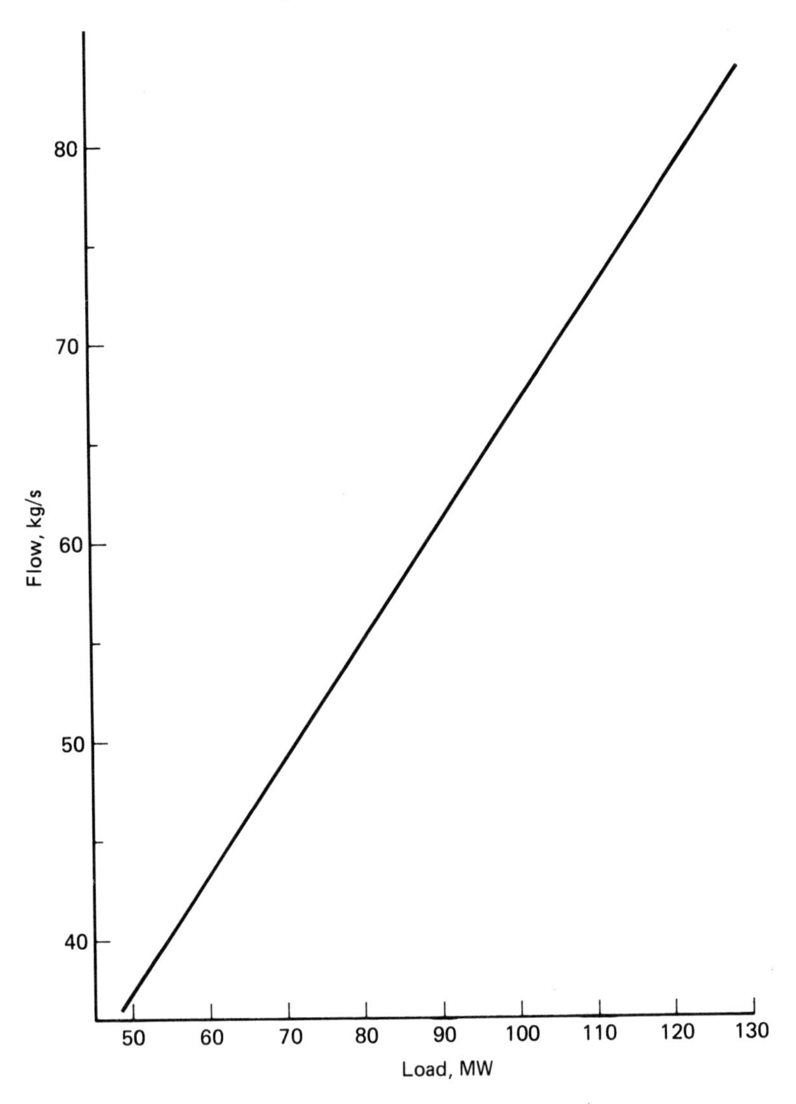

Figure 13.13 Design condensate flow through LP feed heaters

Questions

1 What is the object of testing?
2 How frequently should routine tests be carried out?
3 What is the test code used in the CEGB?
4 What is an electrical transducer?
5 What is the advantage of automatic data aquisition?
6 Name some typical items to be checked on the plant prior to a test.
7 How long should a machine be 'heat soaked 'prior to testing?'

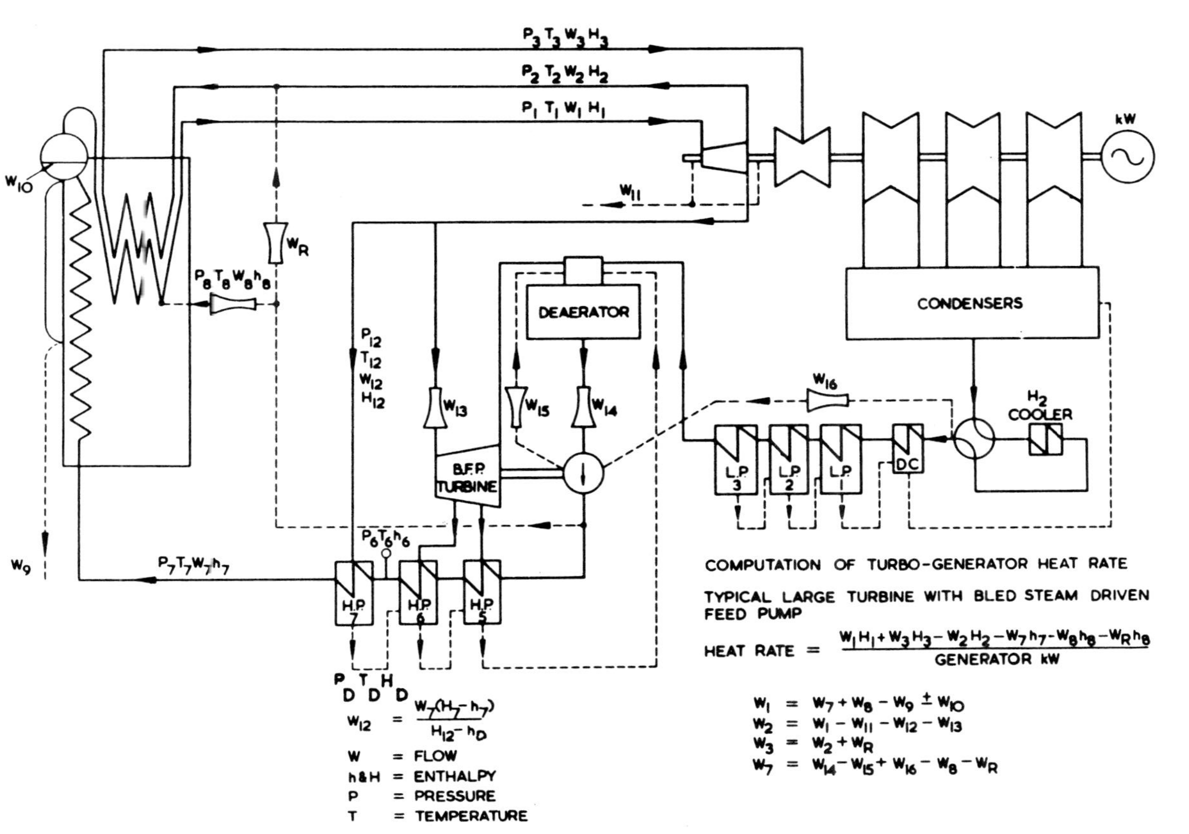

Figure 13.14 Computation of turbo-generator heat rate (CEGB)

1. *Equation for turbine with bled-steam driven feed pump*

$$\text{Turbo-generator heat rate} = \frac{\text{Boiler heat output}}{\text{Generated kW}}$$

$$\text{Boiler heat output} = W_1H_1 + W_3H_2 - WsH_2 - W_7h_7 - (W_8 + W_R)\, h_8$$

Where W_1H_1 = Flow (kg/hr) enthalpy (kJ/kg) at TSV
W_2H_2 = Flow (kg/hr) enthalpy (kJ/kg) of cold reheat
W_3H_3 = Flow (kg/hr) enthalpy (kJ/kg) of hot reheat
W_7h_7 = Flow (kg/hr), enthalpy (kJ/kg) of final feed
W_8h_8 = Flow (kg/hr) enthalpy (kJ/kg) of superheater spray
WR = Reheat spray water flow (kg/hr)

$$W_1 = W_7 + W_8 - W_9 \pm W_{10}$$

Where W_9 = Blowdown flow
W_{10} = Flow due to change in level of boiler drum
$W_2 = W_1 - W_{11} - W_{12} - W_{13}$

Where W_{11} = HP cylinder leak-off missing reheater
W_{12} = Bled steam flow to No. 7 HP heater
W_{13} = Bled steam flow to BFP turbine
$W_3 = W_2 + WR$

Where WR = Reheater spray water flow
$W_7 = W_{14} - W_{15} + W_{16} - W_8 - WR$

Where W_{14} = Flow from deaerator to feed pump suction
W_{15} = Flow from feed pump glands to deaerator
W_{16} = Flow from extraction pump to feed pump glands

2. *Measurements required*

Generator output kW
Pressures and Temperatures at:
(1) TSVs
(2) Cold reheats leaving turbine
(3) Hot reheat entering turbine
(4) Bled steam to No. 7 heater
(5) Bled steam to BFP turbine
(6) Final feed water
(7) Superheater and reheater spray water

Flows at:
W_8 Superheater spray water
WR Reheater spray water
W_9 Blowdown
W_{10} Flow due to change in level of boiler drum
W_{11} HP cylinder leak-off missing reheater
W_{12} Bled steam flow to No 7 heater
W_{13} Bled steam to BFP turbine
W_{14} Main flow from deaerator to BFP suction
W_{15} BFP gland leak-off to deaerator
W_{16} Supply to BFP glands from extraction pumps
Bled steam to last heater calculated by heat balance:

$$W_{12} = \frac{W_7\,(h_7 - h_6)}{H_{12} - hD}\ \text{kg/hr}$$

Table 13.4 Computation of Turbo-Generator heat rate (CEGB)

8 How frequently should main flows be read during a test?
9 Why are several tests required at each loading?
10 What is the 'Willans' line?
11 How is the best straight line determined?
12 What is the efficiency of a machine whose heat rate is 10 000 kJ/kWh?
13 Why does the efficiency reduce as the loading is reduced?
14 What effect does a reduction of stored water (say, in the deaerator) have on a test?

Project 1 (Answer)

	Test No.		*1*	*4*	*Derived*
	Load	MW	120	96	*From*
1	Flow transducer output	mV	43.8597	24.7020	
2	Differential pressure	cm w.g.	461.1216	257.1952	
3	$\sqrt{h} = \sqrt{(2)}$		21.4737	16.0373	
4	Flow constant K	—	4.7018	4.7018	
5	Flow = (3) × (4)	kg/s	100.965	75.40418	
6	Temp. at venturi (HP4 htr. inlet)	°C	128.1	119.1	
7	Press. at venturi (booster pump disch.)	bar(abs)	43.7	44.0	
8	Temp. and press. correction	—	0.9993	1.0030	
9	Corrected flow through main venturi	kg/s	100.894	75.630	
	Boiler feed pump gland sealing water supply				
10	Average head (h) cm Hg under water	cm Hg/H_2O	60.476	51.868	
11	Ambient temperature	°C	12.9	14.5	
12	Density of mercury minus water at 4°C	—	12.5642	12.5607	
13	Corresp. manometer rdg. (10) × (12)	cm w.g.	759.83	651.500	
14	Square root of mano. rdg. $\sqrt{(13)}$	—	27.565	25.524	
15	Flow constant K	—	0.2265	0.2265	
16	Sealing water flow (14) × (15)	kg/s	6.2434	5.7812	
17	Press. of seal water at boost pump disch.	bar(abs)	46.5	44.0	
18	Temp. of seal water at No. 4 htr. inlet	°C	128.1	119.1	
19	Temp. and press. correction	—	0.9993	1.0033	
20	True flow at 127°C/46.5 bar = (16) × (19)	kg/s	6.239	5.8003	
	Boiler feed pump gland sealing water return				
21	Average head (h) cm Hg under water	cm Hg/H_2O	49.29	50.80	
22	Ambient temperature	°C	12.9	14.8	
23	Corresp. density of mercury minus water	—	12.5642	12.5593	
24	Corresp. manometer rdg. (21) × (23)	cm w.g.	619.313	638.012	

	Test No.		1	4	Derived
	Load	MW	120	96	From
25	Square root of mano. rdg. √(24)	—	24.885	25.259	
26	Flow constant *K*		0.2265	0.2265	
27	Press. of seal water return	bar(abs)	4.2	5.1	
28	Temp. of seal water return	°C	128.1	119.1	
29	Temp. and press. correction	—	0.9997	1.0033	
30	True flow to D/A at 127°C/5.2 bar (abs)	kg/s	5.635	1.0033 5.740	
31	Inleakage to boiler feed pump (20) − (30)	kg/s	0.604	0.0603	
	Storage quantities and leaks				
32	2/3 Condenser shell	All in kg/h	0	8.618	
33	1/3 Condenser shell		0	4.082	
34	Stilling chamber		(−)4.990	(−)14.051	
35	Turbine CD Tank		0	0	
36	Drains cooler shell		(−)4.082	0	
37	LP 1 heater shell		0	1.361	
38	Vapour condenser shell		0	0	
39	LP 2 heater shell		0	(−)0.907	
40	LP 3 D/A shell		(−)1269 .605	(−)2 493.397	
41	HP 4 heater shell		0	0	
42	HP 5 heater shell		0	(−)3.175	
43	HP 6 heater shell		0	0	
44	RFT (866.1 kg/cm)		0	0	
45	Hydrogen cooling DW header tank		(−)7.711	0	
46	Hydrogen DW pump gland drips		0	0	
47	Unloading valve (atmospheric drain)		0	0	
48	Chemist's sample at extraction pumps		(+)2.722	(+)2.722	
49	Extraction pumps gland drips		(+)7.25	(+)5.444	
50	Heater drain pumps gland drips		(+)8.165	(+)27.216	
51	Variation in flow through LP heaters Σ (32) to (39) + Σ (45) to (49)	kg/h	(−)6.811	13.009	
52	Net corr. to flow Σ(40) to (44) −(50) +(51)	kg/h	(−)1284. 581	2510.779	
53	Cold R/H desuperheat spray	kg/s	0	0	
	Steam flow to turbine				
54	$(9) + (31) + \frac{(52) - (53)}{3600}$	kg/s	101.141	74.99	
	Calculation of bled steam flow to HP 6 heater				
55	Feed water inlet temperature	°C	189.8	180.8	
56	Feed water inlet pressure	bar(abs)	28.6	21.6	
57	Feed water inlet enthalpy	kJ/kg	808.26	768.3	

	Test No.		1	4	Derived
	Load	MW	120	96	From
58	Feed water outlet temperature	°C	226.6	214.7	
59	Feed water outlet pressure	bar(abs)	28.6	21.6	
60	Feed water outlet enthalpy	kJ/kg	974.41	920.4	
61	Heater drain temperature	°C	230.4	215.6	
62	Heater drain enthalpy	kJ/kg	992.3	923.4	
63	Bled steam temperature	°C	382.2	378.0	
64	Bled steam pressure	bar (abs)	28.6	21.6	
65	Bled steam enthalpy	kJ/kg	3194.6	3195.2	
66	Feed flow through heater (9)	kg/s	100.894	75.628	
67	BS flow $= \frac{(66)\,[(60) - (57)]}{(65) - (62)}$	kg/s	7.612	5.0634	
	Calculation of turbine HP gland leak-off				
68	HP exhaust steam temp. (test)	°C	366.2	362.9	
69	HP exhaust steam press. (test)	bar (abs)	28.2	21.2	
70	Specific volume of HP exhaust steam	dm^3/kg	99.385	133.159	
71	$\left(\frac{(69) \times 1000}{(70)}\right)^{1/2}$	—	16.845	12.6	
72	HP gland sealing steam $Q = \frac{1.366 \times (71)}{17.077}$	kg/s	1.347	1.0079	
	Calculation of steam flow from R/H to IP turbine				
73	LP gland sealing steam supply (design)	all in kg/s	0.3780	0.3780	
74	Spindle leak-off steam (design)		0.3024	0.3024	
75	Steam flow from turbine HP gland leak-off (72)		1.347	1.0079	
76	Steam bled to No. 6 HP heater (67)		7.612	5.0634	
77	Total turbine steam flow (54)		101.141	74.99	
78	Steam from R/H to IP turbine (77) − (73) − (74) − (75) − (76)		91.5016	68.238	
	Electrical output				
79	Main kWh meter	kWh	121658	90289	
80	Correction	—	1.0	1.0	
81	Correction main kWh meter (79) × (80)	kWh	121658	90 289	
82	Check kWh meter	kWh	121628	90515	
83	Correction	—	1.0	1.0	
84	Corrected check kWh meter (82) × (83)	kWh	121628	90 515	
85	Reactive kVAr meter	kVAr	52525	32036	
86	Correction	—	1.0	1.0	
87	Corrected kVAr meter (85) × (86)	kVAr	52525	32 036	
88	Generator output $= \frac{(81) + (84)}{2}$	kWh	121643	90 402	
	Power factor				
89	P.F. $= (88) \div \sqrt{[(88)^2 + (87)^2]}$	—	0.918	0.943	

	Test No.		1	4	Derived
	Load	MW	120	96	From
90	Back pressure at LP exhaust	mbar	31.934	31.460	
	HP turbine heat rate				
91	Total turbine steam flow (54)	kg/s	101.141	74.99	
92	Steam to glands (LP) (design)	kg/s	0.3780	0.3780	
93	HP turbine throttle flow (91) − (92)	kg/s	100.763	74.612	
94	HP throttle steam rate 3600 × (93) / (88)	kg/kWh	2.98206	2.9712	
95	TSV steam temperature	°C	533.8	538.6	
96	TSV steam pressure	bar (abs)	106.8	107.4	
97	TSV steam enthalpy	kJ/kg	3448.8	3460.4	
98	Final feed temp. after bypass	°C	226.6	214.7	
99	Final feed pressure	bar (abs)	40.6	41.6	
100	Final feed enthalpy	kJ/kg	974.8	920.4	
101	Nett heat input (97) − (100)	kJ/kg	2474.0	2540.0	
102	HP throttle heat rate (101) × (94)	kJ/kWh	7377.6	7546.85	
	Turbine gland supply heat rate				
103	LP sealing steam flow (design) (92) × 3600	kg/h	1360.8	1360.8	
104	Gland sealing steam rate (103) ÷ (88)	kg/kWh	0.01119	0.01506	
105	Enthalpy of sealing steam (97)	kJ/kg	3448.8	3460.4	
106	Enthalpy of final feed water (100)	kJ/kg	974.8	920.4	
107	Net heat input (105) − (106)	kJ/kg	2474.0	2540.0	
108	Gland supply heat rate (104) × (107)	kJ/kWh	27.684	38.2524	
	IP turbine heat rate				
	Steam from R/H to IP turbine (78) × 3600	kg/h	329405.8	245 656.8	
109	IP steam rate (78) × 3600 / (88)	kg/kWh	2.708	2.717	
110	IP inlet steam press.	bar (abs)	26.5	20.1	
111	IP inlet steam temp.	°C	538.9	540.6	
112	IP inlet steam enthalpy	kJ/kg	3543.9	3553.4	
113	HP exhaust steam temp.	°C	366.2	362.9	
114	HP exhaust steam press.	bar (abs)	28.2	21.2	
115	HP exhaust steam enthalpy	kJ/kg	3155.9	3162.4	
116	Heat added to R/H steam (112) − (115)	kJ/kg	388.0	391.0	
117	IP heat rate (109) × (116)	kJ/kWh	1050.704	1062.3	
	Reheat spray water heat rate				
118	R/H spray water flow	kg/h	0	0	
119	Water rate (118) ÷ (88)	kg/kWh			
120	IP inlet steam enthalpy (112)	kJ/kg			
121	Boiler feed pump disch. press.	bar (abs)			
122	Boiler feed pump disch. temp.	°C			
123	Enthalpy of spray water	kJ/kg			
124	Heat input (120) − (123)	kJ/kg			
125	R/H spray water heat rate (119) × (124)	kg/kWh	0	0	

	Test No.		1	4	*Derived*
	Load	MW	120	96	*From*
126	*Total 'As-run' heat rate* (102) + (108) + (117) + (125)	kJ/kWh	8455.0	8.647.4	
	Corrections to 'As-run' heat rate				
127	Total steam to turbine (54)	kg/s	101.141	76.3857	
128	Flow through HP heaters (9)	kg/s	100.894	75.628	
129	% devn. in HP flow $\frac{(128) - (127)}{(127)} \times 100$	%	(−)0.2442	(−)0.9919	
130	Correction rate ± 5%	±%	0.55	0.35	
131	Correction factor $\frac{(130)}{5} \times \frac{(129)}{100} + 1$	—	1.0002	1.001	
132	Flow through LP heaters (design)	kg/h	290299.1	218 942.5	
133	Variation in flow (51)	kg/h	(−)6.811	13.009	
134	% varn. in flow $\frac{(133) \times 100}{(132)}$	%	(−)0.002	(−)0.006	
135	Correction rate ± 5% variation	±%	0.26	0.24	
136	Correction factor $\frac{(135) \times (134)}{5 \times 100} + 1$	—	1.0000	1.0000	
137	Correction for TSV pressure		0.9997	0.9996	
138	Correction for TSV temp.		0.9991	1.0002	
139	Correction for IP temp.		1.0003	1.0008	
140	Correction for IP pressure drop		1.0044	1.0047	
141	Correction for back pressure		1.0026	1.0010	
142	Correction for final feed temp.		1.0008	1.0001	
143	Correction for power factor		1.0000	1.0004	
144	Total correction (131) × (136) × (137) × (138) × (139) × (140) × (141) × (142) × (143)		1.0071	1.0078	
145	Corrected test heat rate (126) × (144)	kJ/kWh	8515.0	8714.8	
146	Corrected test heat consumption (88) × (145)	GJ/h	1035.8	787.8	
147	Guaranteed heat rate at test loading	kJ/kWh	8651.5	8813.65	
148	% varn. from guarantee $\frac{(147) - (145)}{(147)} \times 100$	%	(+)1.58	(+)1.13	

Additional Reading

1 Site Test Code No. 2, *Steam Turbine Generator Heat Rate Tests,* CEGB (1978)
2 BS 752, *Test Code for Acceptance of Steam Turbines* (1974)
3 BS 37 Pt. 8: 1959. Pt. 10: 1961 *Electricity Meters* (12 Parts)
4 FENTON, K., *Thermal efficiency and power production*, Pitman (1966)

14 Plant operating parameters

The complexity of a unit offers scope for many parameters to have deviations from optimum, see *Figure 14.1*. It is a fortunate fact, though, that by monitoring just a few terminal conditions it is possible to get a good idea of whether or not the plant is probably satisfactory. The terminal conditions are:

1 Turbine back pressure.
2 TSV steam pressure.
3 TSV and R/H steam temperature.
4 Final feedwater temperature.
5 Boiler excess air (i.e. CO_2% or O_2%)
6 Combustible material in ash.
7 Air heater gas outlet temperature.
8 Make-up.
9 Works power.
10 Unit loading.

If each of the above conditions is at optimum there is a good chance that the unit is being operated at, or near, optimum. Therefore it is good practice to record the above items regularly, say once per shift, and take action on any deviations that are significant.

A shift efficiency control sheet is shown in *Figure 14.2*. Consider each of the parameters in turn.

1 Back pressure

This is the most important condition of all. Every shift the back pressure should be analysed for deviations from optimum on every running unit. Because the back pressure corresponds to the correct value according to the CW inlet temperature it does not necessarily follow that all is well. For example, it may be that there is a deviation due to air ingress, but it is neutralized by having an excessive CW flow – so the final result is that there

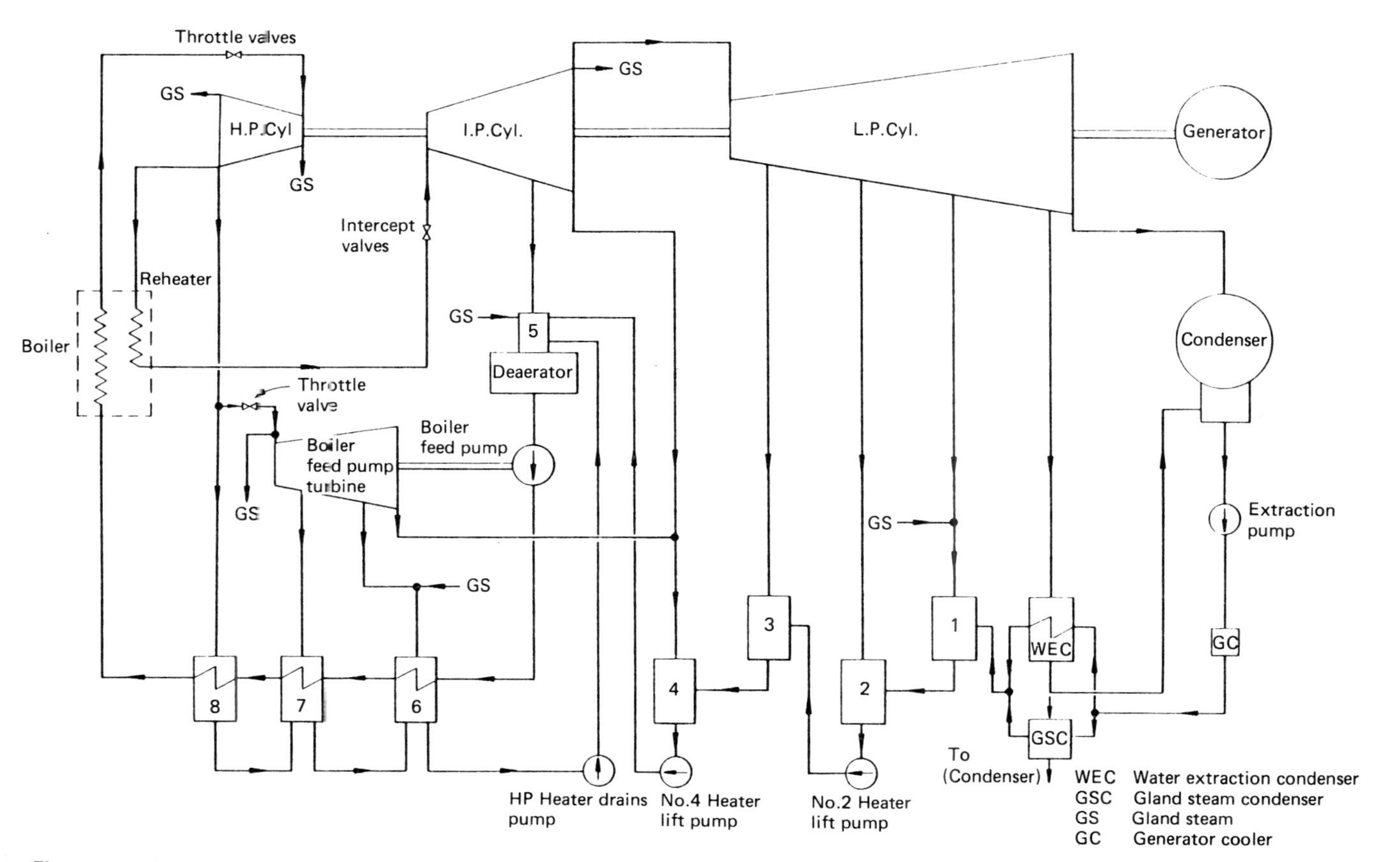

Figure 14.1 Typical plant configuration (CEGB)

Shift control sheet

Parameter		Actual Value	Desired Value	Deviation Limits	Deviation Actual	Action
Instructed load MW				0		
Back pressure mbar (abs.)			See curve	Min BP + 4 mbar		
TSV steam pressure			158.5 bar	± 3 bar		
TSV/IP inlet temp.			566/566°C	± 5°C		
Feed temp. at economizer inlet			See curve	±5°C		
O_2 at A/H inlet			See curve	± 0.2%		
A/H gas outlet temperature			See curve	+ 5°C 0		
Midnight for previous 24 hours	Make-up%		See curve	No min. + 0.2%		
	Works power %		See curve	No min. + 0.2%		

Remarks

Shift Charge Engineer

Unit Operator

Figure 14.2 Shift Efficiency Control Sheet

is zero deviation, despite the two undesirable components.

Regular checks should be carried out to see if air ingress is excessive. The best way to do this is to note the air suction depression when carrying out the shift back-pressure check. Alternatively at regular intervals, say once per week, confirm how long it takes for the back pressure to deteriorate by a set amount when the air pump air suction valves are shut. Comparison with the time taken when the condenser was known to be in good condition will indicate the degree of inleakage.

During icy weather the number of cooling towers in service should be reduced such that the remaining ones have water at a sufficiently high temperature to inhibit icing. On the other hand if the weather is above freezing all the available cooling towers should be kept in service even if some units are off load, so that the maximum cooling can be achieved. Cooling tower irrigation pipework and sprayers should be checked every year and flushed through. The tower ponds should be cleaned as circumstances dictate, usually every two years.

Damaged packings should be removed and replaced as soon as possible after the damage occurs – in this way the towers are kept in good operating condition and the cost at any one time will not be very great. Once wholesale refurbishing becomes necessary the cost will be extremely high. For example, at 1979 prices the cost of re-timbering a fairly small concrete tower of 4.8 m^3/s (17 280 m^3/h) capacity was over £350,000.

Figure 14.3 shows a typical correction curve for variations of back pressure from optimum. The ordinate is a multiplier to correct from actual to optimum conditions, and this applies to later similar curves.

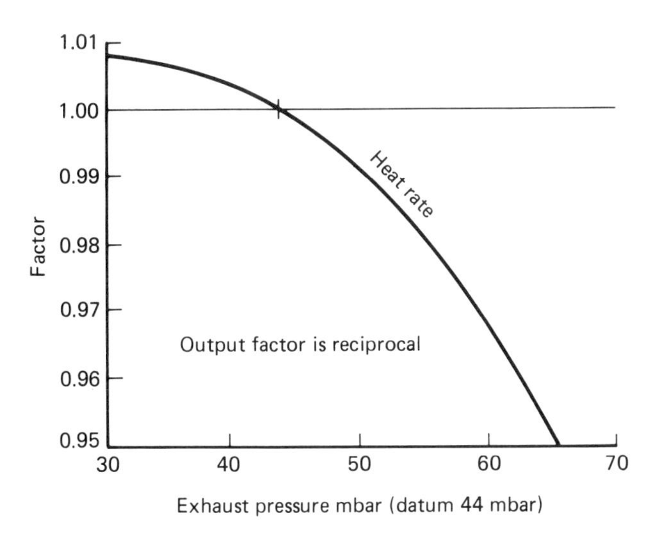

Figure 14.3 Output and heat-rate factor *vs* exhaust pressure (CEGB)

2 Turbine stop valve steam pressure and R/H pressure drop

Steam pressure at TSV

With a throttle-governed turbine the output is proportional to the 'After throttle valve' (ATV) absolute pressure. So if the ATV pressure at full load is 100 bar abs. it will be 50 bar for half load and so on. When the throttle valves are full open there is a pressure drop of about 5% from before the TSV to ATV and the machine loading is dependent upon the TSV pressure. For example, if the TSV pressure is 105 bar for normal full load with the throttles wide open, the load will fall as the pressure is reduced. Suppose the pressure at the TSV fell to 95 bar then the ATV pressure would be about 90 bar and the output of the T/A would become 90/100 = 90% of the original load. So a change of TSV pressure of 10% will result in a change of output of a similar proportion.

Hence, it is most important that when the unit is on full load the TSV pressure is kept at its correct value. Not only is the ATV pressure proportional to T/A output, but so are all the other stage pressures throughout the turbine, as shown in *Figure 14.4*

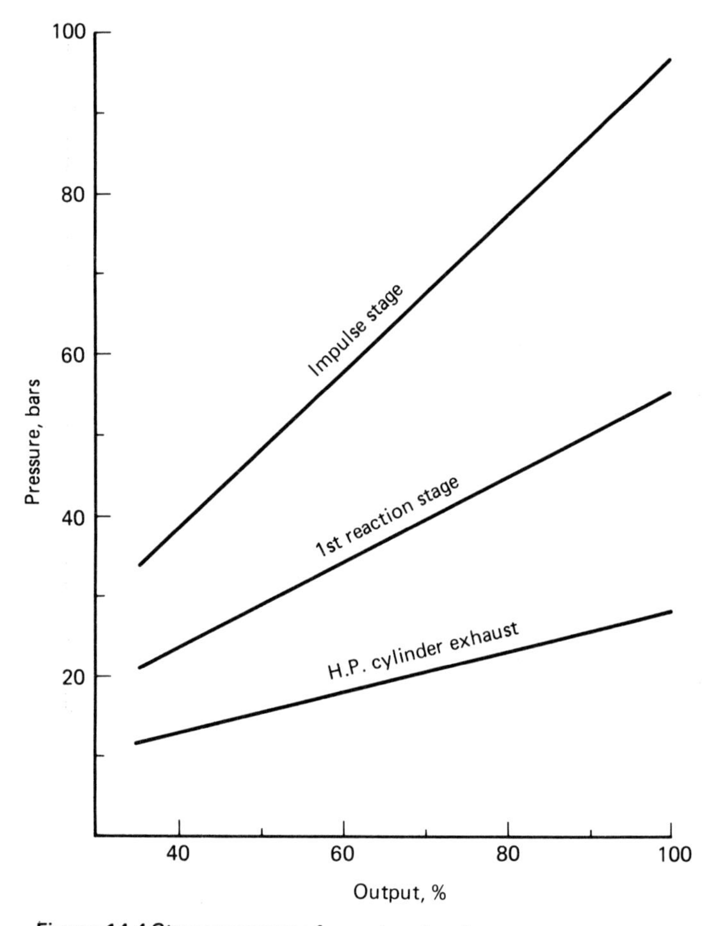

Figure 14.4 Stage pressures for various loadings

On smaller machines it was common to incorporate an overload valve whereby some steam was admitted to the turbine a few stages down the HP cylinder. Thus, from 0 to 80% load steam was admitted normally, and from 80 to 100%, overload steam was admitted. In such a case the proportionality only applies to those stages after the overload admission belt. With nozzle-governed turbines the proportionality applies from the first stage wheel case onward. However, in all turbines the linear relationship does not apply if the flow is very low, and this is particularly so at the last few stages. As load is reduced the available energy in the steam is reduced, as can be seen by reference to *Figure 14.5* which represents the conditions on a non-reheat, throttle-governed machine.

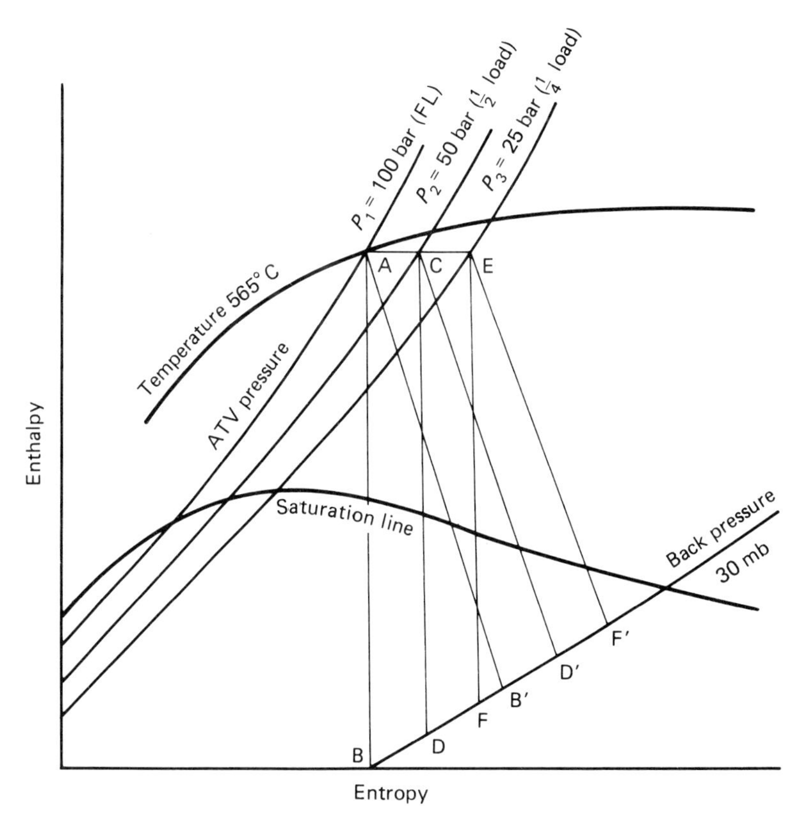

Figure 14.5 Effect of loading on turbine condition line (throttling)

The isentropic and actual conditions for the three loads shown in *Figure 14.5* are given in *Table 14.1*. The values were read from a Total heat–Entropy diagram. At full load for example, the isentropic heat drop is from A to B, whereas at half load it is from C to D. If the turbine efficiency is, say 85%, then the actual expansion lines will be A to B′ for full load and C to D′ for half load.

So part-load operation results in:

1 Reduced available heat in the steam.
2 Reduced wetness at the exhaust.
3 Because of (1), reduced efficiency.
4 Reduced steam temperature after the throttle valves.

Table 14.1

	Units	*Full load*	*Half load*	*Quarter load*
ATV pressure (abs.)	bar	100	50	25
ATV temperature	°C	565	549	538
ATV enthalpy	kJ/kg	3537	3537	3537
Back pressure	mbar	30	30	30
Final enthalpy (isentropic)	kJ/kg	2040	2105	2235
Final enthalpy (actual)	kJ/kg	2265	2320	2430
Heat drop (isentropic)	kJ/kg	1497	1432	1302
Heat drop (actual)	kJ/kg	1272	1217	1107
Exhaust wetness	%	11.5	9.0	4.5

With nozzle control the diagram is different. Each nozzle group has its own throttle valve, and normally these machines are operated with selected valves wide open and the rest shut. At full load the expansion line would be the same as with a throttle-governed turbine as shown in *Figure 14.6* by AB.

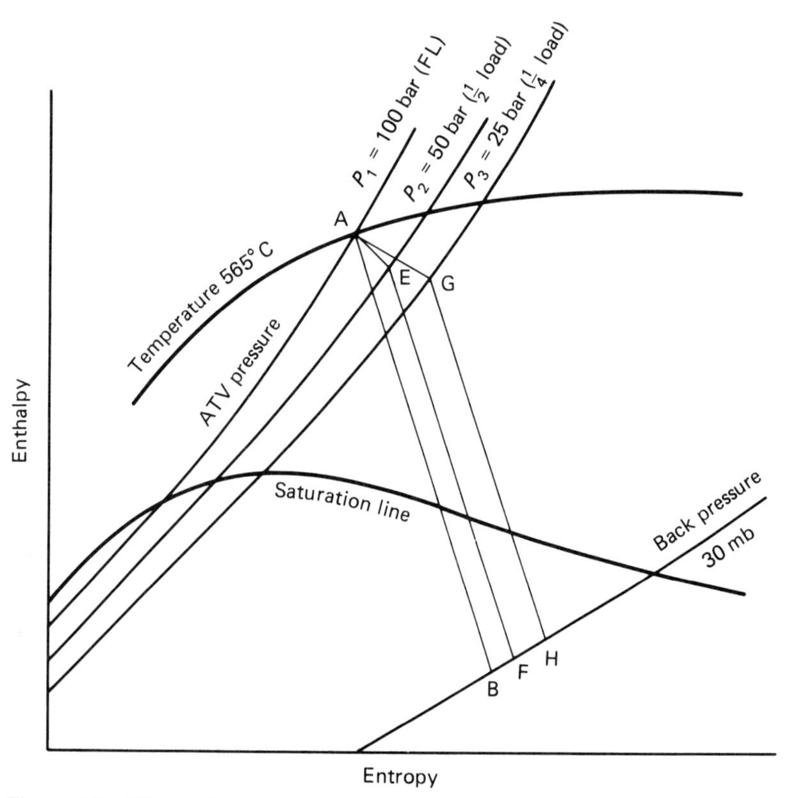

Figure 14.6 Effect of loading on turbine condition bonr (nozzle control)

However, at half load, say, it will only require a proportion of the groups of inlet nozzles in service. The first stage wheel case pressure must be the same as in the throttle governed case, but it is achieved without throttling and so more efficiently. Consequently the first stage wheelcase conditions will be as shown by point E. The *slope* of the expansion lines will be as in the throttle-governed case, but closer together.

So for a nozzle-control turbine, compared to a throttle-governed machine, the changes for part-load operation are:

1 The loss of efficiency due to the control gear is less.
2 The wetness at the exhaust is higher.
3 The controlling valves and operating gear are more complicated.
4 The part-load operating efficiency is better.

Sliding pressure operation

When operating a throttle-governed turbine at part loads the action of throttling the steam results in a reduction of steam temperature as shown by the line AB in *Figure 14.7*. For example, a machine with TSV steam

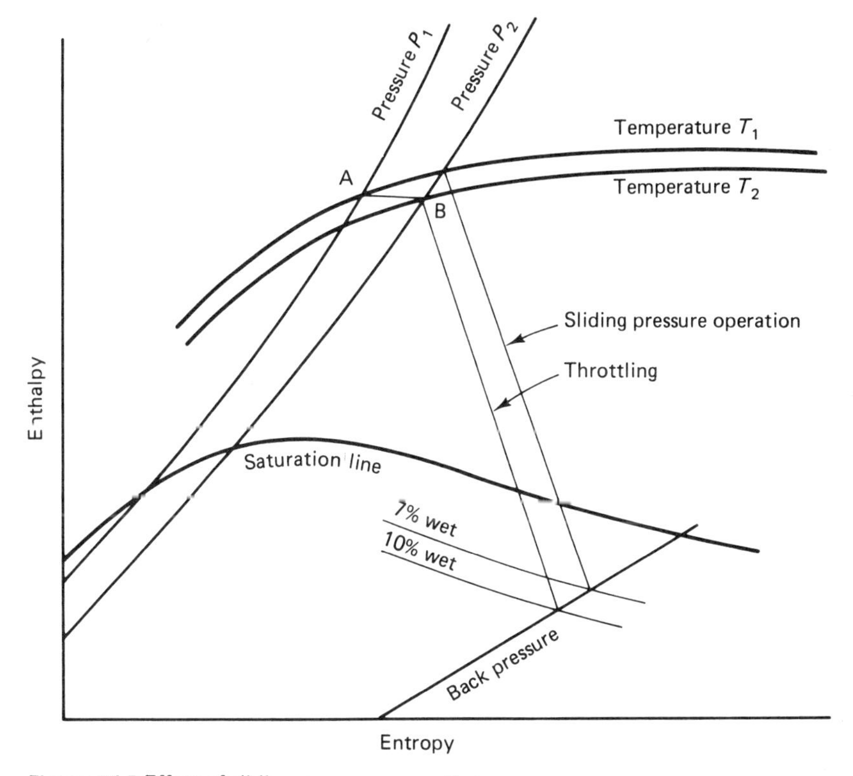

Figure 14.7 Effect of sliding pressure operation

conditions of 105 bar abs. and 566°C would become 547°C if throttled to 50 bar abs. The heat drop available, assuming a non-reheat turbine with an efficiency of 85% and back pressure 30 mbar is, from the H–S chart:

Heat before TSV	3540 kJ/kg
Heat at ATV	3540 kJ kg
Heat at 30 mbar	2325 kJ/kg
Heat drop	1215 kJ/kg

If however, instead of throttling the steam, the boiler pressure were reduced to a value that gave the required ATV pressure with the throttle valves wide open while the steam temperature was kept at optimum (*Figure 14.8*), the heats would be:

Heat at TSV (52.5 bar/566°C)	3585 kJ/kg
Heat at ATV (50.0 bar/566°C)	3585 kJ/kg
Heat at 30 mbar	2350 kJ/kg
Heat drop	1235 kJ/kg

Thus the heat drop per kg of steam has gone from 1215 to 1235 kJ by operating at reduced boiler pressure. The other points to note are:

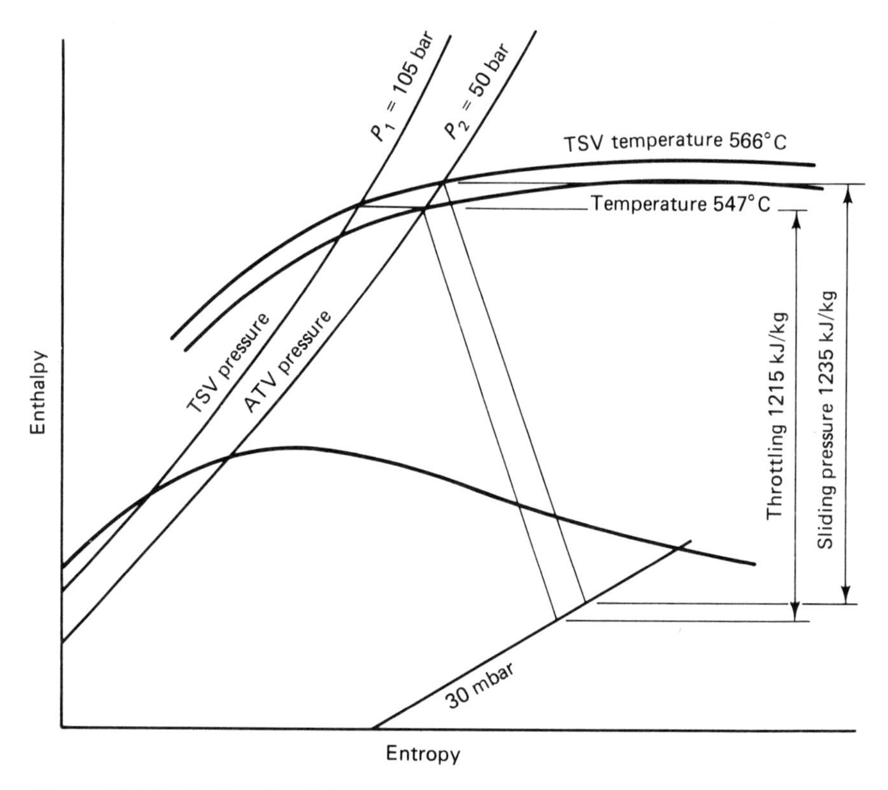

Figure 14.8 Saving heat by sliding pressure operation

(a) The heat of the ATV steam has increased.
(b) The heat of the exhaust steam has increased, but not by as great an amount as the inlet steam.
(c) The wetness at the exhaust has reduced.
(d) The slope of the expansion line is unaltered.

Thus, there is some advantage in operating at part loads with the boiler pressure reduced to the appropriate value. However, care is necessary; for example, if the turbine stop valves should trip but the boiler firing continued a dangerous situation could arise because the boiler pressure would take longer than normal to reach a sufficiently high pressure to operate the safety valves. The delay could be sufficient to cause serious overheating and damage to the tubes. Therefore, before adapting sliding pressure control techniques it is important that consultation be carried out with the manufacturers. Normally they will insist on fitting protection to the boiler which will stop the firing if the steam flow is interrupted.

Deviations from optimum pressure at TSV

Consider *Figure 14.9.* Line AB represents the expansion inside a turbine

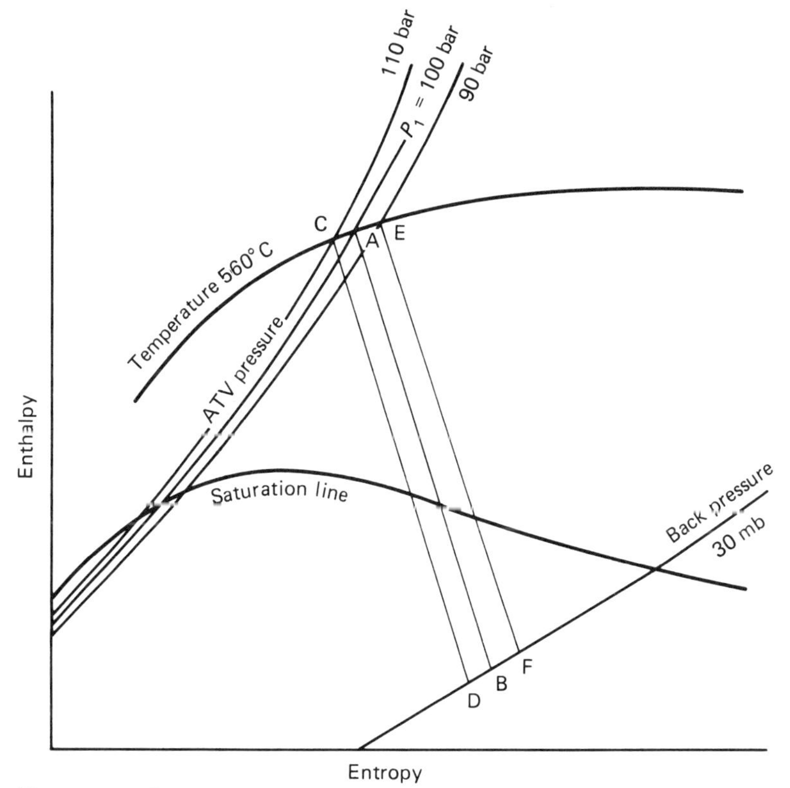

Figure 14.9 Effect of variations of boiler pressure

operating at 100 bar, 560°C steam inlet condition, and exhausting at 30 mbar with wide open throttle valves. If now, the pressure at inlet increased to 110 bar but the temperature remained at 560°C and the exhaust at 30 mbar the total heat of the steam at inlet would be at point C and the exhaust at D. Similarly if the pressure were reduced to 90 bar the expansion would be from E to F. The corresponding changes in heat are shown in *Table 14.2.*

Table 14.2 Effect of variations of boiler pressure (Temperature kept at 560°C and back pressure 30 mbar)

		90 bar	*100 bar*	*110 bar*
Heat in inlet steam	kJ/kg	3534.2	3524.5	3514.8
Heat in outlet steam	kJ/kg	2253.9	2235.5	2222.1
Heat drop	kJ/kg	1280.3	1289.0	1292.7

So the heat drop increases as the pressure increases. Accordingly the output will go up and the heat rate down (i.e. the efficiency will improve) as shown by the typical correction curves in *Figure 14.10*. The ordinates are

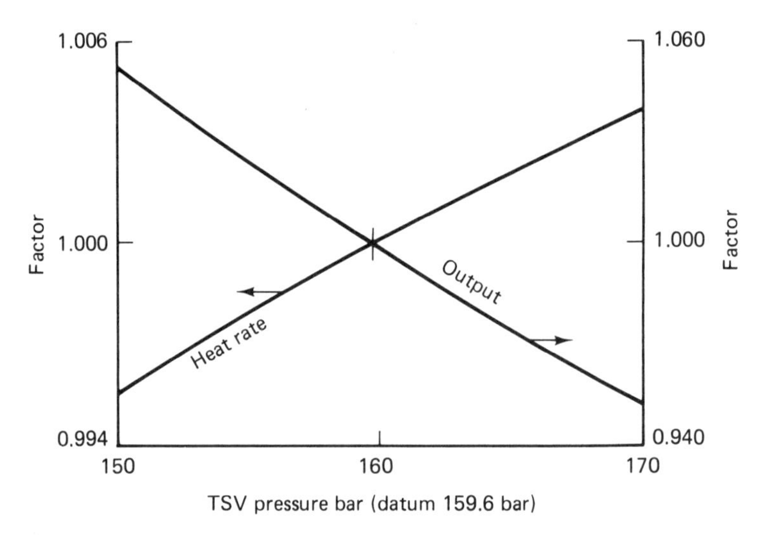

Figure 14.10 Output and reheat factors *vs* TSV pressure drop (CEGB)

multiplying factors to be applied to actual pressures to obtain the equivalent values at optimum pressure. In general the effects of a change of TSV pressure are:

(a) The steam flow will change approximately as:

$$F_a = F_o \sqrt{\frac{P_a v_o}{P_o v_a}}$$

where subscript 'a' = actual condition
'o' = optimum condition
P = pressure at TSV
v = specific volume of steam at TSV
F = TSV steam flow

(b) The changed flow will cause the pressures through the turbine to change, including the bled steam pressures.
(c) Because of (b) the feed heater outlet water temperatures will change.
(d) The total heat of the TSV steam, R/H steam and final feed water will change.
(e) Boiler feed pump output will change to cope with the changed flow.
(f) Because the flow through the turbine has altered so the volumetric flow to the condenser will change.

Thus, the ramifications of a simple change of pressure at the TSV reflect throughout the cycle.

Pressure drop through the reheater

Various things can cause the pressure drop to change, such as:

(a) BFP turbine out of service;
(b) feed heater abnormalities;
(c) R/H safety valves passing, etc.

Such a change will have several effects:

(a) The IP inlet pressure is determined by the flow through the IP cylinder and so a change in the R/H pressure drop will affect the HP cylinder exhaust pressure.
(b) This will cause a change of steam flow to those components using cold reheat steam.
(c) The cold reheat steam total heat will change and so will the feedwater at the last HP heater.
(d) The steam volume to the condenser will alter.

The effect of these changes on heat rate and output is shown in *Figure 14.11*.

3 TSV and R/H steam temperature

Variations in the TSV steam temperature result in variations in the specific volume of the steam, and this results in a change of steam flow in accordance with the formula given in the section for TSV pressure. Other results are:

(a) change of total heat of TSV steam;
(b) change of total heat of HP cylinder exhaust steam;

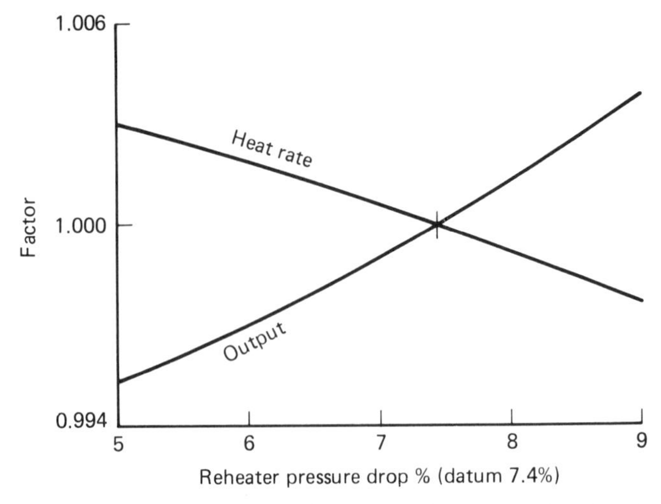

Figure 14.11 Output and reheat factors *vs* R/H pressure drop (CEGB)

(c) the change of flow will alter the pressures throughout the turbine and this will change the bled steam flows, and the flow to the condenser. *Table 14.3* indicates how the heat drop in a non-reheat machine is affected by

Table 14.3 Effect of variations of TSV temperature

		TSV steam temperature		
	Units	*575°C*	*565°C*	*555°C*
ATV pressure	bar abs.	100	100	100
TSV enthalpy	kJ/kg	3561.5	3536.8	3512.1
Back pressure	mbar	30	30	30
Final enthalpy	kJ/kg	2240.0	2265.0	2280.0
Heat drop	kJ/kg	1321.5	1271.8	1232.1

variations of TSV temperature, as depicted in *Figure 14.12(a)*. So operating at a higher temperature increases the heat drop. However, excursions into the higher temperature region can seriously reduce the life of high-temperature components such as the superheater outlet header, and therefore are most undesirable.

Variations of the reheater outlet temperature will cause:

(a) change of total heat of the steam, including bled steam.
(b) Change of steam flow to condenser for a given loading.

Figure 14.12(b) illustrates the effects of variations of reheat temperature on the heat drop and the information is used in *Table 14.4*. *Figure 14.13(a)* illustrates how output and heat rate are affected by variations of TSV and reheat temperature. If it is necessary to control the temperature of the steam

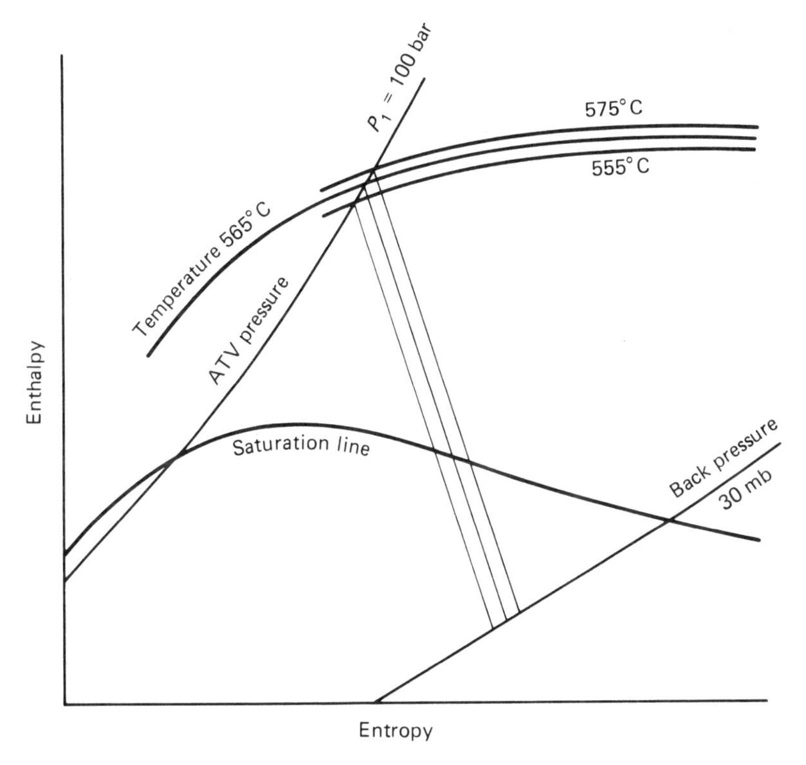

Figure 14.12(a) Effect of variation of TSV steam temperature

Table 14.4 Effect of variations of reheat temperature

	Units	*R/H steam temperature* 575°C	565°C	555°C
R/H pressure	bar abs.	25	25	25
R/H enthalpy	kJ/kg	3628.9	3606.4	3584.1
Back pressure	mbar	30	30	30
Final enthalpy	kJ/kg	2430	2450	2470
Heat drop	kJ/kg	1198.9	1156.4	1114.1

either at superheater or reheater by means of spray injection then there will be a resultant loss of output and an increase in heat rate, as illustrated in *Figure 14.13(b)*.

One interesting type of reheat temperature control is known as the 'Triflux System'. It consists of a section of reheater with large bore tubes, inside each of which is located a small diameter superheater tube. The temperature of the high-pressure steam passing along the inner tubes is regulated by means of spray water injection which, in turn, controls the reheat temperature. This system is installed on No. 12 supercritical boiler at

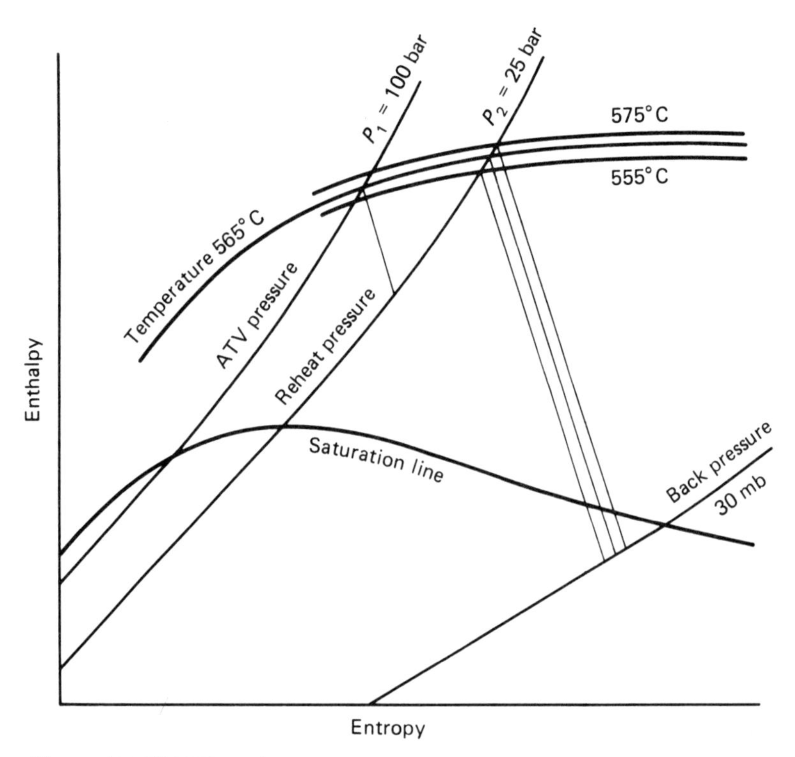

Figure 14.12(b) Effect of variation of R/H steam temperature

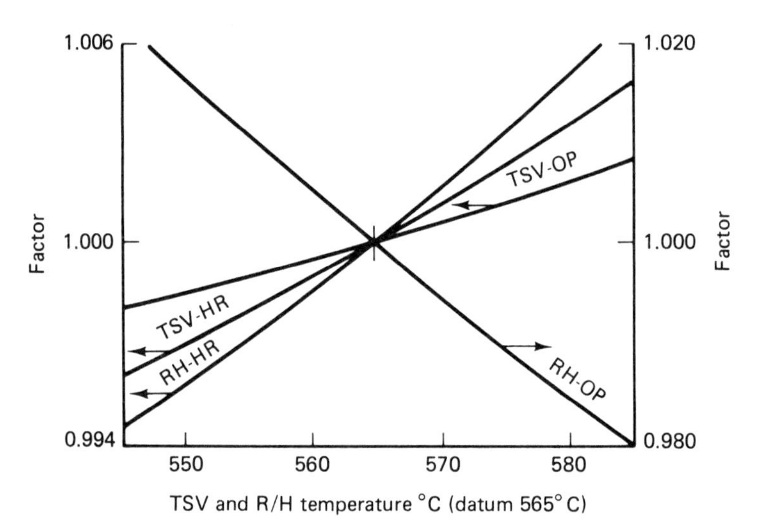

Figure 14.13(a) Output and R/H factors *vs* TSV and R/H steam temperature (CEGB)

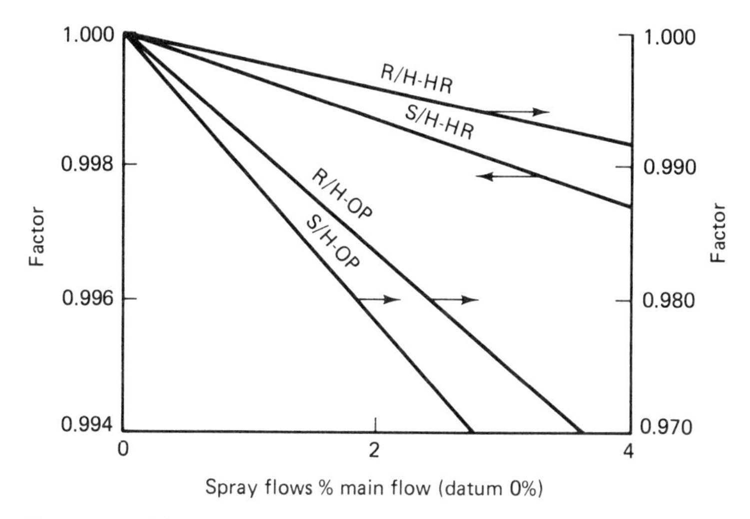

Figure 14.13(b) Output and R/H factors *vs* spray flow (CEGB)

Drakelow and is giving good service. For emergency use there are also spray attemperators fitted to the inlet of the reheater.

4 Final feedwater temperature

The final feedwater temperature should be measured after the last heater bypass has joined the feed line and deviations from optimum should be investigated. Water flowing through the bypass will cause the final feed heater outlet temperature to be higher than the final feed. Variations of feed flow from optimum will cause changes in the bled steam quantity to the affected heater, and this will result in changes of output and heat rate. Typical curves are shown in *Figure 14.14* for HP heater, LP heater and boiler feed pump deviations.

In addition there can be deviations from optimum at individual heaters. Whatever the trouble at a heater it must affect one or more of these parameters:

(a) heater terminal temperature difference;
(b) drain outlet terminal temperature difference;
(c) bled steam pipe pressure drop;
(d) steam temperature at the heater inlet.

Figure 14.15, 14.16, and *14.17* show typical variations of heat rate and output with changes of parameters (a), (b) and (c).

The heater drainage system should be set correctly at all times unless there is some specific reason for departing from it; in any case the system should be returned to normal as soon as possible. Low pressure heater vents to

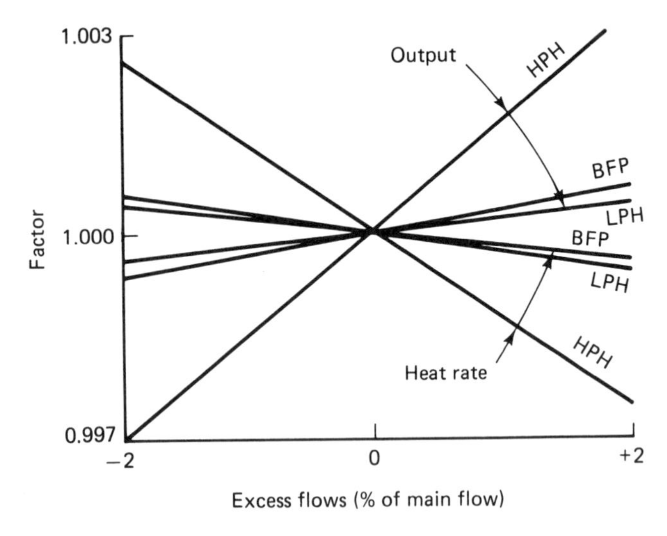

Figure 14.14 Output and heat rate factors *vs* excess flow (CEGB)

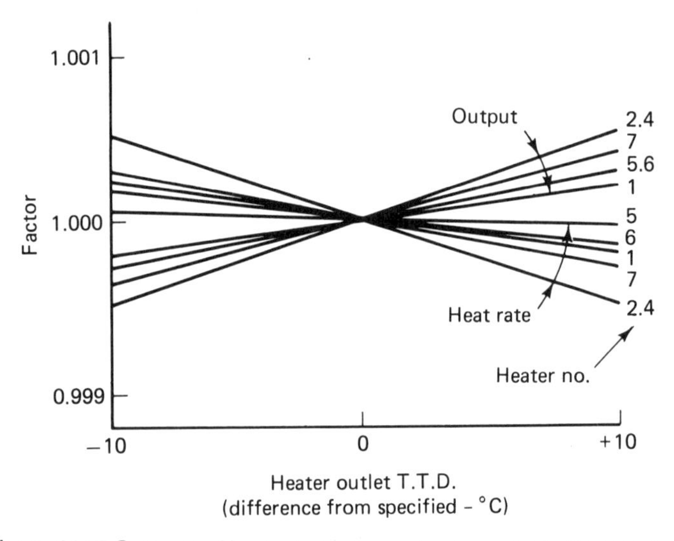

Figure 14.15 Output and heat rate factors *vs* heater outlet TTD (CEGB)

condenser should be left open while on load. The HP heater vents can be left shut but should be opened for a prolonged period when a unit is brought on load to ensure that all the air that may have collected is vented. Thereafter the vent to condenser valves should be opened periodically.

5 Boiler excess air

Boiler combustion efficiency is largely dependent upon supplying the cor-

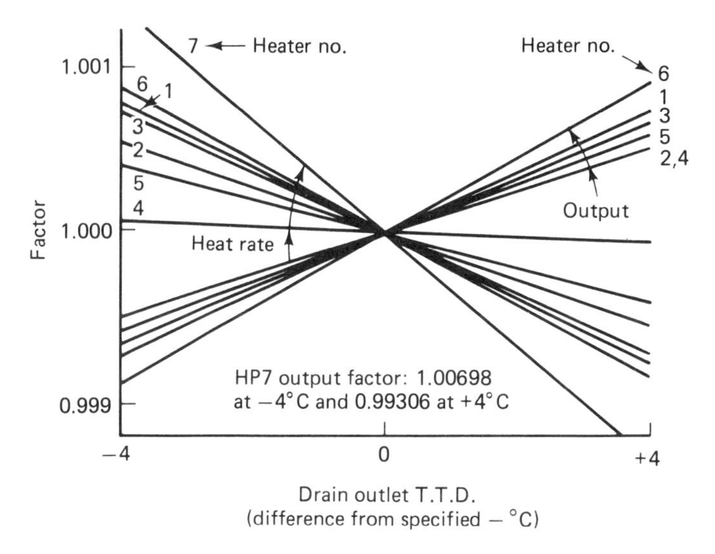

Figure 14.16 Output and heat rate factors *vs* drain outlet TTD (CEGB)

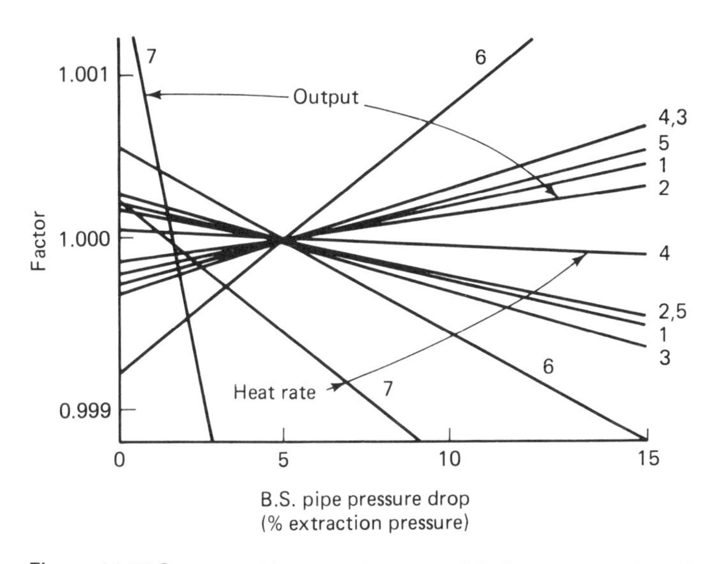

Figure 14.17 Output and heat rate factors *vs* BS pipe pressure drop (CEGB)

rect quantity of excess air at the right place. The introduction of effective CO-monitoring has eased the job of supplying the correct air considerably as discussed in Chapter 8 boiler efficiency. Supplying too much excess air will increase the dry flue gas loss. This is because the *quantity* of gas will increase, and so will the *heat content* as the excess air will absorb heat more readily than will the heat exchange surface, thus increasing the A/H outlet gas temperature.

However, quite apart from the quantity of air deliberately admitted to the boiler being other than optimum there is also the question of air inleakage to consider. Common locations are:

(a) suction milling plant;
(b) expansion seals on ducts, etc.;
(c) openings, such as viewing ports in boiler casings;
(d) ash hopper doors open;
(e) ash hopper seals, etc.

Such inleakage could result in the optimum CO being allied to a high O_2%, (low CO_2%). If serious air ingress is suspected a series of O_2 readings should be taken from boiler outlet to ID fan outlet, and the drops compared with optimum values.

Inleakage beyond the air heater outlet will not affect the boiler efficiency directly. However, if there is serious inleakage at, say, the ID fan inlet seal or precipitator rapping rod holes, then the effect will be to lower the gas temperature, increase the gas quantity and cause the ID fans to be fully loaded earlier than would otherwise be the case, and this would be a cause of load limitation.

6 Combustible material in ash

This subject was dealt with in some detail in Chapter 8, on boiler efficiency, so there is very little to add. Generally we take this material to be carbon in rough ash and carbon in dust. It is uneconomic to eliminate all of it and normally about 1.5% in dust is regarded as optimum when burning bituminous coal. Values lower than this are indicative of excessive milling, while higher values are indicative of:

(a) poor grinding;
(b) incorrect combustion air supplies;
(c) excessive air ingress to mill (suction mills);
(d) incorrect p.f. classifier setting.

Incidentally, 1.5% carbon in ash is the equivalent of about 0.5% boiler loss.

7 Air heater gas outlet temperature

Fuels contain various substances which can attack the metal of an air heater under certain circumstances, such as:

(a) *Water vapour*, which is derived from the original moisture in the fuel and also from the combustion of hydrogen in the fuel.

$$2H_2 + O_2 \rightarrow 2H_20$$

(b) *Sulphur*. Most fuels contain sulphur. It burns to sulphur dioxide (SO_2) and during its passage through the furnace some of the SO_2 is converted to SO_3. The SO_3 may combine with water vapour to form sulphuric acid.

$$2SO_2 + O_2 \rightarrow 2SO_3$$
$$SO_3 + H_2O \rightarrow H_2SO_4$$

(c) *Chlorides* are generally present in coal and are liberated during combustion. Under suitable conditions combination with hydrogen takes place and hydrogen chloride is formed. The hydrogen chloride may then combine with H_2O to form hydrochloric acid.

Therefore there is an economic balance to be struck between the minimum air heater outlet gas temperature (which will increase the boiler efficiency), and higher gas temperatures to prevent deposition of corrosive agents, which necessitate frequent air heater plate renewal. The optimum A/H gas outlet temperature is established by the manufacturers and it should be adhered to if at all possible.

Causes of low A/H gas outlet temperature

The most obvious cause of low temperature is lighting a cold boiler. This is made even worse by the fact that oil is usually being burned and this may condense on the A/H elements. Therefore it is advisable to bypass the A/H on the air and gas sides if possible until such time as the air heater temperature rise gradually permits normal operation.

Another common cause is excessive air leakage across the seals of rotary A/Hs. The rate of leakage varies as the square root of the pressure difference across the seals. Thus care should be taken to keep the seals intact as far as possible. Also, anything which leads to an increased differential pressure should be avoided if possible. Thus, running with a high windbox pressure will mean high air side pressure at the A/H. Boiler fouling will cause increased gas side suction, so either, or both, will increase the leakage across the seals. With seals in good condition on normal main air heaters the leakage is the equivalent of about 1% drop of CO_2 from inlet to outlet.

Causes of high A/H gas outlet temperature

The usual problem is one of high gas outlet temperature. The causes are many and varied, but the main ones are listed here:

1 Ineffective A/H sootblowers, thus the A/H elements become 'lagged' with dust.
2 Holed and torn elements, a particular problem at the cold-end plates because of corrosion.
3 Deposits on boiler heat transfer surfaces. Any covering on the combustion chamber walls or superheaters, etc. will cut down the amount of heat that

can be transferred. Consequently the gas temperature entering the A/H will be higher and so will the exit temperature.
4 Defective sootblowers will result in reduced heat transfer in discrete locations and the result will be as in (3).
5 High excess air increases the gas weight and also elevates the temperature. Of course, if the excess air is very high dilution effects may predominate and the gas temperature will fall.
6 Low final feed temperature has to be remedied by extra firing in the boiler and this will result in high exit gas temperature.
7 Defective baffles and gas bypass dampers are a constant problem where fitted, due to warping and difficulties of locating the baffles.
8 Poor milling and poor combustion result in long burn-off times and result in high gas temperatures at furnace exit in addition to fouling.
9 Using high rows of burners on low loads. Sometimes it may be necessary to use higher burners than desired, but the result will be to elevate the final gas temperature.
10 Passing A/H bypass dampers.
11 Air recirculation damper open. This results in a lower mean temperature difference between gas and air sides and so reduces the heat transfer.
12 Air inleakage before the combustion chamber.

Generally speaking a final gas temperature of about 20°C above the optimum will result in a boiler efficiency loss of 1.0%.

8 Make-up

On modern plants the quality of the make-up water is extremely high, and it follows that it is, therefore, quite expensive. Even so, that is not the main reason for wishing to keep the make-up quantity as low as possible. It is that the make-up is replacing water and steam which have been lost from the system and contain considerable quantities of heat. For the purpose of calculations it is assumed that two-thirds of the make-up is replacing steam lost at boiler stop valve conditions and that one-third is replacing water lost at final feedwater conditions.

There are four usual sources of loss:

(a) *Sootblowng*

If this is carried out too often heat is wasted. If it is not carried out often enough the heat transfer surfaces may become heavily coated and heat transfer will be reduced, and thus the final gas temperature will rise. Hence, there must be some optimum interval between sootblows, but just what it may be difficult to determine. The basic problem is that sootblowing affects both boiler efficiency and boiler availability.

An expression for the heat loss due to carrying out sootblowing is:

$$\text{Loss} = \frac{\text{Heat lost to S/B steam}}{\text{Heat given to TSV steam} + \text{heat given to R/H steam}}$$

$$\text{i.e. loss} = 0.25\,Q_S + \frac{Q_S\,(h_1 - h_5)}{(h_2 - h_5) + Q_R\,(h_4 - h_3)}$$

where Q_S = sootblowing steam as a percentage of TSV steam flow.
Q_R = reheat steam flow as a fraction of TSV steam flow.
h_1 = total heat of steam at A/H gas outlet temperature and pressure.
h_2 = total heat of steam at TSV conditions.
h_4 = total heat of steam before reheater
h_4 = total heat of steam after reheater
h_5 = heat in final feed water

The term $0.25\,Q_S$ is the approximate loss due to raising the temperature of the cold make-up water to final feed temperature.

For example, a test was carried out on a 350 MW unit from which it was determined that the sootblowing steam consumption was about 1.2% of the TSV steam flow. So $Q_S = 1.2$.

Hence loss due to sootblowing (using data for the unit):

$$= (0.25 \times 1.2) + \frac{1.2\,(2737 - 1087)}{(3500 - 1087) + 0.796\,(3603 - 3166)}$$

$$= 1.26\%$$

For operational purposes it is convenient to determine some reference temperature (say, gas temperature leaving the primary superheater) and commence sootblowing when it reaches a certain value, allowance being made for boiler loading. The alternative of blowing at preset times (say once per shift) has little to commend it except convenience.

As a matter of interest, the quantity of steam required for a complete sootblow for a 120 MW unit is about 10 300 kg, and for a 350 MW unit it is about 48 000 kg. The Drakelow 375 MW supercritical units are supplied with such high-quality water that it was decided that it was not economic to use it for sootblowing. Consequently two auxiliary boilers were installed to supply various services to the main plant including sootblowing steam.

One of the main parameters that determines the frequency of sootblowing is the ash content of the fuel. The results of tests on a particular boiler gave a relationship as shown in *Figure 14.18*.

(b) *Boiler blowdown*

This is very wasteful in terms of loss of heat, but is often necessary. Care

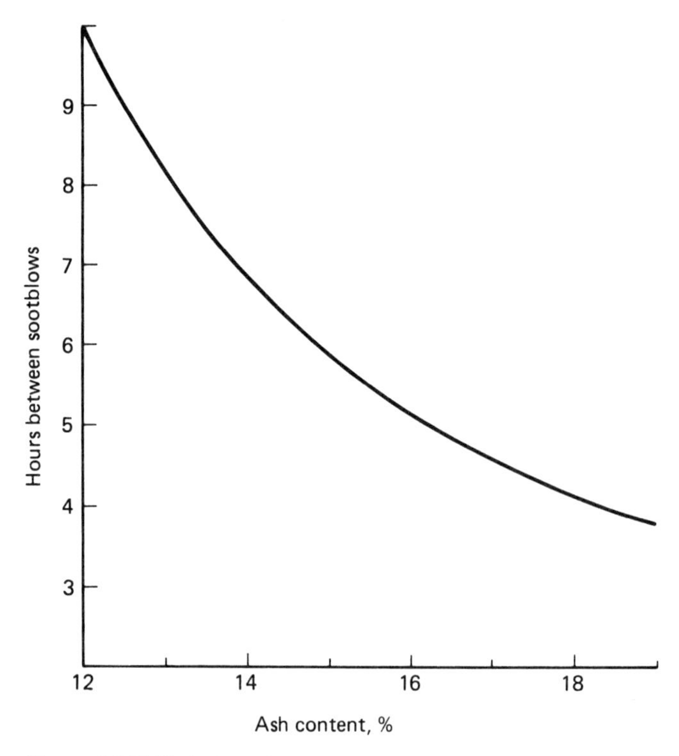

Figure 14.18 Variation of sootblowing interval with ash content

should be taken to prevent dust getting into items of plant while being repaired, e.g. feed pumps, feed heaters, etc. as the dust probably has a significant silica content. It will require a blowdown programme to get rid of it once it gets into the feedwater. The Station Chemist will determine what blowdown, if any, is required. Whatever duration he requests should be adhered to – no more and no less.

The requirement is approximately:

$$\text{Blowdown} = \frac{100\,B\%}{A - B} \text{ of total evaporation}$$

where A = dissolved solids concentration in the feedwater, ppm.
B = maximum permissible concentration in the boiler water, ppm.

(c) *Passing valves and leaks*

Water will leak from a given size opening at a greater rate than steam, as shown by *Table 14.5*. Notice that doubling the size of the hole increases the loss by four times. Of course one would not expect to find a hole of 2.5

Table 14.5 Leakage loss

Dia. of hole (c.m.)	Steam (kg/h)		Water (kg/h)	
	7 bar	20 bar	1.5 bar	7 bar
0.2	7	17	10	23
0.3	28	66	40	90
0.5	63	150	90	200
0.6	112	265	160	360
2.5	1790	4225	2560	5760

cm diameter, but it should be remembered that several small holes will quickly add up to the equivalent of a large one.

Valves passing water or steam to waste are very troublesome. Particularly serious are such items as passing feed line drains, steam traps, safety valves, blow down valves, etc. In other words, those which can pass substantial quantities of very hot substance for long periods of time.

(d) *Tanks overflowing to waste*

Storage tanks, such as RFTs, often have their overflows piped to waste. Thus, if they should overflow considerable quantities of water can be lost without it being particularly obvious. Fortunately the water is not normally very hot. On the other hand the lost water necessitates make-up and this is assumed to be replacing steam and hot water as mentioned earlier.

At a particular 'range' station which shut down at night, the central evaporators were left in service overnight and the RFTs were made up to 3 metres. It was known from experience that with this depth of water the level would rise to 4 metres when the machines were brought up to full load in the morning, i.e. just below the overflow level. Had any more water been put into the tanks during the night it would merely have overflowed to waste the next morning.

It is desirable to have alarms fitted to give warning of overflow of high quality water to waste.

9 Works power

Of all the industries (heavy engineering, shipbuilding, iron and steel, etc.) the one that consumes by far the most electricity is the electricity supply industry itself. Every megawatt of unnecessary works power used by a high merit station means that its output to the grid is reduced by the same amount and must be made good by the running stations at the bottom end of the 'order of merit' table. The cost of 1 MW extra works power at a high merit station could cost about £40,000 per year. There are six main contributors to excess works power:

(a) *Machine loading*

As load is reduced on a unit the required amount of works power falls. However, the *percentage* works power rises as shown in *Figure 14.19*. The

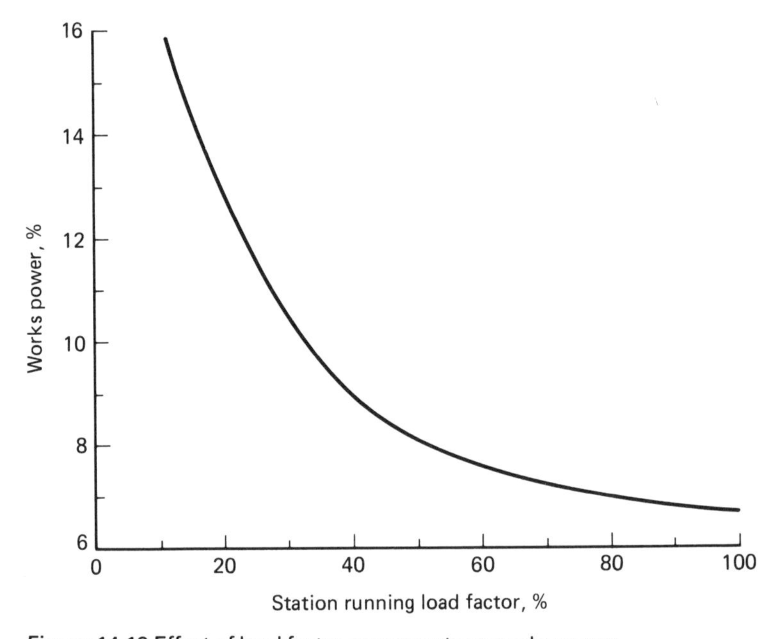

Figure 14.19 Effect of load factor on percentage works power

curve shows the optimum value. In practice, as loading is reduced it is common to leave, say, five mills in service partly loaded rather than four mills fully loaded. Also CW pumps should be operated only in accordance with optimization curves so that the benefit derived from running the pump is greater than the cost of running it.

(b) *Variable-speed drives*

The power consumption of variable-speed drives varies as the cube of the speed, so doubling the speed requires eight times the power. Hence, whenever a variable-speed pump or fan is in service it should be operated at the lowest speed which will do the job. For example, the feedwater regulator differential should be kept at its optimum value at all times so that the feed pump speed can be kept as low as possible. Similarly, the ID fans should not be put into high speed until it is difficult to hold the combustion chamber under suction in low speed. Often ID fans are operated in high speed continuously because the air inleakage to the boiler is so great – the remedy is to stop the inleakage.

(c) *Parallel operation of auxiliaries*

Two pumps in parallel will *not* give twice the output of one pump. In fact it is quite common for the second pump to give only a marginal increase. The reason is illustrated in *Figure 14.20.* With one pump only in service

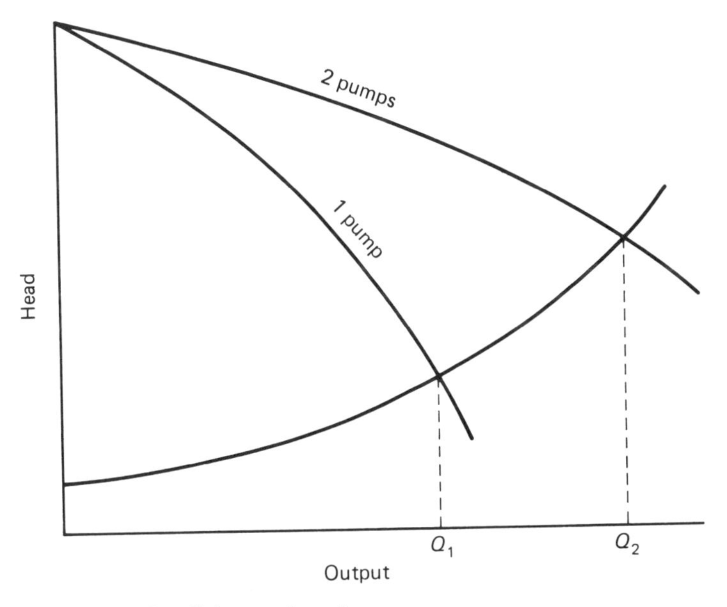

Figure 14.20 Parallel operation of pumps

the output would be Q_1. With two in parallel it would increase to Q_2 which, in the case considered, would be an extra 35% output approximately. To obtain this extra output it is necessary to sustain the no-load losses of the second pump and these can be considerable. *Table 14.6* lists

Table 14.6

Item	*Power consumption (kW)* *No-load*	*Full load*	*No-load % of full load*
CW pump	1600	2460	61
Dust pump	9	18	50
CW MU pump	194	254	76

a few pumps selected at random. It is seen that the no-load power consumption is often more than 50% of the full-load power. The moral is clear – never run an extra auxiliary unless it is genuinely required. Also remember that the extra output obtained by running it may not be as much as expected at first sight.

(d) *Milling plant power consumption*

For some years now pressure mills have been standard on new plant. In general the power consumption of one type of mill compared with another (including mill, feeder and fans) is approximately, in kW/tonne of coal milled:

Low-speed ball (suction)	22.8
Medium-speed (pressure)	16.5
Medium-speed (suction)	19.2
High-speed (suction)	19.5

The mill classifier should be kept at a setting which will give an acceptable but not uneconomic grading. Thus, by reducing the separator speed on an LM 16 mill from 120 to 100 rev/min, the coal throughput was increased by 2 tonne/h without seriously affecting the grading.

The drying capability is sometimes a limiting factor with regard to mill output. *Figure 14.21* illustrates a typical case where maximum output is

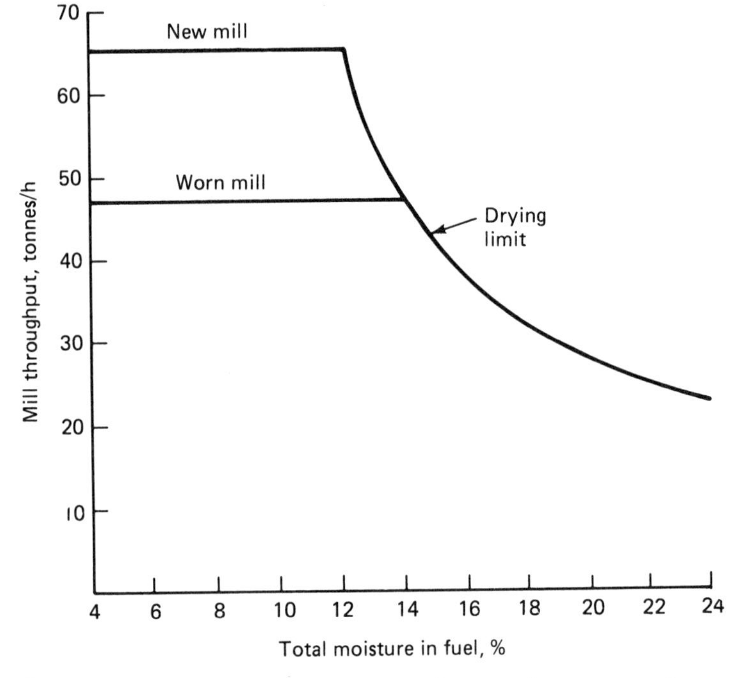

Figure 14.21 Typical mill throughput *vs* moisture performance graph

possible with a mill up to a certain moisture content in the coal. In the case shown it is about 12% for a mill in new condition. Any additional moisture will result in a reduction of load capability. For example, at 16%

moisture the mill throughput capability will be only about 40 t/h compared with over 60 t/h with 12% moisture. With suction mills a common cause of reduced drying capability is excessive air ingress. Every effort should be made to reduce such tramp air to a minimum. On a medium-speed, vertical-spindle mill for example, the tramp air should be less than 10% of the air leaving the mill, but values of 30% and even higher are not uncommon.

(e) *Power consumption of minor auxiliaries*

The majority of motor-driven items of equipment in a power station are of modest proportions, and so attention to these can result in substantial savings. Try to operate the plant with only one 50% rotary air pump in service. Stop the air leaks on the general air service system so that the compressors are normally operating in the de-loaded state. Never fill a boiler via the feed pump, but only via the boiler filling pump. When units are shut down or on survey, isolate all possible minor auxiliaries.

Leaks from the air system were mentioned above, so it may be of interest to note how much air can leak through a hole. Suppose the system is charged to a pressure of 5.5 bar (which is common). Then the loss in cubic metres of 'free' air per minute is:

Dia. of hole (cm)	*Loss (m^3/min)*
0.16	0.1
0.32	0.5
0.48	1.0
0.64	1.9

So a hole 0.5 cm in diameter would allow about 1500 m^3 of free air leakage per day.

The scope for savings of works power is obviously considerable. Probably on every unit *some* savings are possible, and on many the possible savings are considerable.

(f) *Optimizing auxiliary power consumption*

The auxiliary power consumption in a large station could be of the order of 40 MW or more. Therefore, it is important to ensure that it is kept as near to optimum as possible. This is particularly important where large auxiliary plant is involved. For example, CW pumps should be run only when the running cost is outweighed by the benefit derived by the extra output from the main unit. In other words the pump operation should be optimized. A method of doing this is as follows:

Consider a station which has one unit and two CW pumps which can be operated in parallel. Obviously, at least one CW pump must be in service whenever the plant is on load – the question is, 'When is it economic to put the second pump into service?'

Suppose the full-load back pressure correction curve for the unit is that shown in *Figure 14.22*. Then at 43 mbar back pressure the turbine heat

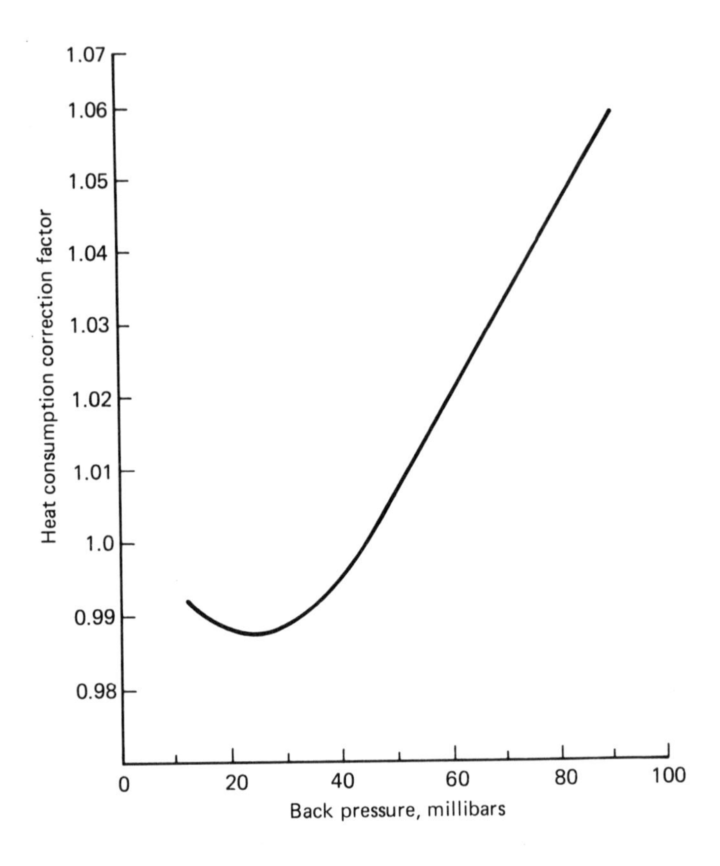

Figure 14.22 Back pressure correction curve for full load

consumption will be at optimum (assuming all the other turbine parameters are at optimum besides the back pressure). At 60 mbar the heat consumption will be 1.018 times the optimum value, whereas at 20 mbar it will be 0.988 times, and so on.

So if the turbine optimum full-load heat consumption is 880 GJ/h at a back pressure of 43 mbar, it will be 896 GJ/h at 60 mbar and 869 GJ/h at 20 mbar. Proceeding in this manner the heat consumption corresponding to any back pressure can be determined. Similarly, if the boiler efficiency is known, the boiler heat input can be determined for any back pressure. For example, if the boiler efficiency is 88.0% and it is assumed that the efficiency does not change for the range of back pressures, then the boiler input heats will be:

Back pressure (mbar)	*Turbine heat (GJ/h)*	*Boiler heat (GJ/h)*
20	869	987.5
43	880	1000.0
60	896	1018.2

Proceeding in this manner an auxiliary scale can be constructed for *Figure 14.22* so that the boiler heat input can be read-off for any back pressure, as has been done on *Figure 14.23*.

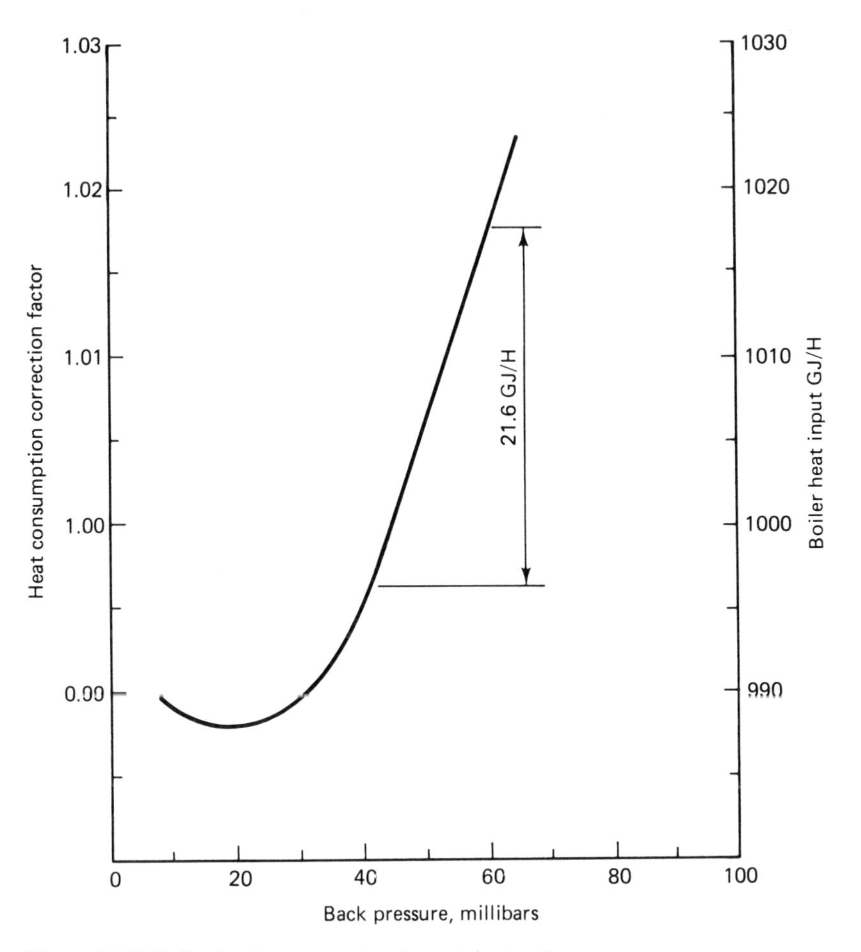

Figure 14.23 Boiler heat consumption for various back pressures

Now, here we are concerned with the improved back pressure which results from running an extra CW pump. Therefore the operation of the pump will be economic only if the heat consumption of the pump motor is equal to, or less than, the heat savings which accrue from the lower back pressure.

Assume the pump brake power is 1500 kW and the motor efficiency is 96%, then the motor input power will be 1500/0.96 = 1562 kW.

However, this power is part of the station works power and if it had not been used to drive the CW pump it would have been available to be sent out to the consumers. As it is not available to consumers, the equivalent amount of power must be supplied by a station lower down the Order of Merit Table, i.e. a higher-cost station. Therefore, running the CW pump should be debited against the higher cost plant which will be assumed to have an efficiency of 26%.

$$\text{Therefore the CW pump heat} = \frac{1562\ \text{kW} \times 3600}{0.26} = 21.6\ \text{GJ/h}$$

Thus, the back pressure improvement necessary to justify running the pump should at least give a reduced boiler heat input of 21.6 GJ/h.

For example, from *Figure 14.23* it can be seen that at 60 mbar it is necessary to improve the back pressure at least to 41 mbar to justify running an extra pump. Proceeding in a similar manner, a series of critical back pressure changes can be determined as shown in *Table 14.7*.

Table 14.7 Critical back pressure change for CW pump operation

Initial back pressure (mbar)	*Final back pressure (mbar)*
62.0	43.0
60.0	41.0
57.0	36.0
55.0	30.0
53.0	20.0

Plotting the values shown in *Table 14.7* enables a curve to be established of critical changes as shown in *Figure 14.24* for use by the operations staff.

10 Unit loading

The efficiency of a *unit* improves as the loading improves. The curve reproduced in *Figure 14.25 is* that for a 120 MW unit at the time of the acceptance tests. It follows that one way to achieve high efficiencies is to run at very high load factors. Hence shortfalls should be kept to an absolute minimum. Even

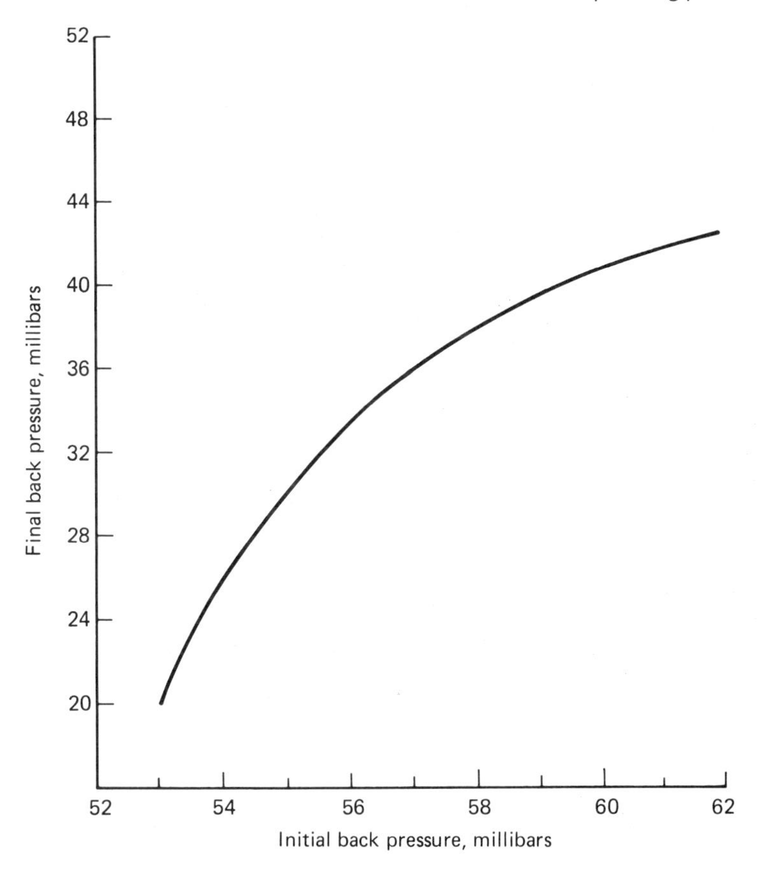

Figure 14.24 Critical back pressure change to justify running an extra CW pump

for mid-merit plant this is important. If they are running at part load it is even more important for them because a small improvement results in a much larger efficiency improvement than at high loads.

The efficiency of T/As improves with load, as shown in *Table 14.8* for

Table 14.8

Capacity (MW)	*Generated efficiency*		
	100% load	*80% load*	*60% load*
60	39.06	38.29	36.89
120	42.49	41.81	40.57
350	45.01	44.43	43.19

some typical throttle-governed machines. This is illustrated by the graph of heat consumption against loading as shown in *Figure 14.26*. The graph is a straight line for throttle-governed turbines, and cuts the *Y*-axis at about 7%

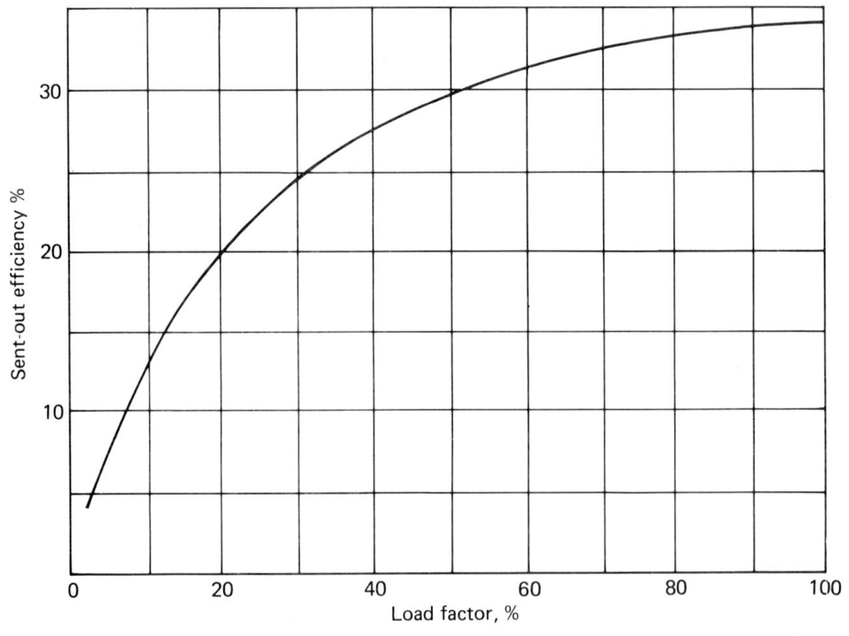

Figure 14.25 Effect of load factor on efficiency

of full-load heat when the loading is zero. This heat has to be sustained at all loads, and consequently it is called the *fixed heat*. The heat required for a change of load is represented by the *slope* of the line. As the line is straight it follows that the heat required for an incremental change of load at lower loads is the same as that at higher loads, and is known as the *incremental heat.*

So heat consumption at any load = Fixed heat ÷ (incremental heat × load)

It follows that it is most important that every possible megawatt should be generated while on high loads. If the machine is supposed to be on full load then every effort should be made to avoid shortfalls. On the other hand, over-generation is very attractive in terms of improved efficiency *provided there are no other limitations* and the Grid Control Engineers do not object. Obviously, if a few hours' operation at overload results in a fouled boiler then it is just not economic to attempt to produce the extra output.

One important way of preventing shortfalls is to ensure that the boiler pressure is controlled by the fuel supply – not, as is so often done, by varying the load on the T/A.

On-load monitoring

The advent of measuring devices with electrical outputs for almost all of the

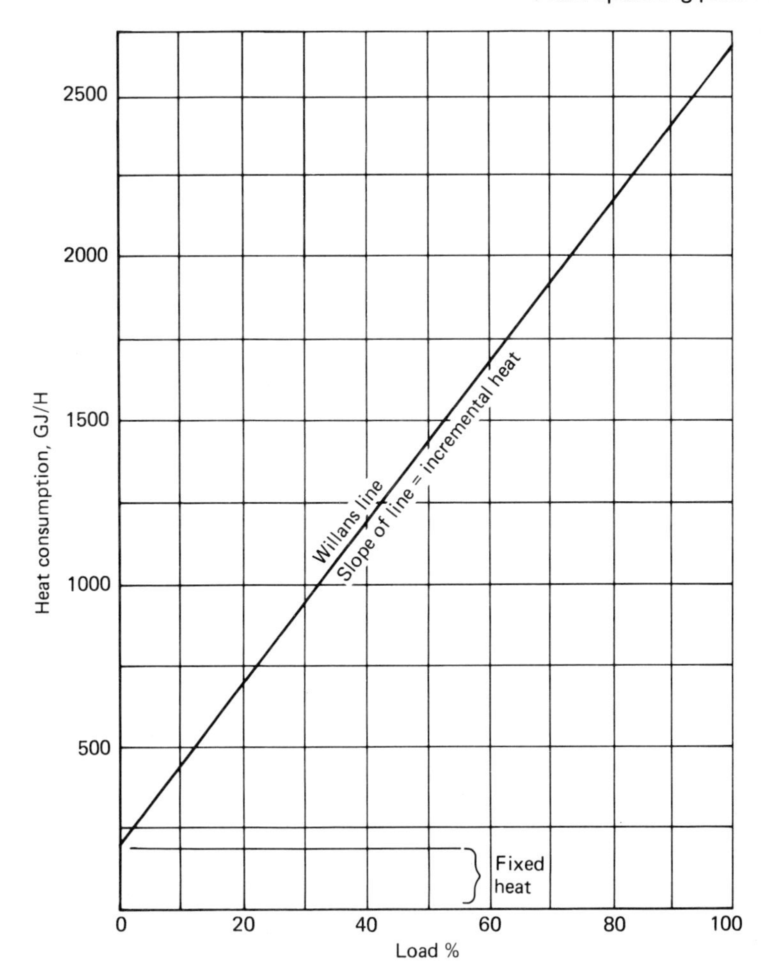

Figure 14.26 Willans line for turbo-alternator

main parameters on a power station unit has made comprehensive on-load monitoring possible. The main items which cannot be so measured are the calorific value of the fuel, the moisture content of coal and the combustible-in-ash loss. Actually the two last named can now be measured quite quickly and in the immediate future it will probably be possible to monitor them continuously. The demand for comprehensive monitoring equipments will probably never be sufficient to make it economic for commercial firms to market them. However, all the components are readily available and so it is easy to design one's own monitoring system.

The automatic data analysis for plant testing (Adapt) system

This is an on-line system assembled by a test team in the Midlands Region of the CEGB. The system is flexible and the boiler, turbine or both can be monitored. It is computer based with facilities for scanning, checking and recording the test information. The results are automatically calculated quickly and then presented graphically. Consequently if the equipment is left on line for several hours the variations of the selected parameters with time can be displayed. *Figure 14.27* shows a typical result, the variations of

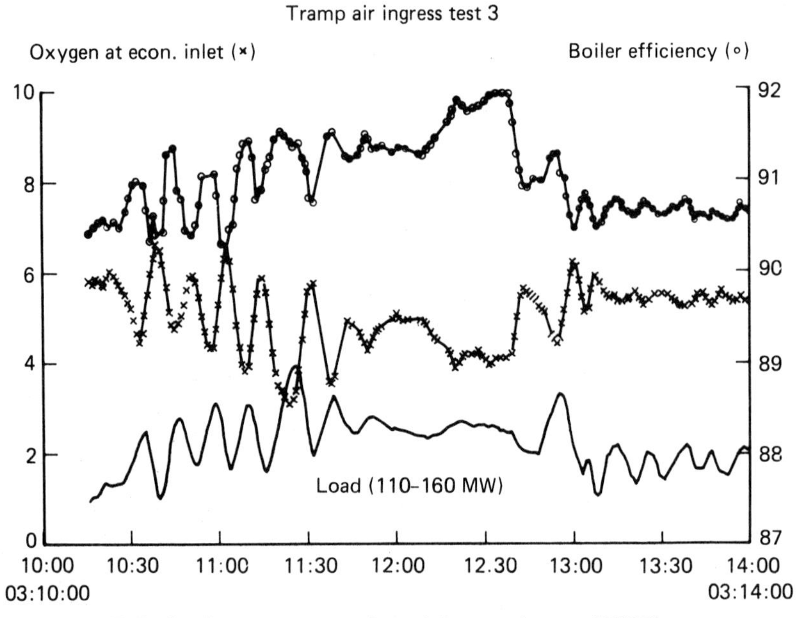

Figure 14.27 Typical parameter trace from Adapt equipment (CEGB)

oxygen at economizer inlet and boiler efficiency with loading, over a six-hour period. One big advantage from the use of this equipment is that it enables on-load optimization to be carried out. For example, *Figure 14.28* shows how the inleakage of a boiler changed with pressure.

The layout of the equipment is shown in *Figure 14.29*. It consists of several remote data aquisition cabinets located at convenient points around the plant to which the outputs of the various sensors are fed. The cabinets contain up to three scanners, a digital voltmeter and an extender. The purpose of the extenders is to convert the data and control information to 'bit-serial' form so that it can be transmitted along a co-axial cable of up to one kilometre in length. The controller is a computer with keyboard, graphics screen and printer. The tape drives provide storage for programmes and data and the discs will hold 240 scans of data.

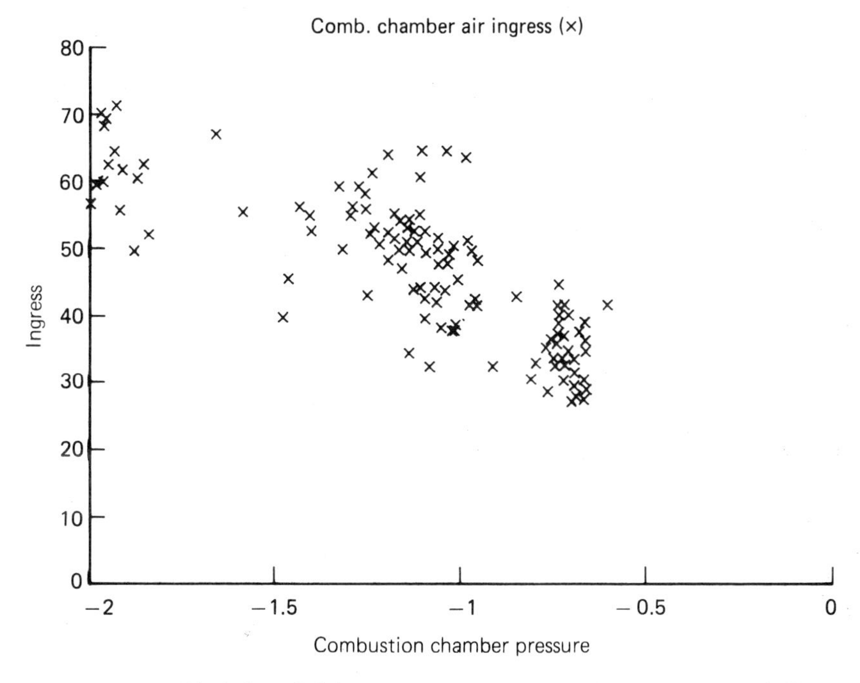

Figure 14.28 Variation of air ingress with combustion chamber pressure (CEGB)

The 'Thermal' system

The largest single loss in a power station is of heat from the steam which is transferred to the CW. *Table 14.9* shows typical losses for a 500 MW turbo-alternator.

Table 14.9

Item		*Heat (GJ/h)*	*Loss (%)*
1	Heat to turbine	4000	100.0
2	Radiation	12	0.3
3	Electrical Auxiliaries	16	0.4
4	Make-up	20	0.5
5	Hydrogen, bearing and transformer coolers	36	0.9
6	Heat to CW in condenser	2180	54.5
	Total loss	2264	56.6

If the heat given to the CW could be measured accurately the turbo-alternator efficiency could easily be determined. Item (2), the radiation loss, will not vary much. Item (3) can be accurately metered and (4) and (5)

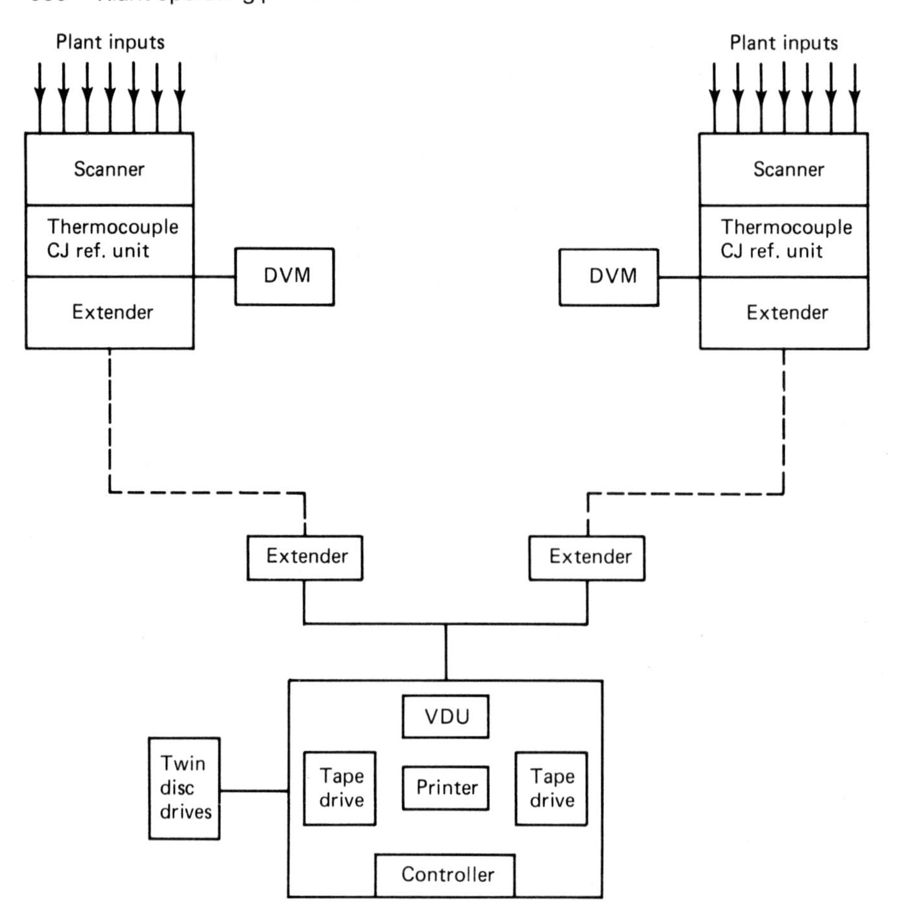

Figure 14.29 Data acquisition and analysis system

estimated closely. Further, because items (2) to (5) inclusive are of small magnitude, errors in their determination will not significantly alter the final result.

Investigations within the CEGB have led to the development of a technique whereby the heat given to the CW can be continuously measured to an acceptable degree of accuracy. It is known as the 'Thermal' system, the name being derived from Turbine HEat Rate Monitoring by Assessment of Losses. The system is described in an Institution of Mechanical Engineers' paper entitled 'Development of a turbine-generator thermal performance monitoring system', by Z.W. Sochaczewski, C.A.E. Clay and J.A. Morris, (Proceedings vol. 195, No. 31). The equipment is shown in *Figure 14.30.*

The principle of operation depends upon transmitting acoustic energy forwards and backwards in an angled direction across the CW pipe and measuring the time of travel. The flowrate of the CW can be determined to an accuracy of better than $\pm 1\%$ and the temperature to $\pm 0.1°C$.

Figure 14.30(a) 'Thermal system. Sensing heads inserted in CW pipe (CEGB)

Figures 14.31 and *14.32* show the results of some early laboratory work. This represents a very significant advance in turbo-alternator efficiency monitoring. With it the efficiency can be determined continuously and the effect of changes of plant parameters shown immediately. For example, operation at other than optimum steam conditions, heaters out of service, bled-steam boiler feed-pump turbine out of service, variations of back pressure, etc. can all be assessed readily.

This equipment is quite cheap and a future development may be to install it on all the main turbines on a system. The results can then be transmitted continuously and automatically to the System Control Centre and so computerized merit order loading will be possible.

Shift monitoring

Small programmable machines are now available very cheaply which are ideal for shift monitoring to provide information for the operations staff. A

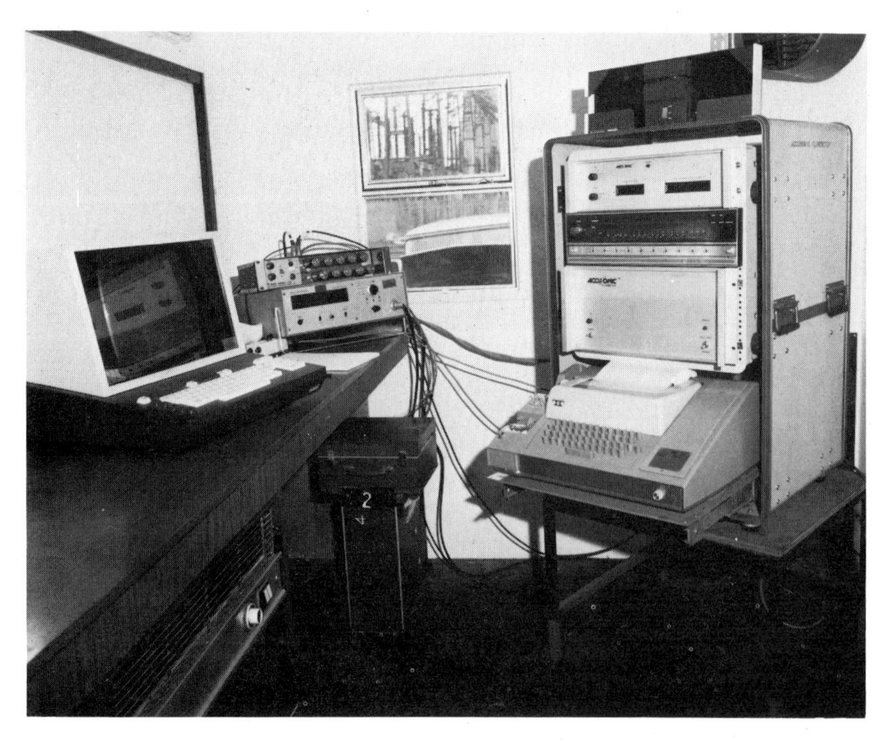

Figure 14.30(b) 'Thermal system. Processing equipment (CEGB)

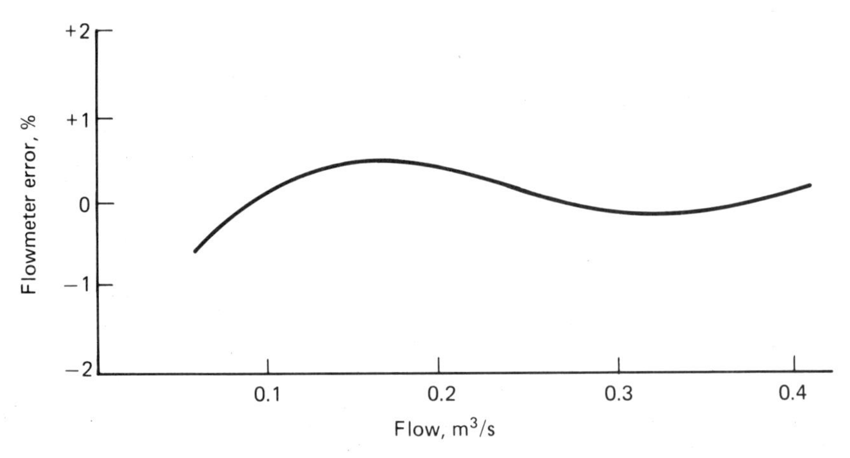

Figure 14.31 Accuracy of CW heat determination using an acoustic flowmeter— accuracy of flow measurement (CEGB)

typical installation consists of a programmed machine with a visual display. The idea is to compare the main unit control parameters (steam temperature and pressure; back pressure; A/H gas outlet temperature, etc.) with the

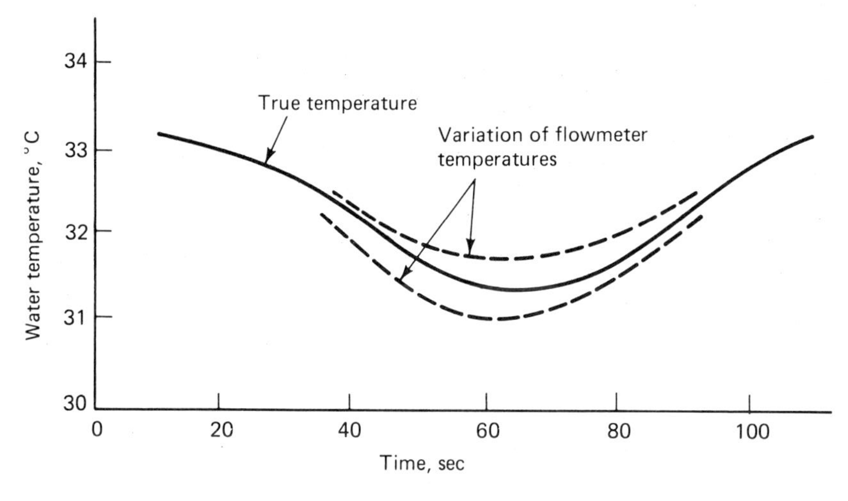

Figure 14.32 Accuracy of temperature determination (CEGB)

optimum values and cost any deviation. Also the efficiency is displayed, allowance being made in the programmes for those items too difficult or impossible to measure. The input to the machine can either be keyed or be fed automatically from the control room instrumentation, the latter being preferred. The inputs are averaged for a preset time, say five minutes, and then the losses and efficiency are displayed. The general layout is shown in *Figure 14.33*.

Questions

1 What are the terminal conditions that should be monitored as a routine?
2 Does the efficiency of a unit improve when the back pressure increases?
3 How does the output of a throttle-governed turbine vary with ATV pressure?
4 Does the available heat increase with throttling?
5 Is throttle governing more efficient for part loading of a turbine? Why?
6 What is sliding pressure operation?
7 What precautions should be taken before implementing sliding pressure control
8 List some typical causes of excessive make-up.
9 List some typical causes of excessive works power.
10 How would you determine the critical back-pressure change to justify running an extra CW pump?
11 Why does the reserve feed tank level rise when a boiler is brought from light load to full load?

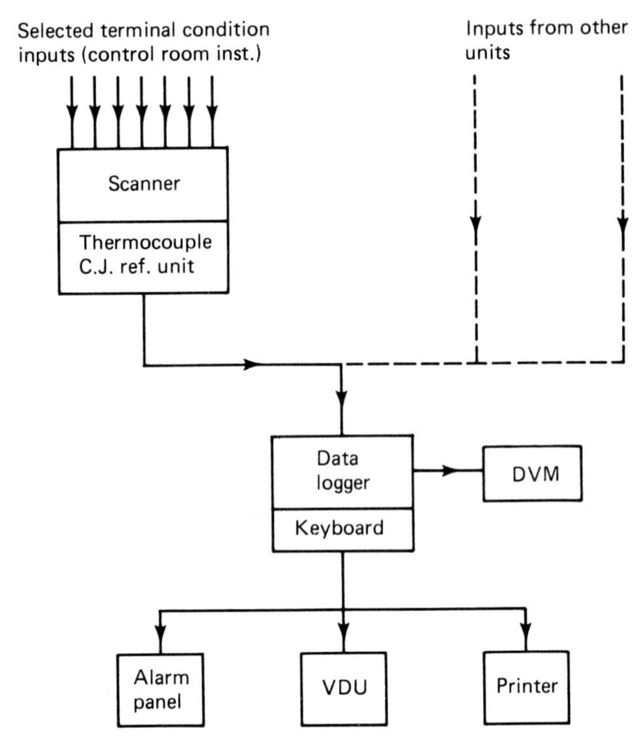

Figure 14.33 Shift control monitoring (Schematic)

Exercise 1

A 120 MW unit was returned to service after survey. It was found that its load capability was only 119 MW with normal steam conditions. Describe the actions you would take to determine the reason for the limitation.

Exercise 1 (Answer)

1 Check the vectormeter accuracy. (This was done by recording the meter over a half-hour while the unit was on steady load and comparing it with the integrator.)
2 Check the output of the unit with the throttle and stop valves full open and steam pressure and temperature indications at optimum.
3 Check pressure drop across the steam strainers.
4 Check the accuracy of the steam pressure gauges and the steam temperature indicators.

If all the above are satisfactory, something inside the turbine is probably the cause of the limitation. Check the back-pressure indication. If this is satisfactory carry out a turbine pressure survey and HP and IP cylinder efficiencies.

In the actual case mentioned the cause of the limitation was that the pressure gauge indication was incorrect. The critical gauge is operated by a signal from the boiler stop valve pressure Bourdon gauge situated at firing-floor level. The static head on this was the equivalent of 3.5 bar and so it should have been calibrated 'slow' by that amount. However, when it was checked during the survey, such calibration was omitted. Hence the critical pressure gauge indicated 3.5 bar high upon return to service of the unit, resulting in the shortfall.

Project 1

On a 375 MW unit trouble is being experienced due to a reheater safety valve lifting at loadings above 314 MW, if one bank of the No. 4 and 8 HP heaters trips while the bled-steam turbine is out of service (see *Figure 14.34*). The associated data is:

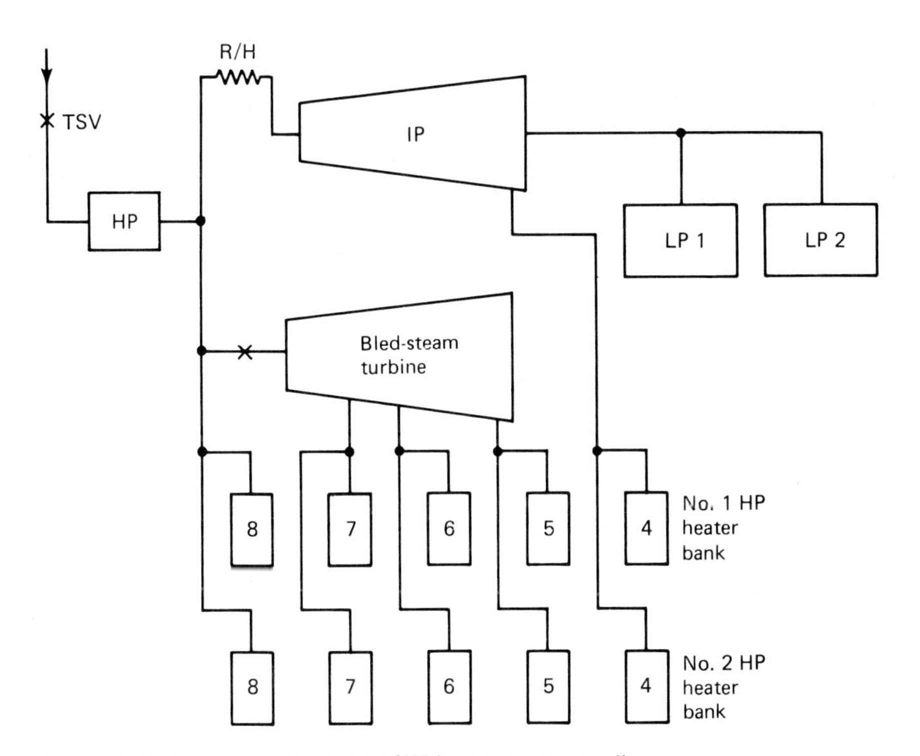

Figure 14.34 Diagrammatic layout of HP heater steam supplies

HP cylinder exhaust pressure at 375 MW = 52 bar abs.
Extra steam flow at 314 MW if the heaters trip = 21% of TSV flow (i.e. BS turbine o/c + 4 and 8 heaters in bank)
Reheater safety valve blow-off pressure = 55 bar abs.

Is the fact that the safety valve lifts indicative of something wrong on the plant or is it to be expected under the stated conditions?

Project 1 (Answer)

HP cylinder exhaust pressure at 375 MW = 52 bar abs.

So HP cylinder exhaust pressure at 314 MW $= \dfrac{314 \times 52}{375} = 43.6$ bar abs.

If the heater bank should trip, the steam that would have been bled to the heaters will flow through the IP and LP turbines. This extra flow will be equal to 21% of the TSV flow and so the pressure at the HP cylinder exhaust will rise by a factor of

$$\frac{100}{100 - 21} = 1.26$$

So the HP exhaust pressure will increase to:
43.6 bar × 1.26 = 54.9, say 55 bar abs.

This is comparable to the safety valve blow-off pressure. Therefore, the safety valve operation being experienced is in accord with what one would expect.

Additional Reading

1 FENTON, K., *Thermal Efficiency and Power Production*, Pitman
2 WADDINGTON, J., and MAPLES, C.C., 'The control of large coal and oil fired generating units', *CEGB Research*, no. 14 (February 1983)
3 ROUGHTON, J.E., 'A proposed on-line efficiency method for pulverised coal fired boilers', *J. Inst. Energy* (March 1980)
4 SOCHACZEWSKI, Z.W., CLAY, C.E.A. and MORRIS, J.A., 'Development of a turbine-generator thermal performance monitoring system', *Proc I Mech E*, **195**, No. 31 (1981)

15 Economics of outages

Items of plant, such as air heaters and condensers, often foul progressively and so sooner or later the unit must be taken out of service for cleaning to be carried out. The cost to the undertaking of an outage can be considerable if high-merit (i.e. low cost of electricity per unit sent out from the station), plant is considered. For example, in the UK a large unit could cost over £150,000 per day to replace with the equivalent electrical output from lower-merit plant. This generation replacement cost varies with such things as the time of year, the cost per unit sent out of the plant concerned, system demand and so on. Normally it is uneconomic to take high-merit plant off load just to carry out efficiency improvements. On the other hand outages occur for other reasons such as boiler tube failures, and so these offer the opportunity to carry out work to improve efficiency, such as condenser cleaning, without incurring generation replacement costs, as they will be debited to the primary cause of the outage.

There must be some optimum time to clean fouled heat exchange surfaces. If cleaning is carried out too early the cost will be greater than the resultant savings. If it is carried out too late the cost of the fouling will be greater than the cost of cleaning. Consequently the ideal time to clean is when the cost of cleaning equals the cost of fouling.

Optimization of cleaning periods

Plant does not normally foul at a uniform rate, but rather as shown in *Figure 15.1* The rate of increase of fouling cost is a maximum in the initial stages and becomes progressively less as the fouling continues. In a way this is analogous to the economics of lagging hot pipes – the first thin coating of lagging has the greatest effect, and that obtained from subsequent layers becomes less.

The precise form of the fouling curve shown in *Figure 15.1* will vary with different items of plant and different circumstances and so its derivation is quite difficult. Fortunately, though, tests have shown that very little

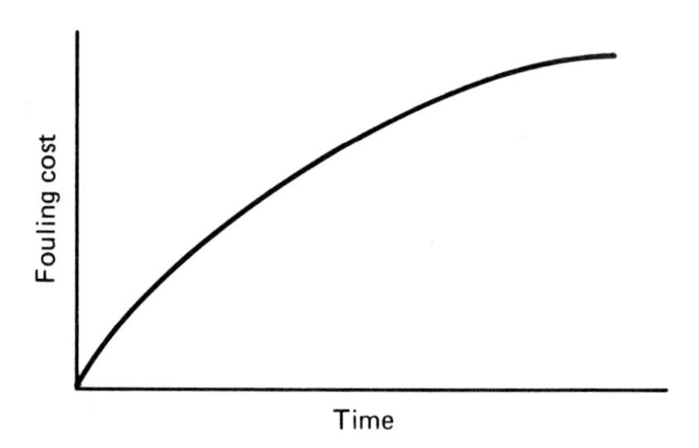

Figure 15.1 Actual fouling curve

accuracy is lost by considering the rate of fouling to be uniform as shown in *Figure 15.2*. The rate of fouling is denoted by R, thus the units of R will be £/h/h. So at any time t hours, the fouling cost in £/h at that time will be given by $R \times t$.

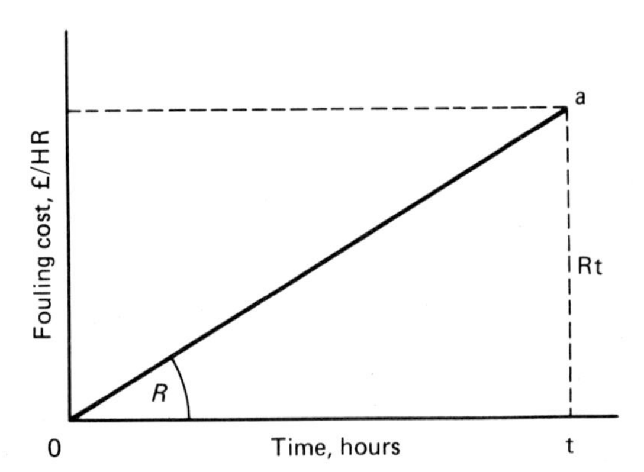

Figure 15.2 Assumed fouling curve

For example, if R = £0.05/h/h then after 200 hours the fouling cost will be 0.05×200 = £10/h. However, the cost at any one time is not particularly important – what is important is the *cumulative* cost of the fouling. In the case just considered the fouling cost has gone from zero at $t = 0$ to £10/h at $t = 200$, and so the cumulative cost is represented by the area of the triangle $0at$.

But $at = Rt$ so the area is given by $\dfrac{Rt \times t}{2} = \dfrac{Rt^2}{2}$

So the cumulative fouling cost for the case considered earlier is given by:

$$\frac{Rt^2}{2} = \frac{0.05 \times 200^2}{2} = £1\ 000$$

As stated earlier, the ideal time to clean the item is when the cost of cleaning equals the cumulative fouling cost, i.e.

$$\text{when total cleaning cost } C = \frac{Rt^2}{2}$$

Included in the cleaning cost may be items such as:

generation replacement cost;
cost of materials;
cost of labour, etc.

$$\text{Thus, the optimum time } t \text{ is found from } C = \frac{Rt^2}{2}$$

$$\text{or } t = \sqrt{\left(\frac{2C}{R}\right)}$$

where t is the running time in hours
C is the total cleaning cost in pounds
R is the rate of change of fouling cost in £/h/h

For example, in the case previously considered, suppose the cleaning cost is £500.

$$\text{Then } t = \sqrt{\left(\frac{2 \times 500}{0.05}\right)} \quad \textbf{141 hours}$$

Example

Consider the fouling of a 375 MW unit condenser. Assume the average running load over the period since the last clean to be 300 MW. From the manufacturers' curves it is concluded that the variation in heat to the unit is 0.1% per mbar change of back pressure. The average cost of fuel is 96.5 pence per gigajoule and the efficiency 32.0%.

$$\therefore \text{The cost of 1 mbar variation} = \frac{300\,000 \text{ kW} \times 3600}{0.32} \times \frac{96.5\text{p}}{10^6} \times \frac{0.1}{100} \times \frac{1}{100}$$

$$= £3.25/\text{h}$$

So if the back pressure worsens by 1 mbar per 100 hours, then

$$R = \frac{3.25}{100} = £0.0325/\text{h/h}$$

A table can now be constructed to cover a range of fouling rates, and a range of cleaning costs can be included (see *Table 15.1*). For example, if

Table 15.1

Rate of deterioration		Total cost of clean, 'C' £		
mbar(100h)	*R (£/h/h)*	50,000	25,000	2,000
			Optimum time t (h)	
5	0.1625	784	554	157
10	0.3250	555	392	110
20	0.6500	392	277	78
30	0.9750	320	226	64
40	1.3000	277	196	55
50	1.6250	248	175	50

generation replacement costs are included, a certain cleaning cost will result. If only part GR costs are included (say most of the clean is done during the time the unit is off for boiler repairs and only a small extension of the outage is required for completion of cleaning) the cost will be less, and if no GR costs are incurred it will be less still. So assume total cleaning costs for the three cases will be £50,000; £25,000; £2,000.
These results are shown in graphical form in *Figure 15.3*, from which the optimum time *t* can be determined for any degree of fouling and any cleaning cost.

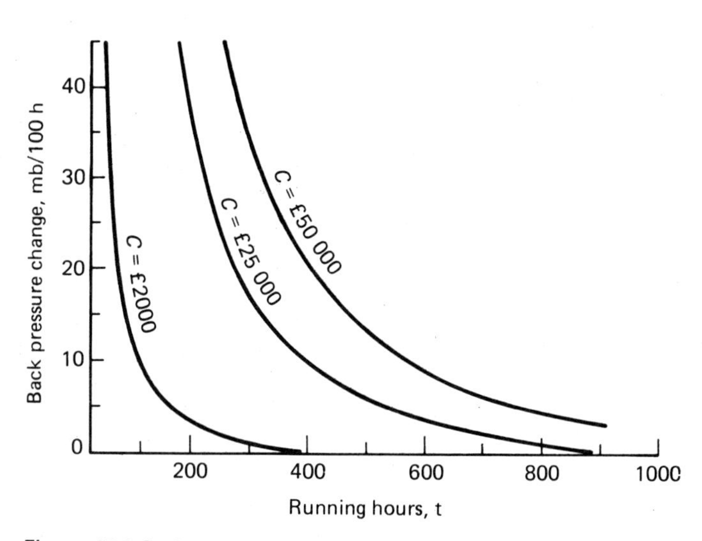

Figure 15.3 Optimum time to clean 375 MW unit condensers

It should be borne in mind that not only is the cost of cleaning higher with high-merit plant, but the *opportunity* for cleaning is less because it is probably running on base load. Therefore there is a double incentive to keep high-merit plant free from fouling if at all possible. For example, ensure that chlorination is satisfactory on the condensers. Staff at two-shifting stations should be able to clean the condensers regularly while off load, even if it is only done partly at a time.

Availability

However, suppose fouling is occurring that is causing loss of *availability* as well as loss of efficiency. This case is quite different to that above as the shortfalls will incur generation replacement costs. For example, some years ago several 120 MW boilers had economizers which were prone to fouling. Every six weeks the boilers had to be taken off load to thoroughly clean the economizers, and this took a week. By the end of the six-week running period the maximum load capability had been reduced from 125 MW to 110 MW. It was abundantly economic to have the boilers out of service for eight weeks to remove and scrap the economizers and replace them with ones with a better tube disposition which prevented fouling. They could then go from one survey to the next without fouling, and so the *availability* was improved considerably.

Incidentally, the boiler efficiency was worse because the heat transfer in the new economizers was not so good as before, but even so it was well worth the considerable cost to improve the availability of the plant which at that time was high in the merit order. By the way, this was a case in point where very *thorough* cleaning of the economiser was essential. The normal rate of fouling was as shown in *Figure 15.4*.

If a thorough clean were carried out the draught loss would be reduced to optimum when the unit was returned to service and it would run for a further six weeks or so. However, if the economizer were returned to service without being thoroughly clean a very much reduced time would elapse before the next clean was necessary. For example, suppose the clean reduced the draught loss to 4 cm from 23 cm. This may sound like a substantial improvement, but the reality is that the unit would then come back to service at a fouling level which it would have taken four weeks running to reach had it been clean. Thus one could only expect two weeks running before another clean was necessary. The importance of thorough cleaning can not be over-stressed. This is even more so if water is being used as a cleaning material. Once boiler deposits have been wetted it is *essential* that they be removed – otherwise when they dry out they will set like concrete.

Improved availability is so desirable on high-merit plant that there is normally an economic case for carrying out even expensive modifications or improvements. Thus, several days can be saved on boiler outages by fitting furnace roof plugs. These plugs, when lifted, allow dust from the top dead space to fall into the boiler gas passes at a controlled rate when the boiler is off load for cleaning. The dust is carried by the air flow through the boiler and deposited in the dust hoppers. Thus a task which used to take several

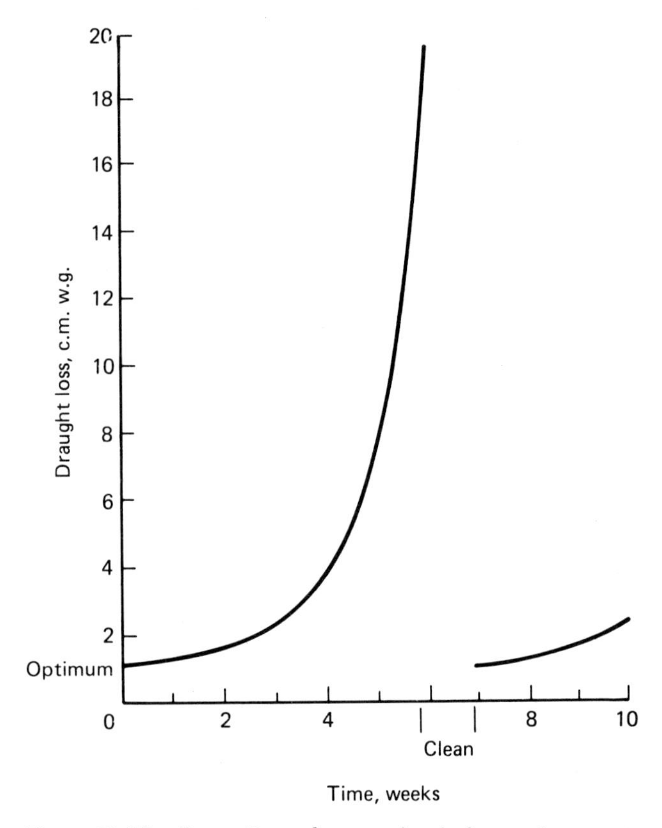

Figure 15.4 Fouling pattern of economiser before replacement

days of manual digging can now be done in a few hours.

Another example is turbine cooling. If it is necessary to stop a turbine shaft while work is carried out it must be cooled until a satisfactory temperature has been reached. On a 500 MW set this may take five days if the rotor is allowed to cool naturally. By blowing air at a controlled rate through the turbine the cooling time can be reduced to a little over a day.

Figure 15.5 shows the improved cooling rate when blowing air through the cylinders. It is apparent that even though the cost of the equipment (blowers, ducts, etc.) is quite high the benefit can be immense.

Proof of time to clean for minimum total cost

Up to now it has been assumed that the optimum time to clean is when the cleaning cost is equal to the cumulative fouling cost. It is now desirable to prove that this is indeed so.

Consider the example used earlier of a 375 MW unit condenser. When the

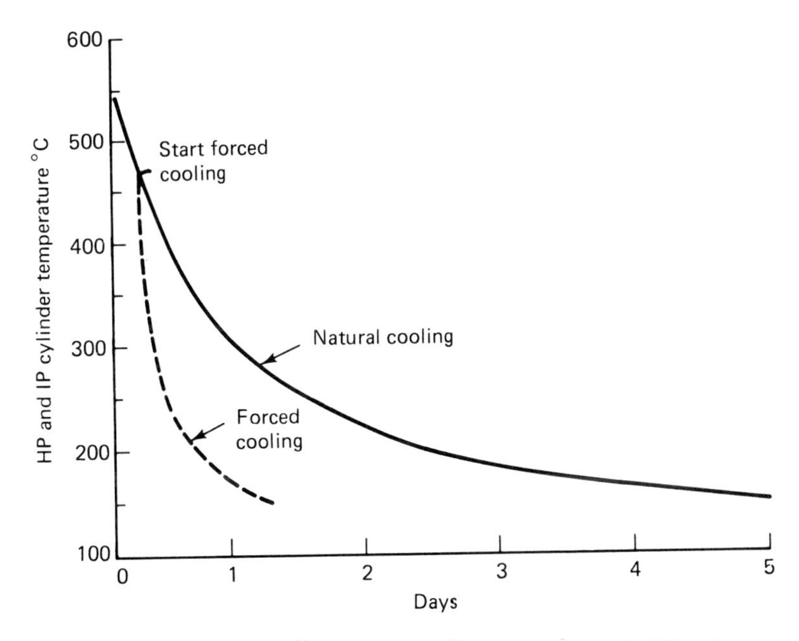

Figure 15.5 Typical natural and forced cooling times for a 500 MW turbine

deterioration rate is, say, 10 mbar/100 hours the value of R is £0.325/h/h. Let the cost of cleaning be, say, £25,000 per time.

Then by calculation, the optimum time is given by:

$$t = \sqrt{\left(\frac{2C}{R}\right)} = \sqrt{\frac{2 \times 25\,000}{0.325}} = \textbf{392 hours}$$

Now consider what will happen if times other than the optimum are chosen. For example, if cleaning were carried out every 300 hours the cumulative fouling cost would be given by:

$$\text{Cumulative cost} = \frac{Rt^2}{2} = \frac{0.325 \times 300^2}{2} = £14,625$$

$$\left(\text{In general terms the cumulative cost} = \frac{0.325 \times t^2}{2} - 0.1625t^2\right)$$

So the total cost per 300 hours' running time is equal to the cumulative cost plus the cleaning cost, i.e.

£14,625 + £25,000 = **£39,625 per time**

Proceeding in a similar manner for other times, a table such as *Table 15.2* can be constructed.

Columns (5) and (6) in *Table 15.2* show how the total cost of fouling plus

Table 15.2 Variation of total cost for various time intervals

1	2	3	4	5	6
Time between cleans, t (h)	*Cumulative fouling cost (£)*	*Cleaning cost (£)*	*Total cost (2) + (3) (£)*	*Total cost per 500 h. (£)*	*Total cost per 1 000 h. (£)*
100	1,625	25,000	26,625	133,125	266,250
200	6,500	25,000	31,500	78,750	157,500
300	14,625	25,000	39,625	66,041	132,082
400	26,000	25,000	51,000	63,750	127,500
500	40,625	25,000	65,625	65,625	131,250
600	58,500	25,000	83,500	69,583	139,166

cleaning differs for the various times between cleans shown in column (1), when reduced to a common basis – in this case arbitrary times of 500 and 1000 hours.

The results are plotted in *Figure 15.6*, and it can be seen that for both

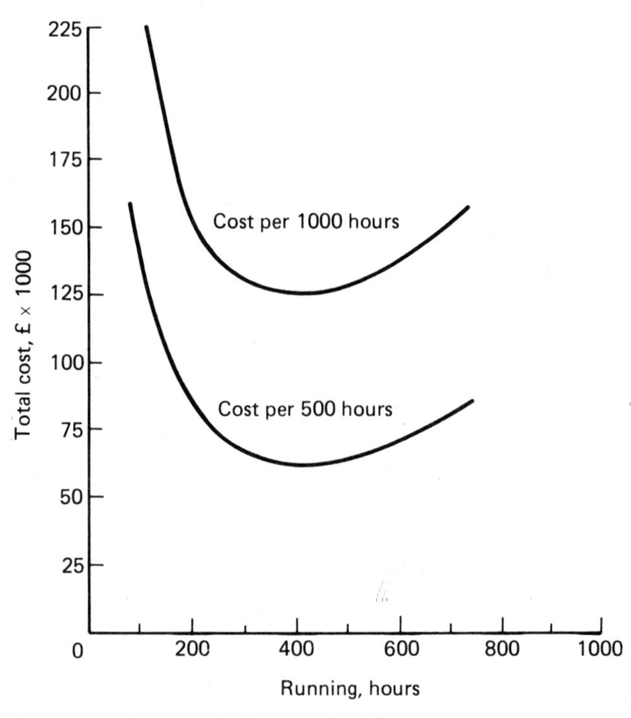

Figure 15.6 Total cost of condenser fouling

curves the minimum cost occurs at 392 hours, the optimum time determined earlier by using the formula. The fact that one curve is lower than the other is of no significance, as the lower curve shows what the total cost is for every

500 hours running, while the upper curve is the cost for every 1000 hours running.

Questions

1 State an expression for fouling cost at any time t.
2 State an expression for the cumulative fouling cost.
3 When is the optimum time to clean a fouled component?
4 State an expression for the optimum time t to clean a component.
5 Is it normally economic to take plant off load just for efficiency improvement?
6 Is it normally economic to take plant off load just for availability improvement?
7 Give some examples of the ways outage times can be reduced.

Project 1

After 250 hours running since its last thorough clean a condenser has a back pressure deviation from optimum of 2 mbar. This will cause a change of heat consumption of 0.2% at full load. The average load is 100 MW, efficiency 30% and fuel cost 103 p/GJ. The total cost of cleaning is £2,000.
Calculate:

(a) the optimum time to clean the condenser if the fouling continues at the same rate;
(b) the fouling cost immediately prior to cleaning.
(c) the cumulative fouling cost at the time of the clean,

Project 1 (Answer)

(a) 1 mbar variation costs $\dfrac{100\,000 \times 3600}{0.30} \times \dfrac{103}{10^6} \times \dfrac{0.1}{100} \times \dfrac{1}{100} = £1.23\text{/h}$

So 1 mbar per 1000 hours variation costs £0.00123/h/h
2 mbar in 250 hours is the equivalent of 8 mbar per 1000 hours.
Hence cost = £0.00123 × 8.0 = £0.00984/h/h = R

So $t = \sqrt{\dfrac{2 \times 2000}{0.00984}} = 638$ hours

(b) Fouling cost = Rt = £0.00984/h/h × 638 h = £6.278/h

(c) Cumulative fouling-cost equals cleaning cost, i.e. £2,000

Useful reference works

1 *Central Electricity Generating Board Site Test Codes*

Site Test Code No. 1	*Boiler Feed Pumps*
Site Test Code No. 2	*Steam Turbine Generator Heat Rate Tests*
Site Test Code No. 3	*Performance of Surface-type Steam Condensers*
Site Test Code No. 4	*Turbine Governors*
Site Test Code No. 6	*Circulating Water Pumps*

2 *British Standards Institution Publications*

BS No.	*Title*
37	Electricity meters (12 parts)
132	Steam turbines
410	Test sieves
599	Methods of testing pumps
752	Test code for acceptance of steam turbines
759	Valves, gauges and other safety fittings for application to boilers and to piping installations for and in connection with boilers.
848	Fans for general purposes (2 parts)
893	Method for the measurement of the concentration of particulate material in ducts carrying gases
1016	Methods for the analysis and testing of coal and coke (17 parts)
1017	Methods for sampling coal and coke (2 parts)
1041	Code for temperature measurement (7 parts)
1042	Methods for the measurement of fluid flow in pipes (3 parts)
1780	Bourdon tube pressure and vacuum gauges (2 parts)
1796	Methods for test sieving
2520	Barometer conventions and tables
2842	Whirling hygrometers
2885	Code for acceptance tests on stationary steam generators of power station type
3405	Simplified methods for measurement of grit and dust emission
4485	Water cooling towers (4 parts)
4937	International thermocouple reference tables (7 parts)
5857	Methods for measurement of fluid flow in closed conduit using tracers (2 parts)

Additional reading – General

1 Various CEGB authors, *Modern Power Station Practice*, Pergamon
2 CRAWFORD, W.R., *Examples in Thermodynamics Problems*, Pitman
3 TOMBS, SIR F. 'Economies of scale in electricity generation and transmission since 1945', *I. Mech. E.* Forty-third Charles Parsons Memorial Lecture, *Proc. I. Mech. E.*, **192** (1978)
4 GRAY, J.L. and JAMES, L.W., 'Economy in capital and specific heat consumption in relation to size of generating sets', 1964 World Power Conference, Paper No. 89
5 DOLLIN, F., 'Design problems in development of large steam turbines', *Proc. I. Mech. E.* (1962)
6 SALISBURY, J.K., *Steam Turbines and their Cycles*, Wiley
7 KEARTON, W.J., *Steam Turbine Theory and Practice*, Pitman
8 HAYWOOD, R.W., 'Research into the fundamentals of boiler circulation theory', *Proc. I. Mech. E.*, General Discussion on Heat Transfer, pp. 63–65, (September 1951)
9 JONES, C.E. and WEINSTEIN, J.L. 'Temperature distribution patterns in furnace wall tubes', *A.S.M.E.*, paper 62 – WA – 131 (1963)
10 LYLE, *The Efficient Use of Steam*, HMSO
11 *The Efficient Use of Fuel*, HMSO
12 MILLER, J.T. *A course in industrial instrument technology*, United Trade Press 1960
13 *Principles and Operation of Power Plant*, Part I, 20 Lessons; Part II, 20 Lessons; CEGB correspondence course
14 SPIERS, H.M. (ed.), *Technical Data on Fuel*, British National Committee, World Power Conference (1962)
15 MANSFIELD. P.H., *Electrical Transducers for Industrial Measurement*, Butterworths (1970)
16 LEWITT. E.H., *Thermodynamics applied to Heat Engines*, Pitman
17 CEGB RESEARCH, Technology, Planning and Research Division of the CEGB

Index